The Theory of Transonic Flow

BY

K. G. GUDERLEY

WRIGHT AIR DEVELOPMENT CENTER
DAYTON, OHIO

Translated from the German by

J. R. MOSZYNSKI

Case Institute of Technology
Cleveland, Ohio

PERGAMON PRESS

OXFORD · LONDON · PARIS · FRANKFURT

1962

ADDISON-WESLEY PUBLISHING COMPANY, INC.

READING, MASSACHUSETTS

PERGAMON PRESS LTD.
Headington Hill Hall, Oxford
4 & 5 Fitzroy Square, London, W. 1

PERGAMON PRESS S.A.R.L.
24 Rue des Écoles, Paris V²

PERGAMON PRESS G.M.B.H.
Kaiserstrasse 75, Frankfurt am Main

This is a translation of the
German Edition, published as
Theorie schallnaher Strömungen
by Springer-Verlag
Berlin, Göttingen, Heidelberg

SOLE DISTRIBUTORS IN THE UNITED STATES
Addison-Wesley Publishing Company, Inc.
Reading, Massachusetts, U.S.A.

Library of Congress Card Number 61-14932

MADE IN ENGLAND

III/18/38

CONTENTS

PREFACE

Transonic flows are characterised by the presence within the flow field of both subsonic and supersonic regions simultaneously. The far-reaching differences between these two types of flow are at the root of many of the difficulties encountered in the analysis of transonic flows. These difficulties are not, as yet, fully surmounted. For example, the apparently simple question of the pressure distribution on a given profile in transonic flow has not been resolved satisfactorily. In fact the theory of transonic flow attempts first of all to explain the fundamental properties of the flow and does not, of necessity, attempt to predict its details.

Even this limited program requires considerable care. For both subsonic as well as supersonic flows, there exist physical analogs which facilitate the interpretation of these phenomena. In addition, the close relationship between the differential equations of subsonic flow and the Laplace equation, as well as that between the equations of supersonic flow and the wave equation, is of great value. The same is not true of transonic flows. There are almost no phenomena analogous to mixed flow and the available theory of mixed elliptic-hyperbolic equations, however valuable, is not quite sufficient to resolve some fundamental mathematical problems.

Thus one cannot rely in the analysis of transonic flow on physical intuition nor on plausibility arguments. The author does not feel that one should therefore proceed in a purely formal manner. In the course of the analysis of examples amenable to an exact treatment, and as a result of careful discussion of the results, it is possible to develop a measure of perception of transonic flow phenomena which permits an extrapolation of the results beyond the range of exact analysis.

In any case, in order to avoid false conclusions, it is necessary in the treatment of transonic flows to rely more strongly on general principles and, occasionally, to demand a more rigorous mathematical approach than is required in the theory of subsonic or supersonic flow. This explains why in the present text the mathematical discussions are more prominent than is usual in the treatment of flow problems.

The book would fulfil its purpose, in the author's opinion, if it explained to the aerodynamicist the mathematical methods and the results of the theory of transonic flows, and if it would point out, to the applied mathematician, the mathematical questions imposed by the physical problem, so that they could fill in the gaps, simplify the reasoning and bring new methods to bear on the field.

Some investigations, conveniently available in the literature, have been left out in order to keep the book within reasonable size limits. These are the discussion of the existence of a supersonic potential flow surrounded by a subsonic flow and the foundations of an airfoil theory in the transonic region.

The following remarks, regarding the arrangement of the book, are in order. Equations from a different section are referred to by number of the chapter, section and, finally, of the equation. A list of symbols, if necessary giving places in the text where the latter are explained, is included after the list of contents. Articles, referred to in the text, are listed separately in the bibliography and reference to them is made in the text by the author's name and by number. The bibliography is not claimed to be complete; it is hoped, however, that the most important schools of thought are represented. It was not attempted to select the references in accordance with the point of view expressed in this book.

Finally, I would like to express my thanks to the Pergamon Press for their excellence in publishing this edition.

Dayton, Ohio, U.S.A. G. GUDERLEY

TRANSLATOR'S PREFACE

This is, as nearly as possible, a literal translation of the original German text. Small changes in the arrangement of the references and in the notation have been introduced to conform with American usage and an attempt has been made to correct some minor errors which have found their way into the original edition. The responsibility for any remaining imperfections is entirely my own.

My thanks are due to Dr. K. G. Guderley for his numerous helpful suggestions and to Dr. G. Kuerti for his continued interest, frequent discussions and extensive help in the preparation of this translation.

I am indebted to Mrs. B. Moszynski and to Mrs. M. Wright for their careful typing of the manuscript and to Pergamon Press for their patience during the frequent delays.

Cleveland, Ohio, U.S.A. J. R. M.

LIST OF FREQUENTLY EMPLOYED SYMBOLS

a	velocity of sound; cf. Eq. I, 2 (5)
a^*	critical velocity; cf. Section I, 2
a_h	coefficient in Eq. VII, 13 (1a)
$b(x)$	in Section III, 3 a function describing the circumference of an infinitely thin wing
$B_{-(4/3)-(h/2)}$, $b_{-(4/3)-(h/2)}$	cf. Eqs. IX, 4 (1) and IX, 4 (7)
$B^{(a)}(\mu), B^{(s)}(\mu)$	cf. Eqs. VII, 12 (13b) and VII, 12 (14a)
b_h	coefficients in Eq. VII, 13 (1b)
c_p, c_v	specific heats at constant pressure and at constant volume respectively
c_L	lift coefficient
c_D	drag coefficient
c_p	pressure coefficient
c_L^*, c_D^*, c_p^*	coefficients as above but referred to stagnation pressure at $M = 1$
c_1, c_2	lower and upper limits of an interval of ξ
C_h	normalising constant [Eq. VII, 9 (8)]; subscript h indicates constant appropriate to the eigenfunction G_h
D	in Section II, 6 characteristic thickness of a profile
D	in Section V, 2 Jacobian of the hodograph transformation
D_1, D_2	real quantities into which the Jacobian D may be split up in the supersonic region
$f(\zeta, n)$	for two-dimensional flows cf. Eq. VII, 2 (2)
$f(\zeta, n)$	for axisymmetric flows cf. Eq. XI, 1 (1)
$f(\xi, \eta, \zeta)$	in Section II, 4 equation of the surface of a shock
$F(a, b, c, x)$	hypergeometric function; cf. Eq. VII, 4 (4b)
$g(\eta, m)$	particular solutions of TRIÇOMI's equation corresponding to CHAPLYGIN's solutions of the hodograph equation; cf. Eq. VII, 1 (2)
$G(\xi, \mu)$	function occuring in the solution of TRICOMI's equation; cf. Eq. VII, 3 (3)
$G^{(s)}$, $G^{(a)}$	functions G for which the appropriate solutions Ψ are respectively symmetric or antisymmetric with respect to the line $\vartheta = 0$
G_1	functions G defined by Eq. VII, 7 (13)
$G_2, G_3, \ldots G_h$	special functions G defined by an eigenvalue problem; Section VII, 9
h	in Sections II, 5 and III, 3 the thickness distribution of a profile
$H_{1/3}^{(1)}$, $H_{1/3}^{(2)}$	HANKEL functions of the first and second kind and of order 1/3
i	specific enthalpy

$I(\mu)$	analytic function defined by Eq. VII, 13 (4)
$J_{1/3}, J_{-1/3}$	BESSEL functions of orders 1/3 and − 1/3 respectively
L	lift
L	in Sections VIII, 4 and VIII, 9 the length of a rhombic profile or of a flat plate
$L(\Phi), L(\varphi)$	differential expression for the boundary conditions of the second kind; cf. Eq. V, 11 (12)
$l^{m,n}$	integrals defined by Eq. VIII, 9 (17)
M	MACH number
M_∞	MACH number at infinity
M_{choked}	MACH number of the approaching flow in a choked wind tunnel
$o(x)$	of order x
p	pressure
p^*	pressure corresponding to critical velocity
p_∞	pressure at infinity
$P\begin{Bmatrix} a & b & c \\ \alpha & \beta & \gamma \\ \alpha' & \beta' & \gamma' \end{Bmatrix} z$	RIEMANN's P function; cf. Sections VII, 2 and VII, 4
$P(x)$	polynomial in x
R	gas constant per unit mass
$R^{-(1/3)-(h/2)}$	functions occuring in the formulation of boundary conditions at a large distance from an obstacle; cf. Eq. IX, 4 (8)
s	specific entropy
T	absolute temperature
u	from Chapter V on, usually the x component of the velocity in two-dimensional problems
v	from Chapter V on, usually the y component of the velocity in two-dimensional problems
$\mathbf{v}$	velocity vector
v_x, v_y, v_z	x, y and z components of the velocity respectively
v_r	radial component of the velocity in axisymmetrical problems
$v_{n\,\text{I}}, v_{n\,\text{II}}$	velocity components normal to a shock and respectively upstream and downstream of the latter
v_t	velocity component parallel to a shock
$\Delta v_x, \Delta v_y, \Delta v_z$	changes in the x, y and z velocity components respectively, in transition through a shock
v_n, v_t	in Section II, 5 respectively the velocity components normal and tangential to an intersection curve between a plane $x =$ const and the surface of an obstacle
w	magnitude of the velocity
$w^* = a^*$	critical velocity; cf. Section I, 2
x_0	characteristic dimension of an obstacle in the x direction, used in formulating the similarity rule

$\tilde{y}, \tilde{z}$	deviations of the y and z coordinates of a streamline from the corresponding coordinates of the same streamline in an undisturbed flow
$\boldsymbol{\alpha}$	MACH angle
α	occasionally the angle of attack
$\alpha_{-1/3}^{-4/3}$ etc.,	constants occuring in an expansion in terms of the "natural" particular solutions, defined in conjunction with Eq. IX, 3 (1b)
$\beta_{-(5/6)-(h/2)}$	constant, cf. Eq. IX, 3 (4)
Γ	circulation integral
Γ	Γ function
γ	ratio of specific heats c_p/c_v
ξ, η, ζ	in connection with the derivation of the similarity rule: space coordinates associated with x, y and z
ζ	independent variable in the hodograph plane; cf. Eq. VII, 2 (1)
ζ	in axisymmetric flows a special variable in the physical plane; cf. Eq. XI, 1 (1a)
ζ_0	in Section XI, 4 the value of ζ corresponding to a compression shock
η	variable describing the deviation of the velocity from the sonic one, defined by Eqs. V, 7 (5) and V, 7 (6)
ϑ	angle included between the velocity vector and the x axis
Θ_0	characteristic angle for an obstacle, e.g. half-angle of a wedge, angle of attack of a plate, also thickness ratio of a rhombic profile
λ, μ	characteristics in the hodograph plane; cf. Eq. I, 7 (3) and I, 7 (4)
λ, λ_h	eigenvalues for the solutions of TRICOMI's equation, cf. Section VII, 9
λ	eigenvalues of a differential equation for axisymmetric flow, cf. Eq. XI, 2 (7)
μ	in connection with $G(\xi, \mu)$ the constant of separation for certain particular solutions of TRICOMI's equation; cf. Eq. VII, 3 (3)
$\mu_h^{(a)}, \mu_h^{(s)}$	cf. Eqs. VII, 12 (13a) and VII, 12 (14b)
ν_1, ν_2	in Sections VI, 5 and VI, 6 cf. Fig. 54
$\boldsymbol{\nu}$	in Sections VI, 5 and VI, 6 cf. Eq. VI, 5 (8)
ν	in Section VII, 11 defined immediately above Eq. VII, 11 (4)
ν	in Section XI, 2 constant of separation defined by Eq. XI, 2 (3)
ξ, ϱ	independent variables of the η, ϑ plane in hodograph problems; cf. Eqs. VII, 3 (1) and VII, 3 (2)
$\tilde{\xi}$	auxiliary variable related to ξ used in establishing the asymptotic representations; cf. Eq. VII, 7 (1a)
ϱ	density
ϱ^*	density corresponding to the critical velocity
ϱ_0	in Section VIII, 10 cf. Fig. 96
$\varrho_1, \varrho_2, \psi_1, \psi_2$	parameters in the formulation of boundary conditions; cf. Eq. IX, 4 (5)
ψ_0, ϱ_0	scale factors for ψ and ϱ in Eq. IX, 4 (7)
ϱ_1	parameter describing the deviation of a flow from $M = 1$ in Section IX, 5

ϱ — independent variable defined by Eq. XI, 2 (9a) in Section XI, 2; cf. Fig. 114

$\sigma(\nu)$ — cf. Eq. VII, 11 (4)

τ — parameter explained in Section I, 12

$\Phi, \bar{\Phi}, \tilde{\Phi}$ etc. potential, perturbation potential or related functions in the physical plane

$\Phi(\eta, \vartheta), \Phi(w, \vartheta)$ change in the LEGENDRE potential caused by a change in the boundary conditions in the physical plane

$\Phi_{-(5/6)-(h/2)}(\xi, \varrho)$ particular solutions for the LEGENDRE potential in the hodograph plane which leave the contour of the profile in the physical plane unchanged

$\varphi(w, \vartheta), \varphi(\eta, \vartheta), \varphi(\xi, \varrho)$ LEGENDRE potential

$\bar{\varphi}, \bar{\bar{\varphi}}, \tilde{\varphi}$ — functions closely related to φ

$\varphi_{-(5/6)-(h/2)}$ — natural particular solutions for φ; these are the same functions as the natural particular solutions for ψ; cf. Section VII, 9

ψ — stream function in the physical and hodograph planes

$\bar{\psi}, \psi_1, \psi_2$ etc. functions closely related to the stream function

$\psi^{(s)}_{-1/3}, \psi^{(a)}_{-5/6}$ etc. natural particular solutions defined in Section VII, 9

$\Psi_{-5/6}, \Psi^{-5/6}$ special particular solutions explained in Section VIII, 3

$\bar{\psi}_{-5/6}(\eta, \vartheta)$ natural particular solution $\psi_{-5/6}$ referred to the variables η, ϑ

$\bar{\psi}$ — explained by Eq. VIII, 7 (2) in Section VIII, 7

$\psi^{m,n}$ — particular solution explained by Eq. VIII, 9 (5)

Ω — in Section V, 8 the complex potential; cf. Eq. V, 8 (2)

ω — in Section V, 2 the complex counterpart of the LEGENDRE potential

ω — angular coordinate in a cylindricale coordinate system

CHAPTER I

GENERAL PRINCIPLES

THE properties of transonic flows can be derived from the general equations of gas dynamics. Their derivation can be found in numerous texts (cf. bibliography on p. 333). Here we shall only present the most important concepts and equations, explaining, however, the logical connection between them. The concept of characteristics will be discussed more fully since some of its consequences are particularly important for the understanding of mixed subsonic and supersonic flows. Finally, a formal procedure will be indicated for the derivation of approximate equations. This will be used repeatedly later, particularly in conjunction with the similarity rule for transonic flows.

1. Fundamental Equations of Frictionless Compressible Flow

In all the considerations to follow friction and the conduction of heat will be neglected. Under such conditions there exists no mechanism in the flow for the transfer of heat between two particles and mechanical energy cannot be converted into heat. Thus the entropy of a particle remains constant.

An exception to this arises in the case of a shock. Physically shocks represent exceedingly narrow regions in which the temperature gradient and the rate of strain of a particle are so large that the entropy increases, however small the heat conduction and internal friction might be. In our calculations, whenever shocks occur, these thin zones will be idealised to an interface between two regions in each of which the flow is frictionless and no conduction of heat takes place. At this interface there occur sudden changes of pressure, entropy and velocity which are governed by the so-called shock equations.

We choose a cartesian coordinate system with coordinates x, y, and z and we shall denote the velocity components in these three directions by v_x, v_y, and v_z respectively. We shall further denote the time by t and the entropy by s. The velocity components and the entropy are considered as functions of the three space coordinates and of time. The conservation of the entropy of a particle is expressed by

Euler's Rule

$$\frac{ds}{dt} = \frac{\partial s}{\partial t} + \frac{\partial s}{\partial x} v_x + \frac{\partial s}{\partial y} v_y + \frac{\partial s}{\partial z} v_z = 0. \tag{1}$$

Since friction forces are neglected, the only forces acting on a particle are those due to pressure and the principle of conservation of momentum in the three directions takes the form

$$\frac{1}{\varrho}\frac{\partial p}{\partial x} + \frac{\partial v_x}{\partial t} + v_x \frac{\partial v_x}{\partial x} + v_y \frac{\partial v_x}{\partial y} + v_z \frac{\partial v_x}{\partial z} = 0, \tag{2a}$$

$$\frac{1}{\varrho}\frac{\partial p}{\partial y} + \frac{\partial v_y}{\partial t} + v_y \frac{\partial v_y}{\partial x} + v_y \frac{\partial v_y}{\partial y} + v_z \frac{\partial v_y}{\partial z} = 0, \tag{2b}$$

$$\frac{1}{\varrho}\frac{\partial p}{\partial z} + \frac{\partial v_z}{\partial t} + v_x \frac{\partial v_z}{\partial x} + v_y \frac{\partial v_z}{\partial y} + v_z \frac{\partial v_z}{\partial z} = 0, \tag{2c}$$

where p is the pressure and ϱ the density. These are the Eulerian equations of motion.

It is, finally, necessary to express mathematically the fact that mass can be neither created nor destroyed. In a fixed element of volume the efflux of mass across the surface of the element must be equal, and opposite in sign, to the increase of the mass contained in the volume during a given interval of time. This results in the equation of continuity

$$\frac{\partial \varrho}{\partial t} + \frac{\partial}{\partial x}(\varrho v_x) + \frac{\partial}{\partial y}(\varrho v_y) + \frac{\partial}{\partial z}(\varrho v_z) = 0. \tag{3}$$

The equations given so far, together with the thermodynamic equations expressing the relationship between pressure, density and entropy, the boundary conditions of the problem and the conditions at the shocks, if any are present, represent the mathematical description of the flow. Strictly speaking, no other statement of physical facts should be necessary, and it should be possible to develop the theory purely mathematically. This does not mean that one is not guided by illustrative physical considerations or that one does not attach physical meaning to the results obtained analytically. On the contrary, physical reasonings constitute one of the most important aids in research. In any case, however, only results which can be derived from the above equations can be considered as valid with certainty. The formulations of the problems themselves stem most frequently from aerodynamics.

For steady axisymmetric flows one usually formulates the problem in a cylindrical coordinate system x, r, ω, where the x-axis coincides with the axis the axis of the cylinder. The continuity equation then takes the form

$$\frac{\partial(\varrho v_x)}{\partial x} + \frac{\partial(\varrho v_r)}{\partial r} + \frac{\varrho v_r}{r} = 0.$$

Here v_r is the velocity component in the direction of increasing r.

2. Bernoulli's Equation

Some further quite general relationships can be derived with a few additiona assumptions. These are stated here without proof.

If the velocities are independent of the time then, as a result of the First Law of Thermodynamics or, in shock-free regions, as a result of integration of EULER's equations we obtain BERNOULLI's equation

$$i + \frac{w^2}{2} = \text{const}, \tag{1}$$

where i is the specific enthalpy and w the magnitude of the velocity. The constant on the RHS can vary from streamline to streamline, often, however, e.g. in all cases of bodies in parallel flows, the constant is the same for all streamlines. The name *isoenergetic* is sometimes therefore applied to such flows. The derivation of BERNOULLI's equation from the First Law indicates that it is valid also in the presence of shocks. It is however not valid if friction or heat conduction occur. Further relations may be obtained if the ratio of the specific heats is assumed constant. We denote by R the gas constant referred to unit mass and by c_p and c_v the specific heats at constant pressure and at constant volume respectively, by γ the ratio of specific heats c_p/c_v and by T the absolute temperature. The equation of state of a gas is then

$$\frac{p}{\varrho} = RT, \tag{2a}$$

while the equation of an isentrope is

$$\frac{p}{\varrho^\gamma} = \text{const}. \tag{2b}$$

Further we have the relations

$$\frac{c_p}{c_v} = \gamma, \tag{3a}$$

$$c_p - c_v = R. \tag{3b}$$

whence

$$c_p = \frac{\gamma}{\gamma - 1} R. \tag{3c}$$

The enthalpy may be expressed by

$$i = c_p T = \frac{\gamma}{\gamma - 1} RT. \tag{4}$$

We introduce further

$$a^2 = \left(\frac{\partial p}{\partial \varrho}\right)_{s\,=\,\text{const}} = \gamma \frac{p}{\varrho}, \tag{5}$$

where the differentiation is to be carried out at constant entropy. From acoustical considerations a is the velocity of sound although this is not apparent in the present context. One obtains then

$$i = \frac{a^2}{\gamma - 1} \tag{6}$$

and from BERNOULLI's equation there results

$$\frac{a^2}{\gamma - 1} + \frac{w^2}{2} = \text{const}. \tag{7}$$

If the velocity w is equal to the corresponding sonic velocity, it is called the critical velocity. All quantities associated with the critical velocity are denoted by an asterisk e.g. $w^* = a^*$, p^*, ϱ^*.

Putting $w = a = w^* = a^*$ the constant on the RHS of Eq. (7) becomes $[(\gamma + 1)/2(\gamma - 1)]\, w^{*2}$. Hence one obtains

$$a^2 = \frac{\gamma + 1}{2} w^{*2} - \frac{\gamma - 1}{2} w^2. \tag{8}$$

The ratio w/a is called the MACH number and is denoted by M.

In deriving BERNOULLI's equation by the integration of EULER's equations one obtains, as an intermediate result for an arbitrary equation of state,

$$\frac{dp}{\varrho} + d\left(\frac{w^2}{2}\right) = 0, \tag{9}$$

where the differentiation is to be performed along a streamline. In an isentropic and isoenergetic flow this equation is valid generally. Finally the following relationships are also valid for an arbitrary equation of state

$$\frac{d}{dw}(\varrho w) = \varrho\left(1 - \frac{w^2}{a^2}\right), \tag{10a}$$

$$\frac{d(p + \varrho w^2)}{dw} = \varrho w\left(1 - \frac{w^2}{a^2}\right). \tag{10b}$$

3. The Equations of Vorticity

If the velocity vector is denoted by $\mathbf{v}$ then the vorticity vector is given by curl $\mathbf{v}$ and represents twice the oriented angular velocity of a particle*.

The following relationship is valid for any vector field

$$\text{div curl}\, \mathbf{v} = 0. \tag{1}$$

Thus if at any given time one considers the vector curl $\mathbf{v}$ as the velocity vector of an incompressible flow, then the continuity equation for this flow is automatically satisfied in accordance with Eq. (1). (EULER's equations would, however, only then be satisfied if the existence of suitable impressed forces were present.)

Upon integration of the vector field of vorticity at any fixed time one obtains so-called vortex lines which are equivalent to the streamlines of the fictitious

* One should actually define what is to be understood under the angular velocity of a particle undergoing deformation.

incompressible flow mentioned above. In a steady flow it is possible to introduce stream tubes which are formed by streamlines originating on arbitrary closed curves. The surface of such a stream tube consists, therefore, always of the same streamlines. In an analogous manner one can define vortex tubes. As a result of the last equation the vorticity flux through a vortex tube is constant. It follows that a vortex tube, and hence also a vortex line, cannot end inside the flow region. They can either be closed within the flow, extend to infinity or end at a boundary of the flow field.

Under the assumption that the density is a function of pressure alone, i.e. that the flow is *barotropic*, which applies for example for incompressible, isothermal or isentropic flows, one finds from EULER's equation that along any closed curve C moving with the gas particles the so-called circulation integral

$$\Gamma = \oint_C (v_x dx + v_y dy + v_z dz) \tag{2a}$$

remains constant with time. With the aid of Stokes' theorem this integral can be expressed in terms of the vector curl $\mathbf{v}$

$$\Gamma = \int_{\mathbf{A}} \operatorname{curl} \mathbf{v}\, d\mathbf{A}\,. \tag{2b}$$

The integration should be extended over the surface $\mathbf{A}$ bounded by the curve C and the vector $d\mathbf{A}$ represents an oriented surface element, i.e. a vector normal to the element considered and equal in magnitude to the surface of the element. The direction of this vector is defined by the sense in which the surface is described. The product curl $\mathbf{v}\, d\mathbf{A}$ is the scalar product of the two vectors.

In accordance with the above result the circulation in a flow which is initially irrotational (i.e. free of vorticity) is zero along all curves which are initially closed and remain so. The vortex sheets which one finds in the wake of an airfoil, or which emanate from the sharp edges of a body immersed in a flow, are compatible with the above principle since the curves which cross such vortex sheets were not closed at an earlier time but ended at the surface of the body considered.

If the condition of barotropic motion is removed, the flow does not have to remain irrotational even if it was irrotational at the beginning. Vorticity is generated for example if the entropy within the field of flows is not constant. For steady isoenergetic flow there exists a simple relationship in the form of CROCCO's equation (OSWATITSCH [67]*)

$$\mathbf{v} \times \operatorname{curl} \mathbf{v} = -T \operatorname{grad} s \tag{3}$$

where the sign $\times$ denotes vector multiplication. This equation determines the component of the vorticity normal to the streamlines. The gradient of entropy is normal to the streamlines since the entropy s is constant along the latter. In order to calculate the tangential component of the vorticity one has to use Eq. (1).

* Numbers is square brackets refer to the bibliography on pp. 333–341.

In plane and axisymmetric flows the vorticity component along the streamline is zero because of symmetry. In such cases the vorticity vector is completely determined by CROCCO's equation.

This latter equation will be employed later to justify the neglecting of the vorticity in transonic flows.

4. The Velocity Potential

If one considers an isentropic flow which is initially irrotational then the flow remains irrotational at any given time except for vortex sheets which may emanate from the edges of a body placed in the flow. The components of the vorticity vector must therefore vanish, i.e.

$$\frac{\partial v_x}{\partial y} - \frac{\partial v_y}{\partial x} = 0; \quad \frac{\partial v_y}{\partial z} - \frac{\partial v_z}{\partial y} = 0; \quad \frac{\partial v_z}{\partial x} - \frac{\partial v_x}{\partial z} = 0 \tag{1}$$

and in view of the above the velocity vector may be expressed by

$$\mathbf{v} = \operatorname{grad} \Phi .$$

This means that the components of the velocity may be written

$$v_x = \frac{\partial \Phi}{\partial x}; \quad v_y = \frac{\partial \Phi}{\partial y}; \quad v_z = \frac{\partial \Phi}{\partial z}. \tag{2}$$

Thus the vector field of velocity is described by the scalar quantity Φ.

If the velocity components are given by Eq. (2), EULER's equations [Eqs. I, 1 (2)] are automatically satisfied. Consider, for example, a steady flow. Let Φ be an arbitrary, twice differentiable function of x, y and z. From this function we can determine the velocity components in accordance with Eq. (2). If the velocities are known then the pressures can be determined from BERNOULLI's equation. If these pressures are now introduced in EULER's equations these latter are identically satisfied and the continuity equation remains as the only relationship to be satisfied by the function Φ.

The continuity equation for an isoenergetic flow, for which, however, constant entropy need not be assumed, can also be written as follows: we consider the pressure and entropy as independent thermodynamic properties of state. The symbol $1/a^2$ has already been introduced for the derivative $\partial \varrho/\partial p$ (which must be always positive for reasons of stability of the gas). The quantity a, the so-called velocity of sound, is a function only of the thermodynamic state and not of the state of the motion. Thus we have

$$\frac{\partial \varrho}{\partial x} = \frac{\partial \varrho}{\partial p}\frac{\partial p}{\partial x} + \frac{\partial \varrho}{\partial s}\frac{\partial s}{\partial x} = \frac{1}{a^2}\frac{\partial p}{\partial x} + \frac{\partial \varrho}{\partial s}\frac{\partial s}{\partial x} \tag{3}$$

and similar equations for the two other coordinate directions. For steady flow the continuity equation [Eq. I, 1 (3)] can be written in partial differential notation

$$\frac{\partial \varrho}{\partial x} v_x + \frac{\partial \varrho}{\partial y} v_y + \frac{\partial \varrho}{\partial z} v_z + \varrho \frac{\partial v_x}{\partial x} + \varrho \frac{\partial v_y}{\partial y} + \varrho \frac{\partial v_z}{\partial z} = 0 .$$

Introduction of Eqs. (3) and the elimination of the derivatives of p with the aid of EULER's equations and those of s with the aid of Eq. I, 1 (1) yields

$$\frac{\partial v_x}{\partial x}\left(1 - \frac{v_x^2}{a^2}\right) + \frac{\partial v_y}{\partial y}\left(1 - \frac{v_y^2}{a^2}\right) + \frac{\partial v_z}{\partial z}\left(1 - \frac{v_z^2}{a^2}\right) - \left(\frac{\partial v_x}{\partial y} + \frac{\partial v_y}{\partial x}\right)\frac{v_x v_y}{a^2}$$

$$- \left(\frac{\partial v_y}{\partial z} + \frac{\partial v_z}{\partial y}\right)\frac{v_y v_z}{a^2} - \left(\frac{\partial v_z}{\partial x} + \frac{\partial v_x}{\partial z}\right)\frac{v_x v_z}{a^2} = 0 . \tag{4}$$

which for potential flow takes the form

$$\Phi_{xx}\left(1 - \frac{\Phi_x^2}{a^2}\right) + \Phi_{yy}\left(1 - \frac{\Phi_y^2}{a^2}\right) + \Phi_{zz}\left(1 - \frac{\Phi_z^2}{a^2}\right) - 2\Phi_{xy}\frac{\Phi_x \Phi_y}{a^2}$$

$$- 2\Phi_{yz}\frac{\Phi_y \Phi_z}{a^2} - 2\Phi_{zx}\frac{\Phi_z \Phi_x}{a^2} = 0 . \tag{5}$$

From BERNOULLI's equation it follows that

$$a^2 = \frac{\gamma + 1}{2} w^{*2} - \frac{\gamma - 1}{2}(\Phi_x^2 + \Phi_y^2 + \Phi_z^2) . \tag{6}$$

The potential equation for axisymmetric flow has the form

$$\Phi_{xx}\left(1 - \frac{\Phi_x^2}{a^2}\right) + \Phi_{rr}\left(1 - \frac{\Phi_r^2}{a^2}\right)^{2} - 2\Phi_{xr}\frac{\Phi_x \Phi_r}{a^2} + \frac{\Phi_r}{r} = 0 . \tag{7}$$

We shall mention here, for the sake of completeness, that a velocity potential exists also in the case of a nonsteady isentropic flow which is initially irrotational. BERNOULLI's equation is then replaced by

$$\Phi_t + i + \tfrac{1}{2}(\Phi_x^2 + \Phi_y^2 + \Phi_z^2) = \text{const.} \tag{8}$$

The EULER's equations are again integrated by the introduction of the potential and the continuity equation takes the form

$$\Phi_{xx}\left(1 - \frac{\Phi_x^2}{a^2}\right) + \Phi_{yy}\left(1 - \frac{\Phi_y^2}{a^2}\right) + \Phi_{zz}\left(1 - \frac{\Phi_z^2}{a^2}\right)$$

$$- \frac{\Phi_{tt}}{a^2} - 2\Phi_{xy}\frac{\Phi_x \Phi_y}{a^2} - 2\Phi_{yz}\frac{\Phi_y \Phi_z}{a^2} - 2\Phi_{zx}\frac{\Phi_z \Phi_x}{a^2} \tag{9}$$

$$- 2\Phi_{xt}\frac{\Phi_x}{a^2} - 2\Phi_{yt}\frac{\Phi_y}{a^2} - 2\Phi_{zt}\frac{\Phi_z}{a^2} = 0 .$$

5. The Stream Function

The continuity equation for a plane steady flow is

$$\frac{\partial(\varrho v_x)}{\partial x} + \frac{\partial(\varrho v_y)}{\partial y} = 0 \tag{1}$$

while for axisymmetric flows one obtains in a cylindrical system of coordinates x, r, and ω

$$\frac{\partial(r\varrho v_x)}{\partial x} + \frac{\partial(r\varrho v_r)}{\partial r} = 0. \tag{2}$$

These equations may be integrated by putting

$$\varrho v_x = \frac{\partial\psi}{\partial y}, \tag{3a}$$

$$\varrho v_y = -\frac{\partial\psi}{\partial x}, \tag{3b}$$

for plane flow and

$$r\varrho v_x = \frac{\partial\psi}{\partial r}, \tag{4a}$$

$$r\varrho v_r = -\frac{\partial\psi}{\partial x} \tag{4b}$$

for axisymmetric flow.

The function ψ is called the stream function and the lines $\psi =$ const are the streamlines. The tangents to the streamlines are parallel to the velocity vector.

Since no assumptions, regarding constant entropy or irrotationality, are implied in the continuity equation, a stream function can also be introduced if such assumptions are not valid. The entropy is constant along a streamline and hence

$$s = s(\psi).$$

For potential flows the function ψ must be such that the curl of the velocity vector vanishes. The equation which results from this condition is, however, quite inconvenient inasmuch as it contains the velocity of sound and the velocity components. The relationships between these quantities and the derivatives of the stream function are somewhat involved. These difficulties do not arise in the linearised treatment of subsonic flow nor in the hodograph equation. In a transonic regime it is much more convenient to use in the physical plane the potential.

6. Characteristics

The concept of characteristics has proved itself to be very useful in supersonic aerodynamics. Since the basis of the method of characteristics plays an important role also in the analysis of the properties of transonic flow, the fundamentals of the theory of characteristics will be discussed briefly.

The derivation of the method of characteristics based on physical reasoning (as was done for example by BUSEMANN) leads to all the results necessary for the calculation of the flow and provides, furthermore, a very lucid picture of the flow process. In spite of this we prefer for the present purposes a formal derivation, since it accentuates more strongly the fundamental concepts (cf. COURANT–HILBERT [2; 7] v. II). For the sake of simplicity only the special case of plane potential flow will be discussed. The flow is described by the continuity equation [Eq. I, 4 (4)]

$$\frac{\partial v_x}{\partial x}\left(1-\frac{v_x^2}{a^2}\right)-\left(\frac{\partial v_x}{\partial y}+\frac{\partial v_y}{\partial x}\right)\frac{v_x v_y}{a^2}+\frac{\partial v_y}{\partial y}\left(1-\frac{v_y^2}{a^2}\right)=0 \tag{1}$$

and by the condition that the vorticity vector must vanish

$$\frac{\partial v_x}{\partial y}-\frac{\partial v_y}{\partial x}=0. \tag{2}$$

The sonic velocity is, in accordance with Eq. I, 2 (8), a function of the magnitude w of the velocity.

Let now the velocity vector be given along a curve C in the physical plane. Along such a curve the velocity vectors are not always independent of one another; we assume, however, that the prescribed velocities are compatible. They could, for example, be obtained from a known flow. We now pose a question which is not immediately connected with the concept of characteristics, namely whether from the prescribed data along the curve C we can calculate the flow field at least in the immediate neighborhood of C.

If the distribution of v_x and v_y on the curve C is known, then their derivatives with respect to x, along C, are also known. They can be expressed in terms of the partial derivatives of v_x and v_y with respect to x and y and of the slope dy/dx of the curve C

$$\frac{\partial v_x}{\partial x}+\frac{\partial v_x}{\partial y}\frac{dy}{dx}=\frac{dv_x}{dx}, \tag{3}$$

$$\frac{\partial v_y}{\partial x}+\frac{\partial v_y}{\partial y}\frac{dy}{dx}=\frac{dv_y}{dx}. \tag{4}$$

Equations (1) through (4) represent a linear system of equations for the four derivatives $\partial v_x/\partial x$, $\partial v_x/\partial y$, $\partial v_y/\partial x$ and $\partial v_y/\partial y$. If this system of equations has a solution then the partial derivatives of the velocity components at any point on C can be determined. By differentiation one can obtain similar equations for the higher derivatives in which process the coefficients of the unknown derivatives on the LHS remain the same. In this way, from the data originally prescribed at all points on a given curve, one can determine all derivatives and hence the flow field in the vicinity of the curve by means of a TAYLOR expansion.

The system of equations has always a unique solution as long as the determinant of the coefficients of the LHS is not zero. The concept of characteristics refers to the exceptional case in which this determinant is zero. The coefficients of the system of equation contain, apart from the velocities v_x and v_y, also the slope of the curve C at the points considered. We seek such directions of the curve C, as described by the slope dy/dx, for which this determinant vanishes. To this end we introduce at a given point P of the curve C a coordinate system x', y', the x'-axis of which is parallel to the local direction of the velocity vector. The introduction of such a system of coordinates does not affect the form of the equations since, in plane flow, there exist no preferred directions. The velocity component in the direction of x' is now w and that normal to x' is zero and the determinant of the coefficients of the system of equations takes the form

$$\begin{vmatrix} 1-\frac{w^2}{a^2} & 0 & 0 & 1 \\ 0 & 1 & -1 & 0 \\ 1 & \frac{dy'}{dx'} & 0 & 0 \\ 0 & 0 & 1 & \frac{dy'}{dx'} \end{vmatrix} = 0$$

from which

$$\frac{dy'}{dx'} = \pm\sqrt{\frac{a^2}{w^2-a^2}}\,.$$

When $w < a$ (or $M < 1$) there are no characteristics. This is the reason for the important differences between subsonic flow ($M < 1$) and supersonic flow ($M > 1$). One introduces normally at this point the Mach angle

$$\alpha = \text{arc sin}\,\frac{a}{w} \tag{5}$$

and the last equation may be written

$$\frac{dy'}{dx'} = \pm\tan\alpha\,.$$

Thus the determinant of the coefficients of the LHS vanishes when the angle between the curve C and the velocity vector is $\pm\alpha$.

Before discussing the system of equations further, we replace the velocity components v_x and v_y by the magnitude of the velocity w and by the angle ϑ between the velocity and the chosen direction of x or x'. Since

$$v_x = w\cos\vartheta, \quad v_y = w\sin\vartheta, \tag{6}$$

one obtains

$$dv_x = dw\cos\vartheta - w\sin\vartheta\, d\vartheta$$

and

$$dv_y = dw\sin\vartheta + w\cos\vartheta\, d\vartheta$$

or, in the coordinate system x', y'

$$dv_x = dw,$$
$$dv_y = w\, d\vartheta.$$

Introducing these results, as well as the equation for dy'/dx', in Eqs. (1) through (4) one obtains

$$\begin{array}{llllll|l}
-\dfrac{\partial w}{\partial x'}\cot^2\alpha & & & +w\dfrac{\partial\vartheta}{\partial y'} & & =0 & \tan\alpha \\[2ex]
 & \dfrac{\partial w}{\partial y'} & -w\dfrac{\partial\vartheta}{\partial x'} & & & =0 & \mp 1 \\[2ex]
\dfrac{\partial w}{\partial x'} & \pm\dfrac{\partial w}{\partial y'}\tan\alpha & & & & =\dfrac{dw}{dx'} & \cot\alpha \\[2ex]
 & & w\dfrac{\partial\vartheta}{\partial x'} & \pm w\dfrac{\partial\vartheta}{\partial y'}\tan\alpha & & =w\dfrac{d\vartheta}{dx'} & \mp 1
\end{array}$$

Since the determinant of the coefficients of the LHS is equal to zero, these equations are linearly dependent. The terms on the right determine which linear combinations of the LHS's are equal to zero. These combinations can be found systematically by eliminating the unknowns.

If the equations are to be satisfied by finite values of the partial derivatives $\partial w/\partial x'$, $\partial w/\partial y'$, $\partial\vartheta/\partial x'$ and $\partial\vartheta/\partial y'$, and this should be the case almost everywhere in the field of flow, then the same linear relationships must exist between the RHS's of the equations as between the LHS's. On the right we have the derivatives in the direction of x' i.e. in the direction of the curve C. One obtains thus

$$\frac{\cot\alpha}{w}\frac{dw}{dx'} \mp \frac{d\vartheta}{dx'} = 0. \tag{7}$$

This last relationship is sometimes referred to as the compatibility equation of the characteristics. The curve on which the determinant of the coefficients of the LHS is zero at all points and on which, in addition, the RHS's satisfy the compatibility condition, is called a characteristic. In the special case of the flow of a gas it may also be called a MACH line or MACH wave. Along a characteristic there exist definite relationships between the infinitesimal changes of state properties, as expressed by Eq. (7) and this fact is employed in calculating the flow field.

The partial derivatives $\partial w/\partial x'$, $\partial w/\partial y'$, $\partial\vartheta/\partial x'$ and $\partial\vartheta/\partial y'$ are not uniquely determined on a characteristic since, in view of the determinant of the coefficients being zero, there exists a non-trivial solution of the system of the homogeneous equations. The complete solution of the system of equations consists of the sum of the solution of the inhomogeneous system and of the solution of the homogeneous system, the latter multiplied by an arbitrary constant. This means that the derivatives of velocity in directions other than that of the characteristic can be different on each side of the curve or that the flow fields on both sides of the curve need not represent analytic continuations of one another. This is also often expressed by saying that a discontinuity in the first derivatives of the velocity can be propagated along a characteristic.

Similar results are valid also for the higher derivatives since the LHS's of the system of equations remain the same and they determine the directions of the characteristics. Thus discontinuities in the higher derivatives are propagated along the same curves as those of the derivatives of the first order. From another point of view, in the case of a potential flow the characteristics are the only curves on which discontinuities in the derivatives of the velocity are permissible.

Whether such discontinuities actually occur in a given field of flow is determined by the boundary conditions. If a sudden change occurs in the curvature of a boundary, a jump occurs in the curvature of all the streamlines along a characteristic which originates at the boundary and at the point of sudden change. The magnitude of the jump in the curvature of the streamlines can be calculated, but it would lead us into too much detail at the present time.

In later considerations the concept of characteristics will be utilised in connection with other equations. If, for example, a similar reasoning to that employed above is to be applied to TRICOMI's equation

$$\varphi_{\eta\eta} - \eta\varphi_{\vartheta\vartheta} = 0,$$

it is convenient to introduce

$$\varphi_\eta = U(\eta, \vartheta),$$
$$\varphi_\vartheta = V(\eta, \vartheta)$$

which results in the following system of equations

$$U_\eta - \eta V_\vartheta = 0,$$
$$U_\vartheta - V_\eta = 0.$$

Corresponding calculations yield for the directions of characteristics

$$\frac{d\eta}{d\vartheta} = \pm\eta^{-1/2} \tag{8}$$

and the condition of campatibility along a characteristic takes the form

$$d\varphi_\eta \mp \sqrt{\eta}\, d\varphi_\vartheta = 0. \tag{9}$$

An approximate equation of axisymmetric transonic flow can, as will be shown later, be written in the form

$$-(\gamma + 1)\Phi_x\Phi_{xx} + \Phi_{rr} + \frac{\Phi_r}{r} = 0.$$

Upon introduction of

$$\Phi_x = u, \quad \Phi_r = v$$

there results the following system of partial differential equations of the first order

$$-(\gamma + 1)uu_x + v_r + \frac{v}{r} = 0,$$

$$u_r - v_x = 0.$$

Applying again the same reasoning we obtain for the characteristic directions

$$\frac{dx}{dr} = \pm(\gamma + 1)^{1/2}\Phi_x^{1/2}, \tag{10}$$

and for the conditions of compatibility

$$-\frac{dx}{dr}\frac{d\Phi_x}{dr} + \frac{d\Phi_r}{dr} + \frac{\Phi_r}{r} = 0. \tag{11}$$

The derivatives dx/dr, $d\Phi_x/dr$ and $d\Phi_r/dr$ should be evaluated along the characteristic curves.

7. Plane Potential Flow

While the preceding considerations are applicable, with small modifications, quite generally (e.g. for non-isentropic or axisymmetric flows) the case of plane potential flow allows certain simplifications which, however, are restricted to that case alone. At the same time some concepts which will prove useful later occur in this case.

Since in potential flow the entropy is constant and the constant in BERNOULLI's equation has the same value for all streamlines, Eq. I, 2 (8)

$$a^2 = \frac{\gamma + 1}{2} w^{*2} - \frac{\gamma - 1}{2} w^2$$

applies. Hence it follows that the MACH angle [Eq. I, 6 (5)] can be a function of only the velocity. Then, upon introduction of

$$J = \int_{w^*}^{w} \frac{\cot\alpha}{w} dw \tag{1}$$

Eq. I, 6 (7) can be integrated yielding for a characteristic

$$J \mp \vartheta = \text{const}. \tag{2}$$

The upper sign applies to characteristics whose direction is obtained by rotating the velocity vector counter-clockwise through a MACH angle while the lower sign applies to the other family of characteristics. The two families of characteristics have been called by TOLLMIEN the *left* and *right* MACH waves* respectively.

Equation (2) indicates that the characteristics of the physical flow plane map in the hodograph plane (the w, ϑ plane) into predetermined curves. These curves, of course, are the characteristics of the hodograph equation since the property, that discontinuities in derivatives are propagated along characteristics, is not affected by the mapping process. These curves are the well-known epicycloids of BUSEMANN's method of characteristic.

* It is easy to see that this nomenclature is independent of the sense of the streamlines or of the velocity vector.

In this method only a preselected group of characteristics is drawn in the physical plane, i.e. only those which in the hodograph plane map into a pencil of lines inclined at a constant angle to one another. This angle is usually made to equal approximately 1°. The direction of the characteristics in the physical plane is determined by the mid-point between two intersection points in the hodograph plane. Since these intersections are fixed by the selected characteristics only the predetermined values of the slope of the characteristics occur in the physical plane. These values can be represented in the form of a table and, once this is done, the characteristic diagram in the hodograph plane is no longer necessary. It retains, of course, its value as an auxiliary illustration (TEMPLE [77]).

To arrive at BUSEMANN's terminology we put

$$\lambda = 400 + \frac{90}{\pi}(-J + \vartheta), \tag{3}$$

$$\mu = 600 + \frac{90}{\pi}(-J - \vartheta), \tag{4}$$

so that for left characteristics λ = const and for right characteristics μ = const. If λ and μ are given we obtain

$$\vartheta = \frac{\pi}{180}(200 + \lambda - \mu), \tag{5}$$

$$J = \frac{\pi}{180}(1000 - (\lambda + \mu)). \tag{6}$$

The coefficient $90/\pi$ was introduced in Eqs. (3) and (4) so that ϑ is obtained from Eq. (5) in degrees. The parameter J, and hence w and all the functions dependent on w, can be expressed in terms of $\lambda + \mu$ with the aid of Eq. (6). These functions have been tabulated, for example by SAUER [2; 1]. The constants 400 and 600 serve to facilitate the differentiation between λ and μ.

BUSEMANN interprets the resulting net of characteristics by considering the flow in each square to be parallel and such that its state corresponds to the center of the image of the square in the hodograph plane. In moving from one square of the net into a neighboring one, across a characteristic, the direction of the velocity vector changes always by the same angle of approximately 1°, as originally chosen, and this change is independent of the point at which a characteristic is crossed. A comparison of the physical plane with the hodograph plane shows that a change in the direction of the velocity vector implies also a change in the magnitude of the velocity. This change has the same sign for a given MACH line independently of the velocity at which it takes place. This can also be seen by inspection of Eq. I, 6 (7). If the pressure increases in crossing a wave then such a wave is called a compression wave. If the pressure decreases, the wave is called a rarefaction wave. One frequently distinguishes between compression and rarefaction, or expansion, waves by employing full lines for the former and dotted lines for the latter in a characteristic diagram.

Thus the waves drawn in the physical flow plane represent changes of state and, if the above rules are observed in the construction of the characteristic net, these changes of state can be calculated by the simple process of counting the waves*.

8. Examples

We shall now illustrate the application of the method of characteristics by an example and we shall see at the same time how the boundary value problems should be formulated.

Let us suppose that the velocity vector is given at every point on a curve AB which intersects any characteristic not more than once (Fig. 1). From the pre-

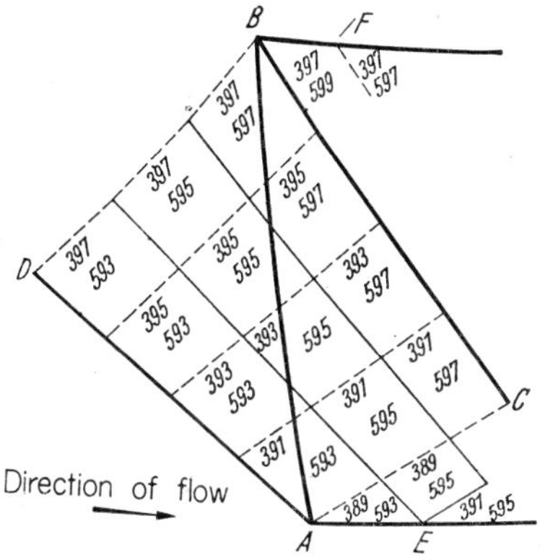

FIG. 1 Application of the method of characteristics.

scribed data the values of λ and μ are calculated and we approximate these functions by stepwise discontinuous curves, since only selected values of λ and μ are employed in the BUSEMANN method. The location of the discontinuities of λ and μ on the curve AB is then known. The characteristics emanate from these discontinuities. For the sake of simplicity, we assume that discontinuities in λ and μ occur also at A and B so that MACH lines originate also from these points. The net of characteristics can then be constructed in the quadrilateral $ACBD$ starting from the curve AB. To this end it is only necessary that μ be constant along right characteristics, while λ is constant along the left ones. The quadrilateral $ABCD$ represents the region of the flow which is determined by the data prescribed on the curve AB. It is, of course, possible, and in fact happens frequently, that along the original curve, the flow is parallel. It follows then that in the region bounded by the four characteristics, which in this case reduces to a parallelogram, the flow is parallel everywhere. In order to determine further regions of the flow field, the curve AB must be extended in such a

* In the more general case of the method of characteristics the latter merely represent curves which are particularly convenient for calculation.

manner that it never intersects a characteristic more than once. The distribution of the velocity vector along this extension must of course also be prescribed.

If the MACH waves emanating from AB intersect boundaries of the flow field, then along these only the direction of the velocity vector or its magnitude, but not both, can be given.

Frequently the boundary is a wall or the surface of an obstacle immersed in the flow. In such cases the direction of the velocity is tangential to this boundary. We assume that along such boundaries there exist only such values of ϑ which result from the values of λ and μ originally selected for the characteristic diagram. The state at the boundary can then be determined from the knowledge of either λ or μ, since the boundary is reached from the field of flow along either a left or a right characteristic. The remaining value of either λ or μ is calculated with the aid of the prescribed direction of the velocity from Eq. I, 7 (5). In Fig. 1 a MACH line intersects a wall at a point E at which there is no change in the direction of the latter. The downstream field of flow is reached from E along a left characteristic and there $\mu = 595$. The value of ϑ is given as $-4°$ and hence $\lambda = 391$.

At the point F the value of ϑ changes from $-2°$ to $0°$. The wall is reached along a right characteristic. The value of λ, both upstream and downstream of F, is 397. With this one finds that downstream of F $\mu = 597$.

Another condition which occurs frequently is that of a boundary on which the pressure is constant. The magnitude of the velocity on such a surface is constant and is best approximated by a value at one of the nodes of the characteristic net prescribed in the hodograph plane. The further treatment is then quite similar to that in the above example.

From these considerations we may formulate the following rule: at a plane wall compression waves are reflected as compression waves and expansion waves are reflected as expansion waves, while at a free surface or, more generally, on a curve of constant pressure which lies within the same included angle between the characteristics as a streamline, compression waves are reflected as expansion waves and vice versa.

These remarks are sufficient to provide an understanding of the method of characteristics but some practical experience is desirable so that the character and properties of a flow can be quickly appreciated. For this experience, as well as for a less formalistic derivation, the reader is referred to the numerous available textbooks on gas dynamics.

9. The Application of the Method of Characteristics to Transonic Flow

We shall now discuss the special form of the method of characteristics applicable to transonic flow. This special discussion is necessary since in the vicinity of $M = 1$, a special analysis is required to determine the directions of the characteristics with sufficient accuracy. In addition, this special method of characteristics provides a very simple illustration of the similarity rule for transonic flows.

We introduce, as a new variable, the deviation of the velocity from the critical value

$$\Delta w = w - a^* \tag{1}$$

so that, with the aid of Eq. I, 6 (5), the compatibility equation of the characteristics [Eq. I, 6 (7)] takes the form

$$\sqrt{\frac{w^2 - a^2}{a^2}} \frac{d\Delta w}{w} \mp d\vartheta = 0. \tag{2}$$

The term $w^2 - a^2$ is now expressed in terms of Δw, using Eq. I, 2 (8) and neglecting terms of second and higher orders in Δw

$$w^2 - a^2 = (\gamma + 1)\, w^*\, \Delta w.$$

To the first approximation $a^2 = w^{*2}$ and hence from Eq. (2)

$$\sqrt{\frac{(\gamma + 1)\Delta w}{w^*}} \frac{d\Delta w}{w^*} \mp d\vartheta = 0. \tag{3a}$$

Integration yields

$$\sqrt{\gamma + 1}\, \frac{2}{3} \left(\frac{\Delta w}{w^*}\right)^{3/2} \mp \vartheta = 0, \tag{3}$$

so that with the above approximation the characteristics in a Δw, ϑ plane are semi-cubic parabolas. To determine the direction of a characteristic we recall that the square root in Eq. (3a) represents an approximation to $\cot \alpha$ so that

$$\tan\left(\frac{\pi}{2} - \alpha\right) = \sqrt{(\gamma + 1)\frac{\Delta w}{w^*}}.$$

Thus the deviation of the MACH angle from $\pi/2$ is proportional to $\sqrt{(\Delta w)}$. Equation (3) indicates that if ϑ is initially zero, then it remains, in the entire field of flow, within the order of magnitude of $(\Delta w)^{3/2}$. The direction of the MACH lines is given by $\vartheta \pm \alpha$. The contribution of ϑ to the above equation, for small values of Δw, is small compared to that of α. One obtains thus, for the direction of the MACH lines

$$\frac{dy}{dx} = (\gamma + 1)^{-1/2} \left(\frac{\Delta w}{w^*}\right)^{-1/2}. \tag{4}$$

Equations (3) and (4) form the foundation of the method of characteristics for transonic flow. Except for the changed form of the basic equations the method is applied in the same way as the more general one discussed previously. We notice from these equations that a known field of flow can be transformed into a series of other fields by the simultaneous distortion of the scales of measurement of the dependent and the independent variables. Specifically one can leave, for example, the x coordinate unchanged and multiply the scale of Δw by a factor τ, the scale of ϑ by $\tau^{3/2}$ and the scale of y by a factor $\tau^{-1/2}$. This scaling of variables leads to an unchanged form of the system of equations. As we shall see later, these scaling factors follow from the similarity rule of transonic flow.

10. General Considerations Related to the Concept of Characteristics

We have introduced the concept of characteristics starting from the problem of determination of a field of flow in the vicinity of a curve C on which the distribution of the velocity vector is known. To this end we have calculated the derivatives of the velocity at all points on the curve from systems of linear equations. In subsonic flow, these systems always possess solutions, since the determinants of the coefficients are never zero. Thus in the subsonic flow regime all the derivatives of the velocity are continuous. In supersonic flow, on the contrary, these derivatives may possess discontinuities along characteristics. The example on which we have shown the application of the method of characteristics indicates that in supersonic flow the velocity can be prescribed on a non-characteristic curve in an arbitrary manner. This is not true in the case of subsonic flow, as may be immediately seen if one considers the potential equation for incompressible flow. The solutions of this equation can always be considered as the real parts of an analytic function of the variable $(x + iy)$. If an analytic function and all of its derivatives are known at one point, then as a result of the principle of analytic continuation, the function is known in the entire x, y plane. Thus, if the solution is known along an infinitesimally short length of the curve, it is known in the entire field of flow and therefore also on the remaining parts of the curve. Thus an arbitrarily prescribed velocity along a curve C would in general result in a contradiction. The conditions are quite similar in compressible subsonic flow.

This remark is not without practical importance. In order to obtain examples of compressible flow, attempts have been made to prescribe the velocity along a given curve, e.g. along the axis of a nozzle or downstream of a shock, and to calculate the flow starting from these values. Such a procedure is, in accordance with the above reasoning, not generally admissible. Admittedly, the velocity distribution is most often chosen in the form of an analytic function and then an analytic continuation exists within an area of sufficiently small radius. Calculation errors, however, can have the same results as if the selected distributions were non-analytic, so that even in such cases, difficulties arise.

11. Some Remarks on the Formulation of Boundary Value Problems in Subsonic and Supersonic Flow

The question of how to formulate boundary value problems is not particularly important from the point of view of an engineer since the physical aspects of a problem indicate quite clearly which quantities must be known in advance*. In transonic flow care must be exercised, however. There exists in fact a case in which the boundary value problem, as formulated on the basis of physical reasoning, need have no solution at all. This is the case of a supersonic region

* It is debatable how far the physical intuition which is usually invoked here is, in fact, based on more rigorous mathematical analysis.

embedded in a subsonic flow. To prepare for a discussion of the proper formulation of boundary value problems in a transonic regime, we shall first describe and compare the most important features of boundary value problems in subsonic and in supersonic flows.

A supersonic problem is completely formulated if the solution may be found by the method of characteristics. An example of this type of problem is given in Fig. 2. The boundary consists of the curve AB, on which the velocity vector is completely known everywhere, and of two curves AC and BD on which either only the direction or only the magnitude of the velocity vector is known. Another possible case is shown in Fig. 3, where the velocities are prescribed on two

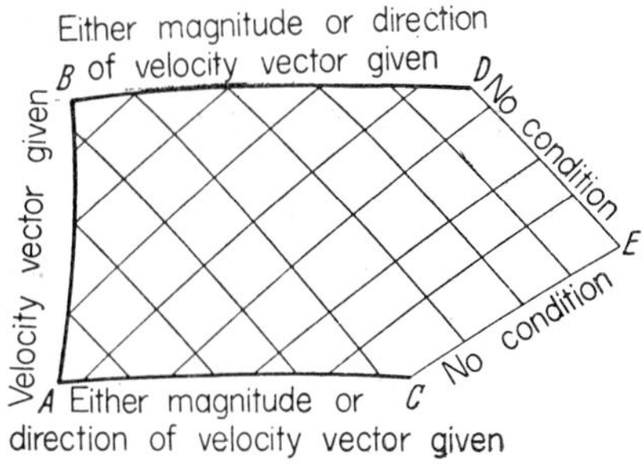

FIG. 2

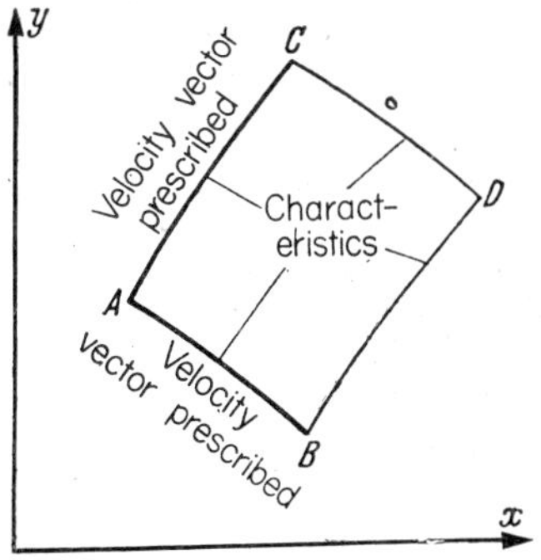

FIG. 3

characteristics AB and AC. Then, however, the compatibility equation [Eq. I, 6 (7)] must be satisfied. The field of flow can be calculated in the characteristic quadrilateral $ABCD$.

It is noteworthy that the boundary values can never be prescribed on a closed curve* but that the region in which a solution can be found is partly bounded by characteristics along which the state of the flow can be calculated.

This is contrary to the situation in subsonic flow problems in which a boundary condition must be prescribed along the entire boundary of the region considered, but this condition can take the form of only one element of the velocity vector, e.g. its derivative in a direction normal or tangential to the boundary. The existence of a solution of a problem depends in these cases also on an integral condition. It is, in general, impossible to prescribe completely the distribution of the velocity vector along a part of the contour, as was shown in the preceding section.

The differences between subsonic and supersonic flows will be illustrated by the following examples. Let us consider a rectangular region in the x, y plane

* This is particularly clear if one considers the analogy between supersonic flow and nonsteady, one-dimensional flow. The course of events cannot be determined by conditions which lie in the future.

bounded by the lines $y = 0$, $y = \pi$, $x = 0$, and $x = b$. As a differential equation, typical for subsonic flow, we select LAPLACE's equation

$$\frac{\partial^2 \Phi}{\partial x^2} + \frac{\partial^2 \Phi}{\partial y^2} = 0$$

with the boundary condition $\Phi = 0$ along $y = 0$ and along $y = \pi$, as shown in Fig. 4.

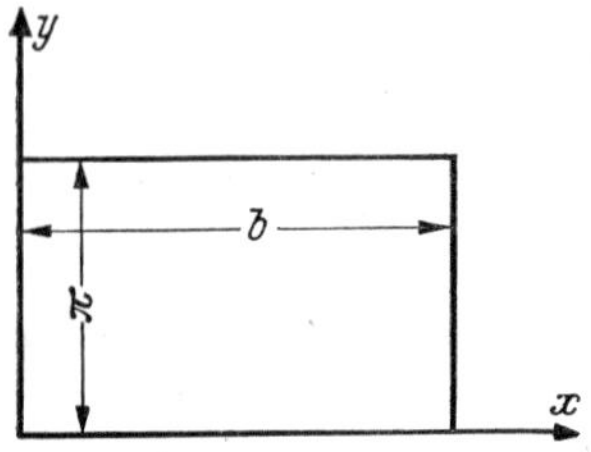

FIG. 4

Particular solutions satisfying these boundary conditions are given by

$$\Phi = e^{\mp m x} \sin m y \qquad (m = 1, 2, \ldots).$$

It is more convenient to employ the following linear combinations of these solutions

$$\Phi = \sinh(m x) \sin(m y)$$
$$\Phi = \sinh[m(b - x)] \sin(m y).$$

Let further conditions be

$$\Phi = f_1(y) \qquad \text{along } x = 0, \qquad 0 < y < \pi$$
$$\Phi = f_2(y) \qquad \text{along } x = b, \qquad 0 < y < \pi.$$

We now assume that the solutions are of the form

$$\Phi = \sum_{m=1}^{\infty} a_m \sinh(m x) \sin(m y) + \sum_{m=1}^{\infty} b_m \sinh[m(b - x)] \sin(m y)$$

where the coefficients a_m and b_m are thus far still unknown. Substituting this solution into the second set of boundary conditions one obtains

$$f_2(y) = \sum_{m=1}^{\infty} a_m \sinh(m b) \sin(m y)$$

$$f_1(y) = \sum_{m=1}^{\infty} b_m \sinh(m b) \sin(m y)$$

and in view of the orthogonality of the solutions, the coefficients are given by

$$a_m = \frac{1}{\sinh(m b)} \frac{2}{\pi} \int_0^{\pi} f_2(y) \sin(m y)\, d y$$

$$b_m = \frac{1}{\sinh(m b)} \frac{2}{\pi} \int_0^{\pi} f_1(y) \sin(m y)\, d y.$$

The convergence of the solution is assured since each term of either sum has the greatest value on the boundaries $x = b$ or $x = 0$ and there the sums converge, since they are FOURIER series representations of $f_1(y)$ and $f_2(y)$.

Were the boundary conditions given in a manner appropriate for supersonic problems, i.e. had there been no condition prescribed for Φ along CD but, along AB, had both $\Phi = f_1(y)$ and $\partial\Phi/\partial x = f_3(y)$ been given then a formal solution* would be

$$\Phi = \frac{1}{\pi}\sum_{m=1}^{\infty}\left\{\int_0^{\pi}\left(f_1(y) + \frac{f_2(y)}{m}\right)\sin[my]\,dy\right\}\sin[my]\,e^{mx}$$

$$+\frac{1}{\pi}\sum_{m=1}^{\infty}\left\{\int_0^{\pi}\left(f_1(y) - \frac{f_2(y)}{m}\right)\sin[my]\,dy\right\}\sin[my]\,e^{-mx}.$$

This expression does not, in general, converge in the entire region considered. The individual terms of the first sum would have, at least within the above region, to remain bounded when m tends to infinity. This would mean that the expressions

$$\left[\int_0^{\pi}\left(f_1(y) + \frac{f_2(y)}{m}\right)\sin my\,dy\right]e^{mb}$$

are bounded, which imposes serious restrictions on the functions f_1 and f_2.

As an example, analogous to a supersonic flow problem, let us consider the differential equation

$$\frac{\partial^2\Phi}{\partial x^2} - \frac{\partial^2\Phi}{\partial y^2} = 0$$

in the same region as above with $\Phi = f_1(y)$ and $\partial\Phi/\partial x = f_2(y)$ prescribed along $x = 0$. One can easily verify that the appropriate solution is

$$\Phi = \frac{2}{\pi}\sum_{m=1}^{\infty}\left(\int_0^{\pi} f_1(y)\sin[my]\,dy\right)\sin[my]\cos[mx]$$

$$+\frac{2}{\pi}\sum_{m=1}^{\infty}\left(\int_0^{\pi} f_2(y)\sin[my]\,dy\right)\frac{1}{m}\sin[my]\sin[mx].$$

These solutions are periodic in x with a period of 2π. If one attempts to prescribe values of Φ along $x = 0$ and along $x = 2\pi$, and in particular if these values differ from one another, a contradiction results. If, however, the values of Φ were the same for both $x = 0$ and $x = 2\pi$ then the solution is indeterminate since there exist solutions for which Φ vanishes on $x = 0$ and $x = 2\pi$, but whose values elsewhere are different from zero. Similar, although not quite so obvious, difficulties arise for regions whose length is other than 2π.

* i.e. a solution whose convergence is not, as yet, certain.

12. A Method of Derivation of the Approximate Equations

A simplification of the differential equation of motion is useful also in the case of transonic flow. It enables us to reduce the mathematical difficulties and to accentuate more clearly the physically important properties. The linearisations usually employed in subsonic and supersonic flows often lead, in the transonic regime, to physically absurd results. We retain therefore in the equations of transonic flow an additional term which, in the sense of the normal linearisation, is of second order. The reasons why this particular second order term, but not the others, is retained are usually given on a purely physical basis. These reasons are, however, only then really convincing when the nature of the flow is already well known*. Although such physical considerations form, as a rule, the starting point from which the simplified equations are derived and although we shall also employ physical reasoning to indicate the meaning of the simplifications, a more formalistic approach is of great value. It presents the process, through which the simplification of the differential equation is achieved, in a concise manner, permits a check on the intuitive physical reasoning and furthermore opens the possibility of systematically simplifying the equations in cases where no physical picture, which could serve as a starting point, exists.

Complicated differential equations are very often simplified by linearisation. The limiting process implied in a linearisation can be generalised only by distorting the coordinates simultaneously with a transition to small disturbances. This is done by considering a family of fields of flow dependent on the space and time coordinates and, in addition, on a parameter τ. Each of the fields in the family is characterised by a specific value of τ and we assume that the field corresponding to $\tau = 0$ is known. The deviations from this particular flow are then determined in the form of expansions in terms of τ. This procedure is known as the method of variational equations.

The mode of dependence of the solutions on the parameter τ determines the resulting degree of approximation. If, for example, the coordinates are independent of the parameter, we have the well-known linearised equations. These and more complicated possible situations can be illustrated on known examples from aerodynamics.

Example 1. The expansion of the potential flow around an airfoil in terms of a thickness parameter.

In this case the linearisation of the equations of motion takes a form known from the derivation of Prandtl's rule. We start from the potential equation for steady, three-dimensional flow [Eq. I, 4 (5)]

$$\Phi_{xx}\left(1-\frac{\Phi_x^2}{a^2}\right)+\Phi_{yy}\left(1-\frac{\Phi_y^2}{a^2}\right)+\Phi_{zz}\left(1-\frac{\Phi_z^2}{a^2}\right)-$$
$$-2\Phi_{xy}\frac{\Phi_x\Phi_y}{a^2}-2\Phi_{yz}\frac{\Phi_y\Phi_z}{a^2}-2\Phi_{zx}\frac{\Phi_z\Phi_x}{a^2}=0. \qquad (1)$$

* This means that the arguments are least convincing when the simplifications of the equations are attempted for the first time.

From Eq. I, 4 (6) the sonic velocity a can be expressed by

$$a^2 = \frac{\gamma+1}{2} w^{*2} - \frac{\gamma-1}{2} (\Phi_x^2 + \Phi_y^2 + \Phi_z^2). \tag{2}$$

We now assume the family of flow fields considered to be described by

$$\Phi = xU + \tau \Phi_1(x, y, z) + 0(\tau^2)^*. \tag{3}$$

In this form the coordinates are independent of τ. For $\tau = 0$ we have parallel flow with a velocity U. This parallel flow represents, naturally, a solution of the differential equations of motion. If Eq. (3) is introduced in Eqs. (1) and (2) and the resulting equations are expanded in terms of τ there results

$$\Phi_{1xx}\left(1 - \frac{U^2}{a_\infty^2}\right) + \Phi_{1yy} + \Phi_{1zz} = 0 \tag{4}$$

where

$$a_\infty^2 = \frac{\gamma+1}{2} a^{*2} - \frac{\gamma-1}{2} U^2.$$

This is the well-known linearised equation of the PRANDTL–GLAUERT approximation. The fact that the process leads to a non-trivial approximate differential equation is already a justification of the assumed form Eq. (3), inasmuch as in accordance with the derivation one can imagine a limiting process whose result is governed by the approximate Eq. (4). It is now necessary to investigate the manner in which the boundaries vary with τ. We shall not, however, do this at this point since a similar analysis will be carried out later for transonic flows.

Example 2. The flow in a nozzle.

Let us consider two-dimensional incompressible flow in a nozzle whose boundary is given by the equation $y = f(x)$. In this example one of the coordinates is distorted by virtue of a dependence on τ.

The velocity potential within the nozzle satisfies LAPLACE's equation

$$\frac{\partial^2 \Phi}{\partial x^2} + \frac{\partial^2 \Phi}{\partial y^2} = 0. \tag{5}$$

To bring the problem into a form dependent on τ we consider a number of similar nozzles which can be generated from one another by a distortion of the scale of x. The contours of the nozzles are therefore described by an equation

$$y = f(\xi), \tag{6}$$

where

$$\xi = x\tau. \tag{6a}$$

When the parameter τ is small, x must be large to yield the same value of the argument of $f(\xi)$. Thus the scale factor in the x direction is τ^{-1}. For the velocity potential we write

$$\Phi = \tau^{-1} g_{-1}(\xi, y) + \tau g_1(\xi, y) + \tau^3 g_3(\xi, y) + \cdots, \tag{7}$$

* An expression $h(x)$ is of the order of magnitude of $g(x)$ if $\lim\limits_{x\to 0} [h(x)/g(x)]$ is bounded. This is written $h(x) = 0\,[g(x)]$.

where g_{-1}, g_1, etc. are functions to be obtained as a result of the calculation. The coefficient τ^{-1} of the first term is necessary in order to maintain the mean velocity constant for all values of τ. It will be seen from the subsequent calculations that the terms containing even powers of τ are in this case unnecessary. Introducing Eq. (7) into the differential equation (5) and collecting terms of equal power of τ, one obtains

$$\frac{\partial^2 g_{-1}}{\partial y^2} = 0,$$

$$\frac{\partial^2 g_1}{\partial y^2} = -\frac{\partial^2 g_{-1}}{\partial \xi^2},$$

$$\frac{\partial^2 g_3}{\partial y^2} = -\frac{\partial^2 g_1}{\partial \xi^2}.$$

The general solutions of these equations are

$$g_{-1} = g_{-1,0}(\xi) + y g_{-1,1}(\xi),$$

$$g_1 = g_{1,0}(\xi) + y g_{1,1}(\xi) - \frac{d^2 g_{-1,0}}{d\xi^2}\frac{y^2}{2} - \frac{d^2 g_{-1,1}}{\partial \xi^2}\frac{y^3}{6},$$

$$g_3 = g_{3,0}(\xi) + y g_{3,1}(\xi) + \frac{d^4 g_{-1,0}}{d\xi^4}\frac{y^4}{24} + \frac{d^4 g_{-1,1}}{d\xi^4}\frac{y^5}{120} - \frac{d^2 g_{1,0}}{d\xi^2}\frac{y^2}{2} - \frac{d^2 g_{1,1}}{d\xi^2}\frac{y^3}{6}.$$

The functions g can be determined from the boundary conditions. The vertical components of the velocity are zero on the axis $y = 0$ and hence the terms $g_{-1,1}$, $g_{1,1}$, $g_{3,1}$, etc. vanish. On the boundary of the nozzle we have

$$\frac{\Phi_y}{\Phi_x} = \tau f'(\xi)$$

and hence

$$-\tau \frac{d^2 g_{-1,0}}{d\xi^2} f(\xi) = \tau f'(\xi) \frac{d g_{-1,0}}{d\xi},$$

$$g_{-1,0} = \text{const} \int \frac{d\xi}{f(\xi)}.$$

The remaining functions $g_{1,0}$ etc. can be determined if one considers higher order terms in the boundary conditions. Physically the last equation represents the solution of the problem in the hydraulic approximation. The succesive terms introduce corrections which account for the pressure differences resulting from the curvature of the streamlines.

This formulation of the solution involves derivatives of higher orders and it is clear therefore that the procedure does not converge in general for arbitrarily prescribed functions f. It is much more probable that the expression in Eq. (7) represents an asymptotic solution of Eq. (5) for very small values of τ. This means that if only a finite number of terms is retained in Eq. (7) and then τ is allowed to approach zero, the expression in Eq. (7) approaches more and more nearly the exact solution for the particular value of τ. The proof of convergence or the proof that an asymptotic representation has in fact been obtained is very difficult, if not impossible, for partial differential equations. The engineer and even the applied mathematician often accept this lack of proof without reflection if the results are plausible from the physical point of view.

Example 3. In connection with the method of characteristics for transonic flow, we have introduced on p. 17 a distortion of the independent and of the dependent variables, by means of which different cases of transonic flow can be generated from one another. The velocity potential corresponding to this distortion is given by

$$\Phi = a^*[x + \tau \Phi_1(x, \eta, \zeta) + O(\tau^2)]$$

with

$$\eta = y\tau^{1/2},$$
$$\zeta = z\tau^{1/2}.$$

If these expressions are introduced into the potential equation for compressible flow, one obtains finally the approximate equation for transonic flow

$$-(\gamma + 1)\Phi_{1x}\Phi_{1xx} + \Phi_{1\eta\eta} + \Phi_{1\zeta\zeta} = 0.$$

The details of the derivation are left to the reader. The present considerations will be later generalised by allowing shocks to occur within the field of flow.

Evidently the assumed form of dependence of the solution on the parameter in question is of fundamental importance in the technique described above. It replaces the order-of-magnitude estimates which are normally made. Several trials may be necessary before the correct form is found. The only criterion available on which the suitability of a particular assumed form of the solution may be judged is that it should lead to non-trivial differential equations.

Another example is offered by the flow at very high Mach numbers (hypersonic flow). Such very high Mach numbers result when at finite flow velocities the velocity of sound becomes very small. As the basic flow one considers a parallel flow with an infinite Mach number ($a = 0$). The term in the potential equation, responsible for the degeneration is $\Phi_{yy}(a^2 - \Phi_y^2)$. In a linearised treatment in the usual sense, this term would vanish, since in the base flow $a = 0$ and also $\Phi_y = 0$. It is therefore necessary to assume such a form for the deviations from the base flow that for small values of τ this term remains finite. The details of this are left to the reader.

CHAPTER II

SIMPLIFIED EQUATIONS AND THE SIMILARITY RULE FOR TRANSONIC FLOW

1. Preliminary Remarks

WITH the exception of such flows which may be computed by means of the method of characteristics or those for which exact solutions may be obtained by a hodograph transformation, one usually has to rely on a simplification of the differential equations of motion when treating compressible flow problems. In the subsonic and supersonic regimes the equations employed are either those of PRANDTL-GLAUERT or those of ACKERET. In the case of transonic flows, the simplification cannot be carried that far since it would frequently result in meaningless solutions and, furthermore, the important consequences of the existence of both subsonic and supersonic regimes in close proximity to one another are always completely obscured. It is, however, necessary also in this case to introduce some measure of simplification of the equations. The resulting equations can, in some special cases, be integrated exactly and, furthermore, new solutions can be generated from known ones by simultaneous distortions of the independent and dependent variables. A number of flows are then related by a suitable similarity rule so that for a given family of flows the number of parameters to be determined experimentally is substantially reduced. The similarity rule was established almost simultaneously be VON KARMAN [54], GUDERLEY [25] and OSWATITSCH.

2. The Prandtl–Glauert Equations

The method of characteristics for transonic flows has already indicated (c.f. p. 17) a distortion of coordinates which leads to a desired simplification of the differential equations. This formulation will be employed as a starting point for our later considerations. At present, however, we shall attempt to estimate the orders of magnitude of the terms neglected in the PRANDTL-GLAUERT approximation in the special case of potential flow. This will afford a better basis for the derivation of the simplified equations of transonic flow.

We start from the special case of the potential equation for plane flow and assume a velocity potential in the form

$$\Phi = Ux + \tilde{\Phi}.$$

The first term represents a uniform parallel flow with a velocity U, while the second term $\tilde{\Phi}$ the deviations from this parallel flow. The complete differential equation for $\tilde{\Phi}$ takes the form

$$\tilde{\Phi}_{xx}(a_\infty^2 - U^2) + \tilde{\Phi}_{yy}a_\infty^2 = \tilde{\Phi}_{xx}\left\{(\gamma+1)\,U\tilde{\Phi}_x + \frac{\gamma+1}{2}\tilde{\Phi}_x^2 + \frac{\gamma-1}{2}\tilde{\Phi}_y^2\right\} +$$
$$+ 2\tilde{\Phi}_{xy}\left\{U\tilde{\Phi}_y + \tilde{\Phi}_x\tilde{\Phi}_y\right\} +$$
$$+ \tilde{\Phi}_{yy}\left\{(\gamma-1)\,U\tilde{\Phi}_x + \frac{\gamma-1}{2}\tilde{\Phi}_x^2 + \frac{\gamma+1}{2}\tilde{\Phi}_y^2\right\}$$

where a_∞ is the sonic velocity of the undisturbed flow. In the usual linearisation the right-hand side of the above equation is neglected. In order to gain an insight into the order of magnitude of the neglected terms we simultaneously introduce a distortion of coordinates, according to the method of PRANDTL-GLAUERT, and represent the solution in the form of an expansion in terms of the parameter

$$\tilde{\Phi} = \tau\bar{\Phi}(\bar{x}, \bar{y}), \tag{1}$$

where

$$x = \bar{x}, \tag{2a}$$

$$\bar{y} = y\sqrt{1 - M_\infty^2}, \tag{2b}$$

$$M_\infty = \frac{U}{a_\infty}. \tag{2c}$$

With this choice of independent variables, namely $\bar{x}, \bar{y}$, the terms retained in the PRANDTL-GLAUERT equations do not change with the MACH number since

$$\tau\bar{\Phi}_{\bar{x}\bar{x}}(1 - M_\infty^2)\,a_\infty^2 + \tau\bar{\Phi}_{\bar{y}\bar{y}}(1 - M_\infty^2)\,a_\infty^2 = \tau^2(\gamma+1)\,U\bar{\Phi}_{\bar{x}\bar{x}}\bar{\Phi}_{\bar{x}} +$$
$$+ \tau^3\frac{\gamma+1}{2}\bar{\Phi}_{\bar{x}\bar{x}}\bar{\Phi}_{\bar{x}}^2 + \tau^3\frac{\gamma-1}{2}(1 - M_\infty^2)\,\bar{\Phi}_{\bar{x}\bar{x}}\bar{\Phi}_{\bar{y}}^2 +$$
$$+ 2\,\tau^2\bar{\Phi}_{\bar{x}\bar{y}}(1 - M_\infty^2)\,U\bar{\Phi}_{\bar{y}} + 2\,\tau^3\bar{\Phi}_{\bar{x}\bar{y}}\bar{\Phi}_{\bar{x}}\bar{\Phi}_{\bar{y}}(1 - M_\infty^2) +$$
$$+ \tau^2(1 - M_\infty^2)\,(\gamma-1)\,U\bar{\Phi}_{\bar{x}}\bar{\Phi}_{\bar{y}\bar{y}} + \tau^3\frac{\gamma+1}{2}(1 - M_\infty^2)^2\,\bar{\Phi}_{\bar{y}\bar{y}}\bar{\Phi}_{\bar{y}}^2 +$$
$$+ \tau^3\frac{\gamma-1}{2}(1 - M_\infty^2)\,\bar{\Phi}_{\bar{y}\bar{y}}\bar{\Phi}_{\bar{x}}^2. \tag{3}$$

The terms on the RHS of this equation are, as we might have expected, at least of second order in τ while those on the LHS are linear in τ. Thus for a given MACH number of the undisturbed flow the importance of the terms on the RHS can be reduced at will by choosing a suitably small value of τ.

A measure of the error committed by neglecting the RHS of the equation is afforded by a comparison of the largest terms on the RHS with one of the terms retained on the LHS of the equation. Assuming the MACH number to be approximately unity, the influence of terms containing the factor $M^2 - 1$ becomes small. The only second order term which remains is $\tau^2(\gamma + 1)\, U \Phi_{\bar{x}\bar{x}} \Phi_{\bar{x}}$. The ratio of this term to the first term on the LHS is

$$\frac{U\tau(\gamma + 1)\,\overline{\Phi}_{\bar{x}}}{a_\infty^2(1 - M_\infty^2)} \cdot$$

If this ratio is small then the problem falls within the range of validity of PRANDTL's rule. To see what this implies let us consider a specific solution of the equations simplified in accordance with PRANDTL's rule. In this solution $\overline{\Phi}_{\bar{x}}$ is independent of the MACH number or of τ. The thickness ratio of a two-dimensional body is proportional to $\widetilde{\Phi}_y$, i.e. to $\tau \sqrt{(1 - M_\infty^2)}$. Consequently τ in the above ratio may be expressed in terms of the thickness parameter. To remain within the range of validity of PRANDTL's rule the thickness ratio must tend to zero as fast as $(1 - M_\infty^2)^{3/2}$ when the MACH number approaches one.

In the case of three-dimensional flows the LHS contains an additional term $\widetilde{\Phi}_{zz}$ and it is then possible that the term $\widetilde{\Phi}_{\bar{x}} \widetilde{\Phi}_{\bar{x}\bar{x}}$, used as basis of comparison above, is small compared to the remaining terms of the LHS. The condition of validity of PRANDTL's rule, formulated above, is then sufficient but it is no longer a necessary condition. In fact such three-dimensional problems in which the thickness of the profile is zero can be analysed on the basis of the linearised theory even when $M = 1$ (c.f. p. 19).

The above discussion suggests a similar formulation to that found in Section I, 9 on the basis of the method of characteristics. The term $(\gamma + 1)\, U \widetilde{\Phi}_x \widetilde{\Phi}_{xx}$ must be retained in the approximate equations of transonic flow. This necessitates a suitable relationship between τ and $(1 - M_\infty^2)$. We may put, for example,

$$(1 - M_\infty^2) \sim \tau .$$

This choice is not unique, a relation of the form

$$2(1 - M_\infty) \sim \tau$$

would serve the same purpose. One might attempt to utilize this comparative freedom of choice in the relation between τ and $(1 - M_\infty^2)$ to satisfy additional conditions in simplifying the differential equations.

3. The Simplified Differential Equations of Flow

We shall now carry out a systematic simplification of the differential equations for the transonic regime. Contrary to our earlier analysis we shall include now the three-dimensional flow problems and we shall further consider the conditions arising in the presence of shock waves. The question of boundary conditions, which thus far has been completely neglected, must now be considered. It may appear superfluous to investigate whether the influence of entropy should be considered in transonic flow problems, since in linearised supersonic flow theory the entropy can always be neglected. There is, however, a measure of uncertainty in this respect in connection with transonic flows since these are very sensitive to changes in cross-section area (in accordance with Eq. I, 2 (10a) the mass flow density is a maximum at $M = 1$) and an increase in entropy has as a consequence an increase in the required cross-section area of a stream tube. For the present, therefore, we shall consider the entropy to be variable although we shall see finally that the changes in entropy can be neglected.

The flow is assumed to be isoenergetic since without this assumption only particular streamlines of the base flow would have a MACH number near unity.

We start from the general equation of continuity for steady flow, Eq. I, 4 (4)

$$\frac{\partial v_x}{\partial x}\left(1-\frac{v_x^2}{a^2}\right)+\frac{\partial v_y}{\partial y}\left(1-\frac{v_y^2}{a^2}\right)+\frac{\partial v_z}{\partial z}\left(1-\frac{v_z^2}{v^2}\right)-\left(\frac{\partial v_x}{\partial y}+\frac{\partial v_y}{\partial x}\right)\frac{v_x v_y}{a^2}-$$

$$-\left(\frac{\partial v_y}{\partial z}+\frac{\partial v_z}{\partial y}\right)\frac{v_x v_z}{a^2}-\left(\frac{\partial v_z}{\partial x}+\frac{\partial v_y}{\partial z}\right)\frac{v_z v_x}{a^2}=0 \tag{1}$$

and from CROCCO's equation

$$\mathbf{v}\times \operatorname{curl}\mathbf{v} = -T \operatorname{grad} s. \tag{2}$$

Introducing a parameter τ and a characteristic length x_0, we assume for the velocities, the following form (GUDERLEY [25])

$$\left.\begin{aligned} v_x &= a^* + \tau\bar{v}_x(\xi,\eta,\zeta),\\ v_y &= \tau^{3/2}\bar{v}_y(\xi,\eta,\zeta),\\ v_z &= \tau^{3/2}\bar{v}_z(\xi,\eta,\zeta),\end{aligned}\right\} \tag{3a}$$

where

$$\xi=\frac{x}{x_0},\qquad \eta=\tau^{1/2}\frac{y}{x_0},\qquad \zeta=\tau^{1/2}\frac{z}{x_0}. \tag{3b}$$

From BERNOULLI's equation we obtain

$$a^2-v_x^2=\tau(\gamma+1)\,a^*\bar{v}_x+0(\tau^2),$$

$$a^2-v_y^2=a^{*2}+0(\tau),$$

$$a^2-v_z^2=a^{*2}+0(\tau)$$

and hence retaining only the terms of lowest order in τ in Eq. (1)

$$-(\gamma+1)\,a^*\bar{v}_x\frac{\partial\bar{v}_x}{\partial\xi}+a^{*2}\frac{\partial\bar{v}_y}{\partial\eta}+a^{*2}\frac{\partial\bar{v}_z}{\partial\zeta}=0. \tag{4}$$

The deviations from the critical velocity appearing in our flow are of the order $0(\tau)$. In accordance with the well-known shock equations the entropy changes are of the order $0(\tau)^3$. To facilitate the substitution of Eq. (3) in CROCCO's equation we calculate separately

$$\left.\begin{aligned} \bar{\mathbf{v}} &= \mathbf{i}(a^* + \tau \bar{v}_x) + \mathbf{j}\tau^{3/2}\bar{v}_y + \mathbf{k}\,\tau^{3/2}\bar{v}_z \\ \operatorname{curl}\mathbf{v} &= \frac{\tau^{1.5}}{x_0}\left(\frac{\partial \bar{v}_x}{\partial \eta} - \frac{\partial \bar{v}_y}{\partial \xi}\right)\mathbf{k} + \frac{\tau^2}{x_0}\left(\frac{\partial \bar{v}_y}{\partial \zeta} - \frac{\partial \bar{v}_z}{\partial \eta}\right)\mathbf{i} + \\ &+ \frac{\tau^{1.5}}{x_0}\left(\frac{\partial \bar{v}_z}{\partial \xi} - \frac{\partial \bar{v}_x}{\partial \zeta}\right)\mathbf{j} \end{aligned}\right\} \tag{5}$$

where **i**, **j** and **k** are unit vectors in the x, y and z directions. Retaining again only the terms of lowest order in τ one obtains from Eq. (2)

$$\frac{\partial \bar{v}_z}{\partial \xi} - \frac{\partial \bar{v}_x}{\partial \zeta} = 0, \quad \frac{\partial \bar{v}_y}{\partial \xi} - \frac{\partial \bar{v}_x}{\partial \eta} = 0. \tag{6}$$

This equation states that the component of the vorticity vector, normal to the streamlines of the undisturbed flow, is zero. This is not unexpected since the influence of entropy in Eq. (2) is negligible and since the streamlines of the undisturbed flow are approximations to those of the actual flow.

Conclusions reaching further with regard to the vorticity vector can be derived from the fact that the velocity components lying in the plane parallel to that of the shock are unchanged across the latter. If the flow was originally irrotational then this means that downstream of the shock the vorticity components normal to the plane of the shock are zero. Since the direction of the normal to the shock plane can never be also normal to the streamlines, as the latter would then lie in the plane of the shock, and since in accordance with Eq. (6) the direction of the vorticity vector coincides with that of the tangent to the streamline it follows that after the first shock and, of course, also after any succesive one, the vorticity remain zero. It is therefore permissible to introduce in the present approximation a velocity potential

$$\Phi = a^* x_0 \tau \bar{\Phi}(\xi, \eta, \zeta) \tag{7}$$

which must satisfy the equation

$$-(\gamma + 1)\,\bar{\Phi}_\xi \bar{\Phi}_{\xi\xi} + \bar{\Phi}_{\eta\eta} + \bar{\Phi}_{\zeta\zeta} = 0. \tag{8}$$

In axisymmetric flows the velocity potential takes the form

$$\Phi = a^* x_0 \tau \bar{\Phi}(\xi, \bar{r}), \tag{9}$$

where

$$\bar{r} = \frac{r}{x_0}\tau^{1/2} \quad \text{and} \quad r = \sqrt{y^2 + z^2}$$

and the potential equation is

$$-(\gamma + 1)\,\bar{\Phi}_\xi \bar{\Phi}_{\xi\xi} + \frac{\bar{\Phi}_{\bar{r}}}{\bar{r}} + \bar{\Phi}_{\bar{r}\bar{r}} = 0. \tag{10}$$

4. The Shock Conditions

Up to the present time our considerations were based on the assumption of velocities being given by Eq. II, 3 (3). Since this assumption led to a non-trivial form of the differential equation of flow, and therefore has proved successful, it remains to investigate how it affects other relationships which are of importance in the flow field. No new assumptions need be made in connection with this investigation. We shall consider the equations governing changes in conditions across a shock in the present section; in Section II, 5 we shall consider the boundary conditions and, finally, on p. 43 the forms of the equations of continuity and of momentum which result under the assumed form of the velocity components.

We have already discussed the condition that the velocity components tangential to a shock cannot undergo any change across the latter. This condition is automatically satisfied by requiring the velocity potential to remain continuous across a shock. The conditions for the velocity components normal to the shock must be considered separately.

Let us denote the states before and after the shock by subscripts I and II respectively and by subscripts n and t the velocity components normal and tangential to the shock. Then for a perfect gas we can write PRANDTL's equation

$$v_{n\,\mathrm{I}}\, v_{n\,\mathrm{II}} = a^{*2} - \frac{\gamma - 1}{\gamma + 1} v_t^2 . \tag{1}$$

Its derivation is based on the assumption of a plane normal shock. The conservation of momentum, energy and mass across the shock is expressed by

Momentum

$$p_\mathrm{I} + \varrho_\mathrm{I}^2 w_\mathrm{I}^2 = p_\mathrm{II} + \varrho_\mathrm{II} w_\mathrm{II}^2 \tag{2a}$$

Energy

$$a_\mathrm{I}^2 + \frac{\gamma - 1}{2} w_\mathrm{I}^2 = a_\mathrm{II}^2 + \frac{\gamma - 1}{2} w_\mathrm{II}^2 \tag{2b}$$

Mass

$$\varrho_\mathrm{I} w_\mathrm{I} = \varrho_\mathrm{II} w_\mathrm{II} \tag{2c}$$

Equation I, 2 (6) was used to transform the energy equation into the above form. For the sake of simplicity the RHS of the energy equation may be denoted by $[(\gamma + 1)/2] a_n^{*2}$. Dividing Eq. (2a) by Eq. (2c) and replacing $\gamma p/\varrho$ by a^2, in accordance with Eq. I, 2 (5), there results

$$\frac{a_\mathrm{I}^2}{\gamma w_\mathrm{I}} + w_\mathrm{I} = \frac{a_\mathrm{II}^2}{\gamma w_\mathrm{II}} + w_\mathrm{II} . \tag{2}$$

We now express a_I and a_II in terms of w_I or w_II and a_n^* with the aid of Eq. (2b), obtaining

$$\frac{\frac{\gamma + 1}{2} a_n^{*2} - \frac{\gamma - 1}{2} w_\mathrm{I}^2}{\gamma w_\mathrm{I}} + w_\mathrm{I} = \frac{\frac{\gamma + 1}{2} a_n^{*2} - \frac{\gamma - 1}{2} w_\mathrm{II}^2}{\gamma w_\mathrm{II}} + w_\mathrm{II} .$$

This is a quadratic equation for w_I one solution of which, namely $w_I = w_{II}$, is known. Multiplying the above equation by $\gamma w_I/(w_I - w_{II})$ we obtain

$$w_I w_{II} = a_n^{*2}. \tag{3}$$

Superimposing an equal velocity component parallel to the shock on both sides of the latter we obtain the conditions pertaining to a plane inclined shock. The quantities w_I and w_{II} are now replaced by the velocity components normal to the shock, viz. v_{nI} and v_{nII}, and the superimposed tangential component is v_t. Since from BERNOULLI's equation

$$a_{II}^2 + \frac{\gamma - 1}{2} w_{II}^2 = \frac{\gamma + 1}{2} a^{*2}$$

and further

$$w_{II}^2 = v_{nII}^2 + v_t^2$$

one obtains

$$a_n^{*2} = a^{*2} - \frac{\gamma - 1}{\gamma + 1} v_t^2$$

which in conjunction with Eq. (3) yields Eq. (1).

Let the surface of the shock be given by

$$f(\xi, \eta, \zeta) = 0 \tag{4}$$

then this surface is affected by the distortion of coordinates given in Eq. II, 3, (3b). In the x, y, z system of coordinates the unit vector normal to the shock is then given by

$$\left(\mathbf{i}\frac{\partial f}{\partial \xi} + \tau^{1/2}\mathbf{j}\frac{\partial f}{\partial \eta} + \tau^{1/2}\mathbf{k}\frac{\partial f}{\partial \zeta}\right)\left[\left(\frac{\partial f}{\partial \xi}\right)^2 + \tau\left(\left(\frac{\partial f}{\partial \eta}\right)^2 + \left(\frac{\partial f}{\partial \zeta}\right)^2\right)\right]^{-1/2}.$$

Employing Eq. II, 3 (5) for the velocity vector and retaining only terms of the first order in τ, one obtains for the component normal to the shock

$$v_n = a^*\left(1 - \frac{\tau}{2}\,\frac{\left(\frac{\partial f}{\partial \eta}\right)^2 + \left(\frac{\partial f}{\partial \zeta}\right)^2}{\left(\frac{\partial f}{\partial \xi}\right)^2}\right) + \tau \bar{v}_x.$$

This equation holds for the normal component both upstream and downstream of the shock depending on whether subscripts I or II are introduced throughout. We can now determine the tangential component v_t as the magnitude of the vector product of the unit vector normal to the shock and of the velocity. Retaining again only terms of first order in τ, we obtain

$$v_t = \tau^{1/2} a^* \sqrt{\frac{\left(\frac{\partial f}{\partial \eta}\right)^2 + \left(\frac{\partial f}{\partial \zeta}\right)^2}{\left(\frac{\partial f}{\partial \xi}\right)^2}}.$$

Introducing these expressions into Eq. (1) and considering only the terms of lowest order in τ, we obtain

$$\bar{v}_{x\,\mathrm{I}} + \bar{v}_{x\,\mathrm{II}} = \frac{2}{\gamma+1}\, a^* \, \frac{\left(\dfrac{\partial f}{\partial \eta}\right)^2 + \left(\dfrac{\partial f}{\partial \zeta}\right)^2}{\left(\dfrac{\partial f}{\partial \xi}\right)^2}. \tag{5}$$

It is noteworthy that the above equation involves the angle of inclination of the shock although the plane of the latter is normal to the direction of the flow in a limiting case of $\tau \to 0$. The shock relationship is apparently not approximated by a normal shock since for this latter case

$$\frac{\partial f}{\partial \zeta} = \frac{\partial f}{\partial \eta} = 0$$

and one obtains

$$\bar{v}_{x\,\mathrm{I}} + \bar{v}_{x\,\mathrm{II}} = 0.$$

The change in the velocity across a shock is given by

$$\tau(\bar{v}_{x\,\mathrm{II}} - \bar{v}_{x\,\mathrm{I}}) = \tau \left(-2\bar{v}_{x\,\mathrm{I}} + \frac{2}{\gamma+1}\, a^* \, \frac{\left(\dfrac{\partial f}{\partial \eta}\right)^2 + \left(\dfrac{\partial f}{\partial \xi}\right)^2}{\left(\dfrac{\partial f}{\partial \xi}\right)^2} \right). \tag{6}$$

The contributions of the changes in the y and z directions can be obtained on the basis of the following reasoning. Since the tangential components of the velocity remain unchanged across a shock, the change in velocity must be in the direction of the normal to the plane of the shock. Hence, from Eq. (4) the components of the change in the velocity in the y and z directions are

$$\Delta v_y = v_{y\,\mathrm{II}} - v_{y\,\mathrm{I}} = \tau^{3/2}(\bar{v}_{x\,\mathrm{II}} - \bar{v}_{x\,\mathrm{I}}) \frac{\partial f}{\partial \eta} \Big/ \frac{\partial f}{\partial \xi}, \tag{7a}$$

$$\Delta v_z = v_{z\,\mathrm{II}} - v_{z\,\mathrm{I}} = \tau^{3/2}(\bar{v}_{x\,\mathrm{II}} - \bar{v}_{x\,\mathrm{I}}) \frac{\partial f}{\partial \zeta} \Big/ \frac{\partial f}{\partial \xi}. \tag{7b}$$

Introducing, in accordance with Eq. II, 3 (3a),

$$\Delta v_y = \tau^{3/2}\, \Delta \bar{v}_y,$$

$$\Delta v_z = \tau^{3/2}\, \Delta \bar{v}_z$$

there results with the aid of Eq. (6)

$$\sqrt{\Delta \bar{v}_y^2 + \Delta \bar{v}_z^2} = \left\{ \frac{\left(\dfrac{\partial f}{\partial \eta}\right)^2 + \left(\dfrac{\partial f}{\partial \zeta}\right)^2}{\left(\dfrac{\partial f}{\partial \xi}\right)^2} \right\}^{1/2} \left[-2\bar{v}_{x\,\mathrm{I}} + \frac{2}{\gamma+1}\, a^* \, \frac{\left(\dfrac{\partial f}{\partial \eta}\right)^2 + \left(\dfrac{\partial f}{\partial \zeta}\right)^2}{\left(\dfrac{\partial f}{\partial \xi}\right)^2} \right].$$

The term

$$\left[\left(\frac{\partial f}{\partial \eta}\right)^2 + \left(\frac{\partial f}{\partial \zeta}\right)^2\right] \Big/ \left(\frac{\partial f}{\partial \xi}\right)^2$$

may be eliminated with the aid of Eq. (5) yielding

$$\frac{\sqrt{\Delta \bar{v}_y^2 + \Delta \bar{v}_z^2}}{a^*} = \sqrt{\frac{\gamma+1}{2}} \sqrt{\frac{\bar{v}_{x\,\mathrm{I}} + \bar{v}_{x\,\mathrm{II}}}{a^*}} \frac{\bar{v}_{x\,\mathrm{I}} - \bar{v}_{x\,\mathrm{II}}}{a^*}. \tag{8}$$

This is the equation of the shock polar diagram for transonic flow and it has been derived by HANTZSCHE and WENDT [47]. The direction of the normal to the plane of the shock can, in accordance with Eq. (4) and with the aid of Eqs. (7a) and (7b), also be expressed in the form

$$\mathbf{i} + \tau^{1/2}\,\mathbf{j}\,\frac{\Delta \bar{v}_y}{\bar{v}_{x\,\mathrm{II}} - \bar{v}_{x\,\mathrm{I}}} + \tau^{1/2}\,\mathbf{k}\,\frac{\Delta \bar{v}_z}{\bar{v}_{x\,\mathrm{II}} - \bar{v}_{x\,\mathrm{I}}}. \tag{9}$$

5. The Boundary Conditions

No particular difficulties are offered by the boundary conditions at a large distance from an obstacle, since there one usually encounters a parallel flow with a MACH number different, in general, from unity. Thus, at that boundary $\bar{\Phi}_\xi = \text{const}$, $\bar{\Phi}_\eta = 0$, $\bar{\Phi}_\zeta = 0$, as may be seen from Eq. II, 3 (7). If, in addition, $\bar{\Phi}_\xi = 0$, the MACH number of the undisturbed flow is unity for all values of τ. In the first approximation the deviations of the MACH number of the undisturbed flow from 1, in the more general case, are proportional to τ.

In considering the boundary conditions on the surface of an obstacle one might be tempted to assume that the profile of the obstacle is affected by the distortion of the y and z coordinates as given by Eq. II, 3 (3b). Actually, however, this is not the case since then the slopes of the streamlines, which to the first approximation are given by v_y/a^* and v_z/a^*, would have to vary in proportion to $\tau^{-1/2}$. Equation II, 3 (3a) shows that this is not the case.

The shape of a streamline, which in the undisturbed flow may be given e.g. by $y_0 = \eta_0 x_0 \tau^{-1/2}$, $z_0 = \zeta_0 x_0 \tau^{-1/2}$ with $\eta_0 = \text{const}$ and $\zeta_0 = \text{const}$, can be obtained by determining the deviations of the y and z coordinates from y_0 and z_0. Denoting these deviations by $\tilde{y}$ and $\tilde{z}$, Eq. II, 3 (3) yields

$$\frac{d\tilde{y}}{dx} = \frac{\tau^{3/2}\bar{v}_y(\xi, \eta_0 + x_0^{-1}\tau^{1/2}\tilde{y}, \zeta_0 + x_0^{-1}\tau^{1/2}\tilde{z})}{a^* + \tau\bar{v}_x(\xi, \eta_0 + x_0^{-1}\tau^{1/2}\tilde{y}, \zeta_0 + x_0^{-1}\tau^{1/2}\tilde{z})} \tag{1}$$

with a similar equation for $d\tilde{z}/dx$.

If the quantities appearing in these equations are differentiable, as is the case almost everywhere within the flow, then the equations may be expanded in series in the vicinity of the undisturbed streamlines, so that when only the terms of lowest order in τ are retained there result

$$\frac{\partial \tilde{y}}{\partial \xi} = \frac{x_0\tau^{3/2}\bar{v}_y(\xi, \eta_0, \zeta_0)}{a^*}; \quad \frac{\partial \tilde{z}}{\partial \xi} = \frac{x_0\tau^{3/2}\bar{v}_z(\xi, \eta_0, \zeta_0)}{a^*}. \tag{2}$$

According to the above equation the deformations of the streamlines are proportional to $x_0 \tau^{3/2}$. The surface of a body submerged in the flow coincides with some of the streamlines and it appears plausible, therefore, that the same dependence on τ will apply to the surface, i.e. that the thickness of the body is proportional to $x_0 \tau^{3/2}$.

In any case the inclination of the streamlines to the x axis tends to zero as $\tau \to 0$ and the obstacle is then represented by sections of a cylindrical surface whose generators are parallel to the x axis. On a swept-back wing these cylindrical surfaces are generated by planes parallel to the x axis and coinciding as closely as possible with the wing itself. For a circular wing one would obtain a circular cylinder. To confirm our above conjecture regarding the dependence of the profile of the body on τ one must assume that for $\tau \neq 0$ the field of flow can be continued to this cylindrical surface, i.e. inside the body itself, both from above and from below, without the occurence of any singularities between the cylindrical surface and the contour of the body proper*. The continuations originating from above and from below the body do not have to be the same on the surface of the cylinder. Thus the above-mentioned cylindrical surface may carry discontinuities in the velocity. Such a cylindrical surface carrying numerous singularities always represents the surface of a body submerged in the flow. Since the solutions for the field of flow are functions of ξ, η and ζ, the positions of these discontinuities are also functions of these variables and hence the position of the surface carrying the discontinuities must be subject to the distortion introduced by the parameter τ and by x_0. We now assume on this cylindrical surface the existence of derivatives required in the simplification of Eq. (1) and we find, as before, that the deviations of the surface of an immersed body from the cylindrical surface are proportional to $x_0 \tau^{3/2}$. This deviation describes both the thickness of the body and the angle of attack. As mentioned above, the shape of the approximating cylinder is distorted with x_0 and τ in the same way as the coordinates.

The boundary conditions at the surface of the submerged body can be stated immediately for those cases which are amenable to calculation. The derivation, therefore, of the boundary conditions for a body of arbitrary shape can be given in an abbreviated form. We start with the cylinder which represents the surface of the body for $\tau = 0$. Let the unit vector normal to this cylinder be $\mathfrak{e}_{n_0}$ while the unit vector in a plane $x = \text{const}$ and tangential to the surface is $\mathfrak{e}_{t_0}$. Finally let the unit vector in the x direction be $\mathfrak{e}_x$. The deviation at $\tau \neq 0$ of the surface of the obstacle from the approximating cylindrical surface can be given in terms of a length $x_0 h^{3/2}$, measured in the direction of the normal to the surface. As a result of this definition, h is independent of τ and x_0. For $\tau \neq 0$ the vector normal to the surface of the body is found to be approximately

$$\mathfrak{e}_n = \mathfrak{e}_{n_0} - \tau^{3/2} \frac{\partial h}{\partial \xi} \mathfrak{e}_x - \tau^{3/2} x_0 \frac{\partial h}{\partial t} \mathfrak{e}_{t_0},$$

* This assumption is made always in the analysis of thin airfoils; it is, however, not always valid. For example, it is certainly violated at all points where there are discontinuities in the derivatives of the profile.

where $x_0\, d\xi$ and dt are linear elements in the directions of $\mathbf{e}_x$ and $\mathbf{e}_{t_0}$ respectively. The velocity vector is resolved in the same three directions $\mathbf{e}_x$, $\mathbf{e}_{n_0}$ and $\mathbf{e}_{t_0}$, and we denote the velocity components in the directions $\mathbf{e}_{n_0}$ and $\mathbf{e}_{t_0}$ by v_n and v_t respectively. Since v_n and v_t result from the components v_y and v_z they are proportional to $\tau^{3/2}$ and we can, therefore, introduce $v_n = \tau^{3/2}\bar{v}_n$ and $v_t = \tau^{3/2}\bar{v}_t$, obtaining

$$\mathbf{v} = (a^* + \tau\,\bar{v}_x)\,\mathbf{e}_x + \tau^{3/2}\bar{v}_n\,\mathbf{e}_{n_0} + \tau^{3/2}\bar{v}_t\,\mathbf{e}_{t_0}.$$

The velocity component normal to the surface of the body must be zero. Hence, retaining only terms of lowest order in τ, the boundary condition may be written

$$\bar{v}_n - a^*\frac{\partial h}{\partial \xi} = 0. \tag{3}$$

If $\partial h/\partial \xi$ is sufficiently smooth, $\bar{v}_n$ may be expressed in terms of $\bar{v}_y$ and $\bar{v}_z$ on the approximating cylindrical surface. The component $\bar{v}_t$ is of no importance in the last equation.

If the deviations from the critical velocity are small, then for the pressure one obtains with the aid of Eq. I, 2 (9)

$$p - p^* = -\frac{\varrho^*}{2}\,(w^2 - a^{*2}) \tag{4}$$

which expression is to be evaluated on the surface of the obstacle. This surface deviates from the approximating cylinder by amounts of the order of magnitude of $\tau^{3/2}$. Since the derivatives of the velocity along the surface must be considered to be bounded, one obtains, as the first approximation for the pressure distribution along the surface of the body,

$$p - p^* = -\tau\,\varrho^* a^{*2}\,\bar{\Phi}_\xi. \tag{5}$$

Here the arguments of $\bar{\Phi}_\xi$ must be those on the approximating cylindrical surface and hence $\bar{\Phi}_\xi$ is independent of τ and one finds that the pressures on the surface of the obstacle are to the first approximation proportional to τ. An axisymmetric obstacle provides an exception to the above considerations; for $\tau = 0$ it degenerates into a segment of the x axis.

Since the differential equation for an axisymmetric flow [Eq. II, 3 (10)] is singular along the axis because of the term $\bar{\Phi}_{\bar{r}}/\bar{r}$, the velocity potential along the segment of the axis contained within the obstacle need not be regular. It is easy to show that the principal terms of a series expansion in the vicinity of the axis are of the form

$$\Phi = a^* x_0\,\tau\,\bar{\Phi}, \tag{6}$$

where

$$\bar{\Phi} = f_1(\xi) + f_2(\xi)\ln\bar{r}. \tag{6a}$$

One should recall that $\bar{r} = (r/x_0)\,\tau^{1/2}$, which is the solution resulting from the omission of the term $(\gamma + 1)\,\bar{\Phi}_\xi\bar{\Phi}_{\xi\xi}$ in Eq. II, 3 (10). The corrections due to this neglected term are of the order of $\bar{r}^2 \ln^2 \bar{r}$. The velocity component in the r direction

$$\Phi_r = a^* x_0 \tau \frac{\partial \bar{\Phi}}{\partial \bar{r}} \frac{d\bar{r}}{dr} = a^* \frac{\tau x_0 f_2(\xi)}{r}$$

is necessary to determine the contour of the body. If the latter is given by

$$r = \tilde{r}(x), \tag{7}$$

we obtain from the condition, that the velocity must be tangential at the surface,

$$\frac{d\tilde{r}(x)}{dx} = \frac{\Phi_r(\tilde{r}, x)}{a^*} = \tau \frac{f_2(\xi)\, x_0}{\tilde{r}(\xi)}$$

and hence

$$\tilde{r} \frac{d\tilde{r}}{d\xi} = \tau x_0^2 f_2(\xi).$$

If we put

$$\tilde{r} = \tau^{1/2} x_0 \bar{\bar{r}}(\xi), \tag{8}$$

then

$$f_2(\xi) = \bar{\bar{r}} \frac{d\bar{\bar{r}}}{d\xi} \tag{9}$$

and thus the diameter is proportional to $\tau^{1/2} x_0$. This last equation represents the boundary condition on the surface of the body immersed in the flow. The body itself is replaced by a distribution of singularities along a segment of the x axis. The coefficient $f_2(\xi)$ of the singular term in Eq. (6) can be calculated with the aid of Eqs. (7), (8) and (9). In order to calculate the pressure distribution on the surface of the obstacle, we start with Eq. (4)

$$p - p^* = -\frac{\varrho^*}{2}[(a^* + v_x)^2 + v_r^2 - a^{*2}] = -\varrho^* \left[a^* v_x + \frac{v_x^2}{2} + \frac{v_r^2}{2}\right]$$

where $v_x^2/2$ can always be neglected in comparison with $a^* v_x$. If, in particular, one introduces the values of r corresponding to the surface, Eq. (6) yields

$$v_x = \tau a^* \frac{df_1}{d\xi} + \frac{df_2}{d\xi} \ln(\tau \bar{\bar{r}}(\xi))$$

and with the aid of Eq. (9) one obtains

$$v_r = a^* \tau^{1/2} \frac{f_2(\xi)}{\bar{\bar{r}}(\xi)} = a^* \tau^{1/2} \frac{d\bar{\bar{r}}}{d\xi}.$$

Hence

$$p - p^* = -\varrho^* a^{*2} \tau \times$$
$$\times \left[\frac{df_1}{d\xi} + \frac{d^2}{d\xi^2}\left(\frac{\bar{\bar{r}}^2}{2}\right) \ln \tau + \frac{d^2}{d\xi^2}\left(\frac{\bar{\bar{r}}^2}{2}\right) \ln \bar{\bar{r}}(\xi) + \frac{1}{2}\left(\frac{d\bar{\bar{r}}}{d\xi}\right)^2\right]. \tag{10}$$

The terms arising from v_x and v_r are of the same order of magnitude except for the expression $[d^2(\bar{\bar{r}}^2/2)/d\xi^2] \ln \tau$. OSWATITSCH and BERNDT [69] have shown that the terms originating from v_r must be considered in calculating the pressures. It is noteworthy that this result has here been obtained in a purely formal manner.

The selection of the scale of τ is unimportant. This means that if a known flow is distorted in accordance with the similarity rule, the same result is obtained irrespectively of the scale of τ. To illustrate this let us compare two fields of flow related by the similarity rule. Let, further, the pressure, similarity parameter and the radius corresponding to the first flow be denoted by p, τ and $\tilde{r}$ respectively and those corresponding to the second flow by p', τ' and $\tilde{r}'$. To calculate p' we must replace τ by τ' in Eq. (10). The term $d^2(\bar{\bar{r}}^2/2)/d\xi^2$ in this equation can be expressed, with the aid of Eq. (8), in the form

$$\frac{d^2}{d\xi^2}\left(\frac{\bar{\bar{r}}^2}{2}\right) = \frac{1}{\tau x_0^2}\,\frac{d^2}{d\xi^2}\left(\frac{\bar{r}^2}{2}\right),$$

i.e. we have

$$p - p^* + \varrho^* a^{*2} \frac{\ln \tau}{x_0^2}\,\frac{d^2}{d\xi^2}\left(\frac{r^2}{2}\right)$$

$$= -\varrho^* a^{*2} \tau \left[\frac{df_1}{d\xi} + \frac{d^2}{d\xi^2}\left(\frac{\bar{\bar{r}}^2}{2}\right) \ln \bar{\bar{r}}(\xi) + \frac{1}{2}\left(\frac{d\bar{\bar{r}}}{d\xi}\right)^2\right]$$

and

$$p' - p^* + \varrho^* a^{*2} \frac{\tau'}{\tau}\,\frac{\ln \tau'}{x_0^2}\,\frac{d^2}{d\xi^2}\left(\frac{\tilde{r}^2}{2}\right)$$

$$= -\varrho^* a^{*2} \tau' \left[\frac{df_1}{d\xi} + \frac{d^2}{d\xi^2}\left(\frac{\bar{\bar{r}}^2}{2}\right) \ln \bar{\bar{r}}(\xi) + \frac{1}{2}\left(\frac{d\bar{\bar{r}}^2}{d\xi}\right)^2\right]. \qquad (11)$$

Elimination of the RHS's yields

$$p' - p^* = \frac{\tau'}{\tau}\left[(p - p^*) - \frac{\varrho^* a^{*2}}{x_0^2} \ln \frac{\tau'}{\tau}\,\frac{d^2}{d\xi^2}\left(\frac{\tilde{r}^2}{2}\right)\right], \qquad (12)$$

which indicates that the pressure p' is a function of the ratio τ'/τ. The term $d^2(\tilde{r}^2/2)/d\xi^2$ is a function of the shape of the body alone.

6. The Similarity Rule

For a wide range of shapes, namely airfoils (quasi-cylindrical bodies) and for axisymmetric bodies, the distortion of the surface and the changes in the pressure are related in a simple manner, in accordance with the results of the preceding section. It is possible to calculate the pressure distribution on the surface of a body which results from the distortion, according to similarity rules, of an experimentally investigated body from only the knowledge of the pressure distribution on the surface of the latter. No further information regarding the field of flow is necessary. These relations form the similarity rules for transonic flows*.

Let us now summarise the results of the preceding section as far as they are of direct importance to the similarity rule.

When in different fields of flow, which are related to one another through the similarity rule, the values of ξ, η and ζ [Eq. II, 3 (3b)] are equal at specific points then these will be referred to as "corresponding" points. The corresponding values of x, y and z vary both with x_0 and with τ. The first of these possibilities simply means a change of scale of the entire field of flow while the second variation describes the appropriate distortion in accordance with the similarity rule. If x_0 is kept constant, then at corresponding points x is proportional to τ^0 and y and z are proportional to $\tau^{-1/2}$. The deviation of the x component of the velocity at corresponding points from the critical velocity is proportional to τ while those of the y and z component are proportional to $\tau^{3/2}$.

An immersed body is represented by a discontinuity in the velocity potential and its derivative along a cylindrical surface whose generators are parallel to the x axis. This surface distorts in the same manner as the coordinates. The deviations of the actual surface of a body from this approximating cylindrical surface are proportional to $\tau^{3/2}$. A body of revolution is represented by a distribution of singularities along a segment of the x axis and its radius is proportional to $x_0\,\tau^{1/2}$.

Deviations of the pressure from the critical pressure on the surface of an obstacle, other than a body of revolution, are proportional to τ.

In the case of a body of revolution the quantity

$$p - p^* + \varrho^* a^{*2} \frac{\ln \tau}{x_0^2} \frac{d^2}{d\xi^2} \left(\frac{\tilde{r}}{2}\right)^2$$

is proportional to τ in accordance with Eqs. II, 5 (10) and II, 5 (8).

The experimental results for cases related by the principle of similarity are best represented in terms of variables independent of τ since then the results corresponding to various values of τ are correlated by single curves. We must consider next the geometrical conditions determining the flow field. An obstacle in the flow is represented by the approximating cylindrical surface and by the deviations of the actual surface of the body from the latter. These deviations must, of course, be proportional to one another at corresponding points. Let the

* Since bodies of revolution and airfoils are distorted in different ways, there exists no similarity rule for flows around bodies consisting of combinations of the two. This is particularly true for the wing-fuselage system. If the entire flow field around the original model were known it would be possible, of course, to calculate the contour of a new body by distorting the flow around the model by means of the parameter τ. Thus the possibility of distortion of the field of flow is more general than the similarity rule. The possibility of such a distortion of the field of flow was already confirmed in Eq. II, 3 (3) by means of which the desired simplification of the differential equation was achieved. It appears that the similarity rule could be derived from the simplified differential equation of flow, Eq. II, 3 (8). This would, however, not fit within the logical framework of our present development.

deviation at a characteristic point be D and let it be proportional to $\tau^{3/2} x_0$, where x_0 is a characteristic length. It follows that

$$\tau = \left(\frac{D}{x_0}\right)^{2/3}.$$

The y and z coordinates of the approximating surfaces are proportional to $x_0 \tau^{-1/2}$. With the aid of the last equation one finds that the quantities

$$\frac{y}{x_0}\left(\frac{D}{x_0}\right)^{1/3} \quad \text{and} \quad \frac{z}{x_0}\left(\frac{D}{x_0}\right)^{1/3},$$

for the approximating cylindrical surfaces are invariant in cases which satisfy the conditions of similarity. It should be noted that the x coordinate behaves in a different manner, i.e. that simply x/x_0 is invariant. The field of flow depends further on the velocity of approach. If the MACH number corresponding to this velocity is M_∞ a further condition of similarity is that

$$\frac{(M_\infty - 1)}{\tau} \quad \text{or} \quad (M_\infty - 1)\left(\frac{D}{x_0}\right)^{-2/3}$$

is invariant.

Such invariant quantities are called similarity parameters. If all the above conditions are satisfied, the fields of flow are similar and the quantities

$$(M_\infty - 1)\left(\frac{D}{x_0}\right)^{-2/3} \quad \text{or} \quad \frac{(p - p^*)}{\varrho^* \omega^{*2}/2}\left(\frac{D}{x_0}\right)^{-2/3}$$

are equal at corresponding points.

As mentioned above (in Section 2), the choice of the physical quantities set proportional to τ is only determined as far as quantities of second and higher orders are concerned. In other words, the similarity parameters are not predetermined. This freedom of choice can be utilized to obtain a better approximation to the exact solutions. SPREITER [71] recommends the following similarity parameter for the MACH number of the undisturbed flow

$$\frac{(M_\infty^2 - 1)}{[(\gamma + 1)\, M_\infty^2 (D/x_0)]^{2/3}}.$$

For the pressure coefficient

$$c_p = \frac{p - p_\infty}{\frac{1}{2}\varrho_\infty w_\infty^2}$$

he obtains the expression

$$c_p \frac{[(\gamma + 1)\, M_\infty^2]^{1/3}}{(D/x_0)^{2/3}}.$$

The ratio of specific heats γ is contained in the above expression in such a form that similarity of transonic flows may result also for varying γ.

Although the improvement in the agreement between theory and experiment obtained by SPREITER in one particular case is quite striking, one should approach his proposed choice of parameters with considerable caution since the reasoning leading to this choice is rather unsatisfactory. In such attempts at improvement one must necessarily accept somewhat rougher approximations. Important features which should be considered have been outlined by OSWATITSCH [68]. Results of any generality can only be obtained at the expense of substantial compromises.

7. Applications of the Similarity Rule

The applicability of the similarity rule for transonic flow is considerably more limited than that of the PRANDTL-GLAUERT rule since it results in a distortion of the shape of the profile immersed in the flow. In the three-dimensional case not only is the thickness of an airfoil changed but also the sweep-back angle if one deals with a swept-back wing. The conditions arising around an airfoil can be easily obtained on the basis of the considerations of the preceding section. At this point we shall derive certain consequences which, although based on the same principles as those considered above, are, however, not immediately obvious.

1. Let the flow over a flat plate be known at $M = 1$ and let further (D/x_0) be taken as equal to the angle of attack α of the plate. The expression

$$\frac{p - p^*}{\varrho^* w^{*2}/2} \left(\frac{D}{x_0}\right)^{-2/3},$$

is then in accordance with the similarity rule invariant at corresponding points. Hence the local pressure coefficient and the lift are proportional to $\alpha^{2/3}$. For a zero angle of attack $dc_L/d\alpha$ is infinite. This fact illustrates the failure of the linearised theory.

2. In the case of a profile of finite thickness the lift is, for small angles of attack, proportional to α even at $M = 1$. Suppose that $dc_L/d\alpha$ is known at $M = 1$ for a given profile and let the lift be L and the thickness ratio D/x_0. In performing the similarity distortion $L(D/x_0)^{-2/3}$ and $\alpha(D/x_0)^{-1}$ remain constant. The lift can also be expressed in the form $L = (dc_L/d\alpha)\,\alpha$. It follows therefore that in the distortion the expression

$$\frac{dc_L}{d\alpha}\,\alpha\,(D/x_0)^{-2/3}$$

and therefore also

$$\frac{dc_L}{d\alpha}\,(D/x_0)^{1/3}$$

are invariant. In other words

$$\frac{dc_L}{d\alpha} \sim (D/x_0)^{-1/3}.$$

Thus the slope of a curve representing the lift, plotted against the angle of attack, increases with decreasing thickness ratio. The range of α in which this is true is proportional, of course, to the thickness ratio D/x_0. For thin profiles this range can be quite small. The above result is worthy of note inasmuch as $dc_L/d\alpha$ is independent of the thickness ratio at a constant MACH number in both subsonic and in supersonic flow.

3. Let us compare the flow around a given profile in a choked wind tunnel with the flow around the same profile at $M = 1$ in an unbounded region. The differences between the pressure distributions around the obstacle in these two cases indicate the influence of the tunnel walls. Let us subject both fields of flow to the same similarity distortion. The relative differences in the pressure distributions are, naturally, preserved. The thickness of the profile is distorted in proportion to $\tau^{3/2}$, the deviations of the choking MACH number from 1 in proportion to τ and the width of the tunnel in proportion to $\tau^{-1/2}$ since the walls are distorted in the same way as the coordinates. Thus for a given chord length the relative influence of the walls is the same for a thick profile in the narrow tunnel as for a thin profile in a wide tunnel. Comparing a thicker profile with a slender one in a tunnel of the same width, the deviation of the pressure distribution from that appropriate to $M = 1$ is smaller in the former case although the choking MACH number is lower. As a result of this the accuracy of wind tunnel measurements can be described in terms of a choking MACH number only if the chords and the thickness ratios of the profiles are about the same.

The application of the similarity rule to the determination of wind tunnel corrections in the transonic regime has been described by GUDERLEY [31].

8. A Simplified Method of Description of the Flow

We have seen how the approximate equations for transonic flow can be derived by means of a limiting process. It is now, therefore, permissible to introduce a less accurate formulation in which the deviations from parallel flow with critical velocity are considered to be "sufficiently" small and the body "sufficiently" slender. We set τ and x_0 simply equal to 1 and do not concern ourselves with the fact that Eqs. II, 3 (8) and II, 3 (10) result from the limiting process but simply consider them to be approximations to the exact differential equations. We denote the cartesian coordinates by x, y and z or cylindrical coordinates by x, r, ω and the velocity potential of the flow by $\overline{\Phi}$. For $\overline{\Phi}$ we assume the following form

$$\overline{\Phi} = a^* (x + \Phi(x, y, z))$$

so that Φ describes the deviation of the flow from a parallel one with critical velocity. The approximate equation for Φ is

$$-(\gamma + 1)\,\Phi_x \Phi_{xx} + \Phi_{yy} + \Phi_{zz} = 0, \tag{1}$$

or in the axisymmetric case

$$-(\gamma + 1)\,\Phi_x \Phi_{xx} + \Phi_{rr} + \frac{\Phi_r}{r} = 0. \tag{2}$$

In the shock conditions, Eqs. II, 4 (8) and II, 4 (9), we replace $\bar{v}_{xI}$, $\bar{v}_{xII}$, $\Delta\bar{v}_x$, $\Delta\bar{v}_y$, and $\Delta\bar{v}_z$ by Φ_{xI}, Φ_{xII}, $\Delta\Phi_x$, $\Delta\Phi_y$ and $\Delta\Phi_z$ respectively. The powers of τ in Eq. II, 4 (9) are ommited. The immersed body is again described by the approximating cylindrical surface and by the deviation h of the actual surface from the latter. The boundary condition at the surface takes the form

$$\frac{d\Phi}{dn} = \frac{\partial h}{dx} \tag{3}$$

and for the pressure distribution one obtains

$$p - p^* = -\varrho^* a^{*2} \Phi_x.$$

A body of revolution is again represented by a distribution of singularities along a segment of the axis. In the vicinity of the axis the predominant terms are

$$\Phi = f_1(x) + f_2(x) \ln r.$$

If the surface of the body of revolution is given by $r = \tilde{r}(x)$ then

$$f_2(x) = \tilde{r} \frac{d\tilde{r}}{dx}.$$

To determine the pressures on the surface of the immersed body it is necessary to evaluate either

$$p - p^* = -\varrho^* a^{*2} \left(\Phi_x + \frac{\Phi_r^2}{2}\right),$$

or

$$p - p^* = -\varrho^* a^{*2} \left(\frac{df_1}{dx} + \frac{df_2}{dx} \ln \tilde{r}(x) + \frac{1}{2}\left(\frac{d\tilde{r}}{dx}\right)^2\right).$$

9. The Equations of Continuity and Momentum for Transonic Flow

In this section we shall indicate the forms of the equations of continuity and momentum which result from the use of the simplified differential equation of flow, Eq. II, 8 (1). These equations may be of importance in the determination of approximate solutions. In such problems the equation of continuity is not always satisfied. To allow for this we admit the existence of sources of strength $\varrho^* a^* q$ within the field of flow. The simplified continuity equation then takes the form

$$-(\gamma + 1)\Phi_x \frac{\partial \Phi_x}{\partial x} + \frac{\partial \Phi_y}{\partial y} + \frac{\partial \Phi_z}{\partial z} = q. \tag{1}$$

Let us consider a volume V bounded by a surface S and let us denote by $d\mathbf{n}$ the vector equal in magnitude to a surface element dS, normal to it and directed outwards, by dV an element of volume and by **i**, **j** and **k** unit vectors in the x, y

and z directions respectively. With the aid of GAUSS' theorem we obtain from Eq. (1)

$$\iint\limits_{0} d\mathbf{n}\left[-\frac{\gamma+1}{2}\Phi_x^2\mathbf{i}+\mathbf{j}\Phi_y+\mathbf{k}\Phi_z\right]=\iiint\limits_{V} q\,dV.$$

If the exact equation of continuity had been employed the LHS of the above equation would take the form

$$\iint\limits_{0} d\mathbf{n}(\mathbf{i}\varrho v_x+\mathbf{j}\varrho v_y+\mathbf{k}\varrho v_z).$$

The term ϱv_x is to the first approximation represented by $\varrho^* a^*$. This term disappears, naturally, upon integration over a closed surface. Taking this fact into account and comparing the last two equations it becomes apparent that the following approximations apply in the transonic regime

$$\varrho v_x=\varrho^* a^*\left(1-\frac{\gamma+1}{2}\Phi_x^2\right),\quad \varrho v_y=\varrho^* a^*\Phi_y,\quad \varrho v_z=\varrho^* a^*\Phi_z. \tag{2}$$

The first of these equations indicates a parabolic relationship between the mass flow density ϱw (which is approximately equal to ϱv_x) and Φ_x. The maximum of the mass flow density occurs thus at the critical velocity in complete agreement with the result of the exact equations of flow [cf. Eq. I, 2 (10a)].

In calculating the forces, exerted on an immersed body, by means of a surface integral and with the aid of the momentum equation, care should be exercised since the momentum is expressed by terms of comparatively high order. The momentum equation should therefore be derived directly from the equation for transonic flow viz. Eq. (1). EULER's equations may later appear to provide a more suitable starting point; they are, however, automatically satisfied by the introduction of a potential, even in the presence of sources within the field of flow. The momentum contributions of these sources must, of course, be taken into account unless the volume is infinitesimally small.

We shall restrict the following discussion to the most sensitive case, namely that of the x component of momentum.

Equation (1) may, upon multiplication by Φ_x, be written in the form

$$-(\gamma+1)\Phi_x^2\Phi_{xx}+\frac{\partial}{\partial y}(\Phi_x\Phi_y)+\frac{\partial}{\partial z}(\Phi_x\Phi_z)-\frac{\partial}{\partial x}(\Phi_y^2)-\frac{\partial}{\partial z}(\Phi_z^2)=q\Phi_x.$$

Hence, with the aid of GAUSS' theorem,

$$\iint\limits_{0} d\mathbf{n}\left\{\mathbf{i}\left(-(\gamma+1)\frac{\Phi_x^3}{3}-\frac{\Phi_y^2}{2}-\frac{\Phi_z^2}{2}\right)+\mathbf{j}(\Phi_x\Phi_y)+\mathbf{k}(\Phi_x\Phi_z)\right\}$$
$$=\iiint\limits_{V} q\Phi_x\,dV. \tag{3}$$

The high power of Φ_x occuring here is surprising. It is easy to show, however, that all the terms are of the same order in τ when the similarity distortion is applied, even if the distortion of the surface elements is taken into account. It is necessary to confirm next that the integral taken over the surface of the immersed body really represents the x component of momentum.

The boundary condition on the surface of the body is

$$d\mathbf{n}a^*[\mathbf{i}(1+\Phi_x)+\mathbf{j}\Phi_y+\mathbf{k}\Phi_z]=0.$$

Substitution of the above expression in Eq. (3) results in

$$\iint d\mathbf{n}\,\mathbf{i}a^*\left\{-(1+\Phi_x)\,\Phi_x-\frac{\varkappa+1}{3}\Phi_x^3-\frac{\Phi_y^2}{2}-\frac{\Phi_z^2}{2}\right\}$$

where $d\mathbf{n}\cdot\mathbf{i}$ is the projection of a surface element in the x direction. The higher powers of Φ_x can be neglected in this case since the surface of the body distorts in a different manner than the coordinates. In the present approximation $(p-p^*)$ is given by

$$-\varrho^*a^{*2}(\Phi_x+\Phi_y^2/2+\Phi_z^2/2)$$

as may be shown in a similar manner to that employed in deriving Eq. (2). The terms $(\Phi_y^2/2)+(\Phi_z^2/2)$ are in general small in comparison with Φ_x. An exception to this was indicated on p. 37 in connection with the analysis of an axisymmetric obstacle. This case is thus included in the formulation of the momentum equation.

CHAPTER III

THE LINEARISED THEORY OF TRANSONIC FLOW

1. Preliminary Remarks

Although we have found the transonic regime to be described by a non-linear equation, it does not mean that this equation must be used exclusively. In a number of problems the non-linear term is of only limited importance. This fact is very helpful since the non-linear equation presents such formidable difficulties that without very great mathematical effort it can be solved only in a few special cases. The problem of determination of the lift of a wing of small aspect ratio is the most important case, from the practical point of view, which can be treated by a linearised theory.

The linearised treatment of a field of flow is not without importance also from the theoretical point of view. It provides an insight into the difficulties which are introduced by the non-linear term even if the numerical results obtained are themselves not very satisfactory.

2. The Linearised Theory of Two-Dimensional and Axisymmetric Transonic Flows

The linearised differential equation of transonic flow is obtained by neglecting the term $-(\gamma + 1)\,\Phi_x \Phi_{xx}$ in Eq. II, 8 (1). For plane flow there results

$$\Phi_{yy} = 0. \tag{1}$$

The general solution of this equation is given by

$$\Phi(x, y) = y\,f(x) + g(x), \tag{2}$$

where f and g are arbitrary functions. Thus Φ_y, i.e. the slope of the streamlines in the present approximation, is constant on each line $x = \text{const}$. The streamlines are therefore of the same shape but displaced from one another in the y direction.

Let us apply this result to the flow around a profile, whose shape can be described by the inclination of the streamlines to the boundary of the profile $\vartheta = \vartheta(x)$. The function $f(x)$ is thus determined by

$$f(x) = \vartheta(x).$$

There remains the problem of obtaining the function $g(x)$. To avoid an immediate absurd result, let us first consider the flow in a free jet of finite width. The boundary of this jet in the linearised treatment is given by the lines $y = \text{const} = \pm y_0$. At the boundary the pressure is equal to the critical pressure and hence, again in the first approximation, $\Phi_x = 0$. This condition is satisfied by a suitable choice of g. Thus, for the upper half of the field of flow the solution is

$$\Phi = y\,\vartheta(x) - y_0\,\vartheta(x). \tag{3}$$

In this approximation the boundary of the jet has the same shape as the profile since all the streamlines are parallel to one another and displaced in the y direction. Upstream and downstream of the profile the boundary of the jet is undisturbed.

The pressures on the surface of the profile are proportional to Φ_x, and there

$$\Phi_{x(y=0)} = -y_0 \frac{\partial \vartheta}{dx}. \tag{4}$$

In the range of validity of the linearised theory the pressures must, of course, be small. This means that either the inclination of the profile or the width of the jet must be of limited magnitude.

What is the physical meaning of this solution? We have found an expression for the mass flow density in the transonic approximation given by Eq. II, 9 (2). If the non-linear term is neglected in the differential equation then one must also neglect the non-linear term in the expression for the mass flow density and hence the latter is constant. In the first approximation this requires a constant distance between the streamlines in the y direction, hence the form of the streamlines is known *a priori*.

The sensitivity of transonic flows to changes in the cross-sections of the stream tubes is indicated by the fact that the mass flow density depends only on second order terms. In order to increase the cross-section of the stream tubes by a small amount a considerable change in the velocity is necessary.

Since the shape of the streamlines is known in the entire flow, the pressures can be determined by the integration of the centrifugal forces. It may be shown, in particular, that this results in the solution given by Eq. (3). If the velocity of the jet tends to infinity, the pressure at the profile tends to $+\infty$ or to $-\infty$ depending on the sign of the curvature of the profile.

In accordance with the above, the difficulties associated with the linearised treatment have their origin in the centrifugal forces which are additive over large distances. The above integration is permissible over a strip of finite width. Only the distant parts of the field of flow force us to abandon the linearised theory. In the linearised theory the disturbances generated by the profile are confined to a strip normal to the velocity of the undisturbed flow and equal in width to the chord of the profile. The non-linear terms of the differential equation are responsible for the spreading of the disturbed region and for the fact that the original disturbances decay with the distance in such a way that the integrated centrifugal forces result in finite pressures at the surface of the profile. This mechanism of spreading and decay is influenced by the non-linear terms also at large distances from the profile. This is somewhat surprising since all the disturbances become very small at a sufficient distance. These facts should be borne in mind when the approximate methods of calculation of transonic flows are reviewed*.

Axisymmetric problems are treated in a quite similar manner. The solution of the linearised potential equation

$$\Phi_{rr} + \frac{\Phi_r}{r} = 0 \tag{5}$$

is

$$\Phi = f(x) \ln r + g(x)$$

and hence

$$\Phi_r = \frac{f(x)}{r},$$

which represents also the inclination of the velocity vector.

If the shape of the body is given by $r = \tilde{r}(x)$ the boundary condition takes the form

$$\frac{f(x)}{\tilde{r}} = \frac{d\tilde{r}}{dx}$$

or

$$f(x) = \frac{1}{2} \frac{d}{dx} (\tilde{r})^2.$$

The function $g(x)$ is again obtained from the boundary conditions at some distance from the body. The solution for a free jet of radius r_0 is

$$\Phi = \frac{1}{2} \frac{d}{dx} (\tilde{r})^2 [\ln r - \ln r_0].$$

The pressure at the surface of the body tends also in this case to infinity as the radius of the jet tends to infinity, but much more slowly than in the plane problem. This is due to the fact that the curvatures of the streamlines, and hence

* The linearisation results in a fundamental change in the differential equation of flow. While in the original form the equation is elliptic or hyperbolic according to the sign of Φ_x, upon linearisation it becomes parabolic. From the point of view of the engineer or the applied mathematician this fact alone could not justify the rejection of the linearised theory. Such simplifications are used quite frequently and usually without serious consequences. One can recall the equations of the boundary layer theory, which are of the parabolic type and which are derived from the elliptic NAVIER–STOKES equations, or the equation of frictionless compressible flow which also results from the NAVIER–STOKES equations. The difficulties introduced by these simplifications are generally confined to small regions which must be excluded or treated separately. Examples of such corrections are furnished by the boundary layers and by compression shocks. The boundary layer theory provides the corrections necessary in view of the fact that the results of frictionless treatment of gas flows do not satisfy the boundary condition at a solid boundary. The compression shocks represent an approximation to those regions of the flow in which very large pressure gradients would result from the application of the NAVIER–STOKES equations. Under the assumption of frictionless flow a folding over of the physical plane would occur.

also the centrifugal forces, decrease with the distance because of the increasing cross-sections*.

One can expect, as a result of these considerations, that the physical difficulties encountered in the transonic regime are less pronounced in axisymmetric flows than in the case of plane two-dimensional ones. This is particularly noteworthy since most of the known exact solutions to transonic problems refer to two-dimensional flows. The extension of the results to the axisymmetric case requires considerable caution.

The result of the linearised theory can be regarded as the first term of an expansion of the flow in terms of the thickness parameter. In an unbounded region, however, already the first term results in infinite pressures. For the inclined plate we have already found, with the aid of the similarity rule, that the tangent at the origin to a curve representing the lift in terms of the angle of attack is vertical. Thus the angle of attack plays a role similar to that of the profile thickness. As a result the linearised theory, although useless in this case, fits, however, well into the general picture.

3. Three-Dimensional Flows

The linearised differential equation takes for three-dimensional flow the form

$$\Phi_{yy} + \Phi_{zz} = 0. \tag{1}$$

Since the derivatives in the x direction are absent from the equation, the latter can be solved for any cross-section $x = \text{const}$ independently of the flow in the neighbouring cross-sections. In a wake of a wing the various cross-sections are, however, related to one another in view of the boundary conditions which must be satisfied in the vortex sheet of the wake.

In accordance with Eq. II, 8 (3) the boundary condition at the surface of an obstacle is

$$v_n = \frac{\partial h}{\partial x}, \tag{2}$$

where v_n denotes the velocity component normal to the surface of the approximating cylindrical surface (c. f. p. 35) and lying in the plane of $x = \text{const}$. The distance between the surface of the body and that of the approximating cylinder, measured in the direction of v_n, is denoted by h.

The fact that only the velocity component lying in the appropriate plane $x = \text{const}$ is present in this equation is quite important. As a result of this, one is confronted in each such plane with a boundary value problem of the second type for a two-dimensional LAPLACE's equation. The requirement that the potential should vanish at infinity provides a further boundary condition, since otherwise finite additional velocities would exist at infinity.

* If the coefficient of Φ_r/r in Eq. (5) were less than unity, the pressures at the surface of the profile would always be finite and the linearised theory could be accepted in the transonic regime without reservation. This fact has been noted by BUSEMANN.

If a plane of $x =$ const cuts the surface of a body in such a way that several curves result, as for example in the case of a swept-back wing at a downstream location, the solution is no longer uniquely determined by the above boundary conditions. A discontinuity in the potential at the trailing edge must be admitted, although the derivative of the potential normal to the surface of the wake is continuous. Immediately above and below the wake, the potential is constant along straight lines parallel to the x axis. At the trailing edge we have Kutta's condition, namely that the velocity cannot become infinite. These conditions lead to an integral equation for the potential in the wake, which completely determines the solution of the flow problem.

The potential Φ in any cross-section $x =$ const is determined by the differential equation and the boundary conditions of a plane incompressible flow. The line integral $\int v_n \, ds$ along the trace of the obstacle in the plane $x =$ const represents, for this incompressible two-dimensional flow, the net outflow of the fluid from the body. If this integral is non-zero, the potential at infinity takes the form corresponding to a source, i.e. the term $\ln r$ predominates. This term, however, was exactly the one that prevented the application of the linearised theory to an axisymmetric body. One must require, therefore, that

$$\int v_n \, ds = 0$$

which, in accordance with Eq. (2), may be written in the form

$$\int \frac{\partial h}{\partial x} \, ds = 0. \tag{3}$$

Since, however, $d\left(\int h \, ds\right)/dx$ represents the derivative of the cross-section of the obstacle in the direction x, Eq. (3) is equivalent to the condition that the cross-sections in the plane $x =$ const are the same for all values of x. The initial cross-section of a body with finite dimensions (e.g. that of a wing) is, however, zero and thus the three-dimensional linearised theory applies only to bodies of zero thickness.

The cylindrical surface to which the surface of the obstacle reduces for $\tau = 0$ is, in the most important practical case viz. that of a wing plane. The wing may be inclined at an angle of attack to the flow; it may be cambered or even twisted. In each plane of $x =$ const the normal derivative of Φ is given along a line representing the intersection of the wing with the plane i.e. along a section of the z axis. The values of this normal derivative are of opposite sign above and below this line for a wing of zero thickness. The solution is obtained systematically by conformal mapping of the line into a circle, within which the boundary value problem is solved in terms of a Fourier series. The problem is occasionally formulated in terms of an integral equation in the y, z plane. This does not, however, affect the method of solution.

As an example we shall give the solution for the case of a constant angle of attack. In this case h in Eq. (2) depends linearly on x and the normal component of the velocity is constant along the lines representing the intersections of the wing with planes $x = $ const. The solution can be found either by the procedure indicated above or it can be immediately written down if it is recalled that an elliptical distribution of the lift in PRANDTL's wing theory results in a constant downwash at infinity. We set, therefore,

$$\Phi = \text{const Re}\left(\sqrt{b^2 + \zeta^2} - \zeta\right),$$

where

$$\zeta = y + iz.$$

The constant occuring in these equations is later chosen in such a way as to obtain the required angle of attack. Expanding the square root, and choosing the positive sign, we notice that the potential vanishes at infinity. For the velocity component in the y direction one obtains

$$\frac{\partial \Phi}{\partial y} = \text{const Re}\left[\frac{\partial}{\partial y}\left(\sqrt{b^2 + \zeta^2} - \zeta\right)\right] = \text{const Re}\left[\frac{d}{d\zeta}\left(\sqrt{b^2 + \zeta^2} - \zeta\right)\right]$$
$$= \text{const Re}\left(\frac{\zeta}{\sqrt{b^2 + \zeta^2}} - 1\right).$$

At the surface of the plate $y = 0$ and hence $\zeta = iz$. Thus the square root reduces to $\sqrt{(b^2 - z^2)}$ which is real for $z < b$. Thus the real part of $\zeta/\sqrt{(b^2 + \zeta^2)}$ is zero at the surface and one obtains

$$\Phi_y = -\text{const}.$$

The equation of the surface of the plate is in the present case $y = -\alpha x$, where α denotes the angle of attack. The boundary condition is therefore

$$\Phi_y = -\alpha.$$

In view of the linearisation this condition must be satisfied along the z axis so that the constant in the assumed expression for Φ must be equal to α. If we assume the contour of the wing to be symmetrical with respect to the x axis and to be given by $b = b(x)$, where for reasons to be discussed later b is a non-decreasing function, there results finally

$$\Phi = \alpha \text{ Re}\left(\sqrt{b^2(x) + \zeta^2} - \zeta\right).$$

Differentiation with respect to x yields the x component of the velocity and the pressures are further obtained with the aid of BERNOULLI's equation.

If b is constant then the potential Φ is, in the present approximation, also constant in the x direction and the pressures on the upper and lower surfaces of the wing are equal to the pressure in the undisturbed flow. Such parts of the wing, therefore, transmit no force and can be omitted. With this we have also found the solution for cases of constant angle of attack in which b decreases. Downstream of the section for which b is a maximum the potential retains the value corresponding to that section and is equal to the potential of the vortex wake.

Calculation of the total lift yields

$$L = 2\varrho^* a^{*2} \iint\limits_{\text{wing surface}} \Phi_x \, dx \, dz = 2\varrho^* a^{*2} \alpha \int\limits_{-b_{\max}}^{+b_{\max}} \sqrt{b_{\max}^2 - z^2} \, dz$$

$$= \varrho^* a^{*2} \alpha \pi b_{\max}^2,$$

where the factor 2 accounts for the contributions of the upper and lower surfaces of the wing. The lift is thus a function of only the angle of attack and of the maximum wing span.

The linearisation is permissible only when the values of Φ_x are not too large, which means that the cross-section cannot change too fast. In the limiting case of an inclined rectangular plate b changes suddenly at the leading edge, Φ_x becomes infinite but, in accordance with the last equation, the lift remains finite and concentrated near the leading edge. The linearised theory is in this case, of course, not applicable.

For a treatment of the delta wing the reader is referred to the original articles of MANGLER [65] and HEASLET, LOMAX and SPREITER [48]. A similar discussion of both the subsonic and supersonic regimes is due to JONES [51].

4. A Body of Finite Thickness

We have found it impossible to determine the flow at $M = 1$ for axisymmetric bodies from the linearised potential equation, since the integration of centrifugal forces yielded infinite pressures. The same is true of more general body shapes whose cross sections in the planes of $x = \text{const}$ are finite.

The flow field and the quantities determining the resistance can, however, still be computed in a comparatively simple manner according to OSWATITSCH and KEUNE [70]. The field of flow around a so-called "equivalent" body of revolution is assumed to be known. This "equivalent" body of revolution has the same cross-section areas in the planes of $x = \text{const}$ as the body under investigation. The field of flow around the equivalent body of revolution must be previously determined from the full approximate equation of transonic flow. The deviation of the actual cross sections from those of the equivalent body is subsequently accounted for with the aid of the linearised potential equation

$$\Phi_{yy} + \Phi_{zz} = 0 \tag{1}$$

The above technique results from the following considerations. Equation (1) may be considered to represent a result of the linearisation, i.e. of an expansion of the field of flow in terms of a thickness parameter, but it may also be interpreted as the result of the calculation indicated on p. 23 under the assumption of a sufficiently slender body. The differential equation is thus compatible with the cross-sections in the planes $x = \text{const}$ remaining similar in the limiting process which leads to the simplification of the differential equations. These cross-sections undergo an affine distortion in the usual linearisation. With the aid of Eq. (1) one could calculate the flow around an arbitrary, but sufficiently slender, body in a free jet flowing with critical velocity, in a manner analogous to the technique outlined on pp. 23–24.

One cannot, of course, allow the radius of the jet to become infinite. If one restricts the region considered to a cylindrical one, enclosing the obstacle, Eq. (1) can be applied without objection. Outside of this region we must employ the complete differential equation of transonic flow. We shall show presently how the solution can be constructed on the basis of the above discussion and also that the necessary omissions are permissible for a sufficiently slender body.

Let the surface of the body be given by

$$F(x, \bar{y}, \bar{z}) = 0,$$

where

$$\bar{y} = y\,\tau^{-1/2},$$

$$\bar{z} = z\,\tau^{-1/2}.$$

The parameter τ expresses the fact that the body is a slender one since when $\tau \to 0$, y and z must be chosen correspondingly smaller if the last two equations are to be satisfied. The cross-sections in the planes $x =$ const are proportional to τ. A vector normal to the surface is given by

$$\frac{\partial F}{\partial x}\,\mathbf{i} + \tau^{-1/2}\frac{\partial F}{\partial \bar{y}}\,\mathbf{j} + \tau^{-1/2}\frac{\partial F}{\partial \bar{z}}\,\mathbf{k} = 0.$$

Recalling that $a^* = 1$, one obtains for the boundary conditions at the surface of the body

$$\frac{\partial F}{\partial \bar{y}}\Phi_y + \frac{\partial F}{\partial \bar{z}}\Phi_z = -\tau^{1/2}\frac{\partial F}{\partial x}. \tag{2}$$

Let the surface of the cylinder, separating the region in which Eq. (1) is applicable from that in which the full differential equation must be used, be given by $y^2 + z^2 =$ const and let, further, the position of this surface be independent of τ. We shall see that for a sufficiently slender body, the flow field outside of this separating surface deviates by arbitrarily small amounts from an axisymmetric field. These deviations can be treated by means of a linearisation.

The solution in the vicinity of the axis is given for the "equivalent" body of revolution by

$$\Phi = f(x)\ln r + g(x). \tag{3}$$

Upon application of the complete equation of transonic flow additional terms of the order of $r^2(\ln r)^2$ would occur in Eq. (3) since the term $\Phi_x\Phi_{xx}$ is of the order of $(\ln r)^2$ and its influence on the potential is the result of an integration. The "equivalent" body of revolution distorts, of course, also with τ; this distortion can be expressed with the aid of the similarity rule for transonic flows, Eq. II, 5 (8). There results

$$\Phi = \tau\,\{f(x)\ln(r\,\tau^{1/2}) + g(x) + O[(r\,\tau^{1/2})^2(\ln(r\,\tau^{1/2}))^2]\}. \tag{3a}$$

The additional terms are thus of the order $\tau^2(\ln\tau)^2$. Suppose that for the obstacle of arbitrary shape Φ_x and Φ_{xx} are bounded which requires that there should be no sudden changes in the cross-section. If that is the case then the term $\Phi_x \Phi_{xx}$ is of the same order of magnitude for both the actual body and for the "equivalent" body of revolution and hence also the error in the potential is of the same order of magnitude.

In the outer region we adopt the solution corresponding to the "equivalent" body of revolution. The difficulties associated with the calculation of such a field are still not completely resolved. From this solution we know, of course, its form in the vicinity of the axis. This is given by Eq. (3a). For sufficiently small values of τ Eq. (3) is valid up to the surface separating the inner and outer regions. The function $g(x)$ is determined by the entire flow field while $f(x)$ is already given by the distribution of the cross-sections of the "equivalent" body of revolution. The expression

$$\tau \{f(x) \ln (r \tau^{1/2}) + g(x)\}$$

describes thus the potential at the separating surface, as calculated from the outer region inwards, to within terms of order $\tau^2 (\ln \tau)^2$. In the inner region one obtains as the solution for the potential

$$\Phi = \tau \{\mathrm{Re}[h(\bar{y} + i\bar{z}, x) + g_1(x)]\},$$

where h must be analytic in $\bar{y} + i\bar{z}$ and must satisfy the boundary conditions given by (Eq. 2) on the surface of the obstacle. The choice of the independent variables $\bar{y}$ and $\bar{z}$ and the presence of the coefficient τ multiplying the solution become clear in view of the above conditions. The expansion of the function h should for $(\bar{y} + i\bar{z}) \to \infty$, in addition to terms vanishing at infinity, contain only $\ln (\bar{y} + i\bar{z})$ and it should contain no terms independent of $\bar{y} + i\bar{z}$. Since both the original obstacle and the "equivalent" body of revolution have the same distribution of cross sections, the real part of $\ln (\bar{y} + i\bar{z})$ is the same in both cases. The function $g_1(x)$ is not determined by the boundary conditions at the surface of the profile and it is taken to be equal to the corresponding function $g(x)$ for the "equivalent" body of revolution.

The error is in part due to the fact that the exact differential equation was not used in the inner region. The order of magnitude of this part of the error has already been determined. The two solutions further do not match exactly along the surface of separation. For example, in the inner region there occur, for large values of $\bar{y} + i\bar{z}$, terms of the order of $\tau^{3/2}/(y + iz)$, in the case of an obstacle at an angle, and terms of the order of $\tau^2/(y + iz)^2$ in the case of a body at zero angle of attack. These terms can be compensated for by the superposition of further solutions in the inner region which correct for the discontinuities in Φ and Φ_r caused by these terms. These corrections are at the most of the order of magnitude of the jumps in Φ and Φ_r and are proportional to $\tau^{3/2}$ and τ^2 in the cases of finite and zero angles of attack respectively. It may be shown that the influence of this term is of the order of magnitude of τ^2 on the surface of an obstacle at an angle.

We have thus shown that the errors are negligible, as long as the body is sufficiently slender. It is noteworthy that the position of the surface of separation is no longer of importance in the final solution since the outer region furnishes only the function $g(x)$.

Estimates of the errors for several concrete examples have been given by LANDAHL [3; 71]. The boundary value problem for the inner region can be solved by means of an expansion in terms of a thickness parameter if the thickness of the cross-section is small. This technique has been developed by KEUNE [55, 56]. In the case of triangular wings, for which the thickness-to-span ratio at any section $x =$ const need not be small, higher order terms in the expansion may become important. With other profiles one can take recourse to methods originating in the theory of functions. The lift and drag of such obstacles are best determined by means of the momentum equation with the control surface formed by the surface of the obstacle and the surface of separation between the inner and outer regions. It may be shown with the aid of Eq. II, 9 (3) that the terms appearing in the momentum balance are the same along the surface of separation whether the term $\Phi_x \Phi_{xx}$ is included in the differential equation of motion or not. For small values of τ the velocity components calculated for the outer region can be used in the computation of the drag. These velocity components have been obtained for the "equivalent" body of revolution and thus the drag on a body of arbitrary shape is equal to that on the "equivalent" body of revolution, except for small quantities of a higher order. This fact was first noticed by OSWATITSCH and KEUNE [70], and by WITHCOMB [83, 84].

It is easy to see that of all the bodies of revolution of a given thickness ratio the one whose cross-section varies most gradually, particularly in the supersonic regime, offers the lowest resistance. It follows from this that in the transonic regime substantial reductions in the drag may be achieved, when the cross-section of the fuselage is reduced in the region of the wings.

The calculation of the lift in the case of slender bodies, and utilising the method outlined above, is well known from both subsonic and supersonic aerodynamics. The transition between these latter results is quite smooth at $M = 1$. The present considerations enable us to apply the method in the transonic regime.

The following peculiarity is worth noting. The linearised theory for supersonic flow around bodies of revolution yields a formula from which a finite value of the drag is obtained also at $M = 1$, although the pressures on the surface of the body become infinite. This result must be regarded with considerable reserve and it does not agree with experimental results. That such a method of calculation is not applicable can be recognised from the fact that by proceeding to the limit of $M = 1$ from the subsonic regime the drag is zero in accordance with D'ALEMBERT's paradox.

5. The Linearised Theory of Non-steady Transonic Flow

Several of the difficulties associated with transonic flows no longer arise if the flow is non-steady and if the accelerations are not too small. This is of importance for aircraft which pass through critical velocity with appreciable accelerations.

It becomes then, in most cases, unnecessary to use the non-linear theory in order to calculate the forces acting on the aircraft.

The investigation of non-steady flow is interesting from the purely physical point of view since the results indicate the manner in which the infinite pressures obtained from the linearised theory for steady flows build up with time.

It is most convenient in these investigations to select a system of coordinates stationary with respect to the surrounding air. Equation I, 4 (9) then takes the form well known from the theory of sound

$$\Phi_{xx} + \Phi_{yy} + \Phi_{zz} - \frac{1}{a_0^2}\Phi_{tt} = 0$$

if one restricts oneself to only terms of the first order. The parameter a_0 is the velocity of sound in the undisturbed flow. For spherical waves the equation takes the form

$$\Phi_{rr} + \frac{2}{r}\Phi_r - \frac{1}{a_0^2}\Phi_{tt} = 0,$$

where

$$r^2 = x^2 + y^2 + z^2$$

and the solution is given by

$$\Phi = \frac{1}{r} f\left(t \pm \frac{r}{a_0}\right). \tag{1}$$

The plus sign applies to waves propagated towards the center, while the minus sign applies to waves propagated outwards from the center of the sphere. Only the second of these two types of waves will be considered here. Equation (1) indicates, incidentally, that a disturbance is propagated in stagnant air with a velocity a_0, i.e. this special case confirms the validity of the description "velocity of sound" which is usually applied to a.

The potential equation is satisfied everywhere with the exception of the center of the sphere. Since the very existence of a potential equation indicates that the continuity equation is satisfied automatically, the singularity in the potential at a point means that a source or a sink must be located at this point. To calculate the strength of the latter we obtain first the velocity, which in this case is directed along r, and then integrate it over a spherical surface of small radius and centered at the origin. In this way we obtain for the mass flow rate across this spherical surface

$$4\pi r^2 \left\{-\frac{1}{r^2} f\left(t - \frac{r}{a_0}\right) - \frac{1}{r a_0} f'\left(t - \frac{r}{a_0}\right)\right\}.$$

Allowing now the radius of the sphere to tend to zero, we obtain for the strength of the source at time t

$$q(t) = -4\pi f(t). \tag{2}$$

In the motion of an axisymmetric body such sources and sinks can certainly not be located outside of the body. We attempt a representation of the motion generated by the body by means of a suitable distribution of sources on the axis of the latter.

The potential, due to a source located at x_1, $y = 0$, $z = 0$ and whose strength at time t_1 is $q(x_1, t_1)$ may be obtained from Eq. (1) by a displacement of the system of coordinates:

$$\Phi = -\frac{1}{4\pi R} q\left(x_1, t - \frac{R}{a_0}\right), \tag{3}$$

where

$$R = \sqrt{(x - x_1)^2 + \tilde{r}^2} \tag{4a}$$

and

$$\tilde{r}^2 = y^2 + z^2. \tag{4b}$$

In accordance with the definition of q its second argument is the instant of time t_1 at which the strength of the source at the point x_1 is to be calculated.

$$t_1 = t - \frac{R}{a_0}. \tag{5}$$

The superposition of such sources yields

$$\Phi = -\frac{1}{4\pi} \int\limits_{x_1 = -\infty}^{x_1 = +\infty} \frac{1}{R} q\left(x_1, t - \frac{R}{a_0}\right) dx_1. \tag{6}$$

The motion of the body can now be represented in a position-time diagram. The motion of the tip of the body is represented by the curve $x = h(t)$, while the motion of the rearmost point is represented by $x = h(t) + L$, if the length of the body is L (cf. Fig. 5). In the region of the x, t plane, contained between those two curves, which region is indicated by shading in Fig. 5, finite values of q can exist. If we focus our attention on a point in space whose coordinates are x and $\tilde{r}$ at a time t then for the second argument of the function q we obtain, in accordance with Eq. (5),

$$t_1 = t - \frac{\sqrt{\tilde{r}^2 + (x - x_1)^2}}{a_0}. \tag{7}$$

Hence at constant x, $\tilde{r}$ and t the following relationship results between the two arguments of q

$$a_0 (t_1 - t)^2 - (x - x_1)^2 = \tilde{r}^2.$$

This is a hyperbola whose asymptotes intersect at $x_1 = x$ and $t_1 = t$. This so-called "hyperbola of influence", corresponding to a point on the surface of the body and mid-way along it, is shown in Fig. 5. The integral in Eq. (6) is thus evaluated along this hyperbola in the x, t diagram. For small values of $\tilde{r}$ the eccentricity of the hyperbola is very small and the integral is evaluated along a curve which almost coincides with the asymptotes.

The function $q(x_1, t_1)$ is, of course, determined by the boundary conditions on the surface of the body. If the shape of the body is given by $\tilde{r} = \bar{r}(\xi)$, where the system of coordinates $\tilde{r}$, ξ moves with the body and the ξ axis coincides with the axis of x, a fixed point on the body is given by

$$x(t) = h(t) + \xi .$$

The vector normal to the surface of the body is

$$-\mathbf{i}\frac{d\bar{r}}{d\xi} + \mathbf{j}$$

where **i** and **j** denote unit vectors in the directions of x and $\tilde{r}$ respectively. The velocity vector relative to the moving body is further

$$\left(-\frac{dh}{dt} + \frac{\partial \Phi}{\partial x}\right)\mathbf{i} + \frac{\partial \Phi}{\partial \tilde{r}}\mathbf{j}.$$

Since the normal component of the velocity vanishes, one obtains

$$\Phi_{\tilde{r}} = -\frac{dh}{dt}\frac{d\bar{r}}{d\xi} \tag{8}$$

if $\partial\Phi/\partial x$ can be considered small in comparison with dh/dt. Thus the values of $\Phi_{\tilde{r}}$ are determined by the boundary conditions. $\Phi_{\tilde{r}}$ can now be expressed in terms of the integral of Eq. (6) yielding an integral equation for q. An approximate solution of this equation can be obtained on the basis of the following reasoning. For a fixed point x, Eq. (6) yields after substitution from Eq. (7)

$$\Phi_{\tilde{r}} = \frac{1}{4\pi}\int_{x_1=-\infty}^{x_1=+\infty}\left[\frac{\tilde{r}}{R^3}q(x_1, t_1) + \frac{\tilde{r}}{R^2 a_0}\frac{\partial q}{\partial t_1}\right]dx_1,$$

i.e. the contributions of the sources decrease rapidly with the distances R between the sources and the point considered. Hence at a given point x, $\tilde{r}$, t only that part of the appropriate hyperbola of Fig. 5 which lies in the immediate vicinity of this point is of importance in the determination of $\Phi_{\tilde{r}}$. This means that the $\tilde{r}$ component of the velocity at a point close to the x axis is determined almost exclusively by the strength, at time t, of the sources located on a section of the axis in the immediate neighborhood of the point. The effect of these sources can easily be visualised. Let the strength per unit length of the axis be $q(x_1, t_1)$. This mass flow per unit time crosses the surface of a cylinder coaxial with the axis, i.e.

$$2\pi\bar{r}\Phi_{\bar{r}} = q(x_1, t_1).$$

The first approximation to q can be obtained from the above equation with the aid of Eq. (9). Hence the expression for the potential takes the form

$$\Phi(\tilde{x}, \tilde{r}, t) = \frac{1}{2}\int_{-\infty}^{+\infty}\frac{1}{R}\frac{dh}{dt_1}\bar{r}(\xi)\frac{d\bar{r}}{d\xi}dx_1,$$

where t_1 is given by Eq. (7) and

$$\xi = x_1 - h(t_1)$$

$$R = \sqrt{(x - x_1)^2 + \tilde{r}^2}$$

in accordance with our earlier definitions. A more rigorous derivation of this result has been given by FRANKL [15].

The pressures on the surface of the body are obtained from the linearised BERNOULLI's equation for non-steady flow.

$$\Delta p = \varrho_0 \Phi_t .$$

It may be noticed from the equation for the point source that Φ_t is proportional to R^{-1}. Thus, although this term decreases with the distance, the integral with respect to x_1 increases logarithmically to infinity which means that the effect of even quite distant parts of the hyperbola of influence on the pressures may be quite considerable.

After this preparation, we can discuss qualitatively the forces on a body in various situations. Let us consider three cases. In the first of these the body starts from rest and suddenly assumes a subsonic velocity. In the second case, this suddenly assumed velocity is equal to the velocity of sound, while in the third case it is supersonic. The corresponding $x_1 - t_1$ diagrams are shown in Figs. 5, 6 and 7. The function q is non-zero in the shaded regions and it depends only on the distance ξ from the tip of the body since the velocity of flight is constant in all three cases.

The hyperbola of influence, corresponding to a point midway along the body, is indicated in these figures. This hyperbola can be considered as moving with the body. It may be noticed that in both the subsonic and supersonic regimes only a limited length of the hyperbola contributes to the pressure. In the supersonic regime these contributions originate from sources which are located in front of the point considered, when referred to the moving system of coordinates. Each source point contributes twice to the pressure, namely when the upstream and downstream waves, originating at the source, reach the point.

In the subsonic regime, the entire body contributes to the pressure at a given point. If the motion takes place with the velocity of sound a finite length of the hyperbola of influence results only when the time elapsed from the beginning of the motion is finite. If the motion starts at $t = 0$ then the hyperbola is cut off at $t = 0$. The length of the branch of the hyperbola becomes longer as the time at which the body is analyzed increases. Since the effect of a source on the pressure is a function of R^{-1}, i.e. for large values of t this effect varies with $(x - x_1)^{-1}$, the integration with respect to x_1 yields a variation of pressure in proportion to $\ln x$ or $\ln t$. The velocity of the body is always the same as that of the disturbances which it generates, and these disturbances are the source of steadily increasing pressures. Large-scale changes of pressure result, of course, also in changes in the velocity of sound and the original disturbances, therefore, become separated from the body. A steady flow field is generated in this manner,

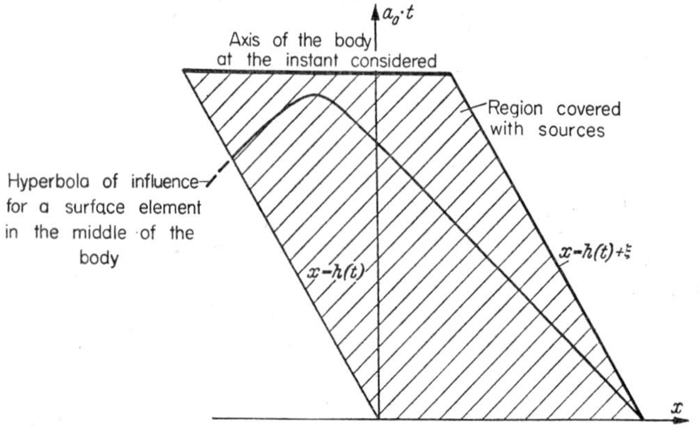

FIG. 5 Illustrating the calculation of the flow past a body of revolution which, starting from rest, suddenly assumes a subsonic velocity.

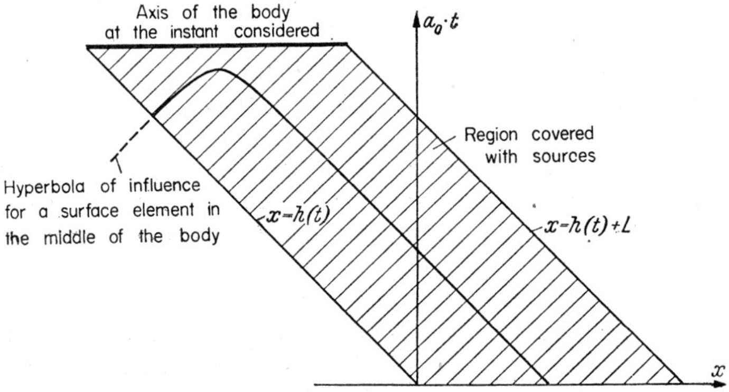

FIG. 6 Illustrating the calculation of the flow past a body of revolution which, starting from rest, suddenly assumes a sonic velocity.

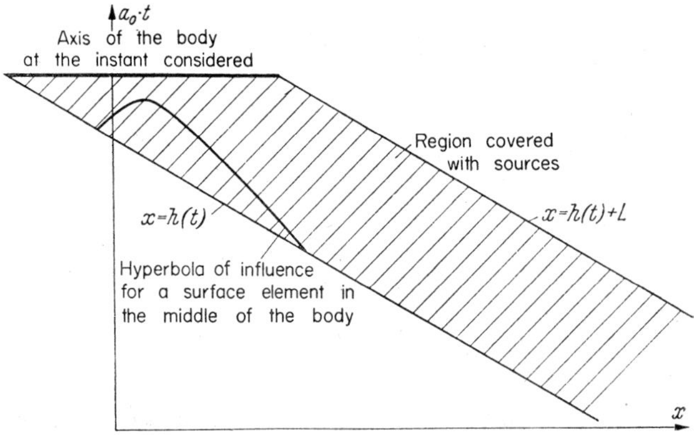

FIG. 7 Illustrating the calculation of the flow past a body of revolution which, starting from rest, suddenly assumes a supersonic velocity.

under the action, however, of the non-linear terms in the differential equation which account for the changes in the velocity of sound.

If the velocity of the body is not constant, then the traces of the foremost and aftermost points of the body in the $x - t$ diagram, are no longer straight lines. A section of the hyperbola of influence which is of importance for a particular point in space and time is, in the case of accelerated motion, finite and the pressures are also finite.

We can assume now that the acceleration is small and determine the deviation of the pressure from that arising in a steady flow. This procedure is applicable to both subsonic and supersonic flows. An example calculated by FRANKL

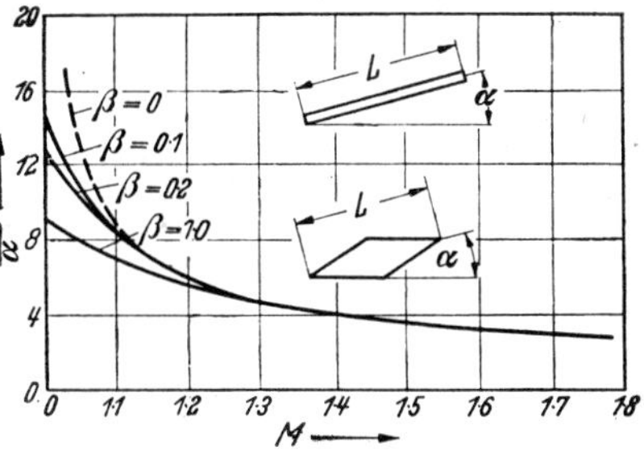

FIG. 8 Variation of the lift coefficient with MACH number for various values of dimensionless acceleration β. (According to GARDNER and LUDLOFF). c_L lift coefficient, b acceleration, a velocity of sound, L length of plate, α angle of attack, β dimensionless acceleration $= 2bL/a^2$.

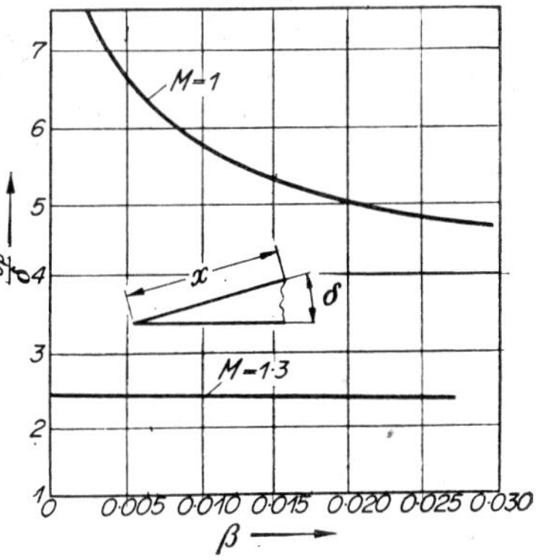

FIG. 9 Variation of the pressure coefficient on a wedge with dimensionless acceleration for MACH numbers $M = 1$ and $M = 13$. (According to GARDNER and LUDLOFF). c_p pressure coefficient, δ wedge angle, x coordinate measured along the wedge, b acceleration, β dimensionless acceleration $= -2bx/a^2$.

[15] shows that the effect of the acceleration on the drag is in all practical cases negligible.

Since in steady transonic flow the pressures are infinite, the above type of analysis cannot be applied to that case. We can investigate, however, what minimum value of the acceleration is required to make the length of the hyperbola of influence so small that the resulting pressures are compatible with the linearised theory. A discussion of this type has been presented by COLE [9], who concluded that although this minimum acceleration lies within the realm of possibilities, it is rarely achieved in practice.

Similar considerations can be applied to plane two-dimensional flows and to wings of finite aspect ratio. The solution is again constructed from three-dimensional sources and the analysis is rather complicated. The principal results obtained by GARDNER and LUDLOFF [22] are shown in Figs. 8–13.

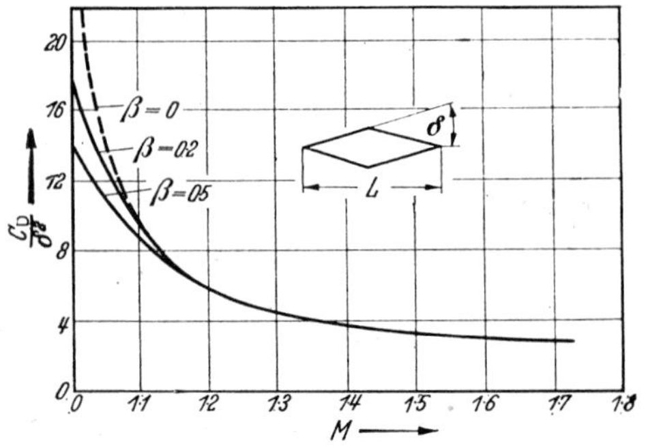

FIG. 10 Variation of the drag coefficient c_D with MACH number M for a rhombic profile. (According to GARDNER and LUDLOFF). Notation as in Fig. 8. δ half-angle at the vertex of the rhombus.

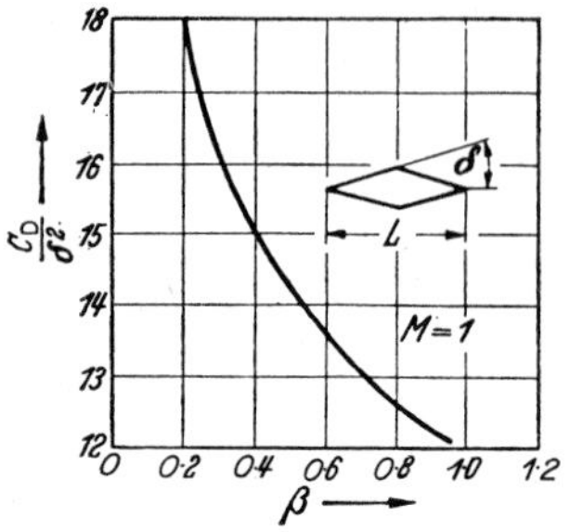

FIG. 11 Variation of the drag coefficient c_D with dimensionless acceleration β at $M = 1$. (According to GARDNER and LUDLOFF). Notation as in Fig. 8.

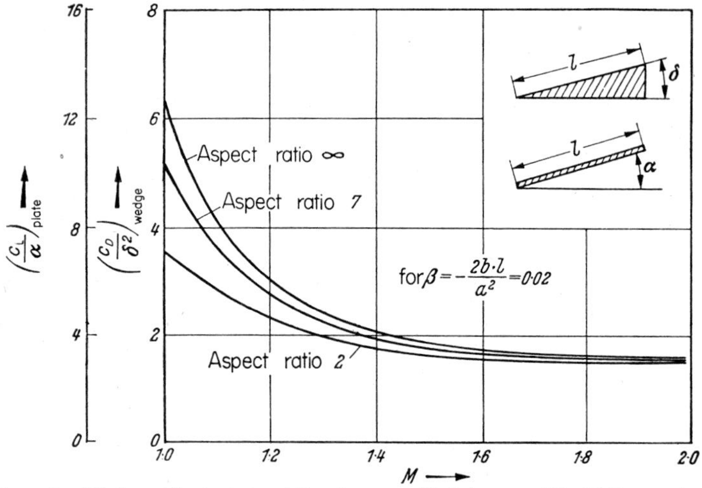

FIG. 12 Wedge: Variation of the drag coefficient c_D with M for various aspect ratios. Plate: Variation of the lift coefficient c_L with M for various aspect ratios. (According to GARDNER and LUDLOFF). Notation as in preceding figures.

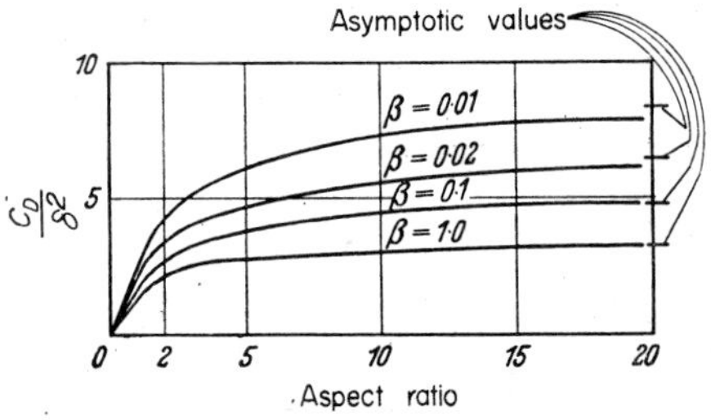

FIG. 13 Variation of the drag coefficient c_D of a wedge with the aspect ratio for various values of dimensionless acceleration β, at $M = 1$. (According to GARDNER and LUDLOFF). Notation as in preceding figures.

Another type of non-steady flow is represented by the motion around a forward moving propeller if one employs a system of coordinates stationary with respect to the surrounding air. If the tips of the propeller move with supersonic velocity then the velocity of the propeller blades with respect to the surrounding air must be sonic at some intermediate radius. BUSEMANN [4] has shown that when the relative velocity of the air is sonic only locally, the linearised theory does not lead to any difficulties.

6. The Limits of Applicability of the Linearised Theory

In view of the fact that the limited number of solutions obtained by means of more exact analyses is far short of the requirements posed by current practice, there exists a strong temptation to use the linearised theory even far outside

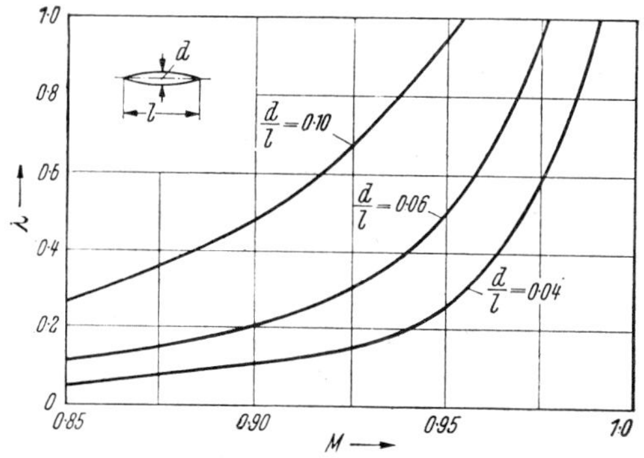

FIG. 14 The ratio λ of the linear to the non-linear terms for an axisymmetric body in steady flow as a function of the MACH number of the approaching flow. (According to GARDNER and LUDLOFF). λ calculated at the point of maximum thickness (According to COLE). l length of the body, d maximum thickness.

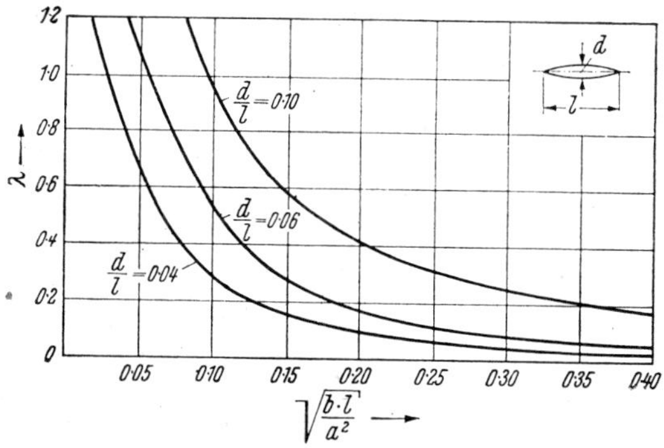

FIG. 15 The ratio λ of the linear to the non-linear terms for an axisymmetric body in transition through $M = 1$ during accelerated flight, as a function of an acceleration parameter. λ calculated for the point of maximum thickness. (According to COLE [9]). b acceleration, l length of the body, d maximum thickness, a velocity of sound.

its limits of applicability. Criteria for the applicability of the linearised theory have been formulated by COLE [9]. He calculates the field of flow on the basis of the linearised theory and then compares the coefficient of the critical term in the linearised theory with the coefficient resulting for this term when the linearised solution is introduced into the non-linear equation. This comparison is carried out for a representative point in the field of flow, e.g. for the point of maximum thickness of the body. It is expressed in terms of a parameter λ defined as the ratio of the difference between the two coefficients to the coefficient occuring in the linearised theory. When $\lambda = 0$ the non-linear terms are of no importance while when $\lambda = 1$ the change introduced by the non-linear terms is equal to the original expression obtained from the linearised theory. Since in general this latter unfavorable case occurs only locally within the field, a value of $\lambda = 1$ can still be considered acceptable. In the case of steady flows $\lambda = 1$ means that locally within the field a MACH number of unity is reached. Some representative result are shown in Figs. 14 and 15.

CHAPTER IV

EXACT SOLUTIONS OF THE POTENTIAL EQUATION OF TRANSONIC FLOW

1. Introductory Remarks

The differences between supersonic and subsonic flows and the fact that both of these can occur side by side in the field of flow have been of no importance in the considerations of the preceding chapters, except as far as non-steady flow problems were concerned. The phenomena associated with the transition from subsonic to supersonic flow could therefore not be explained. In the remainder of the book we shall concern ourselves with problems in which the term expressing the difference between subsonic and supersonic flows is included in the differential equation of flow.

This almost automatically forces us to accept a loss of generality. At the same time particular examples which shed light on a given physical aspect gain in importance although they do not furnish numerical results of general applicability. In addition, one must become resigned to the fact that the examples which immediately suggest themselves, not always have any direct bearing on problems of practical importance. However fascinating this situation might be to a researcher, it is very disappointing to someone concerned with the application of theoretical results to practical problems.

The analysis is most frequently carried out with the aid of the hodograph method. In the present chapter, however, we shall consider two fields of flow directly in the physical plane. These two problems can be extended to the axisymmetric case. Further examples, requiring considerable mathematical resourcefulness, have been treated by TAMADA and TOMOTIKA [75].

2. The Flow in a De Laval Nozzle

The solution of the exact potential equation of the flow in the throat of a DE LAVAL nozzle has been obtained by MEYER [61] in the form of a series expansion. We shall see that the first term of this expansion represents the exact solution of the equation for transonic flow.

Following MEYER we assume that the velocity varies linearly with the distance along the axis of the nozzle. The potential describing the deviation from a one-dimensional flow with the same MACH number is given at $y = 0$ by

$$\Phi = c \frac{x^2}{2}. \tag{1}$$

Successive terms of the solution are obtained by iteration whereby Eq. (1) is introduced into the potential equation for transonic flow

$$-(\gamma + 1)\,\Phi_x \Phi_{xx} + \Phi_{yy} = 0.$$

In this manner one arrives finally at the following exact solution

$$\Phi = c \frac{x^2}{2} + (\gamma + 1)\, c^2 \frac{x y^2}{2} + (\gamma + 1)^2 c^3 \frac{y^4}{24}. \tag{3}$$

This solution determines completely the shape of the streamlines and there remains thus the problem of matching the solution to other nozzle profiles. It may be shown by means of the hodograph method that Eq. (2) represents that part of the solution which is predominant in the vicinity of the throat.

To discuss further the form of the solution, it is convenient to write it in the form

$$\Phi = y^4 \left[\frac{c}{2}\left(\frac{x}{y^2}\right)^2 + \frac{\gamma + 1}{2} c^2 \left(\frac{x}{y^2}\right) + \frac{(\gamma + 1)^2}{24} c^3\right].$$

The variables x and y occur within the square brackets only in the form of a parameter x/y^2. The same parameter is found to occur in the expressions for the velocity components

$$\Phi_x = y^2 \left[c\left(\frac{x}{y^2}\right) + \frac{\gamma + 1}{2} c^2\right], \tag{4}$$

$$\Phi_y = y^3 \left[(\gamma + 1)\, c^2 \left(\frac{x}{y^2}\right) + (\gamma + 1)^2 \frac{c^3}{6}\right]. \tag{5}$$

Thus along the parabolas $x/y^2 =$ const the velocity components are proportional to the second or third power of y respectively. If the above expressions had been written in a somewhat different form the velocity components would have been found to be proportional to some suitable powers of x along these parabolas.

The sonic line, on which the velocity of sound and the flow velocity are equal, is obtained by setting $\Phi_x = 0$. Hence

$$\frac{x}{y^2} = -(\gamma + 1)\frac{c}{2}.$$

The locus of points at which the velocity vector is parallel to the axis of the nozzle is also of interest. There $\Phi_y = 0$ and

$$\frac{x}{y^2} = -(\gamma + 1)\frac{c}{6}.$$

The throat of the nozzle lies on this curve if two streamlines, symmetrical with respect to the x axis, are considered to represent the walls of the nozzle. The sonic line is thus located upstream of the locus of points at which the velocity is horizontal. The direction of the characteristics are obtained from Eq. (2)

$$\frac{dx}{dy} = \pm\sqrt{\gamma + 1}\sqrt{\Phi_x}\,.$$

Let us now consider whether the parabolas $x/y^2 = \text{const}$ can coincide with the characteristics. If we put

$$\frac{x}{y^2} = \zeta$$

then the slope of such a parabola is given by

$$\frac{dx}{dy} = 2\zeta y\,.$$

If this parabola is to be a characteristic, we must have

$$2\zeta y = \pm\sqrt{\gamma + 1}\sqrt{\Phi_x}$$

or

$$\Phi_x = \frac{4\zeta^2 y^2}{\gamma + 1}\,.$$

Substituting in the last equation for Φ_x from Eq. (4) we obtain

$$\frac{4\zeta^2 y^2}{\gamma + 1} = \left(c\zeta + (\gamma + 1)\frac{c^2}{2}\right) y^2\,.$$

Since y^2 can be cancelled on both sides of this equation, a parabola $\zeta = \text{const}$ can in fact coincide with a characteristic along its entire length. The solutions of the last equation are

$$\zeta = -c\,\frac{\gamma + 1}{4} \quad \text{and} \quad \zeta = c\,\frac{\gamma + 1}{2}\,.$$

The location of the special curves discussed above in a field of flow is indicated in Fig. 16.

The equation of the streamlines is obtained by integrating the slope of the streamlines Φ_y along a line $y = \text{const}$. Let the deviation of a streamline from $y = \text{const}$ be denoted by $\tilde{y}$, then

$$\tilde{y} = \frac{y^5}{a^*}\left[(\gamma + 1)\,c^2\,\frac{x^2}{2y^4} + (\gamma + 1)^2\,\frac{c^3}{6}\,\frac{x}{y^2}\right].$$

Two streamlines located at the same distance from the y axis can be considered to form the walls. Choosing such pairs of streamlines at various distances from the y axis, one obtains a family of De Laval nozzles. It may be shown that all these nozzles are related to one another by a transformation according to the similarity rule of transonic flow, i.e. by a simultaneous change in x_0 and τ (cf. p. 29). In other words the application of the similarity rule without change in x_0 amounts in this example to a change of scale in the field of flow.

If two streamlines lying on the same side of the axis are considered to represent the walls, then one obtains a solution describing the transition through the sonic velocity in a curved channel. Flows of this type occur in the blade passages of axial flow turbines (JACOBS [52]).

The following consideration is important to the understanding of mixed subsonic and supersonic flows. Let us consider two streamlines as the boundaries of the flow. It is well known that a change in the shape or position of the wall in a supersonic flow excercises an influence only downstream of the MACH line

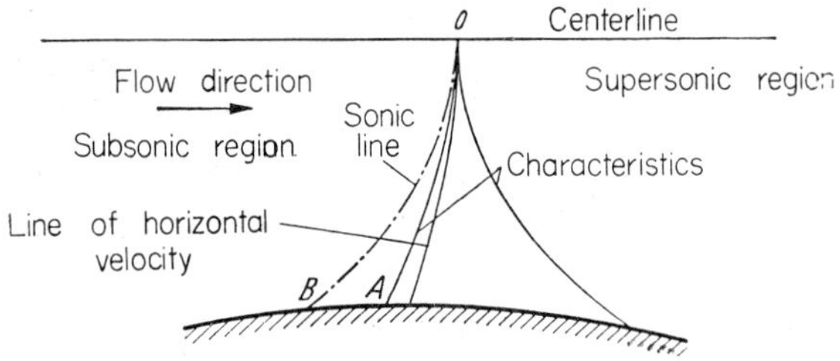

FIG. 16 Flow through a DE LAVAL nozzle.

originating at the point where the change occured. This is, of course, also true when the MACH line, along which the disturbance is propagated, does not reach the sonic line. Thus the shape and position of the wall downstream of point A in Fig. 16 can be changed without influencing the subsonic part of the flow.

We can thus divide the calculation of the flow through a DE LAVAL nozzle into two distinct parts: (1) the calculation of the subsonic region and of that part of the supersonic region which influences the subsonic part and (2) the calculation of the remainder of the supersonic field. For the first part we require the knowledge of the contour of the nozzle, only up a point such as A.

We are confronted here with an example in which the correct formulation of the mixed flow is intuitively obvious. This division of the flow fields will also be important later, when on the basis of the flow in a DE LAVAL nozzle we shall, in the limit, obtain a qualitative picture of a flow with a uniform sonic velocity of approach. The location of the point A was not known in advance in our example. It could be obtained only from the solution of the boundary value problem if such a solution, in general terms, were available. In any case, the point A lies upstream of the throat as will be seen later on the basis of a hodograph transformation*. A MACH line, such as AO, which separates the parts of

* The DE LAVAL nozzle is discussed so frequently in the literature, that one has the impression that it represents a problem of particular importance. It has been shown by G. I. TAYLOR that the DE LAVAL nozzle is of particular interest from the following point of view. If the nozzle is symmetrical with respect to the throat, then as long as the flow is subsonic along the entire length, there exists a symmetry also in the flow field. This is certainly no

the supersonic fields which respectively do or do not influence the subsonic region, is called a limiting MACH line.

For an axisymmetric DE LAVAL nozzle, the corresponding solution is

$$\Phi = \frac{c x^2}{2} + \frac{\gamma + 1}{4} c^2 x y^2 + \frac{(\gamma + 1)^2 c^3}{64} y^4 .$$

The discussion can follow similar lines to that given above. For the sonic line one obtains

$$\frac{x}{y^2} = -\frac{(\gamma + 1)}{4} c ,$$

and for the locus of points in which the streamlines are horizontal,

$$\frac{x}{y^2} = \frac{-(\gamma + 1)\, c}{8} .$$

The MACH lines, finally, are given by

$$\frac{x}{y^2} = -\frac{(\gamma + 1)\, c}{8} (1 \pm \sqrt{5}) .$$

3. The Parallel Sonic Jet

Attempts to calculate the supersonic flow resulting from the expansion of a parallel sonic jet, by means of the method of characteristics, lead to serious difficulties, particularly in the axisymmetric case. These difficulties are due to the fact that the MACH waves which one constructs initially always intersect for the first time at the center of the jet, no matter how fine a characteristic net is chosen. An analytical solution can be obtained (GÖRTLER [23], GUDERLEY [42]) if one puts

$$\left.\begin{aligned} \Phi &= x^3 f(y) \text{ in the two-dimensional case} \\ \Phi &= x^3 f(r) \text{ in the axisymmetric case} \end{aligned}\right\} \qquad (1)$$

The above assumption could be rationalised if the exponent of x were originally considered arbitrary and if Eqs. (1) were introduced into the differential equations of transonic flow, i.e. Eq. II, 8 (1) or Eq. II, 8 (2), respectively. The exponent of x could then be chosen such that the powers of x would cancel out from the equation. As a result one would obtain the form of Eq. (1). Higher powers of x are physically possible and they would denote slower expansions. With the aid of Eq. (1) one obtains for the two-dimensional case

$$f'' - 18(\gamma + 1) f^2 = 0 , \qquad (2a)$$

longer true when the nozzle is acting as a DE LAVAL nozzle. One would expect that a study of the transition from one behaviour to the other would provide an insight into the phenemena of transonic flow. A direct analysis of nozzles has, however, *not in fact led* to this hoped-for result.

and for the axisymmetric case

$$f'' + \frac{f'}{r} - 18(\gamma + 1) f^2 = 0. \tag{2b}$$

One should note that if $F(\zeta)$ is a solution of

$$\frac{d^2 F}{d\zeta^2} - F^2 = 0 \tag{3a}$$

or

$$\frac{d^2 F}{d\zeta^2} + \frac{1}{\zeta}\frac{dF}{d\zeta} - F^2 = 0 \tag{3b}$$

with the initial condition $dF/d\zeta = 0$ at $\zeta = 0$, then the required solutions of Eq. (2) are given by

$$f = C_1^2 \frac{1}{18(\gamma + 1)} F(C_1 y) \quad \text{or} \quad f = C_1^2 \frac{1}{18(\gamma + 1)} F(C_1 r).$$

The solution can be fitted to any width of the jet by a suitable choice of the constant C_1. The function F can be of various types. Let us consider the two-dimensional case a little more fully in order to obtain an insight into the meaning of these solutions. In this case the solution of Eq. (3a) is

$$\zeta = \left(\frac{3}{2}\right)^{1/3} C_2^{-1/6} \int_{\tau=\pm 1}^{\tau = \left(\frac{3}{2} C_2\right)^{-1/3} F} \frac{d\tau}{\sqrt{\tau^3 \mp 1}}.$$

Considering only the upper sign, F varies between a positive value given by

$$\tau = 1 = (\tfrac{3}{2} C_2)^{-1/3} F$$

and infinity and hence y varies from zero to a finite value. The solution corresponds in the vicinity of $F = \infty$ to a PRANDTL–MEYER flow around a corner. This then corresponds also to the outer boundary of the jet. In this solution F is always positive and from Eq. (1) one can see that the jet is supersonic.

Considering now the lower sign, F varies from a negative value to $+\infty$. The region of negative F is interesting. This part of the solution represents the subsonic jet which gradually changes into a sonic one, if only one considers a streamline as a boundary of the jet. Employing the entire region of negative F up to $F = 0$, the pressure on the bounding streamline is, within the limits of our approximation, constant and equal to the critical pressure. The solution can then be interpreted as a free jet flowing with critical velocity. We have shown thus that such a free jet, whose velocity is sonic, becomes parallel within a finite length. Similar conditions arise in the case of an axisymmetrical jet. The functions F and F' for two-dimensional and axisymmetric flow are shown in Figs. 17–20. In the case of supersonic jets $\zeta = 1$ corresponds to the point at

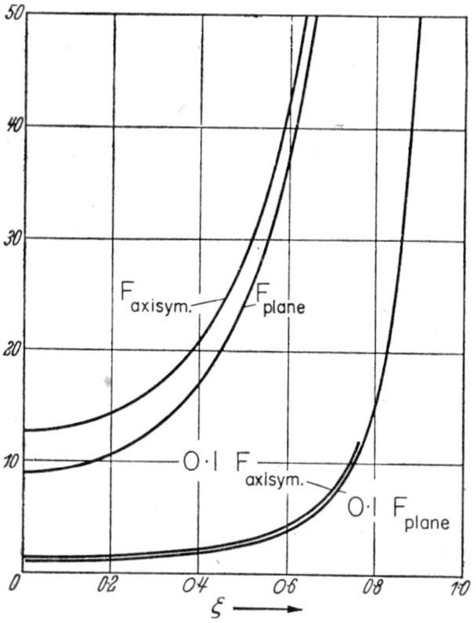

FIG. 17 The functions F for a two-dimensional and for an axisymmetric supersonic jet. $\zeta = 0$ axis of the jet; $\zeta = 1$ boundary of the jet; at $x = \text{const.}$ F is proportional to the deviation of the x component of the velocity from the critical velocity.

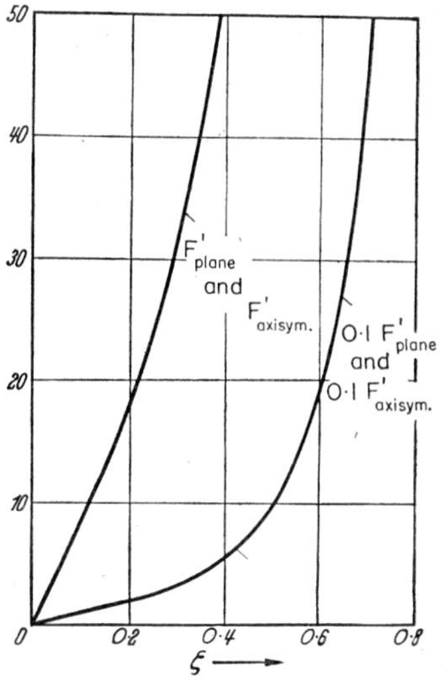

FIG. 18 The functions F for a two-dimensional and for an axisymmetric supersonic jet. $\zeta = 0$ axis of the jet; $\zeta = 1$ boundary of the jet; at $x = \text{const.}$ F is proportional to the velocity component normal to the axis of the nozzle.

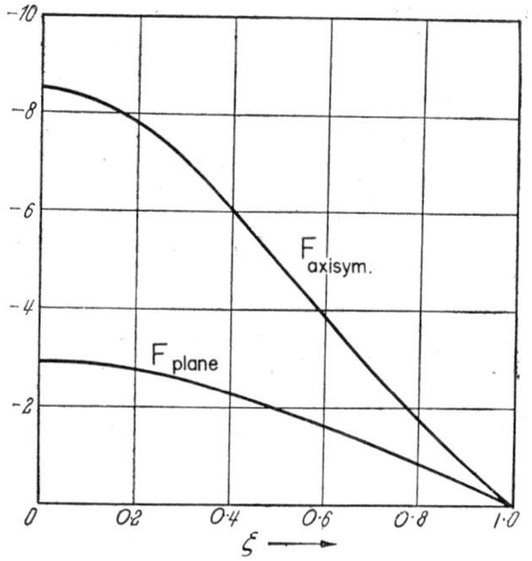

FIG. 19 The functions F for a two-dimensional and for an axisymmetric supersonic jet. $\zeta = 0$ axis of the jet; $\zeta = 1$ boundary of the jet; at $x = \text{const.}$ F is proportional to the deviation of the x component of the velocity from the critical velocity.

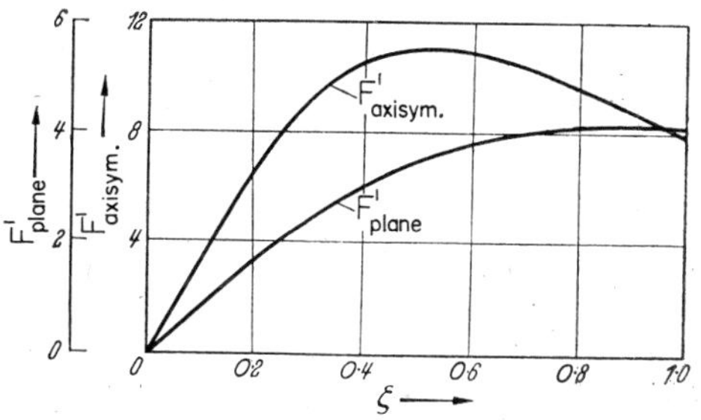

FIG. 20 The functions F for a two-dimensional and for an axisymmetric supersonic jet. $\zeta = 0$ axis of the jet; $\zeta = 1$ boundary of the jet; at $x = \text{const.}$ F is proportional to the velocity component normal to the axis of the nozzle.

which the PRANDTL–MEYER expansion occurs, while in the other case it corresponds to the free surface where the velocity is sonic.

It is well known that a free subsonic jet becomes parallel only at infinity (cf. also Section v·1). By a suitable deformation of the contour of the jet it is possible, on the other hand, to obtain a parallel supersonic jet within a finite length. The last example indicates that with exactly sonic velocity a parallel jet can also be achieved in a finite length even when within the jet only subsonic velocities exist. It is only necessary to provide a constant pressure at the boundary of the jet. An example of this kind is shown in Fig. 48.

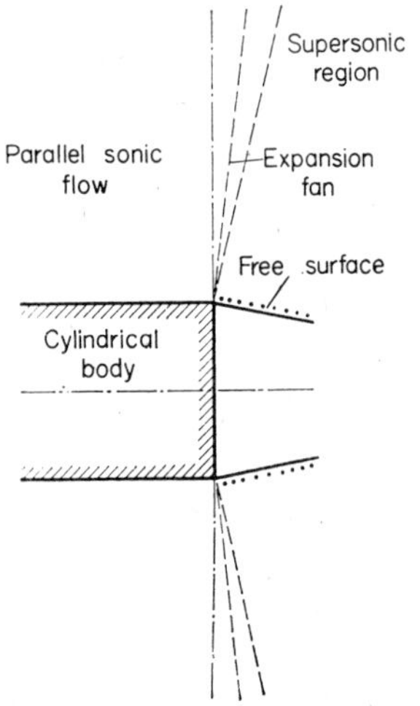

FIG. 21 Expansion behind a cylindrical obstacle in a parallel sonic stream.

By a suitable choice of the integration constant we can extend the solution for the axisymmetric case to a jet issuing from an annular orifice. Allowing the outer boundary of this orifice to become infinite, we obtain the expansion of a sonic parallel flow past a circular cylinder which ends at $x = 0$, at which point a lower pressure is applied. The flow expands inwards, as a result. Such a flow could occur, for example, at the blunt end of a body which is so long that the flow upstream of the end can be considered parallel and sonic. This is case illustrated in Fig. 21 and it has been described by GRAHAM [24].

Both examples considered above are special cases of a more general type of solution which will be discussed in Chapter XI in connection with axisymmetric flows at $M = 1$.

CHAPTER V

FUNDAMENTALS OF THE HODOGRAPH TRANSFORMATION

IF IN the differential equations of flow the velocity components are treated as independent variables then one obtains the so-called hodograph representation. The hodograph transformation is used in hydrodynamics only in such cases in which the boundary conditions in the hodograph plane are very simple. To this group belong two-dimensional flows along whose boundaries either the direction of the velocity or its magnitude and hence, in accordance with BERNOULLI's equation, the pressure are constant. This type of boundary condition lends itself particularly well to a hodograph transformation also in the present analysis and the more general boundary conditions introduce quite serious difficulties. The hodograph transformation is particularly important for transonic flows, since the equations of two-dimensional flow in the hodograph plane are linear. The advantages resulting from this fact by far outweigh the difficulties associated with the boundary conditions which the hodograph transformation introduces.

1. The Equations in the Hodograph Plane

The transformation from the physical to the hodograph plane is obtained quite simply if one starts from the differential equations for the individual velocity components. Putting, for the sake of brevity,

$$v_x = u \quad \text{and} \quad v_y = v .$$

Eqs. I, 6 (1) and I, 6 (2) can be written in the form

$$\frac{\partial u}{\partial x}\left(1 - \frac{u^2}{a^2}\right) - \left(\frac{\partial u}{\partial y} + \frac{\partial v}{\partial x}\right)\frac{u v}{a^2} + \frac{\partial v}{\partial y}\left(1 - \frac{v^2}{a^2}\right) = 0, \tag{1a}$$

$$\frac{\partial u}{\partial y} - \frac{\partial v}{\partial x} = 0. \tag{1b}$$

From BERNOULLI's equation we know that a is a function of $u^2 + v^2$. We now want to transform the equations of the physical plane, namely

$$u = u(x, y) \qquad v = v(x, y)$$

into the corresponding ones of the hodograph plane, i.e.

$$x = x(u, v) \qquad y = y(u, v).$$

From the identity

$$u = u[x(u, v), y(u, v)]$$

we obtain, by differentiating with respect to u and v,

$$1 = \frac{\partial u}{\partial x}\frac{\partial x}{\partial u} + \frac{\partial u}{\partial y}\frac{\partial y}{\partial u},$$

$$0 = \frac{\partial u}{\partial x}\frac{\partial x}{\partial v} + \frac{\partial u}{\partial y}\frac{\partial y}{\partial v}$$

and hence

$$\frac{\partial u}{\partial x} = \frac{\partial y}{\partial v}\Big/D; \quad \frac{\partial u}{\partial y} = -\frac{\partial x}{\partial v}\Big/D, \tag{2}$$

where

$$D = \frac{\partial y}{\partial v}\frac{\partial x}{\partial u} - \frac{\partial y}{\partial u}\frac{\partial x}{\partial v}. \tag{3}$$

In an similar way we find

$$\frac{\partial v}{\partial x} = -\frac{\partial y}{\partial u}\Big/D; \quad \frac{\partial v}{\partial y} = \frac{\partial x}{\partial u}\Big/D. \tag{4}$$

Introducing these results into Eqs. (1) we can cancel D on both sides of the equation and obtain

$$\frac{\partial y}{\partial v}\left(1 - \frac{u^2}{a^2}\right) + \left(\frac{\partial x}{\partial v} + \frac{\partial y}{\partial u}\right)\frac{uv}{a^2} + \frac{\partial x}{\partial u}\left(1 - \frac{v^2}{a^2}\right) = 0 \tag{5a}$$

$$\frac{\partial x}{\partial v} - \frac{\partial y}{\partial u} = 0. \tag{5b}$$

By putting

$$x = \frac{\partial \varphi(u, v)}{\partial u}; \quad y = \frac{\partial \varphi(u, v)}{\partial v} \tag{6}$$

Eq. (5b) is automatically satisfied. Here $\varphi(u, v)$ is a twice-differentiable function of u and v. Substitution into Eq. (5a) yields

$$\varphi_{vv}\left(1 - \frac{u^2}{a^2}\right) + 2\varphi_{uv}\frac{uv}{a^2} + \varphi_{uu}\left(1 - \frac{v^2}{a^2}\right) = 0. \tag{7}$$

The above result is normally derived by applying the LEGENDRE transformation (MOLENBROEK [62]) to the two-dimensional potential equation in the physical plane, Eq. I, 4 (5)

$$\varphi(u, v) = ux + vy - \Phi(x, y). \tag{8}$$

Here φ denotes the transformed potential. Considering x and y to be functions of u and v and using the relations

$$\Phi_x = u \qquad \Phi_y = v$$

we obtain by differentiation with respect to u

$$\varphi_u = x + u\frac{\partial x}{\partial u} + v\frac{\partial y}{\partial u} - \Phi_x\frac{\partial x}{\partial u} - \Phi_y\frac{\partial y}{\partial u}$$

and hence

$$x = \varphi_u.$$

Similarly

$$y = \varphi_v.$$

These above equations are the same as Eqs. (6). The remaining analysis follows the same lines as the one described above, i.e. the derivatives Φ_{xx}, Φ_{xy}, and Φ_{yy}, are determined by a method quite similar to that which led to Eqs. (3) and (4).

The hodograph representation shows no preferred directions. This is most clearly noticeable when polar coordinates are employed. Let w denote the magnitude of the velocity and ϑ the angle between the velocity vector and a fixed straight line, e.g. the x axis. Then

$$w^2 = u^2 + v^2,$$

$$\vartheta = \operatorname{arc\,tg}\frac{v}{u} \tag{9}$$

and one obtains

$$\varphi_{ww} + \frac{1}{w}\varphi_w\left(1 - \frac{w^2}{a^2}\right) + \frac{1}{w^2}\varphi_{\vartheta\vartheta}\left(1 - \frac{w^2}{a^2}\right) = 0. \tag{10}$$

The stream function is frequently chosen as a dependent variable in the hodograph plane. A simple derivation due to BUSEMANN [2] starts from the equations

$$\frac{\partial\psi}{\partial x} = -\varrho v, \qquad \frac{\partial\psi}{\partial y} = \varrho u,$$

$$\frac{\partial\Phi}{\partial x} = u, \qquad \frac{\partial\Phi}{\partial y} = v$$

from which

$$d\psi = -\varrho v\,dx + \varrho u\,dy,$$

$$d\Phi = u\,dx + v\,dy,$$

and

$$dx = \frac{1}{w^2}\left(-\frac{v}{\varrho}\,d\psi + u\,d\Phi\right),$$

$$dy = \frac{1}{w^2}\left(\frac{u}{\varrho}\,d\psi + v\,d\Phi\right).$$

The variables x, y, Φ and ψ are next considered to be functions of w and ϑ. This yields

$$\frac{\partial x}{\partial w} dw + \frac{\partial x}{\partial \vartheta} d\vartheta$$

$$= \frac{1}{w}\left[-\frac{\sin\vartheta}{\varrho}\left(\frac{\partial \psi}{\partial w} dw + \frac{\partial \psi}{\partial \vartheta} d\vartheta\right) + \cos\vartheta\left(\frac{\partial \Phi}{\partial w} dw + \frac{\partial \Phi}{\partial \vartheta} d\vartheta\right)\right]$$

and hence

$$\frac{\partial x}{\partial w} = \frac{1}{w}\left(-\frac{\sin\vartheta}{\varrho}\frac{\partial \psi}{\partial w} + \cos\vartheta\frac{\partial \Phi}{\partial w}\right), \tag{11a}$$

$$\frac{\partial x}{\partial \vartheta} = \frac{1}{w}\left(-\frac{\sin\vartheta}{\varrho}\frac{\partial \psi}{\partial \vartheta} + \cos\vartheta\frac{\partial \Phi}{\partial \vartheta}\right). \tag{11b}$$

Similarly one obtains

$$\frac{\partial y}{\partial w} = \frac{1}{w}\left(\frac{\cos\vartheta}{\varrho}\frac{\partial \psi}{\partial w} + \sin\vartheta\frac{\partial \Phi}{\partial w}\right), \tag{12a}$$

$$\frac{\partial y}{\partial \vartheta} = \frac{1}{w}\left(\frac{\cos\vartheta}{\varrho}\frac{\partial \psi}{\partial \vartheta} + \sin\vartheta\frac{\partial \Phi}{\partial \vartheta}\right). \tag{12b}$$

Since

$$\frac{\partial^2 x}{\partial w\,\partial \vartheta} = \frac{\partial^2 x}{\partial \vartheta\,\partial w}$$

Eqs. (11a) and (11b) yield

$$\frac{1}{w}\left(-\frac{\cos\vartheta}{\varrho}\frac{\partial \psi}{\partial w} - \sin\vartheta\frac{\partial \Phi}{dw}\right) = -\sin\vartheta\frac{d\left(\frac{1}{\varrho w}\right)}{dw}\frac{\partial \psi}{\partial \vartheta} + \frac{d\left(\frac{1}{w}\right)}{dw}\cos\vartheta\frac{\partial \Phi}{\partial \vartheta}$$

and similarly from Eqs. (12a) and (12b) we have

$$\frac{1}{w}\left(\frac{-\sin\vartheta}{\varrho}\frac{\partial \psi}{\partial w} + \cos\vartheta\frac{\partial \Phi}{\partial w}\right) = \cos\vartheta\frac{d\left(\frac{1}{\varrho w}\right)}{dw}\frac{\partial \psi}{\partial \vartheta} + \frac{d\left(\frac{1}{w}\right)}{dw}\sin\vartheta\frac{\partial \Phi}{\partial \vartheta}.$$

Multiplying these equations by $\sin\vartheta$ and $\cos\vartheta$ respectively and adding we obtain

$$\frac{1}{\varrho w}\frac{\partial \psi}{\partial w} = \frac{1}{w^2}\frac{\partial \Phi}{\partial \vartheta},$$

$$\frac{1}{w}\frac{\partial \Phi}{\partial w} = \frac{d\left(\frac{1}{\varrho w}\right)}{dw}\frac{\partial \psi}{\partial \vartheta}.$$

Eliminating Φ by differentiation we obtain finally

$$\frac{\partial}{\partial w}\left(\frac{w}{\varrho}\frac{\partial \psi}{\partial w}\right) - w\,\frac{d\left(\dfrac{1}{\varrho w}\right)}{dw}\,\frac{\partial^2 \psi}{\partial \vartheta^2} = 0 \tag{13}$$

and hence with the aid of Eq. I, 2 (10a)

$$\frac{\partial^2 \psi}{\partial w^2} + \frac{1}{w}\left(1 + \frac{w^2}{a^2}\right)\frac{\partial \psi}{\partial w} + \frac{1}{w^2}\left(1 - \frac{w^2}{a^2}\right)\frac{\partial^2 \psi}{\partial \vartheta^2} = 0. \tag{14}$$

Having found a solution of this equation we can now determine the coordinates in the physical plane from Eqs. (11) and (12) in which, however, Φ must be expressed in terms of ψ.

$$\left.\begin{aligned}
\frac{\partial x}{\partial w} &= \frac{1}{\varrho w}\left(-\sin\vartheta\,\frac{\partial \psi}{\partial w} - \cos\vartheta\,\frac{1-\dfrac{w^2}{a^2}}{w}\,\frac{\partial \psi}{\partial \vartheta}\right)\\
\frac{\partial y}{\partial w} &= \frac{1}{\varrho w}\left(\cos\vartheta\,\frac{\partial \psi}{\partial w} - \sin\vartheta\,\frac{1-\dfrac{w^2}{a^2}}{w}\,\frac{\partial \psi}{\partial \vartheta}\right)\\
\frac{\partial x}{\partial \vartheta} &= \frac{1}{\varrho w}\left(-\sin\vartheta\,\frac{\partial \psi}{\partial \vartheta} + \cos\vartheta\, w\,\frac{\partial \psi}{\partial w}\right)\\
\frac{\partial y}{\partial \vartheta} &= \frac{1}{\varrho w}\left(\cos\vartheta\,\frac{\partial \psi}{\partial \vartheta} + \sin\vartheta\, w\,\frac{\partial \psi}{\partial w}\right).
\end{aligned}\right\} \tag{15}$$

The intimate connection between the LEGENDRE potential φ and the stream function ψ becomes apparent from the following. From the relationship $x = \varphi_u$ and $y = \varphi_v$, which in polar coordinates take the form

$$x = \varphi_w \cos\vartheta - \frac{1}{w}\varphi_\vartheta \sin\vartheta,$$

$$y = \varphi_w \sin\vartheta + \frac{1}{w}\varphi_\vartheta \cos\vartheta$$

one obtains

$$dx = \left(\varphi_{ww}\cos\vartheta + \frac{1}{w^2}\varphi_\vartheta \sin\vartheta - \frac{1}{w}\varphi_{w\vartheta}\sin\vartheta\right)dw +$$
$$+ \left(\varphi_{w\vartheta}\cos\vartheta - \varphi_w \sin\vartheta - \frac{1}{w}\varphi_{\vartheta\vartheta}\sin\vartheta - \frac{1}{w}\varphi_\vartheta\cos\vartheta\right)d\vartheta,$$

$$dy = \left(\varphi_{ww}\sin\vartheta - \frac{1}{w^2}\varphi_\vartheta \cos\vartheta + \frac{1}{w}\varphi_{w\vartheta}\sin\vartheta\right)dw +$$
$$+ \left(\varphi_{w\vartheta}\sin\vartheta + \varphi_w \cos\vartheta + \frac{1}{w}\varphi_{\vartheta\vartheta}\cos\vartheta - \frac{1}{w}\varphi_\vartheta\sin\vartheta\right)d\vartheta.$$

Substituting the above results into

$$d\psi = \frac{\partial \psi}{\partial w} \partial w + \frac{\partial \psi}{\partial \vartheta} d\vartheta = -\varrho v\, dx + \varrho u\, dy$$

and comparing the cofficients of dw and $d\vartheta$ one obtains

$$\left.\begin{aligned} \frac{\partial \psi}{\partial w} &= \varrho\left(-\frac{1}{w}\varphi_\vartheta + \varphi_{w\vartheta}\right), \\ \frac{\partial \psi}{\partial \vartheta} &= \varrho\,(w\varphi_w + \varphi_{\vartheta\vartheta}). \end{aligned}\right\} \qquad (16)$$

Thus, when the transformed potential is known, the stream function can be determined by integration.

The decision as to whether in a given case the equation of the stream function or that of the LEGENDRE potential should be employed depends on the nature of the boundary conditions. The stream function is particularly useful in the treatment of shock conditions and of the flow around a given body. On the other hand, problems which differ so little from a known flow field that the deviations in the contour of the profile, in the physical plane, can be expressed in the hodograph plane by a linearisation of the boundary conditions lend themselves to a very simple representation in terms of the transformed potential.

2. The Jacobian of the Hodograph Transformation

If one considers x and y to be functions of the independent variables u and v then

$$\left.\begin{aligned} dx &= \frac{\partial x}{\partial u} du + \frac{\partial x}{\partial v} dv, \\ dy &= \frac{\partial y}{\partial u} du + \frac{\partial y}{\partial v} dv \end{aligned}\right\} \qquad (1)$$

represents a system of equations in which du and dv are unknown while dx and dy are given. The coefficients $\partial x/\partial u$, $\partial x/\partial v$, $\partial y/\partial u$ and $\partial y/\partial v$ are functions of the point in the flow which is being considered. A necessary condition for the above system of equations to have a unique solution is that the determinant

$$D = \frac{\partial x}{\partial u}\frac{\partial y}{\partial v} - \frac{\partial x}{\partial v}\frac{\partial y}{\partial u} \qquad (2)$$

is not zero. This determinant is called the Jacobian of the transformation and the usual notation employed for it is

$$D = \frac{\partial (x, y)}{\partial (u, v)}.$$

If the Jacobian is equal to zero, Eqs. (1) are linearly dependent and solutions for du and dv can be obtained only if the same linear relationship exists between dx and dy as between the RHS's of Eqs. (1). Then, however, any chosen pair of du and dv yields the same ratio between dx and dy. This means that, when only the linear terms in the expansion for dx and dy are considered, as was done in Eqs. (1), then the neighbourhood of a point in the hodograph plane maps into a line in the physical plane. The Jacobian vanishes also when all the terms of the first order on the RHS's of Eqs. (1) are zero. In such a case the mapping can be carried out only with the aid of terms of higher order. Such a situation can arise at a branch point in the hodograph plane or in the physical plane. We shall not attempt any general discussion of such cases, but we shall later encounter several examples of situations of this type.

The above considerations indicate that there exists a unique relationship between the hodograph plane and the physical plane as long as the Jacobian is neither zero nor infinite. The Jacobian becomes infinite when some of the terms on the RHS's of Eqs. (1) are infinite and in such a case it is possible that for non-zero values of dx and dy the appropriate values of du and dv become zero. The Jacobian can be interpreted as the ratio of the surface element in the physical plane to the corresponding surface element in the hodograph plane. A rectangular element of the surface of the hodograph plane, whose sides are du and dv, maps into a parallelogram whose sides are given by the vectors

$$\mathbf{i}\frac{\partial x}{\partial u}du + \mathbf{j}\frac{\partial y}{\partial u}du$$

and

$$\mathbf{i}\frac{\partial x}{\partial v}dv + \mathbf{j}\frac{\partial y}{\partial v}dv .$$

The oriented surface element of the hodograph plane is given by

$$\mathbf{i}\times\mathbf{j}\,du\,dv,$$

while the oriented surface of the physical plane is

$$\mathbf{i}\times\mathbf{j}\,du\,dv\left(\frac{\partial x}{\partial u}\frac{\partial y}{\partial v} - \frac{\partial y}{\partial u}\frac{\partial x}{\partial v}\right).$$

Hence the above interpretation.

We can, naturally, consider the reciprocal of the ratio and hence

$$\frac{\partial x}{\partial u}\frac{\partial y}{\partial v} - \frac{\partial y}{\partial u}\frac{\partial x}{\partial v} = \left(\frac{\partial u}{\partial x}\frac{\partial v}{\partial x} - \frac{\partial u}{\partial y}\frac{\partial v}{\partial x}\right)^{-1}. \tag{3}$$

The behaviour of the Jacobian of the transformation is important in the hodograph method since whenever it becomes zero or infinite, this indicates the occurence of singularities in the transformation. In the hodograph representation of flow problems, even the simple fact that the Jacobian must be negative is important. This fact will be proved later. As a result of this condition, the possible flow configurations in the hodograph plane are severely restricted (c.f. p. 30). An analytical expression for the Jacobian can be obtained with the aid of Eq. V, 1, (15)

$$\frac{\partial(x, y)}{\partial(w, \vartheta)} = -\frac{1}{\varrho^2 w}\left\{\left(\frac{\partial \psi}{\partial w}\right)^2 + \frac{\left(1-\frac{w^2}{a^2}\right)}{w^2}\left(\frac{\partial \psi}{\partial \vartheta}\right)^2\right\}$$

and, further, from

$$u = w \cos\vartheta,$$

$$v = w \sin\vartheta$$

one obtains

$$\frac{\partial(u, v)}{\partial(w, \vartheta)} = w.$$

Finally, in view of the interpretation of the Jacobian as the ratio of surface elements, we have

$$D = \frac{\partial(x, y)}{\partial(u, v)} = -\frac{1}{\varrho^2 w^2}\left[\left(\frac{\partial \psi}{\partial w}\right)^2 + \frac{1-\frac{w^2}{a^2}}{w^2}\left(\frac{\partial \psi}{\partial \vartheta}\right)^2\right]. \tag{4}$$

The value of the Jacobian is, of course, not dependent on the choice of independent variables in the hodograph plane. If the transformed potential is selected rather than a stream function, then with the aid of Eq. V, 1 (16) there results

$$D = -\left[\left(\frac{1}{w}\varphi_{w\vartheta} - \frac{1}{w^2}\varphi_\vartheta\right)^2 + \left(1-\frac{w^2}{a^2}\right)\left(\frac{\varphi_w}{w} + \frac{1}{w^2}\varphi_{\vartheta\vartheta}\right)^2\right]. \tag{5}$$

In the subsonic regime the Jacobian, which is equal to the negative of a sum of two squares, must itself be either negative or zero. The value zero can occur only at an isolated point since if the Jacobian were zero along a line in the subsonic regime then on this line $\partial\psi/\partial w = 0$ and $\partial\psi/\partial\vartheta = 0$. Thus the analytic continuation must be given by $\psi =$ const. In accordance with our discussion, in connection with the method of characteristics, this can be the only possible analytic continuation. In the supersonic regime the Jacobian vanishes if

$$\frac{\partial \psi}{\partial w} \pm \frac{\sqrt{\frac{w^2}{a^2}-1}}{w}\frac{\partial \psi}{\partial \vartheta} = 0, \tag{6}$$

where the equation has to be satisfied only for one of the two signs. This leads directly to the concept of limiting lines*.

* In the original text the term "edge of regression" has been employed. In view of the strong three-dimensional connotation of the latter the term "limiting line", as employed by several authors, is to be preferred. (Transl.)

3. Limiting Lines

Before undertaking a discussion of limiting lines, we shall first illustrate their properties with the aid of an example.

In the flow due to a source all the streamlines are radial for reasons of symmetry. The velocity is constant on concentric circles. If the radius of one of such circles is r then for reasons of continuity

$$r \varrho w = \text{const.} \tag{1}$$

In accordance with Eq. I, 2 (10a) the mass flow density ϱw has, in the case of isentropic flow, a maximum at the sonic velocity, i.e. the above equation can be satisfied for values of r greater than the minimum value r_0. When $r > r_0$, there exist two solutions corresponding to subsonic and supersonic flow res-

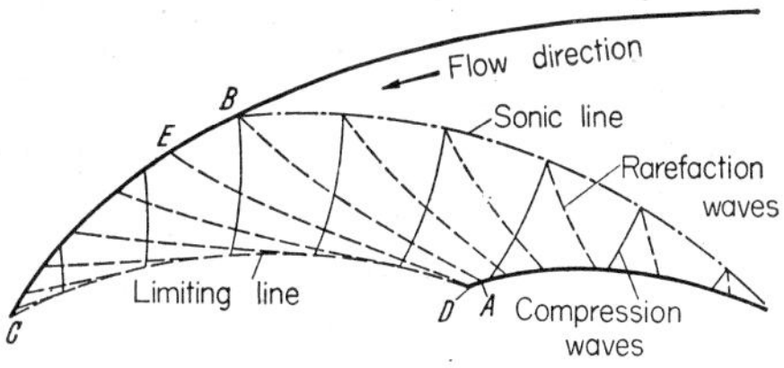

FIG. 22 Limiting line formed by expansion waves.

pectively. These two flows can be considered as forming two sheets of a fold which join along the circumference of a circle with radius r_0. This circle then forms the limiting line. This example is somewhat too specialised to be instructive. All of the important properties become apparent, however, in a flow which one obtains by superimposing in the hodograph plane the flow in a so-called potential vortex on the solution appropriate to the source flow described above. In view of the linearity of the equation for x and y [Eq. V, 1 (15)] the superposition of the solutions in the hodograph plane results in the addition of values of x and y corresponding in the individual cases to the same velocity vector (TOLLMIEN [73]).

Since neither the source nor the potential vortex exhibit a characteristic direction, the same results are true of the flow resulting from their superposition. The supersonic part of the flow can be constructed easily with the aid of the method of characteristics. To this end one assumes, along a given circle, velocity vectors whose magnitude is constant and which are inclined at a constant angle to the tangent to the circle. The magnitude of the velocity must be either supersonic or, at least, sonic. The remainder of the flow is then computed by the method of characteristics with this circle as a starting point. The flow pattern shown in Fig. 22 can be considered as having been obtained in the above manner; only a part of the circle is, however, indicated. Starting from the circle corresponding to the sonic line one finds that the velocities are supersonic within the circle while outside of it they are subsonic. Let us assume the flow to approach from the subsonic regime. The shape of the streamlines in the latter can be pre dicted from the shape of the boundaries, and can be calculated. The dotted MAC lines, obtained by the method of characteristics and originating from the soni line, are propagated upstream and it is seen that they intersect one another an eventually form an envelope. This envelope is the limiting line. In an actu flow corresponding to the above picture the dotted lines would be equivalen to rarefaction waves emanating from the limiting line and propagated dow stream.

The second sheet of the fold is shown in Fig. 23. It is obtained when the con struction by means of the method of characteristics is continued after reachin

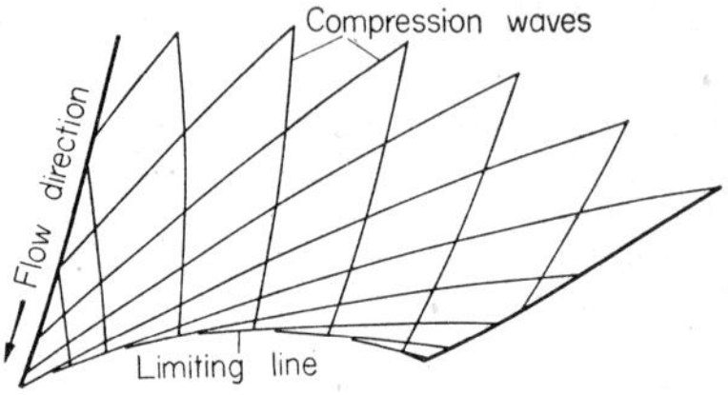

FIG. 23 Limiting line formed by coalescing compression waves.

the limiting line. It covers completely the first sheet discussed before. The hodo graph solution for a source of strength 2π is in the hodograph plane given b

$$\psi = \vartheta. \qquad (1$$

In the case of a potential vortex the magnitude of the velocity is constant alon the streamlines

$$\psi = \psi(w)$$

and hence from Eq. V, 1 (13)

$$\frac{d}{dw}\left(\frac{w}{\varrho}\psi_w\right) = 0 \quad \text{or} \quad \psi_w = \frac{\varrho}{w}. \qquad (2$$

The coordinates of the physical plane corresponding to these solutions can no be determined. This need only be done for a single line, for example, the axis o $u(\vartheta = 0)$ because of symmetry with respect to the origin.

Along the u axis Eq. V, 1 (15) yields for a source

$$\frac{\partial x}{\partial w} = -\frac{\left(1 - \frac{w^2}{a^2}\right)}{\varrho w^2}$$

and hence, with the aid of Eq. I, 2 (10a)

$$\frac{\partial x}{\partial w} = \frac{d\left(\frac{1}{\varrho w}\right)}{dw}.$$

$$x = \frac{1}{\varrho w}.$$

This result could of course be obtained simply by inspection. We find further that

$$y = 0$$

and for the vortex at $\vartheta = 0$

$$\frac{\partial y}{\partial w} = \frac{1}{\varrho w} \psi_w .$$

Since $\psi_w = \varrho / w$, we find

$$\frac{\partial y}{\partial w} = \frac{1}{w^2}$$

or

$$y = -\frac{1}{w} .$$

This last result follows from the solution for the potential vortex in the physical plane.

Multiplying the first of these solutions by c_1 and the second by c_2, and adding, one obtains for the radius r of a circle on which the magnitude of the velocity is w

$$r = \left(\frac{c_1^2}{(\varrho w)^2} + \frac{c_2^2}{w^2} \right)^{1/2} .$$

It should be noted that the two constants c_1 and c_2 have different dimensions.

A limiting line occurs when r is a minimum, i.e. when

$$\frac{dr}{dw} = \frac{1}{r} \left(\frac{-2 c_1^2}{(\varrho w)^3} \frac{d(\varrho w)}{dw} - 2 \frac{c_2^2}{w^3} \right) = \frac{2}{r} \left[\frac{c_1^2}{\varrho^3 w^3} \varrho \left(\frac{w^2}{a^2} - 1 \right) - \frac{c_2^2}{w^3} \right] = 0$$

and hence

$$c_2 = \pm \frac{c_1}{\varrho} \sqrt{\frac{w^2}{a^2} - 1} .$$

Since the expression

$$\frac{1}{\varrho} \sqrt{\frac{w^2}{a^2} - 1}$$

can in the supersonic regime assume all values between zero and infinity, any choice of c_1 and c_2 results in a limiting line. Introducing Eq. V, 2 (4) into Eqs. (1) and (2) one finds that the Jacobian vanishes along the limiting line.

The principal properties of limiting lines become apparent from an inspection of Figs. 22 and 23. They occur whenever either compression waves coalesce (Fig. 23) or when rarefaction waves spread out (Fig. 22). Naturally one should imagine that the increment between the Mach lines had been chosen to be infinitely small. The limiting line represents then, the envelope of one family of Mach lines and as such makes an angle equal to the Mach angle with the velocity vector. Since the second family of Mach lines is inclined at an angle 2α to those of the first family, the limiting line, of course, does not form an envelope of the second family. The waves corresponding to this second family intersect the limiting line at a fixed angle, namely 2α and are reflected from it at the same angle.

The intersection of two MACH lines indicates that even when the increment between successive MACH lines is infinitely small, the density of the MACH lines at the intersection point becomes infinite. This is, of course, true only for those waves which form a limiting line upon coalescing. For the other family the density of the MACH lines remains finite. In the method of characteristics, patterned after BUSEMANN, each wave represents a definite change of state so that, when the limiting line is approached at an angle different from zero, the change of state, i.e. the pressure gradient and the curvature of the streamlines, become

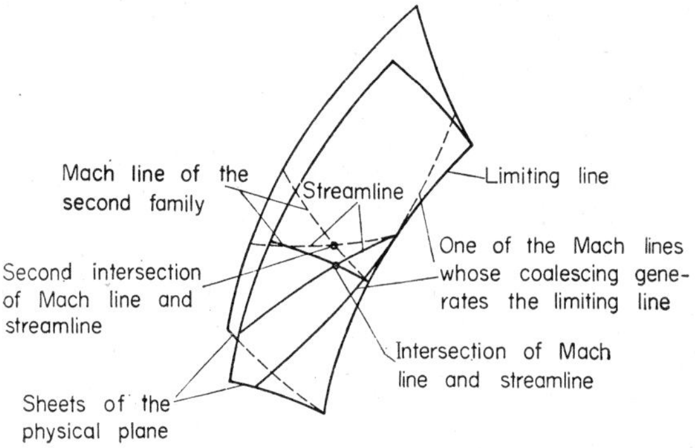

FIG. 24
Structure of the flow in the vicinity of a limiting line.

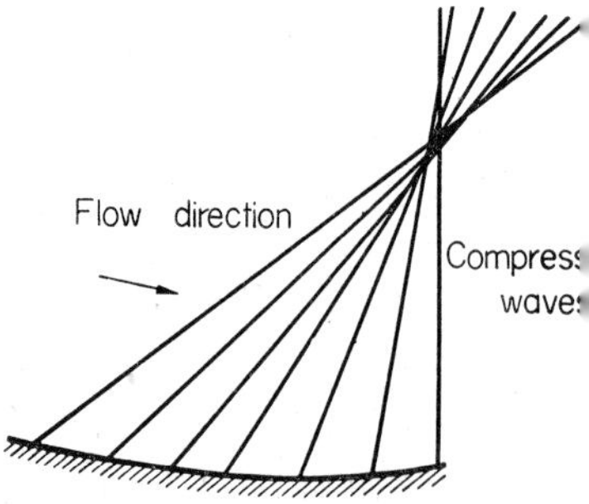

FIG. 25 An example of a limiting line, exhibiting a cusp. The limiting line is the envelope of coalescing waves.

infinite. Similarly the curvature of the MACH lines of the second family becomes infinite since their directions are dependent on the velocity.

Both sheets of the physical plane which are joined along the limiting line are shown in Fig. 24. The family of MACH lines for which the limiting line constitutes an envelope, is shown in these sheets and, furthermore, a single MACH line of the other family and a single streamline are indicated. These last two lines approach the limiting line along one sheet and then regress along the other. If the two lines intersect on one sheet, then they intersect also on the second sheet for a second time since their directions differ only by a small amount from their respective directions at the limiting line and these latter differ from one another by the MACH angle. A MACH line which intersects our streamline exactly on the limiting line has two points in common with the streamline. The streamlines of an analytic solution in the hodograph plane are, in general, free of cusps so that if a streamline has two points in common with a characteristic, this implies that the streamline is tangential to the characteristic. This indicates that the limiting line in the hodograph plane is represented by a locus of points in which the streamlines are tangential to the characteristics.

The limiting line itself can have a cusp as shown in Fig. 25. In this case the waves are generated by a curvature of the wall. It was assumed, for the sake of simplicity, that in this particular example the initial flow was parallel. This assumption results in the presence of a single family of MACH lines in the flow field. On the other hand, the hodograph representation of this flow is singular in that every MACH line of the physical plane is represented by a point in the hodograph plane and the entire physical plane is represented by a characteristic. It is easy, however, to imagine an example in which the second family of MACH lines is present so that the physical plane maps into a surface of the hodograph plane. This does not in any way influence the fact that the limiting line can possess a cusp.

The properties of the limiting line, which up to now has been characterised only by the vanishing of the Jacobian of the transformation, can be derived analytically in the following way. On a line $\psi =$ const one finds from

$$d\psi = \frac{\partial \psi}{\partial w} dw + \frac{\partial \psi}{\partial \vartheta} d\vartheta = 0$$

that the direction of the streamlines is given by

$$\frac{dw}{d\vartheta} = \frac{-\psi_\vartheta}{\psi_w}.$$

If at a given point the Jacobian vanishes but $\psi_w \neq 0$ and $\psi_\vartheta \neq 0$, Eq. V, 2 (6) yields

$$\frac{dw}{d\vartheta} = \mp \frac{w}{\sqrt{\frac{w^2}{a^2} - 1}}.$$

The direction of the characteristics is on the other hand determined by

$$\frac{dw}{d\vartheta} = \pm \frac{w}{\sqrt{\frac{w^2}{a^2} - 1}}, \tag{3}$$

in accordance with Eqs. V, 1 (10) and V, 1 (14). This means that if the Jacobian of the transformation vanishes but both ψ_w and ψ_ϑ do not, the streamlines are tangential to the characteristics in the hodograph plane.

Let us next compute the direction of the limiting line in the physical plane. The direction of an arbitrary curve determined locally in the hodograph plane by the elements dw and $d\vartheta$ is given, in view of,

$$dx = \frac{\partial x}{\partial w} dw + \frac{\partial x}{\partial \vartheta} d\vartheta,$$

$$dy = \frac{\partial y}{\partial w} dw + \frac{\partial y}{\partial \vartheta} d\vartheta$$

by

$$\frac{dy}{dx} = \frac{\dfrac{\partial y}{\partial w}\left(1 + \left(\dfrac{\partial y}{\partial \vartheta}\Big/\dfrac{\partial y}{\partial w}\right)\dfrac{d\vartheta}{dw}\right)}{\dfrac{\partial x}{\partial w}\left(1 + \left(\dfrac{\partial x}{\partial \vartheta}\Big/\dfrac{\partial x}{\partial w}\right)\dfrac{d\vartheta}{dw}\right)}.$$

When the Jacobian is equal to zero, the expressions in brackets on the RHS are equal, and one obtains

$$\frac{dy}{dx} = \frac{\partial y}{\partial w}\Big/\frac{\partial x}{\partial w},$$

so that the direction of the image of the curve in the physical plane is independent of dw and $d\vartheta$. Let us next evaluate dy/dx. Since the hodograph plane does not possess any characteristic direction, we can allow the direction of x to become identical with the direction of the velocity vector. Then, with the aid of Eqs. V, 1 (15) and V, 2 (6) we obtain

$$\frac{dy}{dx} = \mp \frac{1}{\sqrt{\dfrac{w^2}{a^2} - 1}}.$$

This then represents the tangent of the angle between the limiting line and the velocity vector. Since $\sin\alpha = 1/M$, we have $\tan\alpha = 1/\sqrt{(M^2 - 1)}$. Thus our intuitive conclusion that the limiting line is inclined to the velocity vector at the Mach angle is confirmed.

We shall next show that the second sheet of the physical plane does in fact fold back over the first sheet, i.e. that the term limiting line is physically correct. In the vicinity of the limiting line w can be considered as a parameter along a streamline and, since the latter are approximately tangential to the characteristics, dw is certainly non-zero along a streamline. Thus along a streamline we have

$$\frac{dx}{dw} = \frac{\partial x}{\partial w} + \frac{\partial x}{\partial \vartheta}\frac{d\vartheta}{dw} = \frac{1}{\varrho w}\left\{\frac{1 - \dfrac{w^2}{a^2}}{w}\frac{\partial \psi}{\partial \vartheta} + \frac{\partial \psi}{\partial w}\frac{d\vartheta}{dw}\right\}$$

and further

$$\frac{d\vartheta}{dw} = -\frac{\psi_w}{\psi_\vartheta},$$

so that

$$\frac{dx}{dw} = \frac{1}{\varrho w \psi_\vartheta}\left\{\frac{1 - \dfrac{w^2}{a^2}}{w}\psi_\vartheta^2 - \psi_w^2\right\}. \tag{4}$$

Thus on a limiting line dx/dw vanishes. If, further, the second derivative is also zero, than x has an extremum so that the streamline continues on a second sheet which is folded over the first one.

If the second derivative is zero this indicates that Eq. V, 2 (6) is valid at two neighbouring points on a streamline. Since this equation expresses the fact that the streamline in the hodograph plane is tangential to a characteristic, we arrive at the fact that at the point of contact derivatives of higher orders of both the characteristic and the streamline are equal in the hodograph plane. We may state, without proof, that under such conditions an analytic solution in the hodograph plane results in a cusp in the physical plane similar to that shown in Fig. 25.

It is further possible to show analytically that if the limiting line in the hodograph plane does not coincide with a characteristic, then the expression d^2x/dw^2, along a characteristic, can vanish together with dx/dw only at discrete points of the physical plane. If a streamline and a characteristic coincide, then we have at all points on the curves $dx/dw = 0$ and $dy/dw = 0$ [cf. Eqs. V, 1 (15) and (3)], i.e. the entire characteristic maps into a single point in the physical plane. Physically this corresponds to the origin of an expansion fan which is propagated into a non-parallel flow. The particular streamline exhibits a corner from which the Mach lines of the fan originate. If along these Mach lines λ = const [c.f. Eq. I, 7 (3)], then the value of λ depends at the corner on the direction of the velocity of approach. In general, only a single wave of the second family, on which μ = const, will approach a corner. This shows that the corner maps into a section of the curve μ = const in the hodograph plane.

Let us now ask, what is the physical meaning of a limiting line? This question can be formulated in a more precise manner. Let us consider a flow in which a limiting line exists, and which has been determined analytically, and let us ask what kind of boundary conditions could realize such a flow completely or in part. The method of characteristics is in this connection very illuminating, since it shows particularly clearly the influence of the boundary conditions. Two streamlines in such a flow can be prescribed as the boundaries. In the supersonic part of the flow we seek a line which is inclined to the velocity vector everywhere at an angle which is either greater than or equal to the Mach angle. The velocity vector is then calculated along this line from the available analytical solution. The boundary streamlines are allowed to terminate at the limiting line. For example in Fig. 22 the flow can be considered known along the Mach line AB and the prescribed boundaries are BC and AD. These boundary conditions suffice, however, only for the determination of the flow, up to the Mach line DE. There are no boundary conditions given which would cause the Mach lines to emanate from the interior of the flow. Such a situation would require the boundary to fold backwards. The required condition could be provided by guide vanes inserted into the flow. If such artificial situations are excluded, then the occurrence of a limiting line, which represents an envelope of expansion waves, becomes physically impossible (cf. Guderley [41]).

The situation in Fig. 23 is rather different. There the boundaries determine the flow up to the limiting line, and even in a part of the folded-over region of the physical plane. In this case, we have the familiar phenomenon of coalescence of compression waves and the occurence of a compression shock.

Thus the occurrence of limiting lines, as far as they are determined by the boundary conditions, belongs naturally to the phenomena known from supersonic aerodynamics.

In the formulation of the boundary value problem in the hodograph plane, care must be exercised so that the boundaries in the physical plane do not return along the second sheet of the latter. It is therefore not permissible for the boundary streamline to intersect a characteristic more than once.

4. Chaplygin's Particular Solutions

In our future considerations the solutions of the exact hodograph equation will be of no importance since we shall always confine ourselves to the simplified equation, which is mathematically more convenient to handle. We shall, however, frequently ask in what relation are the solutions of the approximate equation to those of the complete hodograph equation. To understand this connection, a certain amount of familiarity with the exact solutions is necessary.

Since ϑ does not appear explicitly in Eqs. V, 1 (10) or V, 1 (14), it appears convenient to assume a solution in the form

$$\left.\begin{aligned} \psi &= g_1(w, m) \begin{Bmatrix} \sin m\,\vartheta, \\ \cos m\,\vartheta, \end{Bmatrix} \\ \varphi &= g_2(w, m) \begin{Bmatrix} \cos m\,\vartheta, \\ \sin m\,\vartheta, \end{Bmatrix} \end{aligned}\right\} \tag{1}$$

where m is a constant. Upon substitution into the hodograph equation, the following ordinary linear differential equations are obtained

$$\frac{d^2 g_1}{dw^2} + \frac{1}{w}\left(1 + \frac{w^2}{a^2}\right)\frac{dg_1}{dw} - \frac{m^2}{w^2}\left(1 - \frac{w^2}{a^2}\right) g_1 = 0 \tag{2a}$$

and

$$\frac{d^2 g_2}{dw^2} + \frac{1}{w}\left(1 - \frac{w^2}{a^2}\right)\frac{dg_2}{dw} - \frac{m^2}{w^2}\left(1 - \frac{w^2}{a^2}\right) g_2 = 0, \tag{2b}$$

where

$$a^2 = \frac{\gamma + 1}{2} w^{*2} - \frac{\gamma - 1}{2} w^2. \tag{3}$$

The velocity w can vary from zero up to $w^*[(\gamma + 1)/(\gamma - 1)]^{1/2}$ since in accordance with BERNOULLI's equation $w^*[(\gamma + 1)/(\gamma - 1)]^{1,2}$ is the maximum value of w which can occur in the flow. It is easy to show that the solutions can be written in series form

$$g_1 = w^{\pm m} \sum_0^\infty a_n w^{2n}, \tag{4a}$$

$$g_2 = w^{\pm m} \sum_0^\infty b_n w^{2n} \tag{4b}$$

where the coefficients a_n and b_n can be calculated by recurrence formulae. When m is an integer, then one of the solutions must be assumed in the form

$$g_1 = w^{-m} \sum_0^\infty \bar{a}_n w^{2n} + c_1 \ln w \, w^m \sum_0^\infty a_n w^{2n}, \tag{5}$$

with the coefficients $\bar{a}_n$ again determined by a recurrence formula. A similar expression results for g_2. The numerical calculation of the solutions of linear differential equations offers no difficulties. Two linearly independent solutions corresponding to $m = 3$ and $m = 10$ are shown in Fig. 26.

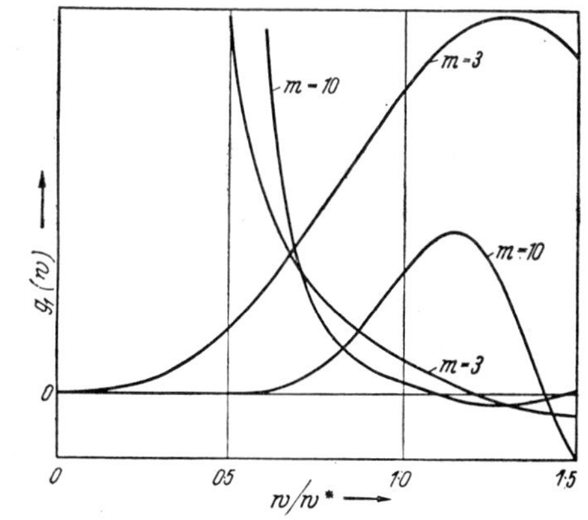

FIG. 26 Two linearly independent functions g_1 for $m = 3$ and $m = 10$. (The vertical scale is unimportant since the functions g_1 are obtained from a linear differential equation.)

The differential equations (2) can be transformed into a well-known form. Introducing a new variable given by

$$\tau = \frac{\gamma - 1}{\gamma + 1}\left(\frac{w}{w^*}\right)^2, \tag{6}$$

one obtains

$$\tau(1-\tau)\frac{d^2 g_1}{d\tau^2} + \frac{dg_1}{d\tau}\left(1 - \frac{\gamma-2}{\gamma-1}\tau\right) - \frac{m^2}{4\tau}\left(1 - \frac{\gamma-1}{\gamma+1}\tau\right)g_1 = 0 \tag{7a}$$

and

$$\tau(1-\tau)\frac{d^2 g_2}{d\tau^2} + \frac{dg_2}{d\tau}\left(1 - \frac{\gamma}{\gamma-1}\tau\right) - \frac{m^2}{4\tau}\left(1 - \frac{\gamma-1}{\gamma+1}\tau\right)g_2 = 0. \tag{7b}$$

These equations have three regular points, namely at 0, 1 and ∞ and they are therefore hypergeometric equations*. Employing the usual notation for hyper-

* Some properties of hypergeometric differential equations are discussed on p. 161.

geometric series we can write the solutions in the form

$$g_1 = \tau^{m/2} F\left\{\left(\frac{m}{2} - \frac{1}{2(\gamma-1)} + \frac{1}{2(\gamma-1)}\sqrt{1+\frac{m^2(\gamma-1)^3}{\gamma+1}}\right),\right.$$

$$\left.\left(\frac{m}{2} - \frac{1}{2(\gamma-1)} - \frac{1}{2(\gamma-1)}\sqrt{1+\frac{m^2(\gamma-1)^3}{\gamma+1}}\right), m+1, \tau\right\} \quad (8a)$$

and

$$g_2 = \tau^{m/2} F\left\{\left(\frac{m}{2} + \frac{1}{2(\gamma-1)} + \frac{1}{2(\gamma-1)}\sqrt{1+\frac{m^2(\gamma-1)^3}{\gamma+1}}\right),\right.$$

$$\left.\left(\frac{m}{2} + \frac{1}{2(\gamma-1)} - \frac{1}{2(\gamma-1)}\sqrt{1+\frac{m^2(\gamma-1)^3}{\gamma+1}}\right), m+1, \tau\right\} \quad (8b)$$

except for the special case given by Eq. (5). When m is a negative integer, Eq. (5) is the most convenient one to use. For the calculation of the functions numerical integration of the differential equation of the series expansion is generally preferable. The first term in these series represents an approximation corresponding to small velocities, i.e. to an incompressible flow. In fact $w^{\pm m} \sin m\vartheta$ and $w^{\pm m} \cos m\vartheta$ can be interpreted as the real and imaginary parts of the complex solution $(u - iv)^{\pm m}$ of the incompressible hodograph equation which is identical with LAPLACE's equation. Thus the connection between the particular solutions for incompressible and compressible flows is established. With appropriate care it is therefore possible to describe a compressible flow with the aid of an analogous incompressible flow. Such calculations, however, do not have any special physical meaning. Tables of CHAPLYGIN's solutions have been given by CHANG and O'BRIEN [7] and by HUCKEL [49].

5. The Solution of a Boundary Value Problem

Let us now show, on an example, the application of the particular solutions discussed above to a given boundary value problem. We consider here the three-dimensional efflux from a sharp-edged orifice*. With reference to Fig. 27a, we assume that to the left of the shaded wall there is an infinitely large container. A subsonic jet issues through the sharp-edged orifice in the wall. The velocity of the jet is determined, of course, by the external pressure. We calculate first the hodograph image, as shown in Fig. 27b. To point out more clearly the correspondence between the physical and hodograph planes, only the lower half of the former is shown in Fig. 27b. The same letters are used to denote the corresponding points in the two planes. In the storage vessel the velocity at infinity is zero. Therefore the image of physical infinity lies in the hodograph plane at the origin. Along a wall we obtain a velocity vector which

* This example was first considered by MOLENBROEK who, however, has not obtained a satisfactory solution in view of an error made in the boundary conditions. The solution has been given by CHAPLYGIN.

is oriented vertically upwards so that the wall maps also into a vertical line in the upper half of the hodograph plane. On the surface of the jet, the pressure is constant, and therefore also, in view of BERNOULLI's equation, the magnitude of the velocity is constant. Thus the surface maps in the hodograph plane into the circular arc BC. If one moves in the direction of flow along the lower boundary of the jet, the velocity vector rotates clockwise. In the free jet the streamlines finally become parallel (point C). The location of this point in the physical plane is at infinity. The boundary conditions are given by $\psi = 0$ along the axis of symmetry and ψ = const along the wall and along the surface of the jet. This

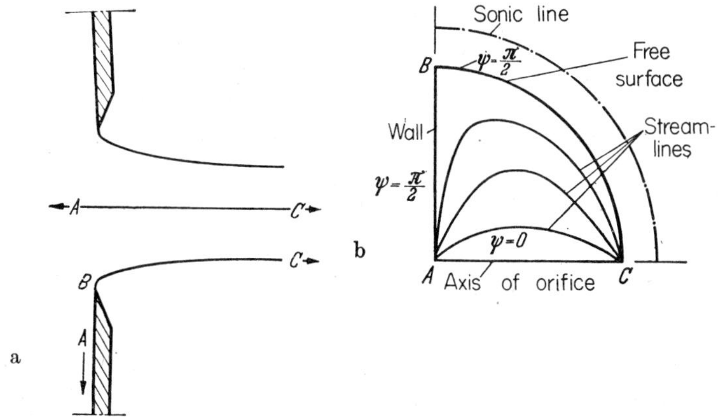

FIG. 27 Discharge through an orifice. (a) physical plane, (b) hodograph plane.

latter constant can be put equal to $\pi/2$ and the actual choice of the value determines the scale of measurement in the physical plane.

The required solution is obtained by superposition of particular solutions. One of the latter, which is zero along AC and has a constant value along AB, is given by

$$\psi = \vartheta .$$

When m is an integer the particular solutions in the form

$$\psi = g_1(w, 2m) \sin(2m\,\vartheta)$$

yield $\psi = 0$ along $\vartheta = 0$ and along $\vartheta = \pi/2$. Thus the expression

$$-\vartheta + \sum_{m=1}^{\infty} a_m g_1(w, 2m) \sin(2m\,\vartheta)$$

satisfies all boundary conditions on $\vartheta = 0$ and $\vartheta = \pi/2$. The coefficients a_m, which thus far are arbitrary, must be calculated in such a manner that the boundary conditions along BC are satisfied. Let the velocity on BC be equal to w_0. Then the required condition is

$$-\vartheta + \sum_{m=1}^{\infty} a_m g_1(w_0, 2m) \sin(2m\,\vartheta) = -\frac{\pi}{2} \qquad 0 < \vartheta < \frac{\pi}{2} .$$

It is therefore only necessary to expand the expression $-(\pi/2)+\vartheta$ in the interval $0<\vartheta\leqslant\pi/2$ in terms of $\sin(2\vartheta m)$ to obtain the constant a_m. In this way one obtains the final solution in the form

$$\psi=-\vartheta-\sum_{m=1}^{\infty}\frac{g_1(w,2m)}{m g_1(w_0,2m)}\sin(2m\,\vartheta).$$

The flow, and in particular the shape of the boundary of the jet, can now be calculated with the aid of Eq. V, 1 (15). We shall not consider this problem any further, since from the physical point of view the example is of only limited interest. The form assumed by the efflux from a vessel is qualitatively quite obvious. The example, however, gives us a first glimpse of the hodograph method. Much more difficult problems have been treated, particularly by LIGHTHILL [58].

6. Approximate Representations of Chaplygin's Solutions

We have seen in the preceding section that the solution of boundary value problems by the hodograph technique leads very rapidly to infinite series of particular solutions of the CHAPLYGIN type. We are therefore led to an attempt to represent the higher terms of these series by approximate expressions so that the exact calculations of these functions become unnecessary. One of these approximate solutions represents, incidentally, an exact solution of the partial differential equation which approximates the hodograph equation in the transonic regime. The transition from the solutions of the approximate equation to those of the exact hodograph equation can be effected with the aid of the above expressions.

Approximations to CHAPLYGIN's solutions are valid for large values of m. After some trial and error one can derive such expressions as formal series expansions in terms of $1/m$. Alternatively the following, more systematic, method may be employed. We transform the dependent and independent variables in Eq. V, 4 (2a) in such a manner that the term containing the first derivative vanishes and the coefficient of the term containing m^2 becomes constant. In more general terms we consider the differential equation

$$g''+p(w)\,g'+m^2\,q(w)\,g=0, \tag{1}$$

where p and q are known continuous functions. We put

$$g=h(w)\,z(x), \tag{2a}$$

where

$$x=x(w). \tag{2b}$$

It should be noted that the quantities z and x have, of course, nothing in common with the coordinates of the physical plane. From the above we obtain

$$\frac{dg}{dw}=\frac{dh}{dw}z+h\frac{dz}{dx}\frac{dx}{dw},$$

$$\frac{d^2g}{dw^2}=\frac{d^2h}{dw^2}z+2\frac{dh}{dw}\frac{dx}{dw}\frac{dz}{dx}+h\frac{d^2z}{dx^2}\left(\frac{dx}{dw}\right)^2+h\frac{dz}{dx}\frac{d^2x}{dw^2}.$$

Substitution in Eq. (1) yields

$$\frac{d^2 z}{dx^2} h \left(\frac{dx}{dw}\right)^2 + \frac{dz}{dx}\left[2 \frac{dh}{dw}\frac{dx}{dw} + h \frac{d^2 w}{dx^2} + p(w) \frac{dx}{dw} h\right] +$$

$$+ z \left[\frac{d^2 h}{dw^2} + p(w) \frac{dh}{dw} + m^2 q(w)\, h\right] = 0 .$$

If the coefficient of the term containing m^2 is to be constant, we must put

$$\frac{dx}{dw} = \sqrt{|q(w)|} \tag{3}$$

and at the same time the coefficient of d^2z/dx^2 becomes equal to ± 1. The condition that dz/dw should not appear in the differential equation yields

$$2 \frac{dh}{dx}\frac{dx}{dw} + h \frac{d^2 x}{dw^2} + p(w)\, h \frac{dx}{dw} = 0$$

and hence

$$h = \left(\frac{dx}{dw}\right)^{-1/2} e^{-1/2 \int p(w)\, dw} \tag{4}$$

so that finally

$$\frac{d^2 z}{dx^2} + (\pm m^2 + r(x))\, z = 0 . \tag{5}$$

The sign of m^2 is the same as that of the original function $q(x)$. The function $r(x)$ contains terms independent of m^2 and can be expressed in terms of $h(x)$.

It is plausible that $r(x)$ may be neglected for large values of m^2. Thus the approximate solutions are represented by

$$z = \begin{Bmatrix}\sin\\ \cos\end{Bmatrix} (m\, x) \tag{6a}$$

when the sign of m^2 in Eq. (5) is positive and by

$$z = e^{\pm m x} \tag{6b}$$

when the sign is negative.

Succesive terms of an expansion in terms of $1/m$ can be determined without difficulties. The above derivation should not be construed as a proof of the validity of the approximation. It may be shown, however, that expressions of the type of Eq. (4), augmented if necessary by a finite number of additional terms, are capable of representing suitably chosen exact solutions with any required degree of accuracy, provided the value of m is large. The expansion in terms of $1/m$ does not, in general, converge which means that for any fixed value of m the accuracy of the approximation cannot be increased by including more and more terms of the series.

We introduce next some considerations which add plausibility to the rules which have to be followed in assigning exact solutions to given approximate solutions.

The asymptotic representations, as given by Eq. (6b), increase or decrease exponentially in the direction of increasing or decreasing x, depending on the sign. The rate of increase depends on the value of m. The exact solution is chosen in such a manner, that at a given point both the function and the derivative are the same for the solution and for the asymptotic approximation. It is to be expected that the behavior of the exact solution is similar to that of the asymptotic one, which means that one of the linearly independent exact solutions should increase exponentially with x and the other one should exponentially decrease. If we assume that we have assigned at the point P an exact solution to that asymptotic solution which increases in the direction of positive x, then the two agree exactly at P. In general this exact solution will consist of a part increasing with x and a part decreasing with x. Naturally, in the present example, the first component of the solution will have a larger coefficient, but the contribution of the second component is in general not equal to zero. This contribution due to the component which increases with decreasing x can very rapidly become large when m is large and when the negative value of x increases. In fact, this contribution can exceed that due to the other component whose value decays rapidly with increasing negative values of x. It is therefore possible that to the left of P the exact solution deviates considerably from the approximate one. To the right of P this situation cannot arise, since there the undesirable component of the exact solution decays very rapidly. These considerations are included in the following theorem whose proof, under somewhat more general conditions, can be found in the literature (cf. e.g. SEIFERT [72]).

An expression $z = e^{+mx}$ or $z = e^{-mx}$ represents asymptotically an exact solution of Eq. (5) if the value of the function and that of the first derivative at a point P in the complex x plane agree with those of the exact solution. The asymptotic representation is valid for such values of x which can be reached along a path, along which the real part of e^{+mx} or e^{-mx} does not decrease.

These approximations can now be determined for Eq. V, 4 (2a). The integrals occuring in the calculation of h and x can be expressed in closed terms but the results are rather complicated. The solutions g are written in the form

$$g_1 = h(w)\, W(w)^{\pm m} \tag{7}$$

where

$$W(w) = e^{x(w)}.$$

The functions h and W are shown in Fig. 28.

In accordance with the above considerations the correspondence between the exact solutions of CHAPLYGIN's equation and the approximate expressions depends on the choice of the sign in Eq. (7). If this sign is positive, then the exact and approximate solutions must coincide at $w = 0$. If the sign is negative, then one could demand agreement at a high subsonic velocity, although the approximations would subsequently only be valid for lower velocities. To obtain as large a domain of validity as possible the velocity, at which the asymptotic and exact solutions are required to agree, should be chosen as high as possible. A difficulty arises in view of the fact that the approximation of Eq. (7) apparently fails at the critical velocity, as shown by the curve representing $h(w)$ in Fig. 28. The approximate solutions there become infinite although the exact solution remains finite. The singularity of the approximate solution is caused by the transformation of Eqs. (2a) and (3) in which the coefficient q of the term containing m^2 has been transformed into a constant. In the original differential equation q is equal to zero at the critical velocity so that the condition of Eq. (3) has introduced a very serious restriction on the differential equation. We can eliminate this difficulty by allowing the corresponding term in the approximate differential equation also to become equal to zero at the critical velocity. To this end, we again employ the substitution of Eq. (2a) but require that

$$x = \frac{q(w)}{\left(\frac{dx}{dw}\right)^2}.$$

This results in

$$\sqrt{x}\,dx = \sqrt{q}\,dw$$

and hence

$$x = \left(\tfrac{3}{2}\int_{w^*}^{w}\sqrt{q}\,dw\right)^{2/3} \tag{8}$$

where $h(w)$ is again of the form of Eq. (4). Thus the transformed differential equation takes the form

$$\frac{d^2 z}{dx^2} - (m^2 x + r(x))\,z = 0. \tag{9}$$

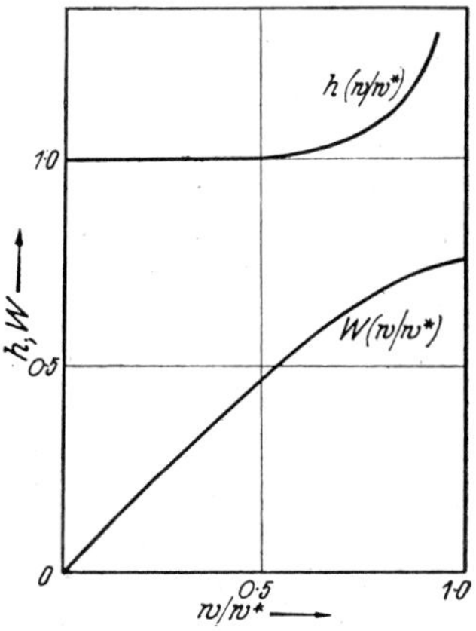

FIG. 28 Functions occuring in the approximate representation of CHAPLYGIN's solutions.

The approximate solutions are then obtained from the following differential equation

$$\frac{d^2 z}{dx^2} - m^2 x z = 0. \tag{10}$$

Solutions of this equation can be expressed in terms of BESSEL functions of order $\frac{1}{3}$. These functions have been tabulated by the COMPUTATION LABORATORY OF THE NATIONAL BUREAU OF STANDARDS [12]. The solutions are

$$z = \sqrt{|x|}\,[-c_1 e^{-i\pi/6} J_{1/3}(\tfrac{2}{3} i m |x|^{3/2}) + c_2 e^{i\pi/6} J_{-1/3}(\tfrac{2}{3} i m |x|^{3/2})] \tag{11a}$$

for negative x and

$$z = \sqrt{x}\,[c_1 J_{1/3}(\tfrac{2}{3} m x^{3/2}) + c_2 J_{-1/3}(\tfrac{2}{3} m x^{3/2})] \tag{11b}$$

for positive x.

In these equations c_1 and c_2 are constants. Their choice is not quite arbitrary since $J_{1/3}(\frac{2}{3} i m |x|^{3/2})$ and $J_{-1/3}(\frac{2}{3} i m |x|^{3/2})$ have the same asymptotic expansions so that the two asymptotic expressions are not linearly independent. The choice of $c_1 = c_2$ eliminates from the solutions the components which are important for large values of m and one obtains an expression which in the asymptotic case is linearly independent of all the others in which c_1 and c_2 are not equal. The asymptotic representation of this solution [Eq. (11a)] decreases exponentially as $x \to -\infty$. All the other solutions increase exponentially when $x \to -\infty$. The functions h and x which result from the application of the above considerations to Eq. V, 4 (2a) are shown in Fig. 29, where the variable x is denoted by η. All the quantities plotted in this figure are considered to be functions of η. It is possible, in fact, to prove that for large values of m the expressions of Eqs. (11) can approximate suitably chosen exact solutions g_1 as closely as desired once when we put $c_1 = c_2 = 1$ and again if another linear combination is employed. The conditions which govern the assignment of corresponding exact solutions to the asymptotic expression must be followed also in this case. The

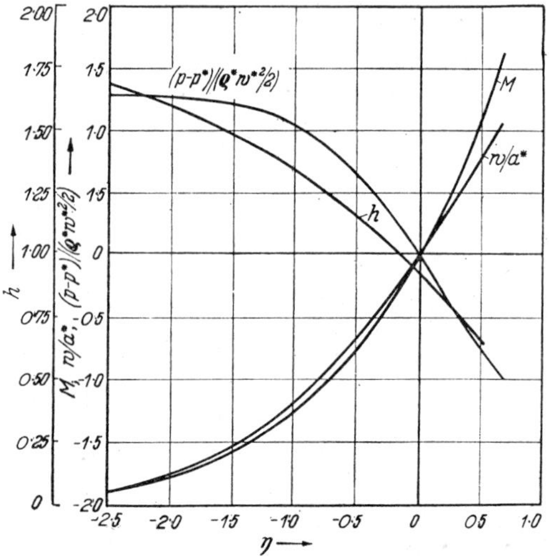

FIG. 29 Some functions occurring in the asymptotic representation of the solutions of TRICOMI's equation. (According to GUDERLEY [32]).

formulation of these conditions must be slightly modified since the BESSEL functions behave exponentially only for very large values of the argument. The solution for $c_1 = c_2 = 1$ represents asymptotically the expression which agrees with it at $\eta = -\infty$, i.e. when $w = 0$. These are the solutions g_1 in Eq. V, 4 (4a) which correspond to positive values of m. The second linear combination must be required to agree with the exact solution at the sonic velocity or even at a supersonic velocity. In any case one obtains a representation valid for the entire velocity range. The mathematical theory is due to LANGER [59] (cf. also FRANKL [17], IMAI [50] and GUDERLEY [40]).

7. Tricomi's Equation

In the following analysis we shall always employ a simplified hodograph equation. It would be convenient if this equation were such that CHAPLYGIN's particular solutions were in the form of Eq. V, 6 (11). This would imply a simple transition from the solutions of the approximate equation to those of the hodograph equation. To achieve this condition, we apply the transformation

$$\psi(w, \vartheta) = h(w)\,\overline{\psi}(\eta(w), \vartheta), \tag{1}$$

which corresponds exactly to Eq. V, 6 (2a), to the complete hodograph equation and in analogy with Eq. V, 6 (9) we obtain

$$\overline{\psi}_{\eta\eta} - \eta\,\overline{\psi}_{\vartheta\vartheta} = r(\eta)\,\overline{\psi}. \tag{2}$$

In analogy to Eq. II, 3 (3), which resulted in a simplification of the differential equation of transonic flow in the physical plane, we introduce a distortion in terms of a parameter τ by means of

$$\overline{\psi} = \widetilde{\psi}\,(\widetilde{\eta}, \widetilde{\vartheta}),$$

where

$$\widetilde{\eta} = \eta\,\tau^{-1},$$

$$\widetilde{\vartheta} = \vartheta\,\tau^{-3/2}. \tag{3}$$

Substituting the above in Eq. (2) and retaining only the terms of lowest order in τ we obtain

$$\widetilde{\psi}_{\widetilde{\eta}\widetilde{\eta}} - \widetilde{\eta}\,\widetilde{\psi}_{\widetilde{\vartheta}\widetilde{\vartheta}} = 0. \tag{4}$$

Chaplygin's solutions of this equation are actually the asymptotic expressions for the Chaplygin's solutions of the complete hodograph equation. The above transition from an approximate to an exact solution can be visualised (in principle) as follows. We expand a solution of the approximate differential equation (4), which solution does not necessarily have to consist of a superposition of Chaplygin's solutions, in terms of these solutions. The difference between the Chaplygin's solutions and the exact ones is expressed in terms of corrections*. Examples of this kind have so far not been calculated. They would give an insight into the errors which result from the application of the approximate equation.

Equation (4) is called Tricomi's equation since the first analysis of boundary value problems associated with this equation has been performed by Tricomi. This equation is most frequently derived by substituting a form corresponding to Eq. (3) not into the transformed hodograph equation but directly into the original hodograph equation

$$\left.\begin{aligned} \psi &= \widetilde{\psi}\,(\widetilde{\eta}, \widetilde{\vartheta}), \\ \widetilde{\eta} &= (\gamma + 1)^{1/3}\left(\frac{w - w^*}{w^*}\right)\tau^{-1}, \\ \widetilde{\vartheta} &= \vartheta\,\tau^{-3/2}. \end{aligned}\right\} \tag{5}$$

Upon substitution into Eq. V, 1 (14) and with the aid of Eq. I, 2 (8), there results

$$\widetilde{\psi}_{\widetilde{\eta}\widetilde{\eta}}(\gamma + 1)^{-2/3}\tau^{-2} + 2\widetilde{\psi}_{\widetilde{\eta}}(\gamma + 1)^{-1/3}\tau^{-1} - (\gamma + 1)^{-2/3}\tau^{-2}\,\widetilde{\eta}\,\widetilde{\psi}_{\widetilde{\vartheta}\widetilde{\vartheta}} + (\text{terms of higher order in } \tau) = 0.$$

* This procedure cannot always be performed in such a simple manner. In particular, if the solution to be expanded has a singularity in the subsonic regime, difficulties can arise.

Hence by retaining only terms of lowest order in τ one obtains Eq. (4). The relationship between the independent variable and the velocity is shown in Fig. 29. If the substitution of Eq. (5) is employed, this relationship is replaced by a linear one which represents the tangent to the first curve at the sonic velocity. The function $h(w)$ introduced a complication into the assumed form of Eq. (1). This difficulty becomes apparent in particular when one investigates the distortion of the contour of an obstacle with the aid of the similarity rules. In view of this one frequently prefers the alternative derivation. Further difficulties arise in passing from a solution $\bar{\psi}(\bar{\eta}, \bar{\vartheta})$, interpreted in the

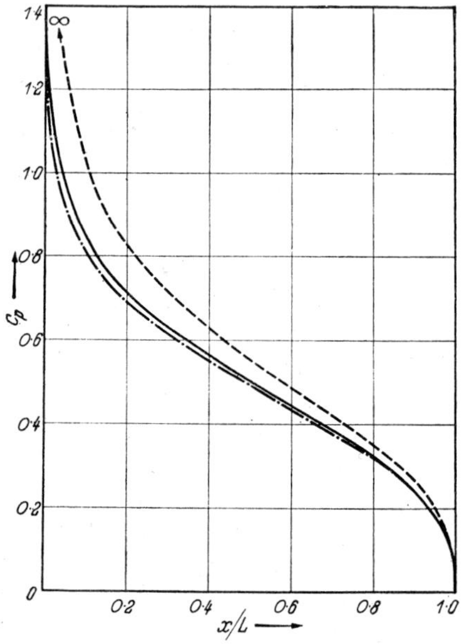

Fig. 30 Pressure distribution on the pressure side of an inclined plate. Length of plate L; angle of attack 13°. Calculated using the exact hodograph equation and the approximations Eqs. V, 7(3) and V, 7(5). (According to VINCENTI, WAGONER and FISHER).

——— exact solution
– – – – Eq. V, 7(5)
–·–·–· Eq. V, 7(3)

sense of the second derivation, to the exact hodograph equation. An example calculated by VINCENTI, WAGONER, and FISHER [81], and shown in Fig. 30 indicates that in particular the approximation of Eq. (3) yields very useful results. Equivalent simplifications applied to the equation of the transformed potential result also in TRICOMI's equation

$$\tilde{\varphi}_{\tilde{\eta}\tilde{\eta}} - \tilde{\eta}\,\tilde{\varphi}_{\tilde{\vartheta}\tilde{\vartheta}} = 0. \qquad (6)$$

For the sake of simplicity we shall write in future $\psi, \varphi, \eta, \vartheta$, in place of $\tilde{\psi}, \tilde{\varphi}, \tilde{\eta}, \tilde{\vartheta}$ and the parameter τ will be put equal to 1 after performing the ex pansion. Let us next summarize briefly some results which are obtained by substituting Eq. (5) into the exact equations and by the retention of only those terms which contain the lowest powers of τ. The relationships between the potential and the stream function given by Eq. V, 1 (16) take the form

$$\psi = \varrho^* \varphi_\vartheta . \tag{7}$$

The equations of the coordinates are

$$\left.\begin{aligned} \frac{\partial x}{\partial \eta} &= \frac{1}{\varrho^* w^*}(\gamma+1)^{1/3}\eta\psi_\vartheta, & \frac{\partial y}{\partial \eta} &= \frac{1}{\varrho^* w^*}\psi_\eta, \\ \frac{\partial x}{\partial \vartheta} &= \frac{1}{\varrho^* w^*}(\gamma+1)^{1/3}\psi_\eta, & \frac{\partial y}{\partial \vartheta} &= \frac{1}{\varrho^* w^*}\psi_\vartheta \end{aligned}\right\} \tag{8}$$

or

$$y = \frac{1}{\varrho^* w^*}\psi \tag{9}$$

so that with the introduction of the transformed potential

$$\left.\begin{aligned} x &= \frac{(\gamma+1)^{1/3}}{w^*}\varphi_\eta, \\ y &= \frac{1}{w^*}\varphi_\vartheta . \end{aligned}\right\} \tag{10}$$

Further one obtains

$$\left.\begin{aligned} w - w^* &= w^*(\gamma+1)^{-1/3}\eta, \\ p - p^* &= -\varrho^* w^{*2}(\gamma+1)^{-1/3}\eta, \\ c_p^* = \frac{p-p^*}{\varrho^* w^{*2}/2} &= -2(\gamma+1)^{-1/3}\eta, \\ M - 1 &= \tfrac{1}{2}(\gamma+1)^{2/3}\eta . \end{aligned}\right\} \tag{11}$$

The Jacobian of the hodograph transformation becomes

$$D = -\frac{(\gamma+1)^{2/3}}{\varrho^{*2} w^{*4}}\{\psi_\eta^2 - \eta\psi_\vartheta^2\}. \tag{12}$$

TRICOMI's equation, Eq. (6), can incidentally be obtained by the application of the LEGENDRE transformation to the approximate equation of transonic flow in the physical plane. The transformation to an equation for the stream function is then effected with the aid of Eq. (7). A considerable saving in computation time can be made by introducing instead of φ and ψ new variables φ/w^* and $\psi^*/\varrho^* w^*$ which have the dimensions of a length. This is equivalent to putting $\varrho^* = w^* = 1$ in Eqs. (7), (8), (9), (10) and (12). We shall make use of this simplification in some later calculations.

8. Examples of Hodograph Transformations

In the present section we shall discuss some examples which will enable us to become familiar with the form which various flow fields assume when transformed into the hodograph plane.

Let us consider first some cases of incompressible flow*. Let

$$z = x + iy \tag{1}$$

then in a two-dimensional incompressible flow the potential and the stream function can be expressed as the real and imaginary parts, respectively, of a complex function of z, i.e.

$$\Phi(x, y) + i\,\psi(x, y) = \Omega(z). \tag{2}$$

If we treat the above as an equation in two independent variables x and y, then

$$\frac{\partial \Phi}{\partial x} + i\frac{\partial \psi}{\partial x} = \frac{\partial \Omega}{d z}$$

and further since

$$\frac{\partial \Phi}{\partial x} = u,$$

$$\frac{\partial \psi}{\partial x} = -v$$

one obtains

$$u - iv = \frac{d\Omega}{dz}. \tag{3}$$

The expression

$$w = u - iv$$

is called the complex velocity**. If the x, y plane is identified with the complex z plane, then the complex velocity vector is obtained from the physical velocity vector by a reflection with respect to the x axis. We thus have

$$w = \frac{d\Omega}{dz} = \Omega'. \tag{4}$$

In the hodograph plane the stream function is interpreted as a function of the velocity. Therefore Ω must be expressed as a function of w which requires that z be eliminated from Eqs. (2) and (4).

* It was believed for quite some time that the principal characteristics of transonic flow can be obtained by constructing compressible hodograph solutions from solutions of similar structure corresponding to incompressible flow in the hodograph plane (the equivalence principle). A great deal of caution is called for, however. It was possible for Ringleb [3–91] to show by this method that there exist flows in which a smooth transition both from subsonic to supersonic velocities and vice versa is possible; on the other hand the procedure has led to a fallacy when applied to the problem of the origin of compression shocks in mixed subsonic and supersonic flows. This is due to the fact that in spite of its greater generality the procedure does not encompass all possible flow fields.

** In other sections the symbol w is used to denote the magnitude of the velocity.

A particularly simple treatment is often afforded by the LEGENDRE transformation. The original equation of the transformation, Eq. V, 1 (8),

$$\varphi = -\Phi + ux + vy$$

can be written

$$\varphi = \mathrm{Re}(zw - \Omega) = \mathrm{Re}(\omega), \tag{5}$$

where w is given by Eq. (4). On the other hand

$$\frac{d\omega}{dw} = z \tag{6}$$

where ω is called the transformed complex potential. The independent variable is, of course, again w.

Examples

The potential of a source flow is given by

$$\Omega = \ln z, \tag{7}$$

which yields

$$w = \Omega' = \frac{1}{z}$$

and hence

$$\Omega(w) = -\ln w. \tag{8}$$

The LEGENDRE potential takes the form

$$\omega = 1 - \ln w. \tag{9}$$

An interpretation of this equation is left to the reader, since in the present connection, personal experience is of particular value.

The potential of a doublet is given by

$$\Omega = z^{-1}, \tag{10}$$

and hence

$$w = -z^{-2},$$

$$\Omega = \sqrt{-w}, \tag{11}$$

$$\omega = -\frac{2}{z} = -2\Omega = -2\sqrt{-w}. \tag{12}$$

It can be noticed that the hodograph plane consists of two RIEMANN sheets with a branch point at the origin.

The flow around a half-body, as shown in Fig. 31, is given by the equation

$$\Omega = Uz + \ln z \tag{13}$$

where U is the undisturbed velocity. From this we obtain

$$w = U + \frac{1}{z},$$

$$z = \frac{1}{w - U},$$

$$\Omega = \frac{U}{w - U} - \ln(w - U), \tag{14}$$

$$\omega = -1 + \ln(w - U). \tag{15}$$

Thus at the point $w = U$ a singularity results. This is understandable since the point represents the hodograph image of infinity in the physical plane. The two

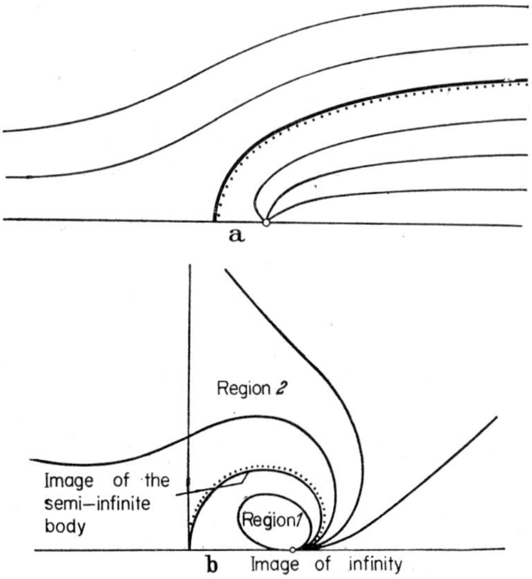

FIG. 31 Flow past a semi-infinite body. (Source in parallel flow). (a) physical plane (b) hodograph plane. Regions within and outside of the boundary of the body are respectively denoted by 2 and 1.

expressions which become singular at this point are superimposed when the stream function is employed.

In the physical plane there exists a close relationship between a source and a half-body. This relationship is lost, to a large extent, in the hodograph plane. In the vicinity of the singular point, $w = U$, the first term of Eq. (14) predominates so that the flow is of the doublet type. At infinity of the hodograph plane the second term predominates so that there the character of a source flow is preserved. The infinity of the hodograph plane represents the source placed within the half-body. Therefore the streamlines going to infinity correspond to those streamlines which are confined within the boundary of the body. Even these streamlines in the physical plane approach the undisturbed velocity U at infinity so that in the hodograph they must end at the point $w = U$. At the origin of the hodograph plane, the flow must have a branch point which corresponds to the stagnation point of the physical plane. If the term $\ln(w - U)$ in Eq. (14) is multiplied by a positive non-zero factor, which one might be tempted to consider as a rather unimportant modification, then the branch point of the streamlines is displaced to a new position and a completely different flow field results. The representation in terms of a LEGENDRE potential is then much simpler.

The above remarks prompt us to ask what is the meaning of a hodograph solution in which the origin is not the branch point of the streamlines. Such a situation can arise if one constructs a hodograph solution without sufficient attention being paid to the origin. The principal characteristics of the flow field in the vicinity of the origin can be determined by considering only the first term of a TAYLOR series. Apart from a constant, which is of little interest, one obtains

$$\Omega = w. \tag{16}$$

If the first term of the TAYLOR series is of a higher order then the origin is a branch point of the streamlines. The definition of the complex velocity vector yields [Eq. (4)]

$$dz = \frac{d\Omega}{w}$$

from which, for the present case there results

$$dz = \frac{dw}{w},$$

$$z = \ln w.$$

This shows that the origin of the hodograph plane is mapped into infinity in the physical plane. This, incidentally, is also true for compressible flow. The transformation to the physical plane yields

$$w = e^z,$$

$$\Omega = e^z,$$

$$\psi = e^x \sin y \tag{17}$$

which represents the flow between two parallel straight lines given by $y = 0$ and $y = \pi$. The streamline pattern of this flow is shown in Fig. 32. We can treat this as a limiting case of flow inside a corner where the angle of the latter tends to zero. This transition from a corner to two parallel straight lines is sketched in Fig. 33.

When the solution in the physical plane is known, the transformed potential can be calculated

$$\omega = w(\ln w - 1). \tag{18}$$

Thus the origin of the hodograph plane is a singularity of the transformed potential if it does not represent the branch point of the streamlines. In most cases physical reasons demand that the origin of the hodograph plane be a branch point of the streamlines. This then requires that, in terms of the stream function, a TAYLOR expansion can contain no linear term. For the transformed potential the requirement of regularity is sufficient. The solution for the transformed potential $\omega = w$ yields, in accordance with Eq. (6), $z = 1$. Superposition of such a solution in the hodograph plane is equivalent to the addition of a constant to all the coordinates in the physical plane. If the hodograph representation employs the stream function, then the coordinates in the physical

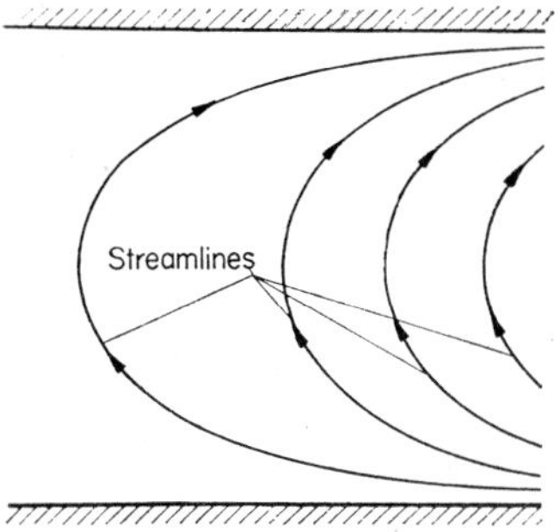

FIG. 32 Interpretation of a hodograph solution which has no branch point of the streamlines at zero velocity.

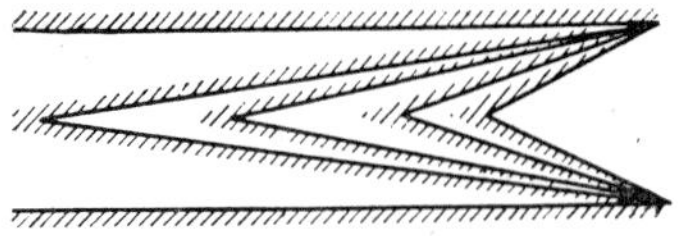

FIG. 33 Transition from the flow past a concave corner to the flow between two parallel walls.

plane are obtained by integration. The same translation of the physical plane is effected by the choice of an integration constant.

The next term in the TAYLOR series for the transformed potential is

$$\omega = w^2$$

and hence

$$\left.\begin{aligned} z &= 2w, \\ \Omega &= w^2, \\ \Omega &= \left(\frac{z}{2}\right)^3 \end{aligned}\right\} \tag{19}$$

which represents the flow near a stagnation point.

Let us next consider the meaning of a branch point of the streamlines which occurs at a non-zero velocity. Let us suppose that

$$\Omega = (w - a)^2, \tag{20}$$

and hence

$$dz = \frac{d\Omega}{w} = \frac{2(w-a)}{w} dw$$

which, with a suitably chosen integration constant yields

$$z = 2(w - a) - 2a \ln w.$$

To facilitate further discussion we expand this expression in the vicinity of the point $w = a$. Putting

$$-2a \ln a = z_0,$$

one obtains

$$z - z_0 = \frac{(w-a)^2}{a} - \frac{2}{3}\,\frac{(w-a)^3}{a^2} + \cdots$$

and hence

$$z - z_0 = \frac{1}{a}\,\Omega - \frac{2}{3a^2}\,\Omega^{3/2}.$$

A solution for Ω yields

$$\Omega = a(z - z_0) + \tfrac{2}{3}\, a^{1/2}(z - z_0)^{3/2} \tag{21}$$

and thus

$$w = \frac{\partial \Omega}{\partial z} = a + a^{1/2}(z - z_0)^{1/2},$$

so that for real a we have, in the first approximation,

$$u = a, \quad v = I\,m\, a^{1/2}(z - z_0)^{1/2}$$

or

$$v = 0 \qquad \text{for} \qquad y = 0,\ x > x_0$$

$$v = a^{1/2}\,|x - x_0|^{1/2} \qquad \text{for} \qquad y = 0,\ x < x_0.$$

The slope of the streamlines is given in the first approximation by

$$0 \qquad \text{for} \qquad x > x_0$$

$$a^{-1/2}|x - x_0|^{1/2} \qquad \text{for} \qquad x < x_0$$

and hence the streamlines are given by

$$\tilde{y} = 0 \qquad \text{for} \qquad x > x_0$$

$$\tilde{y} = -\tfrac{2}{3} a^{-1/2}\,|x - x_0|^{3/2}. \tag{22}$$

This flow is similar to that in the vicinity of the trailing edge of a JOUKOWSKI profile. The physical plane branches into two RIEMANN sheets. The flow can naturally take place only in a single sheet. The two sheets are shown separately in Fig. 34b. The heavy line represents in both cases the branching streamline. The two RIEMANN sheets should be considered as joined along lines labelled with the same letters. The corresponding hodograph representation is sketched in Fig. 34a.

The flow around a circle

$$\Omega = U z + \frac{b}{z} \tag{23}$$

yields in the hodograph plane

$$\Omega = U \sqrt{\frac{b}{U - w}} + \sqrt{b}\,\sqrt{U - w} \tag{24}$$

and by means of a LEGENDRE transformation one obtains

$$\omega = -2\sqrt{\frac{b}{U - w}}\,. \tag{25}$$

In this case, a single sheet of the physical plane maps into two sheets in the hodograph plane. One of the latter, corresponding to the upper half of the physical plane and including the branching streamline and two other streamlines, is sketched in Fig. 35.

Very frequently the hodograph representations of flows which appear quite simple are exceedingly complicated. This can be noted, for example, in the case

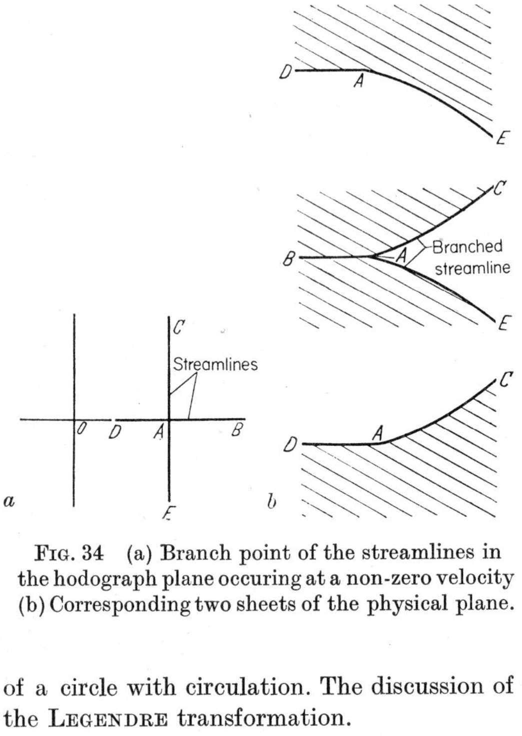

FIG. 34 (a) Branch point of the streamlines in the hodograph plane occuring at a non-zero velocity (b) Corresponding two sheets of the physical plane.

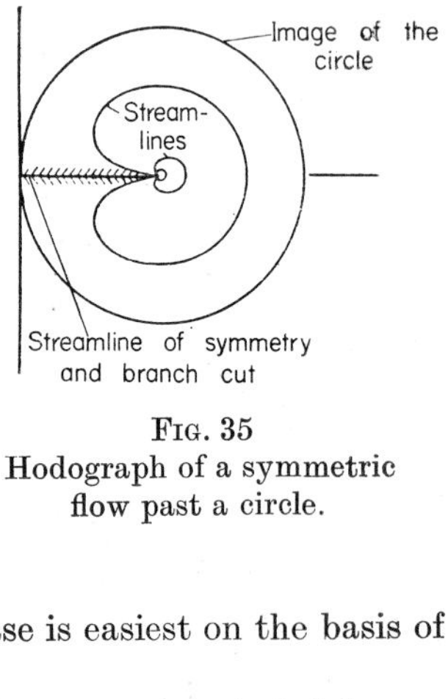

FIG. 35
Hodograph of a symmetric flow past a circle.

of a circle with circulation. The discussion of this case is easiest on the basis of the LEGENDRE transformation.

The classical examples of the hodograph method were not included in our above discussion. One of these, namely, the discharge from a vessel, has been considered in Section V, 5. Further cases will be discussed in the next chapter. In most cases, these examples result in comparatively simple hodograph images, although considerable complications can arise as a result of small changes in the boundary conditions in the physical plane.

As a last example we shall consider the flow through a DE LAVAL nozzle for which a solution was given on p. 66. Since this was a solution of the approximate transonic potential equation, its transformation into the hodograph plane satisfies TRICOMI's equation. The variables Φ_x and Φ_y of Eqs. IV, 2 (4) and IV, 2 (5) express the deviations from a parallel flow with sonic velocity. Employing the notation of the preceding section, one obtains

$$\Phi_x = w - w^* = w^* (\gamma + 1)^{-1/3} \eta; \quad \Phi_y = w^* \vartheta. \dagger$$

Equations IV, 2 (4) and IV, 2 (5) may be written

$$\eta = (\gamma + 1)^{-2/3} y^2 \left[c_1 \frac{x}{y^2} + \frac{c_1^2}{2} \right], \tag{26a}$$

$$\vartheta = (\gamma + 1)^{-1} y^3 \left[c_1^2 \frac{x}{y^2} + \frac{c_1^3}{6} \right], \tag{26b}$$

where

$$c_1 = (\gamma + 1)\, c. \tag{26c}$$

A line $y =$ const represents a streamline in the present approximation. The elimination of x from the last equation yields

$$\vartheta = -(\gamma + 1)^{-1/3} c_1 \eta y + \frac{(\gamma + 1)^{-1}}{3} c_1^3 y^3 \tag{27}$$

and $y =$ const results in a straight line in the η, ϑ plane. The characteristic in the η, ϑ plane, which passes through the origin, forms an envelope of these straight lines. The slope of the line is given by

$$\frac{d\vartheta}{d\eta} = -(\gamma + 1)^{-1/3} c_1 y.$$

The slope of the characteristics is, in accordance with Eq. I, 6 (8), given by

$$\frac{d\vartheta}{d\eta} = \pm \eta^{1/2}$$

so that for a straight line, whose slope is equal to that of a characteristic at a certain value of η_0 one obtains

$$(\gamma + 1)^{-1/3} c_1 y = \pm \eta_0^{1/2}$$

and Eq. (27) takes the form

$$\vartheta = \mp \eta_0^{1/2} \eta + \tfrac{1}{3} \eta_0^{3/2}.$$

For $\eta = \eta_0$ one obtains

$$\vartheta = \mp \tfrac{2}{3} \eta_0^{3/2},$$

so that the particular point of the straight line lies on one of the characteristics which pass through the origin and which are described by this equation.

† From this point on the symbol w is again used to denote the magnitude of the vector.

The special curves in the physical plane shown in Fig. 16 have all been characterized by the behaviour of the velocity vector and can therefore be easily mapped into the hodograph plane.

The hodograph representation is shown in Fig. 36. The most notable result is that the region contained between the two characteristics passing through the origin is covered three times. At each point in this region there exist three straight

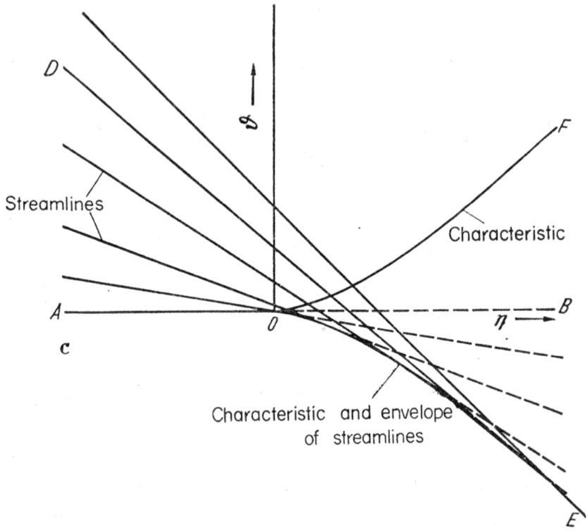

FIG. 36 Hodograph of a solution for the flow in a De Laval nozzle.

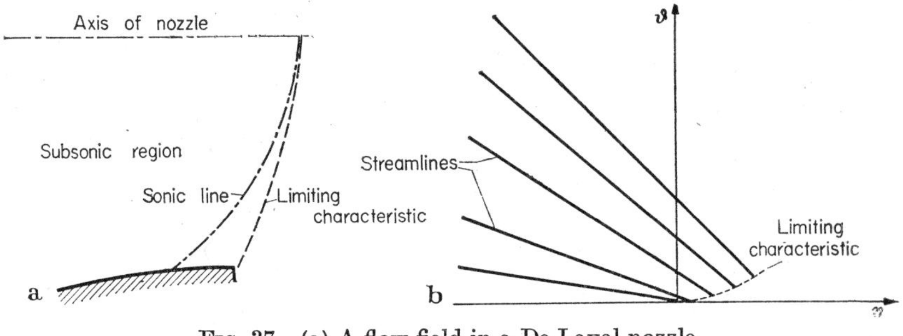

FIG. 37 (a) A flow field in a De Laval nozzle
(b) Representation in the η, ϑ plane.

cines, each one tangential to one of the characteristics. Figure 36 refers only to the lower half of the flow field, the region $AOBFD$ is covered once and the region BOE twice. The triple coverage of the region EOF would result if the upper half of the physical plane were included. Such a behaviour of the streamlines is to be expected from their form in the physical plane.

If the flow is considered from the point of view of a boundary value problem (Fig. 37), the multiple coverage does not appear very meaningful. In line with the considerations on p. 68 we ask which part of the nozzle boundary must be prescribed to determine the subsonic region of the nozzle and that part of the supersonic region which affects the subsonic part. Evidently one requires the boundary of the subsonic regime as well as that part of the boundary of the supersonic region which extends from the intersection with the sonic line to the characteristics passing through the origin. These latter characteristics are the limiting ones. One may note that for a prescribed contour in the physical plane, the boundary conditions in the hodograph plane cannot be stated along a given contour. In any case, however, the limiting characteristic is known and it is clear that conditions prescribed on the other side of the limiting characteristic cannot influence the subsonic region. The part of the flow field, described above, is only covered once. The continuation of the flow can be determined with the aid of the method of characteristics which is best applied to the physical plane. If the resulting flow is subsequently transformed into the hodograph plane, the multiple coverage of the supersonic part of the flow is obtained automatically*.

9. Branch Lines in the Hodograph Plane

We have found in the last example that two sheets of the hodograph plane can be joined along the characteristic passing through the origin so that along a streamline one can move from one sheet to the other. Let us consider the conditions necessary for such a structure of the hodograph plane to be possible.

Let the curve in the hodograph plane, along which the two sheets of the latter are joined, be denoted by C and let us use the same notation for the image of this line in the physical plane. Conceivably the solutions on both sides of C in the physical plane may not be analytic continuations of one another. This can, however, occur only if C is a characteristic in both the physical and hodograph planes.

We leave this case out, assum ing that the solution in the physical plane is analytic along C and ask whether in this case the curve C also has to be a characteristic. In general we have

$$du = \frac{\partial u}{\partial x} dx + \frac{\partial u}{\partial y} dy,$$

$$dv = \frac{\partial v}{\partial y} dx + \frac{\partial v}{\partial y} dy.$$

If the determinant of the coefficients of these equations (which is equal to the reciprocal of the Jacobian $\partial(x, y)/\partial(u, v)$, is non-zero, then the RHS's are linearly independent and a one to one correspondence exists between the hodograph plane and the physical plane. Evidently this cannot be the case if a line C represents a junction between two sheets of the hodograph plane, therefore we must have

$$\frac{\partial u}{\partial x}\frac{\partial v}{\partial y} - \frac{\partial v}{\partial x}\frac{\partial u}{\partial y} = 0.$$

* In the literature one may find a derivation of the hodograph solution which utilizes this multiple coverage in the definition of the solution. This is not very satisfactory from the physical point of view.

The introduction of the velocity potential in the above yields

$$\Phi_{xx}\Phi_{yy} - \Phi_{xy}^2 = 0. \tag{1}$$

For the sake of simplicity, the following analysis will be based on the equation of transonic flow, Eq. II, 8 (1)

$$-(\gamma + 1)\,\Phi_x \Phi_{xx} + \Phi_{yy} = 0. \tag{2}$$

Let the slope of the curve C be dy/dx. Then differentiating along this curve one obtains

$$\frac{d\Phi_x}{dx} = \Phi_{xx} + \Phi_{xy}\frac{dy}{dx}; \tag{3a}$$

and

$$\frac{d\Phi_y}{dx} = \Phi_{xy} + \Phi_{yy}\frac{dy}{dx}. \tag{3b}$$

From Eqs. (1) and (2) we find

$$(\gamma + 1)\,\Phi_x \Phi_{xx}^2 - \Phi_{xy}^2 = 0. \tag{4}$$

This shows that such a junction of two sheets can occur only in the supersonic regime ($\Phi_x > 0$), since in the subsonic regime the LHS of Eq. (4) is the negative of a sum of two quadratic terms. On the other hand, if both Φ_{xx} and Φ_{xy} are zero along a curve in the subsonic region, it may be easily shown that the flow is parallel. From the last equation one obtains

$$\pm\sqrt{\gamma + 1}\,\sqrt{\Phi_x}\,\Phi_{xx} = \Phi_{xy}$$

and, with the aid of Eqs. (4) and (2), Eq. (3) yields

$$\frac{d\Phi_x}{dx} = \Phi_{xx}\left(1 \pm \sqrt{\gamma + 1}\,\sqrt{\Phi_x}\right)\frac{dy}{dx};$$

$$\frac{d\Phi_y}{dx} = \Phi_{xx}\left(\pm\sqrt{(\gamma + 1)}\,\sqrt{\Phi_x} + (\gamma + 1)\,\Phi_x\frac{dy}{dx}\right).$$

Hence

$$d\Phi_y \mp \sqrt{\gamma + 1}\,\sqrt{\Phi_x}\,d\Phi_x = 0$$

or

$$d\vartheta \mp \sqrt{\eta}\,d\eta = 0.$$

This is the differential equation of the characteristics in the η, ϑ plane. We find, therefore, that two sheets of the hodograph plane can be joined only along a characteristic. It remains to be shown that this is also the case in the physical plane. One of the conditions, the so-called compatibility condition, for the characteristics in the physical plane is satisfied, since the curve C maps into a characteristic in the hodograph plane. There remains only the question whether C in the physical plane has the direction of a characteristic. The form of the hodograph representation is naturally independent of whether one employs the stream fun-ion or the transformed potential as a dependent variable. For the latter, one ›btains along a characteristic

$$\sqrt{\eta}\, d\varphi_\eta \pm d\varphi_\vartheta = 0 .$$

)nly derivatives calculated along the characteristic occur in this equation. The quation is, therefore, valid also when the derivatives of $d\varphi_\eta$ and $d\varphi_\vartheta$ do not xist in other directions as is the case, for example, in a De Laval nozzle. In iew of Eqs. V, 7 (5) and V, 7 (10), the last equation can be interpreted as

$$(\gamma + 1)^{-1/2} \left(\frac{\Delta w}{w^*}\right)^{1/2} dx \pm dy = 0$$

vhich is the same as Eq. I, 9 (4) for the direction of the characteristics in the hysical plane. The branch lines of the hodograph plane are the counterparts of he limiting lines of the physical plane. In this latter case, the limiting line is in ;eneral, however, not a characteristic, while the branch line of the hodograph s always a characteristic. This is, of course, closely connected with the linearity f the hodograph equation.

In the example of the De Laval nozzle, the branch line of the hodograph is hat characteristic of the physical plane which runs downstream from the interection point of the sonic line with the axis of the nozzle. In the lower half of he physical plane this is a right Mach line. Such Mach lines in the lower half f the physical plane denote compression waves when they originate from the onic line and expansion waves when they originate from the nozzle wall. This s the reason for the fact that the hodograph consists of two planes which is lways the case if such changes from compression to expansion waves, or vice ersa, occur.

0. The Lost Solutions

We shall now, finally, discuss the hodograph representation which corresponds o a flow field resulting from an originally parallel flow around a curved wall. . construction by the method of characteristics results only in Mach lines corsponding to one family, say only the left characteristics as shown in Fig. 38. he flow maps therefore into only a single characteristic in the hodograph plane. ach point of this characteristic represents a single wave in the physical plane. uch solutions are, of course, discontinuous in ie hodograph plane. For example on our chacteristic of the hodograph plane, ψ varies beween the two limits determined by the bounary streamlines of the flow. This solution, ierefore, represents only a ridge normal to the odograph plane. In general, such solutions are illed *lost solutions* (cf. Tollmien [74]).

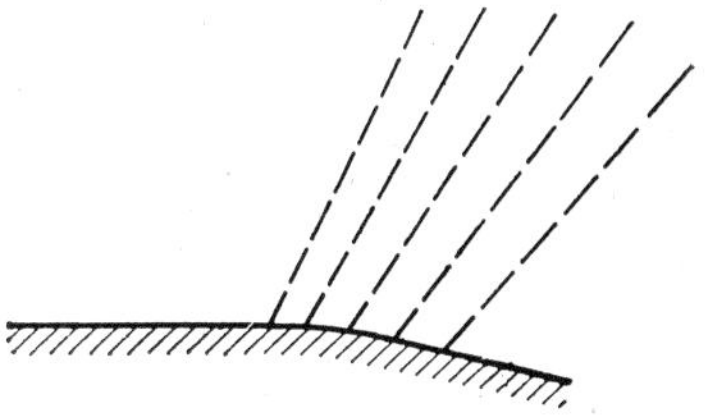

Fig. 38 A "lost" solution in the physical plane.

The singularity is less dangerous in the case a transformed potential. This may be seen from a comparison with Eq. V, 7 (7). Let φ_1 and φ_2 be two different analytical solutions of TRICOMI's equation for the transformed potential, which are equal along a characteristic C of the hodograph plane and whose derivatives in directions other than that of C are not equal. Let the corresponding coordinates x and y be x_1, y_1 and x_2, y_2 respectively. In view of the equality of φ_1 and φ_2 along C we have

$$\frac{\partial \varphi_1}{\partial \eta} + \frac{\partial \varphi_1}{\partial \vartheta}\frac{d\eta}{d\vartheta} = \frac{\partial \varphi_2}{\partial \eta} + \frac{\partial \varphi_2}{\partial \vartheta}\frac{d\eta}{d\vartheta}$$

or

$$(\gamma + 1)^{-1/3} x_1 + y_1 \frac{d\eta}{d\vartheta} = (\gamma + 1)^{-1/3} x_2 + y_2 \frac{d\eta}{d\vartheta},$$

$$x_1 - x_2 = -(\gamma + 1)^{1/3} (y_1 - y_2) \frac{d\eta}{d\vartheta}.$$

As a result of this, for any given point for the characteristic C, the corresponding point of the second flow must, in the physical plane lie on a straight line which passes through the corresponding point of the first flow and whose slope dx/dy is given by

$$-(\gamma + 1)^{1/3} \frac{d\eta}{d\vartheta}.$$

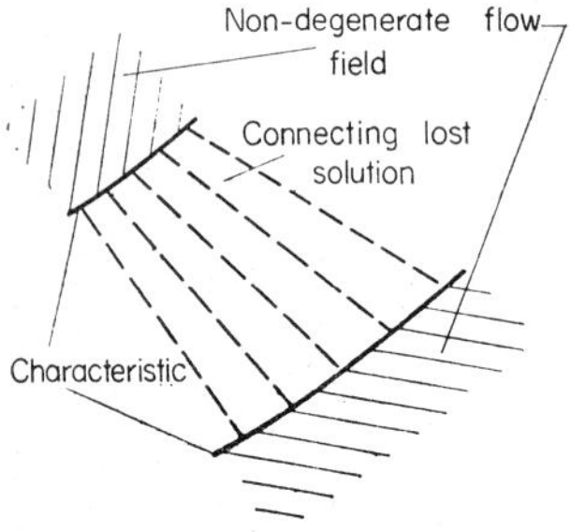

FIG. 39 Joining of two non — degenerate solutions by a "lost" solution.

Here $d\eta/d\vartheta$ is to be calculated at the given point on the characteristic. With the aid of Eqs. I, 6 (8) and V,7 (11) one obtains

$$\frac{dx}{dy} = (\gamma + 1)^{1/2} \left(\frac{\Delta w}{w^*}\right)^{-1/2}.$$

These straight lines are characteristics in the physical plane and in particular when C is a right characteristic, the slope of the straight line corresponds to a left characteristic. We have arrived, thus, at the result shown in Fig. 39. Two solutions, for which the transformed potential is the same along a characteristic in the hodograph plane, but whose derivatives differ in directions outward from the curve, represent two flow fields which can be connected together by a suitable lost solution. In this manner such lost solutions can be included in analytical investigations.

11. Boundary Value Problems in the Hodograph Plane

We have seen in several examples that the boundary value problems in subsonic and supersonic flow take on different forms. Evidently, therefore, a degree of caution must be exercised in formulating mixed flow problems. We shall summarise in the following the known features of such boundary value problems. The proofs will not be included but we shall attempt to illustrate the formula tion on the basis of physical examples. The fundamental result is due to Tricomi, who considered the differential equation

$$\psi_{\eta\eta} - \eta\psi_{\vartheta\vartheta} = 0 \tag{1}$$

which we have already obtained as the approximate hodograph equation of transonic flow. In Fig. 40 A and B are two points on the sonic line. The origin of the coordinate system is at A. The region considered is bounded by a curve C which lies in the subsonic regime and which connects A and B. The normal assumptions for the treatment of boundary value problems are made with respect to this curve. Let us draw the characteristics AD and BD through the points A and B. These represent the boundary of the supersonic regime of the region considered. Let ψ be prescribed along the curve C and along the characteristic BD; ψ is finite and furthermore it must satisfy certain more or less self-explanatory conditions with regard to its derivatives formed in the direction of the curve. We require that the second derivatives of the solution should exist everywhere within the region considered and, furthermore, that along the sonic line, the expression $\psi_\eta \vartheta^{5/6}$ should be bounded. This last condition we shall call Tricomi's condition. Tricomi has shown that under the above assumptions a unique solution of the above differential equation, which satisfied the prescribed boundary conditions, does exist.

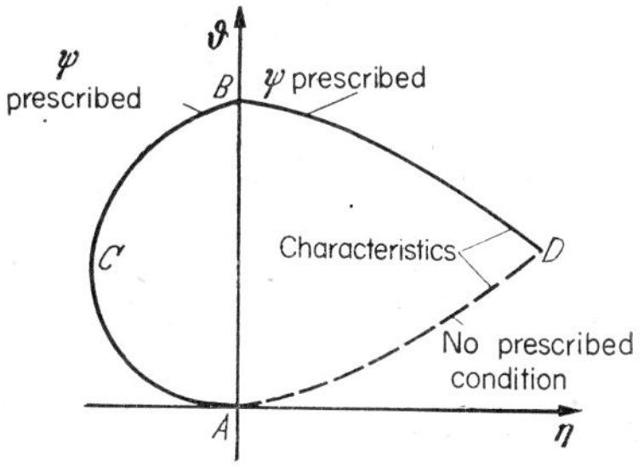

Fig. 40 The boundary of Tricomi's boundary value problem.

The formulation of this boundary value problem combines features of a subsonic problem with those of a supersonic one. For example, the contour along which the values of ψ are prescribed is closed in the subsonic regime and has a gap, which extends along a characteristic, in the supersonic regime.

To visualise this better, let us formulate in the physical plane the boundary value problem which leads to Tricomi's equation in the hodograph plane. A de Laval nozzle with straight walls is shown in Fig. 41. We consider only the lower half of the physical plane. The axis of symmetry of the nozzle and the nozzle wall are then lines of constant ψ in the η, ϑ plane. We prescribe $\psi = 0$ along the axis of the nozzle and $\psi = -1$ along the image of the wall. It is further necessary to say something about the inlet cross-section. For example, we can prescribe the values of ψ along a line $\eta = \text{const}$ which connects the streamline of symmetry and the streamline representing the wall. It is simpler, however, if the inlet cross-section is placed at infinity in both the physical and the hodograph planes. It is then only necessary to say that at the inlet cross-section ψ should increase monotonically from zero to one. In accordance with Tricomi's formulation we then prescribe $\psi = -1$ along the characteristic DE and give no condition along the characteristic EA. If $\psi = \text{const}$ along a characteristic, i.e. when a streamline and a characteristic coincide, then the latter maps into a point in the physical plane [cf. Eqs. V, 1 (15) and V, 3 (3)]. Since the direction of the velocity vector changes along DE this implies that a corner exists in the flow (point $D \equiv E$). A MEYER expansion fan forms at this corner as we have seen in the supersonic case. This explains the flow field shown in Fig. 41. The MACH lines of the expansion fan correspond to the characteristics of the hodograph, which originate from DE and are propagated towards the sonic line, e.g. the characteristic GH.

From the point of view of the flow alone, Fig. 41 differs little from Fig. 16, which represents a more general case of flow through the DE LAVAL nozzle. In the subsonic regime changes in the contour of the nozzle are, in general, inconsequential. An important difference lies in the supersonic regime in which the line element AB of Fig. 16, which determines the MACH lines propagated towards the sonic line, has degenerated into a point $D \equiv E$ in Fig. 41. It is probable

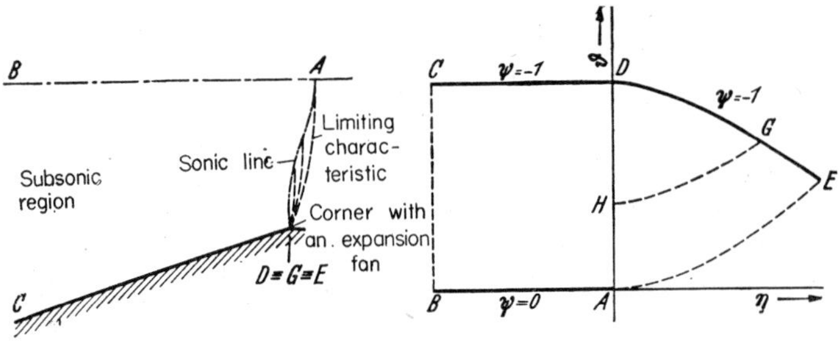

FIG. 41
A flow whose hodograph is of the form of TRICOMI's problem.

that a boundary value problem as shown in Fig. 16 also has a unique solution. How is one to formulate the analogous boundary value problem in the hodograph plane? The choice of the subsonic contour in TRICOMI's problem is, within physically reasonable limits, almost unlimited. As regards the supersonic contour, there exists an important difference. The corner at the throat, as shown in Fig. 41, appears quite arbitrary. When, however, in the physical plane there is no corner, then the boundary does not map into a characteristic in the hodograph plane. Along the boundary ψ = const. Hence on the boundary

$$\frac{\partial \psi}{\partial w}\frac{dw}{d\vartheta} + \frac{\partial \psi}{\partial \vartheta} = 0; \quad \frac{dw}{d\vartheta} = -\frac{\partial \psi}{\partial \vartheta}\Big/\frac{\partial \psi}{\partial w}.$$

Since the Jacobian is negative in the subsonic regime, it must remain negative also in the supersonic region, otherwise one would obtain a flow which cannot be physically realised. As a result of this and in accordance with Eq. V, 2 (4)

$$\left|\frac{\partial \psi}{\partial w}\right| > \frac{\sqrt{M^2 - 1}}{w}\left|\frac{\partial \psi}{\partial \vartheta}\right|.$$

The contour, therefore, must at every point have a slope $|dw/d\vartheta|$ which cannot exceed that of a characteristic*. These considerations have led us to a boundary value problem in which the subsonic contour has the same generality as in TRICOMI's problem. The supersonic contour consists of a characteristic (AB in Fig. 42) and of a more general curve BC whose slope $|dw/d\vartheta|$ does not exceed the local slope of the characteristic. The values of ψ are prescribed along the subsonic contour and along CB. This boundary value problem has not been investigated as fully as that of TRICOMI. Uniqueness proofs have been given by FRANKL [20], MORAVETZ [64] and GUDERLEY [29].

Further generalisations result from the fact that in Fig. 16 the upper half of the DE LAVAL nozzle can evidently be included in the flow field and that the

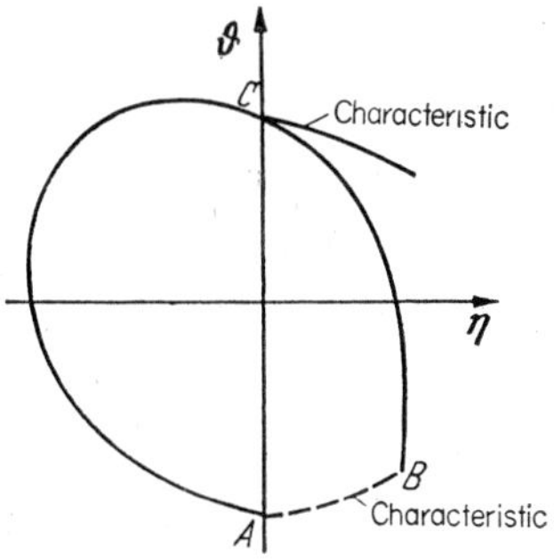

FIG. 42
The contour for a generalised form of TRICOMI's boundary value problem.

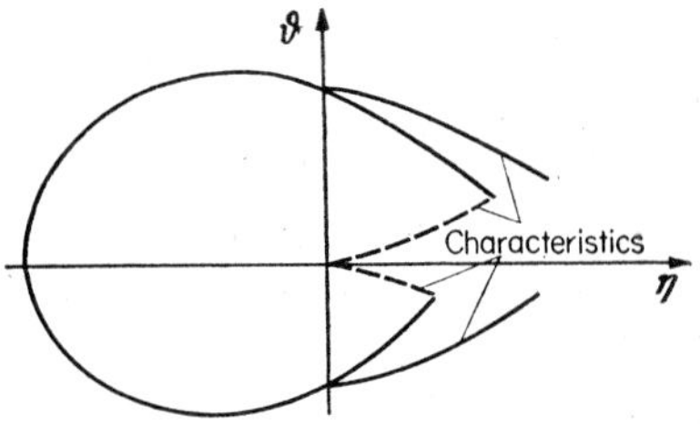

FIG. 43
Further generalisation of TRICOMI's problem.

latter need not always be symmetric. This leads to a form of the boundary as shown, for example, in Fig. 43. The uniqueness theorems mentioned above are applicable also to such cases.

Shocks in parallel flow map in the hodograph plane into the shock polar, i.e. into a prescribed curve. A linear boundary condition exists on this curve (FRANKL [20], GUDERLEY [26]) and this condition will be derived presently. The transonic approximation of the shock polar has already been derived previously and is given by Eq. II, 4 (8). We now have

$$\Delta v_z = 0,$$

$$\Delta v_y = a^* \vartheta,$$

$$v_{x_{\mathrm{I}}} = (\gamma + 1)^{-1/3} a^* \eta_{\mathrm{I}},$$

$$v_{x_{\mathrm{II}}} = (\gamma + 1)^{-1/3} a^* \eta_{\mathrm{II}}$$

* From the mathematical point of view, the conditions that the Jacobian must be negative, and that along the contour $\psi = 0$, are external to the boundary value problem. This line of thought is, however, permissible in a heuristic discussion leading to a proper formulation of the boundary value problem.

which yields

$$\vartheta_{II} - \vartheta_{I} = \sqrt{\frac{\eta_I + \eta_{II}}{2}}\,(\eta_I - \eta_{II}), \tag{2}$$

where, as before, the subscripts I and II refer to conditions before and after the shock, respectively.

The boundary condition to be satisfied along the shock polar expresses the fact that in moving along the shock polar one simultaneously moves in the physical plane in a prescribed direction, namely in the direction of the shock. This direction is determined solely by the velocities before and after the shock. Since the change in the velocity vector, occuring at the shock, is normal to the latter, one obtains for it

$$\frac{dy}{dx} = (\gamma + 1)^{1/3}\,\frac{\eta_I - \eta_{II}}{\vartheta_{II} - \vartheta_I}. \tag{3}$$

The direction of propagation along the shock is obtained from Eq. (2) by differentiation

$$\frac{d\vartheta_{II}}{d\eta_{II}} = \mp\,[8(\eta_{II} + \eta_I)]^{-1/2}\,(3\,\eta_{II} + \eta_I). \tag{4}$$

Further

$$dx = \frac{\partial x}{\partial \eta}\,d\eta + \frac{\partial x}{\partial \vartheta}\,d\vartheta,$$

$$dy = \frac{\partial y}{\partial \eta}\,d\eta + \frac{\partial \eta}{\partial \vartheta}\,d\vartheta.$$

Introducing this in Eq. (3) and eliminating the partial derivatives of x and η with the aid of Eq. V, 7 (8), and finally substituting from Eq. (4), the following linear boundary condition for the shock polar is obtained

$$\psi_\eta \mp \psi_\vartheta \sqrt{\frac{\eta_{II} + \eta_I}{2}}\,\frac{7\eta_{II} + \eta_I}{5\eta_{II} + 3\eta_I} = 0. \tag{5}$$

It can be interpreted in the following manner. Along a line $\psi = \text{const}$

$$\psi_\eta + \psi_\vartheta\,\frac{d\vartheta}{d\eta} = 0.$$

Hence the slope of such a line is

$$\frac{d\vartheta}{d\eta} = -\,\frac{\psi_\eta}{\psi_\vartheta}.$$

This expression can be also calculated from the boundary condition on the shock polar

$$\frac{d\vartheta}{d\eta} = \mp\sqrt{\frac{\eta_I + \eta_{II}}{2}}\,\frac{7\eta_{II} + \eta_I}{5\eta_{II} + \eta_I}. \tag{6}$$

Thus the slope of the streamlines is prescribed along the shock polar.

The shock polars for $\eta_{\rm I} = 1$, 0·8, 0·6, 0·4 and 0·2 are shown in Fig. 44. The directions of the approaching streamlines are shown on the shock polar corresponding to $\eta_{\rm I} = 1$. At S $\eta =$ const along the streamlines, at Q (CROCCO's point) $\vartheta =$ const along the streamlines, at R the value of $\vartheta_{\rm II} - \vartheta_{\rm I}$ is a maximum for the shock polar. A few characteristics are also shown. The characteristic passing through $\eta_{\rm I} = 1$, $\vartheta_{\rm II} - \vartheta_{\rm I} = 0$ lies within the shock polar through that point.

A comparatively simple boundary value problem, involving the occurence of a shock, is offered by a wedge in supersonic flow whose velocity is such that an

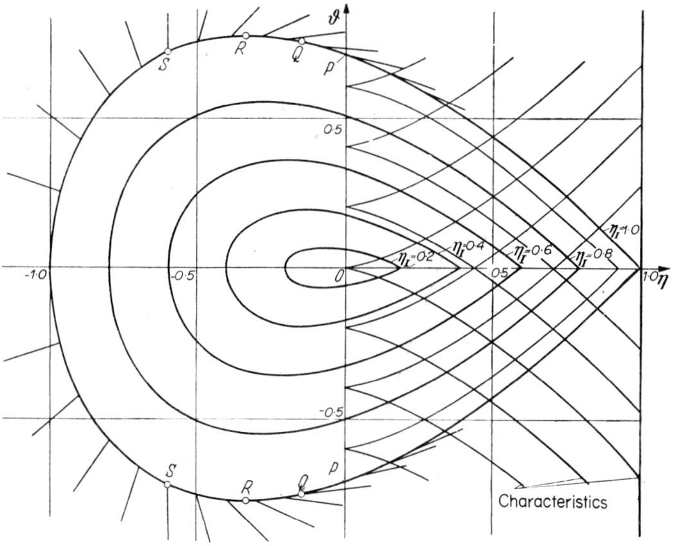

FIG. 44 Shock polars in the η, ϑ plane showing directions of streamlines. (According to GUDERLEY [26]).

attached shock cannot exist. In the case of a symmetrical wedge the resulting shock is, of course, also symmetrical with respect to the axis of the wedge. On the axis of the flow (cf. point A in Fig. 45), the shock is normal. The velocity along the axis changes from a value corresponding to that downstream of a normal shock to zero at the leading edge of the wedge (line AB in the hodograph representation in Fig. 45). At the leading edge the velocity vector assumes the direction of the face of the wedge and thus transforms into a line $\vartheta =$ const in the hodograph plane. At the shoulder of the wedge $C \equiv D$ the velocity becomes sonic and the corner maps into the characteristic CD in the hodograph plane. An explanation of why the velocity cannot become sonic along the face of the wedge was given in Section IV, 4.

In Fig. 45c the hodograph plane has been transformed into the η, ϑ plane. The origin of the former maps into $\eta = -\infty$. The boundary conditions are given by $\psi = 0$ along AB and along BCD and, further, by the shock conditions along the shock polar. Since all the boundary conditions are homogeneous, it must obviously be possible to introduce a further condition which determines the scale of measurement in the physical plane. For example, the length of the face of the wedge can be prescribed or, alternatively, the value of the stream function at the point E. This latter condition is physically of little interest. A uniqueness proof of the boundary value problem of the type described above has been given by FRANKL [20].

Another type of boundary condition results from the following considerations. One of the principal problems of analytical fluid mechanics is the determination

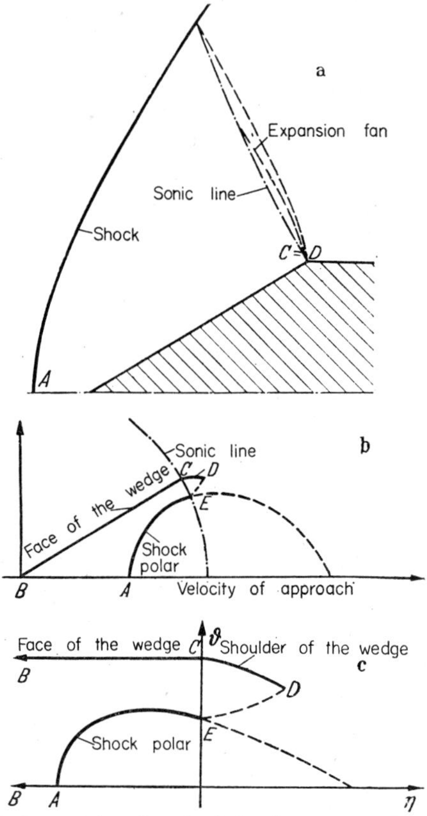

FIG. 45 Supersonic flow with a detached chock past a wedge. (a) physical plane, (b) hodograph plane, (c) η, ϑ plane.

of the flow around a given profile. This boundary value problem, however, is insoluble in practice. As a partial step in this direction one may consider the following problem. Let us suppose that the hodograph solution for a flow around a given body is known. Let us determine the boundary conditions which arise when the physical contour of the body is changed by a prescribed small amount. Boundary conditions of this type are important in the analysis of flows in the vicinity of $M = 1$, as well as in deciding whether shocks occur in a mixed subsonic flow, when the contour of the profile is changed in a prescribed manner.

A small change of the contour in the physical plane can be accounted for in the hodograph plane by a linearisation of the boundary conditions. The resulting condition is then derived for the general hodograph equation and subsequently it is specialised to the transonic approximation.

The boundary in the physical plane can be described by the following parametric equations for x and y

$$x = f_1(\vartheta),$$

$$y = f_2(\vartheta),$$

where f_1 and f_2 are related by

$$\frac{dy}{dx} = \frac{f_2'}{f_1'} = \tan\vartheta .$$

In the hodograph plane the contour is given by

$$w = w_0(\vartheta).$$

The coordinates x and y can be expressed in terms of the transformed potential by

$$x = f_1(\vartheta) = \varphi_w(w_0, \vartheta)\cos\vartheta - \frac{1}{w_0}\varphi_\vartheta(w_0, \vartheta)\sin\vartheta, \tag{7a}$$

$$y = f_2(\vartheta) = \varphi_w(w_0, \vartheta)\sin\vartheta + \frac{1}{w_0}\varphi_\vartheta(w_0, \vartheta)\cos\vartheta \tag{7b}$$

from which the values of φ_w and φ_ϑ, occuring along the contour, can be calculated. This calculation takes the form

$$\varphi_w(w_0, \vartheta) = f_3(\vartheta), \tag{8a}$$

$$\frac{1}{w_0}\varphi_\vartheta(w_0, \vartheta) = f_4(\vartheta). \tag{8b}$$

The functions f_3 and f_4 are the same as f_1 and f_2 in a local system of coordinates, whose origin is the same as that of the original x, y-system and whose x axis coincides with the direction of the velocity vector. Let us denote such a coordinate system by $\bar{x}, \bar{y}$. Once chosen, this $\bar{x}, \bar{y}$ system must be held constant in any differentiation process. Let the angle which the velocity makes with the $\bar{x}$ axis be $\bar{\vartheta}$. Naturally, at the point considered $\bar{\vartheta} = 0$. The application of Eq. (7b) to the new coordinate system yields

$$\frac{d\bar{y}}{d\bar{\vartheta}} = f_3 - f_4'.$$

Since at the point considered $\bar{y}' = 0$, we have

$$f_3 = f_4'$$

and the boundary conditions may be written as

$$\frac{1}{w_0}\varphi_\vartheta(w_0, \vartheta) = f_4(\vartheta), \tag{9a}$$

$$\varphi_w(w_0, \vartheta) = f_4'(\vartheta). \tag{9b}$$

In accordance with the above, f_4 is the normal distance from the origin of co-ordinates to the tangent to the surface at the point considered, as shown in Fig. 46.

Let us now change the value of f_4 by a small quantity F_4. The solution satisfying the new boundary conditions differs from φ by a small quantity Φ. The

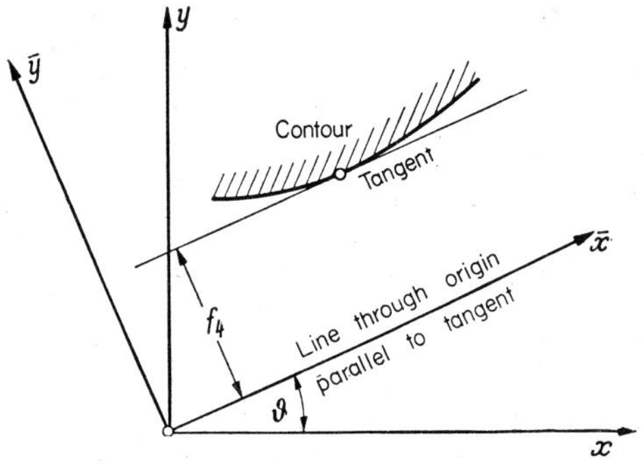

FIG. 46 Geometrical interpretation of f_4. (According to GUDERLEY [26]).

location of the contour in the hodograph plane will also change slightly so that the function $w_0(\vartheta)$ must be replaced by a function $w_0(\vartheta) + W_0(\vartheta)$. Thus in the new flow the boundary conditions are given by

$$\frac{1}{w_0 + W_0}[\varphi_\vartheta(w_0 + W_0, \vartheta) + \Phi_\vartheta(w_0 + W_0, \vartheta)] = f_4(\vartheta) + F_4(\vartheta),$$

$$\varphi_w(w_0 + W_0, \vartheta) + \Phi_w(w_0 + W_0, \vartheta) = f_4'(\vartheta) + F_4'(\vartheta).$$

If F_4, W_0 and Φ are regarded as small, the above equations can be linearised, yielding

$$\frac{-\varphi_\vartheta(w_0, \vartheta)}{w_0^2} W_0 + \frac{\varphi_{w\vartheta}(w_0, \vartheta)}{w_0} W_0 + \frac{1}{w_0}\Phi_\vartheta(w_0, \vartheta) = F_4(\vartheta),$$

$$\varphi_{ww}(w_0, \vartheta)\, W_0 + \Phi_w(w_0, \vartheta) = F_4'(\vartheta)$$

and upon elimination of W_0

$$-\Phi_w\left(\frac{-\varphi_\vartheta}{w_0^2} + \frac{\varphi_{w\vartheta}}{w_0}\right) + \Phi_\vartheta \frac{1}{w_0}\varphi_{ww} = F_4\,\varphi_{ww} - F_4'\left(\frac{-\varphi_\vartheta}{w_0^2} + \frac{\varphi_{w\vartheta}}{w_0}\right).$$

In the original flow, expressed in terms of the new coordinate system, $d\bar{y} = 0$ and hence in accordance with Eq. (7b)

$$\varphi_w(w_0, \vartheta)\, d\bar{\vartheta} - \frac{1}{w_0^2}\varphi_\vartheta(w_0, \vartheta) + \frac{1}{w_0}\varphi_{w\vartheta}(w_0, \vartheta)\, dw + \frac{1}{w_0}\varphi_{\vartheta\vartheta}\, d\bar{\vartheta} = 0.$$

From this, with the aid of Eq. V, 1 (10), we obtain

$$\frac{dw_0}{d\vartheta} = \frac{w_0 \varphi_{ww}(w_0, \vartheta)}{\left(1 - \frac{w^2}{a^2}\right)\left(-\frac{1}{w_0^2}\varphi_\vartheta + \frac{1}{w_0}\varphi_{w\vartheta}\right)}.$$

As a result, the boundary condition, which is to be satisfied along the hodograph image of the contour of the original problem, takes the form

$$-\Phi_w \frac{w_0^2}{1 - \frac{w_0^2}{a^2}} + \Phi_\vartheta \frac{dw_0}{d\vartheta} = -F_4' \frac{w_0^2}{1 - \frac{w_0^2}{a^2}} + F_4 w_0 \frac{dw_0}{d\vartheta}, \tag{10}$$

where $F_4(\vartheta)$ and $w_0(\vartheta)$ are known functions (cf. GUDERLEY [25]).

This linear boundary condition may appear somewhat complicated. It is, however, related to the differential equation of the transformed potential in the same way in which the normal derivative is related to the solution of LAPLACE's equation. By integrating, for example, LAPLACE's equation over a surface

$$\iint_S \left(\frac{\partial^2 \varphi}{\partial x^2} + \frac{\partial^2 \varphi}{\partial y^2}\right) dx\, dy = 0$$

one obtains

$$\oint_C \left(\frac{\partial \varphi}{\partial x} dy - \frac{\partial \varphi}{\partial y} dx\right) = 0.$$

Here S denotes a surface element and C its boundary. The integrand of this last expression is closely related to the normal derivative. A similar relationship occurs in our present problem. In order to show this, we write the differential equation, Eq. V, 2 (10), in the form

$$\frac{\partial(\varrho w \varphi_w)}{\partial w} + \frac{\varrho}{w}\left(1 - \frac{w^2}{a^2}\right)\varphi_{\vartheta\vartheta} = 0,$$

which is easily derived with the aid of Eqs. I, 2 (10a). A suitable integration of

$$\iint_P \left[\frac{\partial(\varrho w \Phi_w)}{\partial w} + \frac{\varrho}{w}\left(1 - \frac{w^2}{a^2}\right)\Phi_{\vartheta\vartheta}\right] dw\, d\vartheta$$

yields

$$\int_C \varrho w \Phi_w\, d\vartheta - \frac{\varrho}{w}\left(1 - \frac{w^2}{a^2}\right)\Phi_\vartheta\, dw = 0. \tag{11}$$

The integrand is proportional to the LHS of Eq. (10). In view of the analogy with the boundary value problem of the second kind of the potential theory, we speak in the present connection also of a boundary value problem of the second kind.

Equations (11) and (10) represent, for a closed contour, a condition of solubility of the boundary value problem in analogy to the corresponding condition in the potential theory. The contours of interest to us possess, however, frequently a gap in the supersonic regime and then it is not obvious whether such a condition arises. Certain heuristic considerations (cf. p. 239–40) allow us to conclude that in this case an additional condition is also necessary.

The corresponding boundary condition for TRICOMI's equation can be obtained either directly or by introducing the same simplifications as in the actual derivation of TRICOMI's equation. If we put, for example, $\Phi = \tau\tilde{\Phi}(\tilde{\eta}, \tilde{\vartheta})$ where $\tilde{\eta}$ and $\tilde{\vartheta}$ are given by Eq. V, 7 (5), then $F_4(\vartheta) = \tau^{3/2}\tilde{F}_4(\tilde{\vartheta})$ is compatible with this assumption. Substituting into the boundary condition, Eq. (10), replacing $\tilde{\Phi}$ and $\tilde{F}_4$ by Φ and F_4 and retaining only terms of lowest order in τ one obtains

$$L(\Phi) = \Phi_\eta + \Phi_\vartheta \eta_0 \frac{d\eta_0}{d\vartheta} = \frac{dF_4}{d\vartheta}. \tag{12}$$

The original boundary is given in the η, ϑ plane by $\eta = \eta_0(\vartheta)$ and, in accordance with Eq. (9b), $df_4/d\vartheta$ represents the values of x for a given slope of the surface ϑ except for a factor $(\gamma + 1)^{-1/3}$. The change in $df_4/d\vartheta$ caused by the deformation of the contour is given by $dF_4/d\vartheta$. The uniqueness theorem for this problem has been given by MORAVETZ [63].

In most of the applications which we shall meet the boundary conditions are homogeneous. For example, the surface of an obstacle in the flow is given by $\psi = 0$. Alternatively, the requirement that the surface of the obstacle is to remain unchanged during superposition of another solution on the given flow leads to the condition of Eq. (12), where the RHS of the equation is zero. These hodograph solutions possess then at least one singular point. This singular point is located very frequently on the sonic line, and the singularity is described by a particular solution of TRICOMI's equation. The homogeneous boundary conditions are then satisfied by adding to the solution, describing the singularity, a further solution of TRICOMI's equation which satisfies TRICOMI's condition and which, along the contour of the region considered, gives the same contribution to the boundary value as the singular solution, except for an opposite sign. If the singular solution is given then the complete solution is unique for the boundary value problem of the first kind.

We have mentioned that in a boundary value problem the prescribed boundary values may have to be subjected to an additional condition. We then need two singular solutions. One of these is prescribed and the other is multiplied by a suitable factor and then superimposed. The multiplication factor should be chosen in such a manner that the boundary conditions of the remaining regular portion of the solution satisfy the conditions of solubility.

CHAPTER VI

DISCUSSION OF TRANSONIC FLOWS ON THE BASIS OF THE HODOGRAPH TRANSFORMATION

1. Introductory Remarks

THE hodograph transformation can provide an insight into the general properties of a flow field in cases in which a direct transformation into the hodograph plane is possible. Such flows are rarely of direct practical interest; they permit us, however, to achieve a degree of familiarity with the properties of transonic flows and a better understanding of boundary value problems in the transonic regime. In some cases, the physical interpretation of theoretical results obtained by a different method, and whose understanding may previously have been difficult, becomes much easier.

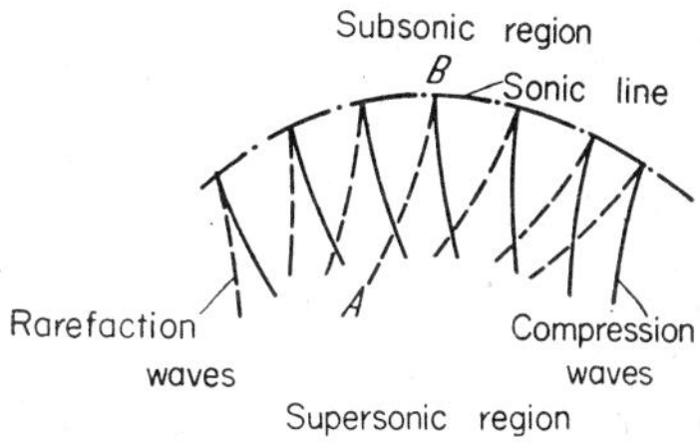

FIG. 47 The structure of a supersonic flow field adjoining a subsonic region.

The attempt to find the hodograph mapping of a given flow alone provides significant information about the field of flow. This is due to the general rules governing the hodograph transformation. Although these rules have already been discussed in the previous chapter, we shall summarise them here again, for convenience.

The sense in which a surface element is described changes sign in the transformation to the hodograph plane in the case of subsonic flow, since the Jacobian of hodograph transformation is negative. The same is true in the supersonic regime for reasons of continuity and also since we have excluded limiting lines from our considerations. From this we can derive a rule for the sign of MACH lines which originate or end on the sonic line. The rule is easiest derived following BUSEMANN*.

Changes of state, along a given MACH line, are caused only by the waves belonging to the other family of MACH waves. On a MACH wave which ends on the sonic line, e.g. the line AB in Fig. 47, the pressure increases as the sonic line is approached, since one is then moving from supersonic to subsonic flow. This wave, therefore, is being intersected by compression waves which, however, are propagated from the sonic line. As a result of this all waves originating on the

* Similar ideas can be found in an article by NIKOLSKI and TAGANOFF [66].

sonic line are compression waves and, since the pressure on the sonic line is constant, all waves approaching the sonic line must be rarefaction waves.

It is quite obvious that the physical plane consists of a single sheet. The hodograph plane, on the other hand, can consist of a number of sheets. We have already met several examples in which such a possibility arose. In subsonic flow the transition from one sheet to another takes place when circumscribing a singular point. It is impossible for two such sheets, covering one another, to be joined along a line in the subsonic regime, since then such a line would have to be a characteristic and these do not exist in subsonic flow.

There exist in subsonic flow points in which a number of streamlines meet or, more exactly, for which the stream function assumes different values depending on the direction from which the point is approached. These points are always mapped into infinity. This is so because when the flow is parallel, along a curve in the physical plane in the subsonic regime, and this is the case when a number of streamlines meet at a single point in the hodograph plane; then the analytic continuation of such a flow is also parallel in the entire physical plane. As there are no characteristics in the subsonic regime, a flow cannot change from a parallel one into another form. A singular point occuring at sonic velocity need not be mapped into infinity as indicated by the example in Section 3 of Chapter 4. Singularities of the type discussed there do not occur in subsonic flow.

If a characteristic intersects a streamline in the hodograph plane more than once we have a limiting line and the streamline reverses its direction. For the bounding streamlines, at least, such behaviour is not permissible. We obtain thus the requirement that a streamline which represents the boundary of a flow can intersect each characteristic not more than once. It is possible for a streamline to coincide with a characteristic in which case the former exhibits a corner (cf. Fig. 41). If a streamline crosses a characteristic and is at the same time tangential to it, then in the physical plane we have a point of infinite curvature.

2. The Discharge from a Vessel

The elementary theory of discharge from a vessel shows that the mass flow depends on the pressure as long as the pressure ratio is such that the issuing jet is subsonic. If the external pressure falls below the so-called critical value, then it no longer exerts any influence on the mass flow. Such a sudden change in the nature of the discharge is unlikely from the physical point of view. In the following we shall find a more accurate description of the transition.

The subsonic discharge problem has already been considered earlier (cf. Fig. 27). The calculation method described at that time applies as long as the velocity of the issuing jet is subsonic or, at most, sonic. In the former case, the streamlines become parallel at a point at infinity. If the velocity of the jet is sonic, then with the aid of the asymptotic representation of CHAPLYGIN's functions [Eq. V, 6 (11a)], it may be shown that at the corresponding point the x coordinate is finite (Fig. 48). We have already seen that a sonic jet can become parallel in a finite length. The above results will help in understanding the transition from a subsonic to a supersonic jet.

The boundary value problem for a supersonic jet has been formulated by GUDERLEY [26] and by FRANKL [18, 20]. The pressure on the outer surface of the jet is again constant and is represented by a circular arc in the hodograph plane. To construct a boundary of the hodograph image, based on the subsonic problem,

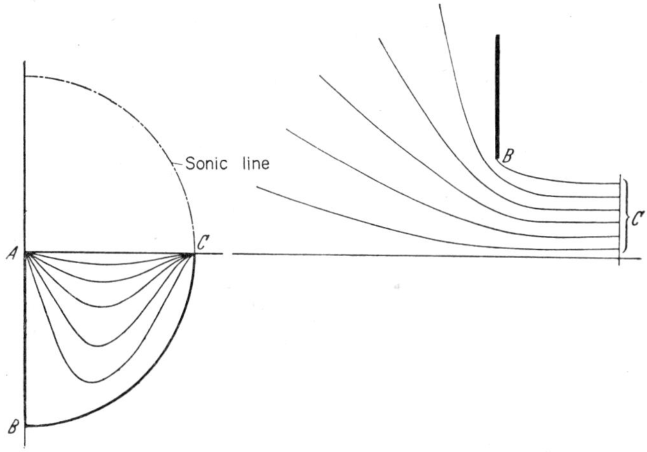

FIG. 48 Sonic discharge from a vessel. (According to GUDERLEY [26].)

(line $ABCD$ in Fig. 49) would certainly be wrong. A streamline in the vicinity of the boundary would be intersected twice by the same characteristic so that a limiting line would occur. It is physically possible, on the other hand, that the boundary coincides with a characteristic (BD_1 in Fig. 50). Then in the physical plane an expansion cone emanates from the boundary and the bounding streamline exhibits a sudden change in direction. This expansion leads to the external pressure, i.e. to the point D_1 in the hodograph plane. The original inclination of the free surface of the jet is determined by this point. The waves emanating from the corner are, of course, rarefaction waves and they are reflected as compression waves at the sonic line. If the external pressure is close to the critical one, the MACH lines are reflected several times from the sonic line and from the surface of the jet. The compression waves originating at the sonic line change into rarefaction waves upon reflection at the surface of the jet so that only the latter type of wave approaches the sonic line.

One of the MACH lines originating from the surface of the jet intersects the sonic line finally at a point on the axis of the nozzle (line D_2C in Fig. 50). The local conditions at this point are the same as in the throat of a DE LAVAL nozzle. The MACH waves located downstream of this characteristic can no longer influence the subsonic region of the flow. Thus the MACH line D_2C represents the boundary of that part of the supersonic regime which must be calculated simultaneously with the subsonic part of the flow. No boundary conditions can, of

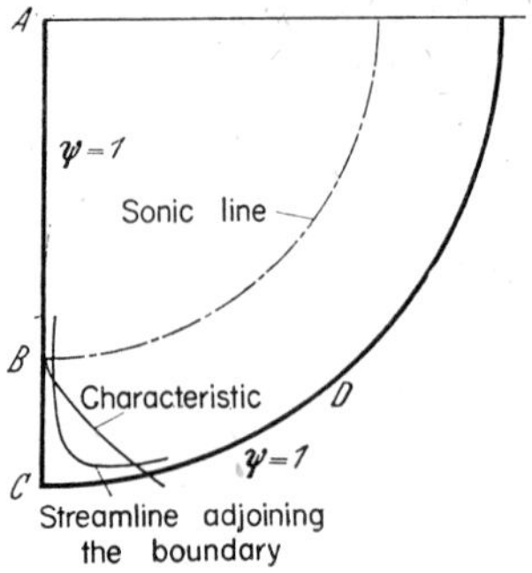

FIG. 49 Hypothetical hodograph image. (According to GUDERLEY [26]).

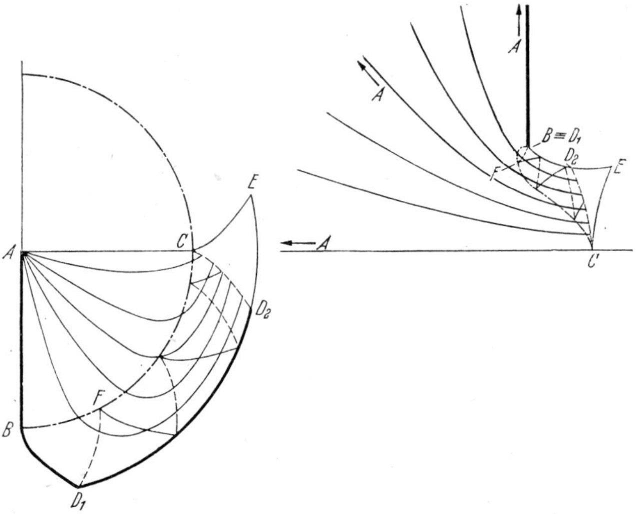

FIG. 50 Supersonic discharge from a vessel. (According to GUDERLEY [26]).

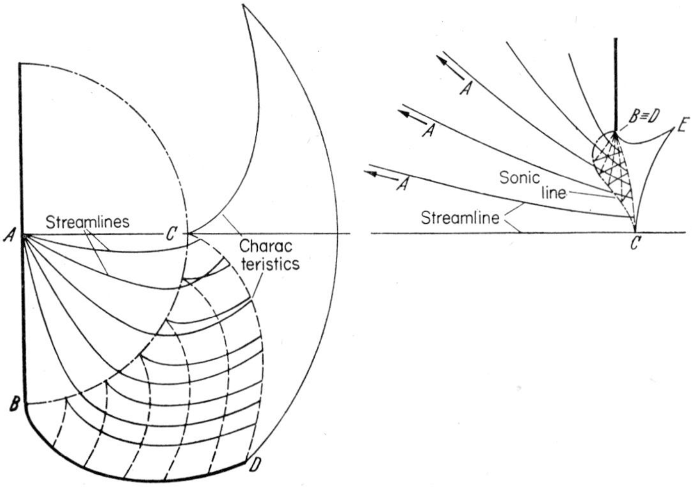

FIG. 51 Discharge from a vessel at a high subsonic velocity.

course, be prescribed along this MACH line since it runs across the jet. Thus the boundary value problem has a characteristic gap as has already been mentioned in connection with Fig. 41.

Upon further reduction in the external pressure, i.e. as the jet velocity is further increased, the hodograph remains qualitatively unchanged except that the expansion is extended further and the region, in which the MACH lines travel several times between the jet surface and the sonic line, is reduced.

Below a certain value of the external pressure only waves emanating from the original expansion fan can reach the sonic line (cf. Fig. 51). This type of boundary value problem corresponds to TRICOMI's formulation.

As long as the MACH lines, travelling from the surface of the jet, can reach the sonic line the pressure at the surface of the jet exercises an effect on the subsonic part of the flow. As a result of this the mass flow is influenced by the external pressure even at supersonic velocities. It becomes independent of the pressure only when the latter becomes so low that no waves emanating from the surface of the jet can reach the sonic line.

Up to now we have only considered the flow field which is of importance for the upstream subsonic flow. The further development of the jet is a problem in purely supersonic flow and can be handled by the method of characteristics. In this case a part of the hodograph plane consists of three sheets, as we have already seen in the case of the DE LAVAL nozzle.

Quite similar hodograph images are obtained if the walls of the vessel are inclined to one another. The smaller the angle between the walls, the smaller the MACH number of the jet at which the mass flow becomes independent of the external pressure. In the limiting case of a slender nozzle one obtains, in fact, the same result as that predicted by the simple hydraulic theory. It should be noted that the entire series of flows considered above can be developed continuously from one another. This can be seen in particular if one considers the gradual change in the shape of the sonic line or the natural manner in which the free sonic jet fits into the entire series of flow patterns.

If one of the walls of the vessel is moved in a direction normal to its plane, the hodograph image of the wall does not change. The direction of the free jet, i.e. the location of the point C, however, does change in view of the asymmetric character of the flow. For supersonic jets the gap CD_2 is displaced. This is the first example of a change in the physical plane producing a change at a completely different point in the hodograph plane.

. The Flow around a Sharp Corner

In the flows considered above we have encountered an expansion cone of the PRANDTL-MEYER type which penetrated into the subsonic region and made the transition to sonic velocity possible. At such a point there is a discontinuity in the direction of the streamline. It is well known that in the case of incompressible flow over a convex corner one obtains an infinite velocity and an infinite negative pressure. The present example indicates what one should expect in reality:

sonic velocity is reached at the corner and the pressure is reduced by an amount determined by the change in the direction of the streamline, in accordance with the equations of a PRANDTL-MEYER expansion.

It is not easy to comprehend the further particulars of the flow. If the wall downstream of the corner is, for example, flat, then the compression waves approaching from the sonic line are reflected as compression waves. These reflected compression waves travel subsequently towards the sonic line. Since they cannot reach it, in accordance with the discussion in Section I of Chapter 6, they result in a shock which then limits the supersonic region. Such a shock has been calculated by YOSHIHARA [87]. A continuation of the flow past the corner would be possible if the wall in the above example had a similar curvature to that of the surface of the free jet discussed previously, so that the compression waves emanating from the sonic line could, upon reflection, change into rarefaction waves.

A semi-analytical treatment of the flow past a corner can be undertaken with the aid of the particular solutions of Chapter VII (GUDERLEY [27]). This analysis shows that a bounding streamline which could convert compression waves to rarefaction waves would have to have an infinite curvature at the corner. Similarly, the curvature of the sonic line at the corner is infinite. In the case of a wall, which downstream of the corner is flat, the shock originates immediately at the corner; it is, however, very weak. Further downstream one obtains a rather rapid pressure increase in view of the compression waves arriving from the sonic line.

These effects are in practice obliterated by the interaction with the boundary layer. It is, in fact, possible to obtain a separation of the flow, followed very closely by a re-attachment of the boundary layer. Upstream of the corner the pressure decreases and the gradient is infinite.

A certain similarity exists between the flow described above and the suction region which occurs at high subsonic speeds near the sharp leading edge of an inclined wing.

4. Supersonic Flow past a Wedge

We have seen that shocks, occuring in parallel flow, can be easily represented in the hodograph plane and we have also encountered the supersonic flow around a wedge. Let us now consider the results of varying the angle of the wedge while the MACH number of the flow remains supersonic and constant. We shall see that the flow changes from purely supersonic, when the wedge angle is small, to the flow shown in Fig. 45.

We shall denote by Roman figures the points in the hodograph plane corresponding to a parallel supersonic velocity. For example, the undistrubed velocity of approach is indicated in Fig. 52a by I. The same notation will be used for the shock polar, e.g. shock polar I. Let us first assume the angle of the wedge to be so small that an attached shock is possible and that the velocity after the shock is supersonic (II), as shown in Fig. 52*.

* Only half of the flow field is shown in Fig. 52 so that the correspondence between the physical plane and the hodograph plane can be more clearly perceived. In addition, the hodograph plane is replaced by the η, ϑ plane.

If the angle of the wedge is allowed to increase, while the MACH number of the undisturbed flow remains constant, then the point II moves along the shock polar towards the sonic line. When the point II reaches the intersection of the sonic line and the shock polar, then the flow after the shock is sonic and parallel.

A further increase in the angle of the wedge causes the point, which up to now has been denoted by II, to move into the subsonic region. Now, however, it is no longer possible for a parallel flow to exist downstream of the shock. In view of the principles of analytic continuation, this would require the entire flow

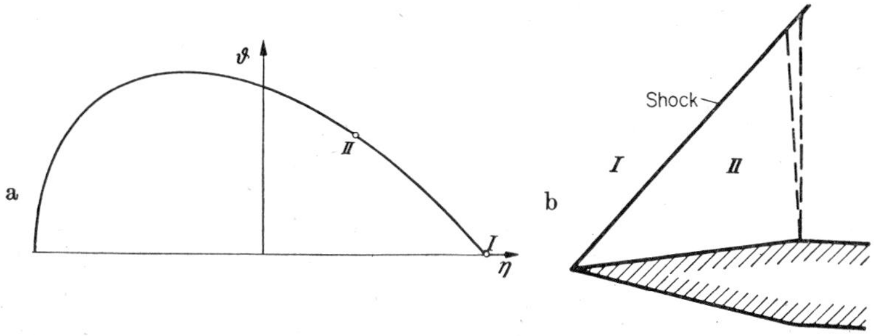

FIG. 52 Supersonic flow past a wedge. (According to GUDERLEY [26]).

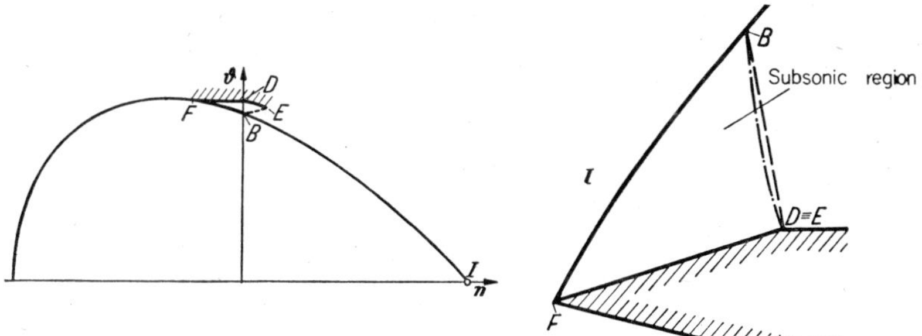

FIG. 53 Supersonic flow with an attached shock past a wedge. (According to GUDERLEY [26]).

downstream of the shock to be parallel and this is not compatible with the boundary conditions further downstream on the surface of the wedge. Thus one obtains a slightly curved shock. We know in advance that the surface of the wedge must map into a straight line, i.e. into the line FD in Fig. 53. The corner where the inclined and the horizontal faces of the wedge meet is represented by the characteristic DE in accordance with our previous experience. The subsonic regime is further limited, of course, by a section of the shock polar. As a result of this, the subsonic regime which develops along the inclined surface of the wedge is represented by the region DFB. The transition to supersonic velocities takes place through an expansion fan attached to the corner of the wedge. The sonic line extends from the corner to the shock. Some of the expansion waves originating from the corner end on the sonic line. The remaining ones, those which are of no importance as far as the subsonic regime is concerned, end at the shock.

At this point one is faced with the question, why does the sonic line originate at the corner of the wedge? This question has been answered by LIEPMANN, who showed that if the sonic line originated at a point on the inclined face of the wedge, then the position of this point, and hence the entire subsonic regime, would not be described by a characteristic length associated with the boundary value problem; therefore, the uniqueness of the solution would be lost. The following explanation goes a little further into the particulars of the flow. Moving along the sonic line from the wedge towards the shock one crosses the streamlines at an angle to the direction of flow (crossing exactly at right angles would imply the existence of a limiting line). If the direction in which the streamlines are crossed is oriented partly against the flow, then the sonic line generates compression waves which travel towards the shock. In view of this, the latter would become progressively stronger. This is in contradiction, however, to the fact that when one moves along the shock in the direction of the flow, one encounters first subsonic and then supersonic velocities. If the sonic line is oriented partly with the flow (when moving from the wedge to the shock), then the compression waves are propagated towards the sides of the wedge where they cause an increase in pressure, which is again incompatible with a transition from subsonic to supersonic velocities along the side of the wedge.

From the first argument it follows that the sonic line must have a downstream component, when moving from the profile towards the shock. From the second argument we see that the sonic line can originate only at a point of the contour of the profile at which the convex curvature is such that a decrease in pressure is possible in spite of the compression waves emanating from the sonic line.

If the angle of the wedge is increased further, the nature of the flow remains unchanged until the maximum possible angle for a compression shock is reached.

At this point we reach a new region in the hodograph plane which includes the stagnation point and we obtain the boundary value problem already indicated in Fig. 45.

The continuous series of flows obtained as a result of the above consideration lets us speculate that a similar continuous transition from one flow field to another would be obtained in an actual experiment.

5. The Analysis of the Flow near the Edge of a Wedge with an Attached Shock

We shall now describe a supplementary analysis, referring in particular to the vicinity of the leading edge of the wedge profile, i.e. to the vicinity of the point F in Fig. 53, when the shock is attached. The boundary condition is given by $\psi = 0$ along the edge and by the shock conditions [Eq. V, 11 (5)] along the shock polar. In the general case the direction of the streamline at F, prescribed by the above equation, differs from the direction of the line FD and then F in the hodograph plane is a singular point. We shall calculate the first term of the expansion which describes the solution in the vicinity of this point. In Section 14 of Chapter 7, we shall obtain the exact solutions which possess a given type of singularity at any arbitrary point of the η, ϑ plane. For an extension of the present analysis these exact solutions would be preferred. At this point we shall restrict ourselves to simpler expressions which are, however, applicable only in the immediate vicinity of F.

Let $|\eta_F|$ denote the absolute value of η and ϑ_F the value of ϑ at the point F. TRICOMI's equation can for this case be written in the form

$$\psi_{\eta\eta} + \{|\eta_F| - \eta - |\eta_F|\}\, \psi_{\vartheta\vartheta} = 0. \tag{1}$$

Let further

$$u = \sqrt{|\eta_F|}\,(\eta + |\eta_F|) \tag{2a}$$

or

$$\eta = -|\eta_F| + u\,|\eta_F|^{-1/2} \tag{2b}$$

and

$$\vartheta - \vartheta_F = v. \tag{3}$$

Hence Eq. (1) may be written

$$\frac{\partial^2 \psi}{\partial u^2} + (1 - u|\eta_F|^{-3/2})\,\frac{\partial^2 \psi}{\partial v^2} = 0.$$

The term $u\,|\eta_F|^{3/2}$ can be neglected in the immediate vicinity of $F(u = 0, v = 0)$ and the following simplified equation is obtained*

$$\frac{\partial^2 \psi}{\partial u^2} + \frac{\partial^2 \psi}{\partial v^2} = 0. \tag{4}$$

The general solution is given by

$$\psi = \operatorname{Im} F(w), \tag{5}$$

where

$$w = u + iv,$$

and F is an arbitrary analytic function of w. Re F and Im F denote the real and imaginary parts of the function F respectively. With the aid of Eq. (2b), we can calculate the values of x

$$dx = \frac{\partial x}{\partial \eta}\,d\eta + \frac{\partial x}{\partial \vartheta}\,d\vartheta = \frac{\partial x}{\partial \eta}\,|\eta_F|^{-1/2}\,du + \frac{\partial x}{\partial \vartheta}\,dv.$$

If ψ is given by Eq. (5), then for small u and v we obtain from Eq. V, 7 (8)

$$\begin{aligned} dx &= \frac{1}{\varrho^* w^*}\,(\gamma + 1)^{1/3}\,|\eta_F|^{1/2}\,(-\psi_v\,du + \psi_u\,dv) \\ &= \frac{1}{\varrho^* w^*}\,(\gamma + 1)^{1/3}\,|\eta_F|^{1/2}\,\operatorname{Im}\left(-i\,\frac{dF}{dw}\,du + \frac{dF}{dw}\,dv\right). \end{aligned}$$

Integration yields

$$x - x_0 = \frac{1}{\varrho^* w^*}\,(\gamma + 1)^{1/3}\,|\eta_F|^{1/2}\,\operatorname{Re} F(w) \tag{6}$$

* With the aid of a transformation similar to Eq. V, 6 (2) one could obtain an approximation which would be valid in a wider region and which would exhibit a similar degree of simplicity.

where x_0 denotes the integration constant. The origin of the u, v plane is at F as shown in Fig. 54, and the u axis is formed by the image of the surface of the wedge. A tangent to the shock polar is inclined at an angle ν_1 to the u axis and the direction of the streamlines on the shock polar is given by ν_2. Let us focus our attention on a point on the lower half of the shock polar in both the hodograph and the physical planes so that v in the region is positive. At this point, the shock travels from upper left to lower right. In the region between the point on the shock polar at which ϑ is a maximum and the point corresponding to sonic velocity, the angle ν_1 is positive for such shocks. The sign of ν_2, on the other hand, changes in this region. The point at which $\nu_2 = 0$ is called CROCCO's point. Between CROCCO's point and that at which the maximum value of ϑ occurs ν_2 is negative, while between the point of sonic velocity and CROCCO's point ν_2 is positive.

At F the shock polar can, in the first approximation, be replaced by its tangent. The boundary conditions require that

$$\psi = 0 \quad \text{when} \quad v = 0 \tag{7a}$$

and that for $\arctan (v/u) = \nu_1$ we have, along a line of $\psi = \text{const}$

$$\frac{dv}{du} = \tan \nu_2 . \tag{7b}$$

If

$$w = r e^{i\nu} \tag{8}$$

then from

$$\psi = \operatorname{Im} w^m \tag{9}$$

one obtains

$$\psi = r^m \sin(m\nu).$$

At $u = 0$ $\nu = 0$ and therefore the assumed solution [Eq. (9)] satisfies the first condition. Further

$$\frac{\partial \psi}{\partial u} = m \operatorname{Im} w^{m-1} = m r^{m-1} \sin[(m-1)\nu]$$

and

$$\frac{\partial \psi}{\partial v} = m \operatorname{Im}(i w^{m-1}) = m r^{m-1} \cos[(m-1)\nu].$$

Thus, on a line of $\psi = \text{const}$

$$\frac{\partial v}{\partial u} = -\frac{\partial \psi}{\partial u} \Big/ \frac{\partial \psi}{\partial v} = -\tan[(m-1)\nu].$$

This shows that the lines $\psi = \text{const}$ are inclined to the u axis at an angle $-(m-1)\nu$. On the shock polar one obtains thus the following condition

$$\nu_2 = -(m-1)\nu_1$$

from which

$$m = 1 - \frac{\nu_2}{\nu_1} .$$

The slope of the shock in the physical plane varies, to the first approximation, linearly with the distance of the point considered from F in the hodograph plane. This last distance is, also to a first approximation, proportional to r. The y co-ordinate is, in the first approximation, proportional to ψ and hence along the shock it is proportional to r^m. Thus the slope of the shock is proportional to $y^{1/m}$. The curvature of the shock is proportional to

$$\frac{1}{m}\,y^{1/m-1} = \frac{\nu_1}{\nu_1-\nu_2}\,y^{\nu_2/(\nu_1-\nu_2)}.$$

If F is located between CROCCO's point and the critical velocity, it is obvious from Fig. 54 and from the above considerations that ν_2 is positive and smaller than ν_1. When y tends to zero, i.e. when one approaches the leading edge of the wedge

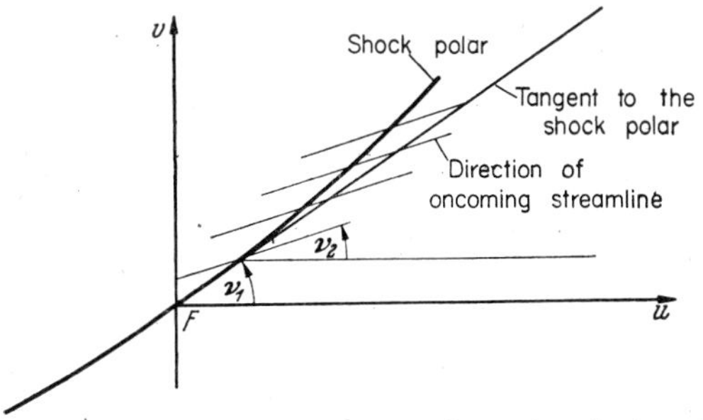

FIG. 54 Illustrating the calculation of the singularity at the point F.

along the shock, the curvature of the latter becomes zero. At CROCCO's point $\nu_2 = 0$ and the shock has a finite curvature although the curvature of the face of the wedge is zero. If F is located between CROCCO's point and the point corresponding to a maximum of $|\vartheta|$, then ν_1 and ν_2 are of opposite sign. The expression for the curvature contains a negative power of y so that the curvature at the leading edge of the wedge is infinite.

Thus if the angle of the wedge corresponds exactly to the intersection of the shock polar with the sonic line one obtains a normal shock and, downstream of the latter, a sonic velocity. If F lies between the critical velocity and CROCCO's point then, although the shock is generally curved, its curvature at the leading edge is zero. At CROCCO's point the shock has a finite non-zero curvature also at the leading edge. In the region between CROCCO's point and the point of maximum of ϑ the initial curvature of the shock is infinite. The continuous transition between these three cases is again worthy of note.

6. The Wedge with Curved Surfaces

CROCCO's discovery of the point named after him resulted from an analysis which related the initial curvature of the compression shock to the curvature of the faces of a wedge. With an initial slope of the shock corresponding to CROCCO's point his analysis has shown that for a finite curvature of the surfaces the initial curvature of the shock must be infinite. For larger included angles of the wedge, which still, however, permit the existence of an attached shock, the curvature of the latter was found to be opposite in sign to the curvature of the face. Since this appeared nonsensical from the physical point of view, the question arose as to whether the shock does not already become detached at CROCCO's point. CROCCO's solution corresponds in the hodograph plane to the expression

$$\psi = r \sin(\nu - \nu_2).$$

It is easy to show that for each line of $\psi = \text{const}$

$$\frac{dv}{du} = \tan \nu_2,$$

so that the condition along the shock polar is satisfied. The boundary streamline $\psi = 0$ is given by $\nu = \nu_2$. Along this streamline the inclination of the velocity vector can be expressed as

$$\vartheta = \vartheta_F + r \sin \nu_2.$$

Since the present solution is regular at F, the length of the boundary streamline in the physical plane is proportional to the distance in the hodograph plane of the point considered from F, i.e. it is proportional to r. Thus the curvature of the boundary streamline becomes proportional to $\sin \nu_2$. We require further the curvature of the compression shock. The direction of the latter is, in the physical plane, proportional to r (measured along the shock polar), in the first approximation. The length of the compression shock, measured from the leading edge, is proportional to y, i.e. to $r \sin(\nu_1 - \nu_2)$. Thus the ratio of the curvature of the shock to that of the boundary streamline is proportional to

$$(\sin \nu_2)^{-1} \sin(\nu_1 - \nu_2)^{-1}. \tag{1}$$

This expression becomes infinite at CROCCO's point and at the same time changes its sign. We have already found that the zero curvature of the face of the wedge results in a finite curvature of the shock.

The above solution in the region between the critical velocity and CROCCO's point is easily understood. The situation is more difficult, however, if F is located between CROCCO's point and that corresponding to a maximum value of ϑ. Moving along a boundary streamline from F towards the sonic line the slope of the streamline increases so that the contour is concave. One would expect that the solution for concave contours would not differ substantially from that for a wedge with plane faces. The flow in the vicinity of F may, in fact, be obtained by adding a correction term which accounts for the curvature of the faces to the solution corresponding to a wedge with plane faces. The resulting solution takes the form of a series expansion in powers of $w^{-\nu_2/\nu_1}$. In the expression given below, the first term originates from the solution for a wedge with plane faces, while the second term is due to the curvature (GUDERLEY [26]).

$$\psi = \text{Im}\left(C w^{1-\nu_2/\nu_1}\left[1 - w^{-\nu_2/\nu_1} K C \frac{\nu_1 - \nu_2}{\nu_1 \sin \nu_2} e^{i\nu_2}\right]\right) \tag{2}$$

where K and C are constants. Differentiation yields

$$\frac{\partial \psi}{\partial u} = \frac{\nu_1 - \nu_2}{\nu_1} C \operatorname{Im} \left[w^{-\nu_2/\nu_1} - w^{-2\nu_2/\nu_1} K C \frac{1 - 2\frac{\nu_2}{\nu_1}}{\sin \nu_2} e^{i\nu_2} \right],$$

$$\frac{\partial \psi}{\partial v} = \frac{\nu_1 - \nu_2}{\nu_1} C \operatorname{Im} i \left[w^{-\nu_2/\nu_1} - w^{-2\nu_2/\nu_1} K C \frac{1 - 2\frac{\nu_2}{\nu_1}}{\sin \nu_2} e^{i\nu_2} \right].$$

With the aid of Eq. VI, 5 (8) we obtain for the derivative along a streamline

$$\frac{du}{dv} = \frac{-r^{-\nu_2/\nu_1}\left\{-\sin\left(\frac{\nu_2}{\nu_1}\nu\right) - K C r^{-\nu_2/\nu_1} \frac{1 - 2\frac{\nu_2}{\nu_1}}{\sin \nu_2} \sin\left(\nu_2 - 2\frac{\nu_2}{\nu_1}\nu\right)\right\}}{r^{-\nu_2/\nu_1}\left\{\cos\left(\frac{\nu_2}{\nu_1}\nu\right) - K C r^{-\nu_2/\nu_1} \frac{1 - 2\frac{\nu_2}{\nu_1}}{\sin \nu_2} \cos\left(\nu_2 - 2\frac{\nu_2}{\nu_1}\nu\right)\right\}}.$$

On the shock polar the condition of Eq. VI, 5 (7b) must be satisfied. In fact the above equation yields for $\nu = \nu_1$

$$\frac{du}{dv} = \frac{\sin \nu_2}{\cos \nu_2} \frac{1 - K C r^{-\nu_2/\nu_1} \frac{1 - 2\frac{\nu_2}{\nu_1}}{\sin \nu_2}}{1 - K C r^{-\nu_2/\nu_1} \frac{1 - 2\frac{\nu_2}{\nu_1}}{\sin \nu_2}} = \tan \nu_2 .$$

To obtain the equation of the line $\psi = 0$, Eq. (2) must be put into a real form

$$\psi = C r^{\frac{\nu_1 - \nu_2}{\nu_1}} \left\{ \sin\left(\frac{\nu_1 - \nu_2}{\nu_1}\nu\right) - \right.$$

$$\left. - r^{-\nu_2/\nu_1} K C \frac{\nu_1 - \nu_2}{\nu_1 \sin \nu_2} \sin\left[\left(1 - 2\frac{\nu_2}{\nu_1}\right)\nu + \nu_2\right]\right\} = 0$$

so that from the terms of lowest order in $r^{-\nu_2/\nu_1}$ one obtains

$$\nu = 0 .$$

An improved result, obtained by an iteration procedure, is

$$\nu = K C r^{-\nu_2/\nu_1} .$$

The deviation of the direction of the streamline from that at F is given by

$$v = \nu r = K C r^{1 - \nu_2/\nu_1} . \tag{3}$$

The length of a streamline measured from F is given by an expression proportional to the real part of $F(w)$ in accordance with Eq. VI, 5 (6). This expression, to the lowest order in $r^{-\nu_2/\nu_1}$ is

$$x - x_F \sim C r^{1-\nu_2/\nu_1} \cos\left\{\left(1 - \frac{\nu_2}{\nu_1}\right) K C r^{-\nu_2/\nu_1}\right\}.$$

If $r^{-\nu_2/\nu_1}$ is small, then the cosine can be replaced by 1 and one obtains

$$x - x_F \sim C r^{1-\nu_2/\nu_1}. \tag{4}$$

Equations (3) and (4) show that the curvature of the surface at F has a finite non-zero value. The assumed form of solution given by Eq. (2) fails between CROCCO's point and the critical velocity since then $r^{-\nu_2/\nu_1}$ is a negative power or r. Also at CROCCO's point this solution cannot be used. This case was also discussed by GUDERLEY [26].

We can now see why CROCCO's solution is not applicable between CROCCO's point and that of maximum of ϑ. In this region the dominating part of the solution at F is that due to the wedge with flat surfaces while the curvature of the surface produces a higher order effect. Between CROCCO's point and the sonic velocity the curvature of the faces exerts a dominating influence so that CROCCO's solution, which tacitly assumes this, is justified.

7. Transition from an Attached to a Detached Shock

The transition from a shock attached to the leading edge of the wedge to a detached shock appears to introduce such a radical change in the flow field that one would expect quite abrupt changes in flow characteristics such as the drag. The analysis of this transition is, therefore, of particular interest.

Let us first determine the approximate solution of TRICOMI's equation which is valid in the vicinity of the maximum of ϑ on the shock polar. Let us consider this point to be the origin of a system of coordinates with axes of u and v, there being no connection between these variables and the similarly denoted variables of the preceding section. Putting for the velocity upstream of the shock $\eta = 1$, Eq. V, 11 (2) yields at the point of maximum of ϑ

$$\eta = -\frac{1}{3}, \quad \vartheta = \pm\frac{4}{\sqrt{27}}. \tag{1}$$

The coordinates u and v are then given by

$$u = \eta + \tfrac{1}{3}, \tag{2a}$$

$$v = \vartheta \mp \frac{4}{\sqrt{27}}. \tag{2b}$$

Along the shock v is a function of u which we can express by writing $v_s(u)$. For small values of u the equation of the shock polar [Eq. V, 11 (2)] yields

$$v_s = \mp\frac{\sqrt{27}}{8} u^2. \tag{3}$$

The hodograph equation takes the form

$$\psi_{uu} + (\tfrac{1}{3} - u)\,\psi_{vv} = 0 \tag{4}$$

and the boundary condition on the shock polar is given by

$$\frac{\partial \psi}{\partial u} \pm \sqrt{\frac{1}{3}}\left(1 - \frac{33}{4}u\right)\frac{\partial \psi}{\partial v} = 0. \tag{5}$$

Let the angle of the wedge exceed the maximum value of ϑ possible along the shock polar by an amount c. Let us consider the lower half of the shock polar since then v is positive. We now look for a solution of TRICOMI's equation in the form of Eq. (4) which satisfies the following boundary conditions, which correspond to Fig. 55. At $v = -c$

$$\psi = 0 \tag{6a}$$

while at

$$v = v_s = \frac{\sqrt{27}}{8}u^2,$$

$$\frac{\partial \psi}{\partial u} - \sqrt{\frac{1}{3}}\left(1 - \frac{33}{4}u\right)\frac{\partial \psi}{\partial v} = 0. \tag{6b}$$

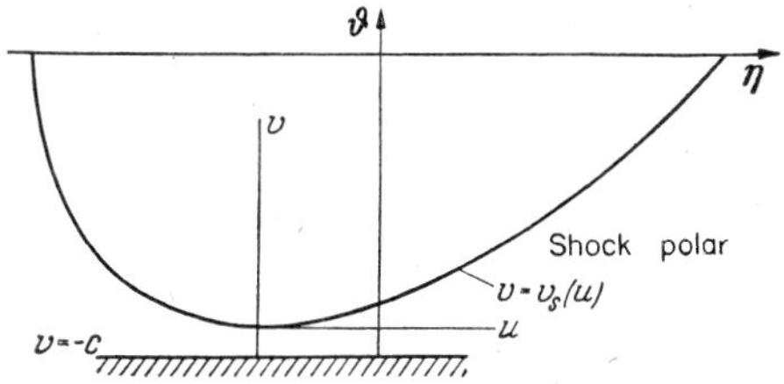

FIG. 55 Illustrating the calculation of the flow in the vicinity of the point $u = 0$, $v = 0$.

The solutions derived below are valid for small values of c or, more precisely, for values of c of the order of magnitude of v_s or of u^2. The assumed form of the solution is based on the following considerations. If c is chosen progressively smaller and if the scale of measurement of u and v is changed simultaneously so that, in terms of the new coordinates, the distance between the shock polar and the boundary streamline at F remains constant, then one obtains the family of configurations in which the changes in the distance between the shock polar and the image of the wall decrease as c becomes smaller. One would thus expect that the solution is very similar to that obtained for a constant distance between the two boundaries. Solutions which satisfy the differential equations and the boundary conditions at the point of minimum distance are given by

$$\psi = \exp\left[3^{-1/2}\pi\left(\frac{1}{4} + n\right)c^{-1}u\right]\sin\left[\pi\left(n + \frac{1}{4}\right)\left(1 + \frac{v}{c}\right)\right],$$

where n is an integer. We shall now attempt to modify this expression so that it retains its validity, at least approximately, at a finite distance from the throat. If one were to consider a position other than that of minimum distance between boundaries and assumed the distance occuring there to be constant, the solution would be

$$\psi = \exp\left[3^{-1/2}\pi\left(\frac{1}{4} + n\right)\bar{c}^{-1}u\right]\sin\left[\pi\left(n + \frac{1}{4}\right)\frac{c + v}{\bar{c}}\right], \tag{7}$$

where

$$\bar{c} = c + \frac{\sqrt{27}}{8} u^2 .$$

The distance between the two boundaries is here given by $\bar{c}$ and is considered constant. This distance is in reality variable. If its changes are, however, small in comparison to a length, measured in the direction of u, in which the exponential function changes by a significant amount, then the correct solution should not differ much from the expressions given above. Thus the condition for the validity of the following solutions is

$$\frac{d\bar{c}}{du} \ll \bar{c}^{-1} n \quad \text{or} \quad \frac{\sqrt{27}}{4} u \ll \frac{n}{c + \frac{\sqrt{27}}{8} u^2}, \tag{8}$$

where the LHS denotes the derivative of the distance between the two boundaries with respect to u while the RHS represents approximately the derivative of the exponential function with respect to u. The following expression, which differs from Eq. (7) particularly as regards the form of the first term, is especially useful for the approximate representation of the solution

$$\psi = \exp\left[3^{-1/2} \pi \left(\frac{1}{4} + n\right) \int \bar{c}^{-1}(u)\, du\right] \sin\left[\pi \left(n + \frac{1}{4}\right) \frac{c + v}{\bar{c}(u)}\right]. \tag{9}$$

This expression need not, as yet, represent the actual solution. Although the terms of lowest order in a series expansion of the differential equation in terms of u are immediately eliminated, this would also be true if they were to be multiplied by an arbitrary function $h(u)$, e.g. by a power of $\bar{c}$. Since this factor can change substantially for small values of u, the solution given by Eq. (9) need not be even approximately correct. It is evidently insufficient to consider only the terms of lowest order in the differential equation even if only the first term of an approximate solution is desired. The correctness of this first term is assured only if terms of next highest order are included in the differential equation. To this end, the expression of Eq. (9) must be extended. It has been shown in a different connection (cf. GUDERLEY [25]) that this extension can in general be performed quite systematically. BUSEMANN in a similar problem has guessed the term of the next order (cf. BUSEMANN and GUDERLEY [5]). This can also be done in the present case so that the extended solution is given without derivation and its correctness will then be verified*. Let

$$\bar{v} = \pi \left(n + \frac{1}{4}\right) \frac{c + v}{c + \frac{\sqrt{27}}{8} u^2} \tag{10a}$$

* One may validly object that this is only a formal development. The engineer will consider this fact as urging caution but will not be deterred from employing the solution.

and

$$\bar{\lambda} = 3^{-1/2}\pi\left(n + \frac{1}{4}\right)\left(c + \frac{\sqrt{27}}{8}u^2\right)^{-1}. \tag{10b}$$

We have previously shown that $c = 0(u^2)$ so that

$$\bar{\lambda} = 0(u^{-2}). \tag{10c}$$

Then the solution takes the form

$$\psi = \bar{\lambda}^m \exp\left(\int \bar{\lambda}\, du\right)\{\sin\bar{v} + u(a_1\bar{v}\cos\bar{v} + a_2\bar{v}^2\sin\bar{v})\}. \tag{11}$$

The first term corresponds to the previous expression. Along the image of the wall, i.e. when $v = -c$, $\bar{v} = 0$; along the shock polar $\bar{v} = 1$. The term $\bar{\lambda}$ is inversely proportional to the width of the cross-section and the constants m, a_1 and a_2 are given by

$$m = \tfrac{1}{2} + \tfrac{2}{3}\pi(n + \tfrac{1}{4}), \tag{12a}$$

$$a_1 = -\tfrac{9}{8}[\pi(n + \tfrac{1}{4})]^{-1}, \tag{12b}$$

$$a_2 = \tfrac{9}{8}[\pi(n + \tfrac{1}{4})]^{-1}. \tag{12c}$$

We must show next that the expression given in Eq. (11) satisfies the differential equation and the boundary conditions. Differentiation yields

$$\frac{d\bar{\lambda}}{du} = -\frac{9}{4}\frac{u\bar{\lambda}^2}{\pi(n + \frac{1}{4})}, \tag{13a}$$

$$\frac{d\bar{v}}{dv} = \sqrt{3}\,\bar{\lambda}, \tag{13b}$$

$$\frac{d\bar{v}}{du} = -\frac{9}{4}u\frac{\bar{\lambda}\bar{v}}{\pi(n + \frac{1}{4})}, \tag{13c}$$

so that

$$\frac{\partial\psi}{\partial v} = \bar{\lambda}^m \exp\left[\int\bar{\lambda}\, du\right]\sqrt{3}\times$$
$$\times\,\bar{\lambda}\{\cos\bar{v} + u[a_1(\cos\bar{v} - \bar{v}\sin\bar{v}) + a_2[2\bar{v}\sin\bar{v} + \bar{v}^2\cos\bar{v}]\}, \tag{14a}$$

$$\frac{\partial^2\psi}{\partial v^2} = \bar{\lambda}^m \exp\left[\int\bar{\lambda}\, du\right]3\bar{\lambda}\{-\sin\bar{v} +$$
$$+\, u[a_1(-2\sin\bar{v} - \bar{v}\cos\bar{v})] + a_2[4\bar{v}\cos\bar{v} + 2\sin\bar{v} - \bar{v}^2\sin\bar{v}]\}. \tag{14b}$$

For the derivatives with respect to u we introduce now the terms of the two lowest orders so that, recalling Eq. (10c),

$$\frac{\partial\psi}{\partial u} = \bar{\lambda}^m \exp\left[\int\bar{\lambda}\, du\right]\bar{\lambda}\left\{\sin\bar{v} + u\left[a_1\bar{v}\cos\bar{v} + a_2\bar{v}^2\sin\bar{v} -\right.\right.$$
$$\left.\left. - \frac{9}{4}\frac{m}{\pi(n + \frac{1}{4})}\sin\bar{v} - \frac{9}{4}\frac{\bar{v}}{\pi(n + \frac{1}{4})}\cos\bar{v}\right]\right\}, \tag{15a}$$

$$\frac{\partial^2 \psi}{\partial u^2} = \bar{\lambda}^m \exp\left[\int \bar{\lambda}\, du\right] \bar{\lambda}^2 \left\{ \sin \bar{v} + u \left[a_1 \bar{v} \cos \bar{v} + a_2 \bar{v}^2 \sin v - \right.\right.$$

$$\left.\left. - \frac{9}{4} \frac{(2m+1)}{\pi(n+\frac{1}{4})} \sin \bar{v} - \frac{9}{4} \frac{1}{\pi(n+\frac{1}{4})} \bar{v} \cos \bar{v} \right] \right\}. \tag{15b}$$

Introducing this into the differential equation (4) the factor $\bar{\lambda}^m \exp\left[\int \bar{\lambda}\, du\right]$ cancels out. The terms of lowest order in u, as well as some terms of the next higher order, also cancel. We are left with

$$-\frac{9}{4} \frac{2m+1}{\pi(n+\frac{1}{4})} \sin \bar{v} - \frac{9}{4} \frac{1}{\pi(n+\frac{1}{4})} \bar{v} \cos \bar{v} - 2a_1 \sin \bar{v} + 4a_2 \bar{v} \cos \bar{v} +$$

$$+ 2a_2 \sin \bar{v} + 3 \sin \bar{v},$$

which vanishes because of Eq. (12).

Since at $v = -c$ the variable $\bar{v}$ is zero, it may be seen immediately that the boundary condition given by Eq. (6a) is satisfied. For $v = v_s$ we have in accordance with Eqs. (6b) and (10a) $\bar{v} = \pi(n + \frac{1}{4})$ which results in

$$\sin \bar{v} = \cos \bar{v}.$$

Substituting Eqs. (14a) and (15a) in Eq. (6b), and noting the above result, the terms of lowest order in u can be immediately canceeled. The terms of the next highest order vanish as a result Eq. (12).

The terms of the orders occuring in Eq. (11) are not fully determined since the expression

$$u \exp\left[\int \bar{\lambda}\, du\right] \sin \bar{v},$$

would introduce an error of an order higher than those considered up to now in both the differential equation and in the boundary condition. It is therefore useless to include in the result the terms of order u. Thus the approximate solution takes the form

$$\psi = \bar{\lambda}^m \exp\left[\int \bar{\lambda}\, du\right] \sin \bar{v}$$

and omitting a constant

$$\psi = \left(c + \frac{\sqrt{27}}{8} u^2\right)^{-\left(\frac{1}{2} + \frac{2}{3}\pi\left(n + \frac{1}{4}\right)\right)} \times$$

$$\times \exp\left[\pi\left(n + \frac{1}{4}\right) 3^{-\frac{1}{2}} \int \left(c + \frac{\sqrt{27}}{8} u^2\right)^{-1} du\right] \times$$

$$\times \sin\left[\pi\left(n + \frac{1}{4}\right) \frac{c + v}{c + \frac{\sqrt{27}}{8} u^2}\right]. \tag{16}$$

The exponential term is here of particular importance. The sign of the exponent depends on that of n. Thus both solutions which increase exponentially with u and which decrease exponentially with u are possible. If $c = 0$, i.e. if in Fig. 54 one considers the neighborhood of the point F, and when the angle of the wedge is equal to the maximum angle occuring on the shock polar then the particular solutions are given by

$$\psi = u^{-1-\frac{4}{3}\pi\left(n+\frac{1}{4}\right)} \exp\left[-\pi\left(n+\frac{1}{4}\right)\frac{8}{9}u^{-1}\right] \sin\left[\pi\left(n+\frac{1}{4}\right)\frac{v}{\frac{\sqrt{27}}{8}u^2}\right] \qquad (16\text{a})$$

except for an unimportant constant. Since ψ cannot for physical reasons become infinite at F, only non-negative values of n are admissible. The solution of Eq. (16a) replaces then the particular solution given by Eq. VI, 5 (9). Let now c be different from zero and let us investigate the behaviour of the hodograph solution as c varies. Since the solution cannot be given explicitly, the argument must unavoidably remain fairly abstract.

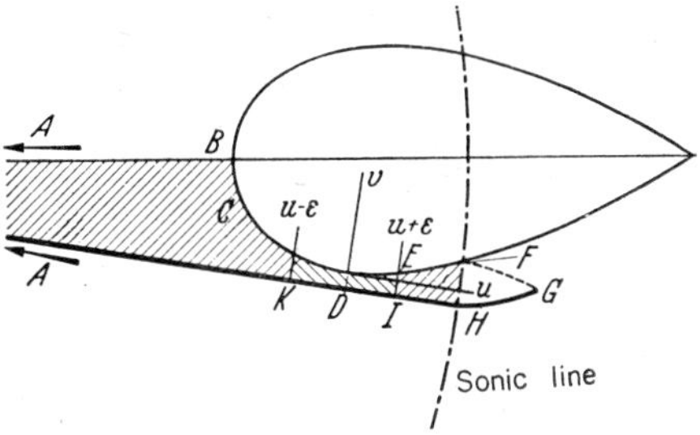

FIG. 56 Transition from a detached to an attached shock.

In Fig. 56 we choose two points $u = -\varepsilon$ and $u = +\varepsilon$ located so close to the narrowest section that between them the solution for ψ can be expressed as by means of superposition of the particular solutions calculated above. Along the line $u = \varepsilon$ the solution of the boundary value problem for $c = 0$ is certainly different from zero. We assume further that the solution varies continuously with c so that for small values of c the solution along this line differs only by a small amount from that corresponding to $c = 0$. We shall try next to establish a relationship between the solution for $u = \varepsilon$ and that in the region $ABCK$. This latter solution is determined by the values of ψ for $u = \varepsilon$ and by the known boundary conditions for the region $ECBAKDI$.

We obtain first (in principle) a family of particular solutions which satisfy the boundary conditions along $ECBAKI$ and which assume the value

$$\sin\left[\pi\left(n+\frac{1}{4}\right)\frac{c+v}{c+\frac{\sqrt{27}}{8}\varepsilon^2}\right]$$

for non-negative values of n along $u = \varepsilon$. This last expression agrees with our particular solutions given by Eq. (16) for the case of $u = \varepsilon$ except for a multiplying factor. With the aid of the above system the solution in the region $ECBAKI$ can be found by expanding ψ along $u = \varepsilon$ in terms of these particular solutions. That our present system is sufficient to establish such a solution may be seen intuitively by comparison with the system

$$\sin\left[\pi\left(n+\frac{1}{2}\right)\frac{c+v}{c+\frac{\sqrt{27}}{8}\varepsilon^2}\right]$$

for which a proof of completeness follows from theory of FOURIER Series or from the theory of eigenvalue problems. Our present system is very similar to the above.

The particular solutions required can be obtained as follows. We start with a solution $\overline{\psi}_n$ which along $u = -\varepsilon$ exhibits a jump both in the value of the function and in the value of the derivative. In the region $KCBAK$ $\overline{\psi}_n \equiv 0$ while in the region $-\varepsilon < u < \varepsilon$ it is given by

$$\overline{\psi}_n = \left[\frac{c+\frac{\sqrt{27}}{8}u^2}{c+\frac{\sqrt{27}}{8}\varepsilon^2}\right]^{-\left(\frac{1}{2}+\frac{2}{3}\pi\left(n+\frac{1}{4}\right)\right)} \times$$

$$\times \exp\left[\pi\left(n+\frac{1}{4}\right)3^{-\frac{1}{2}}\int_{\varepsilon}^{u}\left[c+\frac{\sqrt{27}}{8}u^2\right]^{-1}du\right] \times$$

$$\times \sin\left[\pi\left(n+\frac{1}{4}\right)\frac{c+v}{c+\frac{\sqrt{27}}{8}u^2}\right].$$

This is again one of the solutions given by Eq. (16) except for a multiplying factor. The jump or discontinuity of $\overline{\psi}_n$ occuring along $u = -\varepsilon$ is thus

$$\Delta\overline{\psi}_n = \exp\left[-\pi\left(n+\frac{1}{4}\right)3^{-1/2}\int_{-\varepsilon}^{\varepsilon}\left[c+\frac{\sqrt{27}}{8}u^2\right]^{-1}du\right] \times$$

$$\times \sin\left[\pi\left(n+\frac{1}{4}\right)\frac{c+v}{c+\frac{\sqrt{27}}{8}\varepsilon^2}\right].$$

A similar expression results for the derivative with respect to η. The order of magnitude of these jumps is

$$O\left\{\exp\left[-\pi\left(n+\frac{1}{4}\right)3^{-1/2}\int_{-\varepsilon}^{\varepsilon}\left[c+\frac{\sqrt{27}}{8}u^2\right]^{-1}du\right]\right\}$$

$$= O\left\{\exp\left[-\frac{\pi\left(n+\frac{1}{4}\right)}{\sqrt{c}}\,\frac{2}{3}\sqrt[4]{\frac{4}{3}}\,2\arctan\frac{\sqrt[4]{27}}{\sqrt{8}}\,\varepsilon\right]\right\}.$$

Since

$$\lim_{c \to 0} 2 \arctan \frac{\sqrt[4]{27}}{\sqrt{8c}} \varepsilon = \pi$$

we obtain, after some calculation, for small values of c the following expression for the order of magnitude of the discontinuity

$$O\left\{\exp\left[-\pi^2\left(n+\frac{1}{4}\right)\frac{2}{3}\sqrt[4]{\frac{4}{3}}\frac{1}{\sqrt{c}}\right]\right\}.$$

We now superimpose on $\overline{\psi}_n$ another solution $\overline{\psi}'_n$ which satisfies the boundary conditions along $ECBAKI$ and such that $\overline{\psi}' = 0$ along EJ and which, finally, has the same jumps in its value and in its derivative along the line $u = -\varepsilon$ as $\overline{\psi}_n$ except for an opposite sign. The uniqueness of such a solution can be shown by FRANKL's method, while the solution itself could also be obtained by the superposition of singularities along the boundary with the aid of an integral equation. Of importance is the fact that the solution is proportional to the inhomogeneous quantities by which it is determined. These are the jumps in $\overline{\psi}_n$ and $\partial \overline{\psi}_n / \partial u$ which occur in the first part of the solution so that the second part of the solution must be of the order

$$O\left\{\exp\left[-\pi^2\left(n+\frac{1}{4}\right)\frac{2}{3}\sqrt[4]{\frac{4}{3}}\frac{1}{\sqrt{c}}\right]\right\}.$$

In the region $u < -\varepsilon$ this last expression forms, however, the sole contribution to the solution, i.e. the particular solutions are in that region of the above order of magnitude. Let us now express ψ, for $c = 0$, along the line $u = \varepsilon$ by

$$\psi = \sum_{n=0}^{\infty} a_n \sin\left[\pi\left(n+\frac{1}{4}\right)\frac{c+v}{c+\frac{\sqrt{27}}{8}\varepsilon^2}\right].$$

In view of the continuous dependence of the solution on c this is also an approximation valid for small values of c. Then the solution in the region $ECBAKI$ takes the form

$$\psi = \sum_{n=0}^{\infty} a_n O\left\{\exp\left[-\pi^2\left(n+\frac{1}{4}\right)\frac{2}{3}\sqrt[4]{\frac{4}{3}}\frac{1}{\sqrt{c}}\right]\right\}.$$

The first term predominates for sufficiently small values of c so that the solution for such cases is

$$\psi = a_0 O\left\{\exp\left[-\frac{\pi^2}{6}\sqrt[4]{\frac{4}{3}}\frac{1}{\sqrt{c}}\right]\right\}.$$

The image of the length AB gives the distance of the shock from the leading edge. The order of magnitude of this distance is expressed in terms of c by the last equation. It is a function which vanishes together with all of its derivatives for $c = 0$. Thus the transition from an attached shock to a detached one is completely continuous.

8. Forked Shocks

The situation in which two compression shocks intersect one another is well known in supersonic flow from solutions obtained by means of the method of characteristics. Under such conditions from the point of intersection of the two shocks there either are propagated two new shocks or one shock and an expansion fan. If downstream of the point of intersection the velocity is subsonic then, although the conditions at the shock can be formulated mathematically (WEISE [82], EGGINK [13]), the role of such shocks in the flow is not at all clear. These difficulties can be resolved by the hodograph representation.

A typical case in which a subsonic field can occur results in the outflow of a parallel supersonic jet into a region of higher pressure. Let the state of the

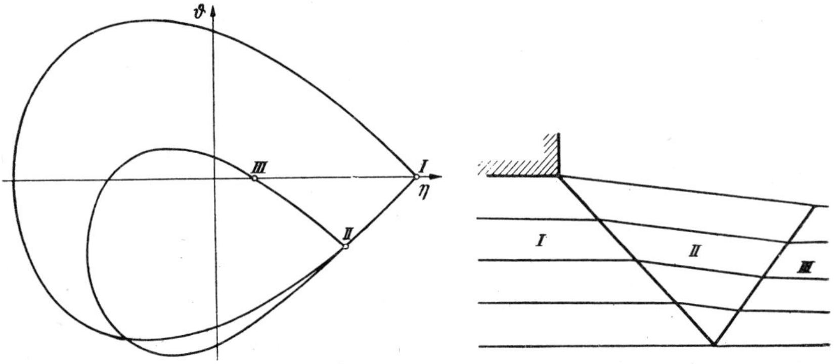

FIG. 57 A supersonic jet issuing against excess pressure. (According to GUDERLEY [26]). A purely supersonic problem.

original jet correspond to the point I in the hodograph, as shown in Fig. 57, and let a velocity be associated with the external pressure and let it be represented by the line η = const passing through the point II. The shock polar through I represents the locus of all states which can be reached from I across a shock. Since in the upper half of the hodograph plane the shock is evidently propagated from the orifice downwards, the state after the shock must be located in the lower half of the hodograph. This shock reaches the axis of the jet which, because of symmetry, may be regarded as a rigid wall. Along this wall we then have the condition that the velocity vector must be horizontal. One would expect that this boundary condition is reached through a second shock which forms the downstream boundary of the region in which the state corresponds to II. The shock polar passing through II is the locus of the states which can be reached from the state II. If the external pressure is fairly low, then the second shock polar intersects the axis $\vartheta = 0$ at a point in the supersonic region. This point of intersection is denoted by III and it corresponds to the state after the second shock. This simple supersonic flow problem will form the starting point for our considerations.

When the external pressure increases the points II and III move towards lower velocities. The flow remains unchanged, in principle, until the point III crosses the sonic line, as shown in Fig. 58. When this happens the entire flow downstream of the second shock can no longer correspond to the state III since the only continuation of such a flow is a parallel one and this does not satisfy the boundary conditions at the boundary of the jet. At the boundary one must obtain, in any case, an expansion leading to the prescribed value of the external pressure, i.e. to the value of η which corresponds to II. Such an expansion at the boundary of the jet can be imagined if, after the second shock, the velocity at the boundary is sonic. It is not possible for the velocity to become sonic

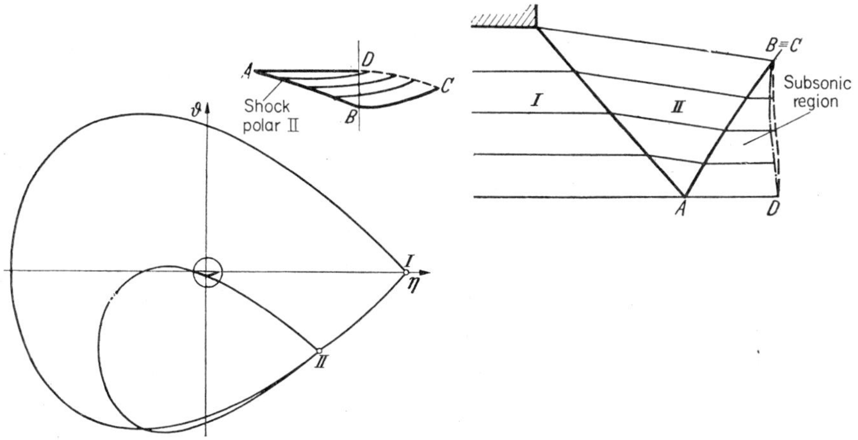

FIG. 58 A supersonic jet issuing against low pressure. A subsonic region forms downstream of the second shock. (According to GUDERLEY [26]).

after the second shock before reaching the boundary of the jet, since then one would obtain, downstream of the shock, a sonic line which would naturally originate at this shock. The compression waves emanating from the sonic line would end at the shock and would cause an increase in pressure. Such an increase in pressure would contradict the assumption that, when one moves downstream along a shock, a transition from subsonic to supersonic flow takes place.

The expansion waves originating at the intersection of the shock with the boundary of the jet are propagated in the direction opposite to that of the shock. Since they are not propagated upstream they do not directly influence the shock. Indirectly, however, the shock is, of course, determined by the expansion fan, namely, by the subsonic regime between the shock and the fan itself.

These considerations explain the hodograph image of this part of the flow field. One should still investigate the orientation of corresponding surface elements in the hodograph and physical planes. A discussion, similar to that presented with reference to a shock attached to a wedge, can be made with reference to the shape of the shock at the point A (originally denoted by III). The curvature of the shock at A is zero if this point is located between CROCCO's point and the critical velocity, it is finite at the CROCCO's point and finally infinite between CROCCO's point and that of the maximum of ϑ on the shock polar II.

If the shock polar II no longer intersects the ϑ axis, we have a situation similar to that occuring in the detachment of a compression shock from the leading edge of a wedge, i.e. a new region of the hodograph plane is reached, as shown in Fig. 59.

To visualise the corresponding flow field we assume that both the shock polars have an intersection point in the subsonic regime. The streamline located on the axis originates in Fig. 59 from the point E, i.e. from a point which can be reached by a normal shock located in the region I. Moving along the shock one crosses all states which correspond to points lying between E and F. From F on-

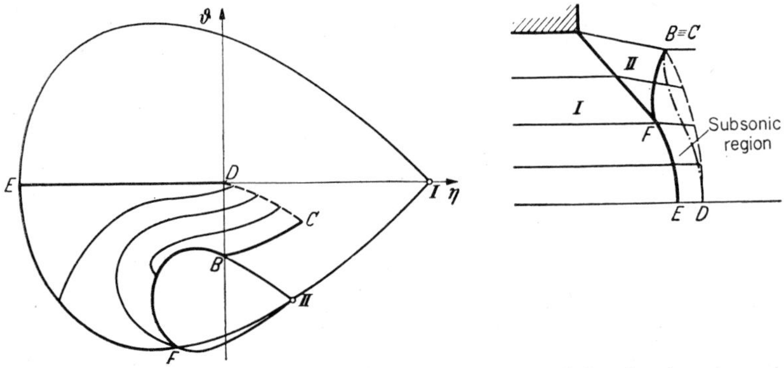

FIG. 59 Supersonic jet issuing against high pressure. A local subsonic region occurs at the reflection of the shock. (According to GUDERLEY [26]).

wards the shock polar of the region II represents the boundary of the subsonic regime. The streamline passing through F separates the streamlines which have crossed only one shock in the region I from those which also pass through another compression shock II. Along this boundary the direction of the velocity and the pressure in the flow on both sides of it must be the same. Since changes in entropy can be neglected in transonic flows, this implies a continuity of the velocity vector. The point F is the only one in the hodograph plane which is located immediately after the shock and in which the equality of the two flow fields is possible. Moving now along the shock polar II one reaches the boundary of the jet at the point B where the velocity has the critical value. It is noteworthy that the boundary of the subsonic regime consists of a segment of the shock polar II which is located partly above and partly below the axis of symmetry. With reference to the streamlines, the shock is therefore propagated partly to the left and partly to the right. This may appear strange if one recalls a rule of supersonic aerodynamics which states that a disturbance can never be propagated upstream. In the present example one would be tempted to consider the point F as the origin of the disturbance. If one reflects, however, that the flow downstream of the shock is subsonic one must conclude that the term "propagation of disturbances" is completely inapplicable in this connection. This is particularly true since, in order to deflect the flow in the vicinity of the axis of the jet, a subsonic pressure field must be generated which maintains the shock in the upstream supersonic region. As a result of this one finds that a part of the compression shock II runs upstream if one moves from the point A towards the boundary of the jet. Actual experimental observations of this behaviour are unknown to the author. If a more accurate picture of the flow in the vicinity of F were desired, in order to allow comparison with experimental results, one could develop a method similar to that of Section VI, 5. In this manner, for example, the ratio of the radii of curvature of the shocks could be determined.

9. A New Type of Forked Shock

It was assumed in the preceding section that the intersection of the two shock polars is located in the subsonic region. If the Mach number of the original jet is close to one no such intersection exists at all. Cases do arise, however, where the intersection can exist only in the supersonic regime. A flow field, such as described above, is then no longer possible. On the other hand, it would be rather surprising if the outflow of the supersonic jet against a high pressure should have no solution or if the solution were to differ radically from the flow described above.

To understand what can happen at a point corresponding to F in Fig. 60 let us assume that both after the shock I and after II the velocity is critical. As may be seen from the hodograph representation the corresponding velocity vectors diverge. Such a discrepancy could be compensated for in the supersonic regime by means of an expansion fan on either side of the streamline through F. This would simultaneously cause the necessary change in the direction of the velocity and generate pressure distributions in the two regions such that they would match each other along the common boundary. This is, in fact, possible for the region after the compression shock II since the latter is oriented in such a way that it cannot be reached by the waves of the expansion fan. The flow here is similar to that found at the point B in Fig. 58. In the region I, the expansion fan would interact with the shock so that supersonic velocities would be reached along the shock polar. The state, a short distance downstream of F, would then be given by the intersection of the shock polar I with the characteristic through F, since the latter represents the expansion fan originating at the point F of the physical plane. The waves of the fan are naturally rarefaction waves and they are reflected as compression waves at the sonic line, following which, they end at the shock I. They cause in the process a pressure rise which is finally responsible for the transition to a subsonic velocity along the shock polar I. This type of flow field can be visualised without difficulty.

The region FGK does not agree with the conditions which we have discussed in Section V, 11, with reference to mixed boundary value problems, inasmuch as the supersonic contour has no gap. This gap was necessary in Tricomi's problem in order to assure the existence of a solution which would satisfy certain continuity conditions. One could assume that the boundary conditions

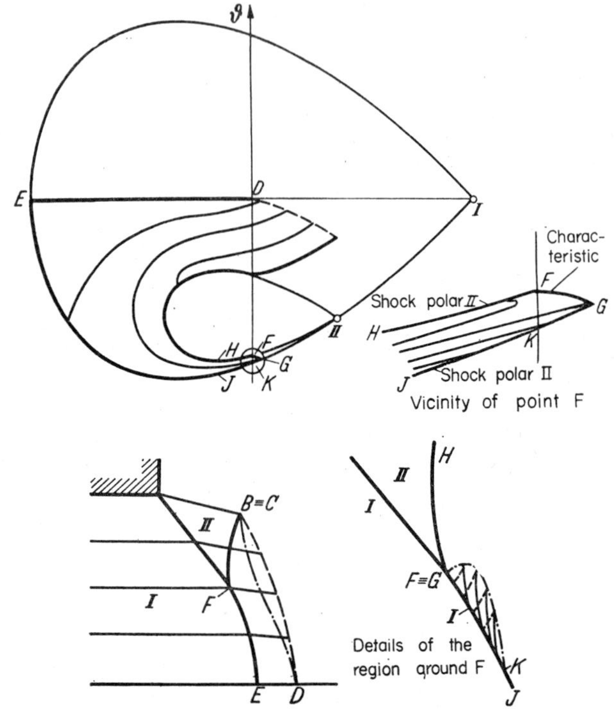

Fig. 60 Supersonic jet issuing against high pressure. A local subsonic region occurs at the reflection of the shock. (According to Guderley [26]).

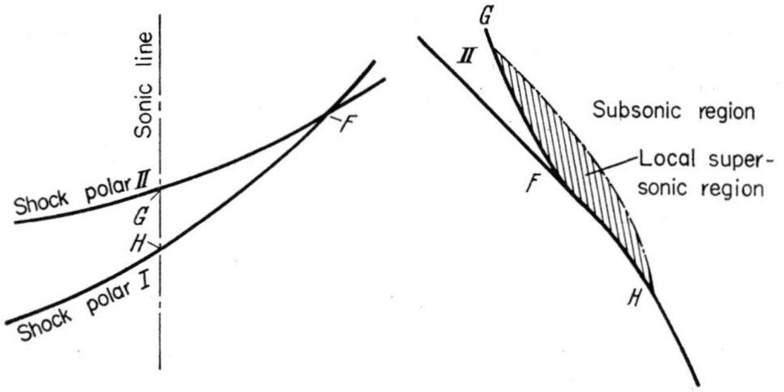

Fig. 61 Hypothetical (but impossible) form of a forked shock. (According to Guderley [26]).

along the shock polar, which differ substantially from those of Tricomi's problem, allow the supersonic boundary to be of a different character. Careful analysis (cf. Guderley [26]) indicates, however, that a singularity results at the point K or that also in this case a solution in Tricomi's sense is not possible.

From the practical point of view the details of the structure of the flow field are greatly complicated by this singularity. In general the form of the flow developed above is correct.

The flow, just described, occurs also when both shock polars intersect in the supersonic regime. It should be noted that we have assumed so far that, with the exception of point II, no other intersection point of the two shock polars exists. In Fig. 61 an attempt is made to sketch out the flow assuming that an intersection of the shock polars in the supersonic regime has the same effect as a similar intersection in the subsonic regime. As a result of the hodograph representation a sonic line, leading from one shock polar to the other, is obtained. Since the Mach waves propagated from the sonic line are compression waves, the transition from sonic to supersonic velocity along FH, as required by the hodograph representation, is impossible.

The type of forked shock which results depends thus on whether the shock polars intersect in the subsonic region. The intersection points in the supersonic region are physically meaningless. These shocks are often classified in the literature according to total number of intersection points. From a physical point of view such a classification is not satisfactory.

10. The Meaning of the "Second" Solution for the Supersonic Flow Past a Wedge

It is known that in order to determine the supersonic flow past a wedge, whose included angle is not too large, the shock polar must be intersected with a line passing through the origin of the hodograph plane and whose direction is equal to that of the face of the wedge. This results, however, in two such intersection points which correspond to shocks of different strength. Only the weaker of the two is observed experimentally. The second solution is, however, physically possible, as shown by all flows with detached shock waves, since in those cases all the states occuring on the shock polar can occur along the shock. The question arises, how could the stronger shock on a wedge be realised experimentally. Busemann supposed that this would require an obstruction downstream of the wedge so as to maintain a higher pressure in that region. It would therefore be interesting to attempt to construct an example of a flow which would illustrate such behaviour and which would permit a simple mapping of the flow field into the hodograph plane.

Let us consider a wedge whose half angle at the apex exceeds the maximum angle of deflection of the shock polar so that a detached shock would have to occur. On the upstream part of the wedge we attach a second wedge, with a smaller half angle, which permits an attached shock. Let us further assume that the ratio of the lengths of the faces of the two wedges can be varied. If the blunt wedge is very large, then one obtains a detached shock located far upstream of the leading edge. If this wedge, on the other hand, is very small, then one certainly obtains a shock attached to the leading edge of the slender wedge. Thus, by changing the length of the blunt wedge, the stagnation effect can be varied at will. The flow with the detached shock is shown in Fig. 62. On the axis of symmetry the shock is normal, in accordance with the shock polar I for the undisturbed flow. From that point onwards the zero streamline proceeds towards the stagnation point at the apex of the slender wedge E_2. Between E_2 and E_1 the velocity is parallel to the face of the slender wedge. The points E_1 and E_2 are stagnation points; between them the velocity has a maximum and thus the face of the first wedge maps into the line E_2FE_1. The location of F in the hodograph plane is not known in advance; it depends on the ratio of the length E_2E_1 and E_1C in the physical plane. If E_1C is very large, then the entire first wedge lies within the stagnation region so that the length E_1F in the hodograph plane is very small. Thus E_1F can be considered as a parameter determining the ratio of the sizes of the two wedges of the hodograph plane*. If the length of the face of the second wedge is gradually allowed to decrease,

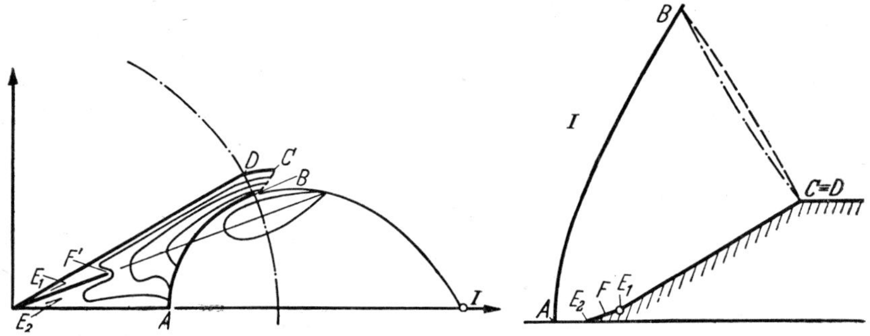

FIG. 62 Twin wedge in supersonic flow. Shock upstream of the foremost wedge. (According to GUDERLEY [26]).

then the point F finally reaches the shock polar I as shown in Fig. 63. The region AFE is then fully enclosed, and no streamline can leave it. The zero streamline starts at F and is immediately directed along the face of the foremost wedge. At the leading edge of the first wedge one obtains then, in fact, the stronger of the two shocks which can arise at this point.

Let us discuss next the behavior of the flow when the length of the face of the second wedge is further shortened. A change must occur since the hodograph representation uniquely determines the physical flow and all the dimensions occuring in the physical plane. If the dimensions of the thicker wedge are held constant, then the solutions, discussed up to now, can be interpreted as indicating that a detached shock occurs upstream of this wedge. The more slender wedge emerges, as it were, from the thicker one influencing, of course, the flow field to some extent. This wedge moves initially in the stagnation regime and then gradually approaches the detached shock. Figure 63 shows the flow when the slender wedge just reaches the shock. If its motion is now continued further,

* Sometimes the existence of such parameters in a hodograph formulation is overlooked and the possibility of satisfying all physically prescribed conditions in the physical plane is lost. This is particularly deceptive if one calculates not the entire flow field but only some technically interesting data.

one should assume that it penetrates the detached shock as shown in Fig. 64. Then, at the leading edge of the slender wedge, a shock of the weaker type is generated. The state after this shock is denoted by II. Outside of the region downstream of the shock II one finds still the original shock which exists in the region I. This latter shock then proceeds into the region II and reaches the face of the slender wedge. This continuation maps into a section of the shock polar II. The point H is the junction of the two shocks and can represent a fork

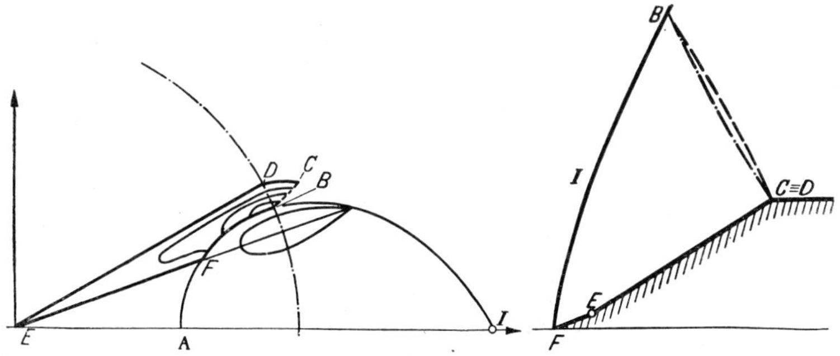

FIG. 63 Supersonic flow past a twin wedge. Attached shock at the foremost wedge shows the stronger of the two possible solutions. (According to GUDERLEY [26]).

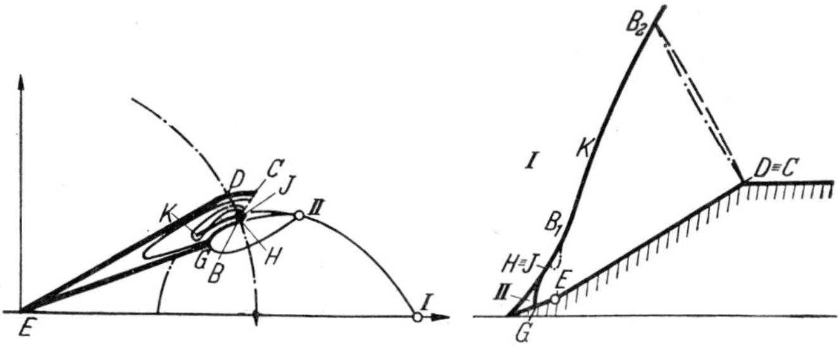

FIG. 64 Twin wedge in supersonic flow. The shock leading to the subsonic region starts on the face of the foremost wedge. (According to GUDERLEY [26]).

of the first or the second kind. The transition from Fig. 63 to the present flow takes place because of the occurence of a gap in the hodograph plane at the point K. The shock in the region I is then represented by the two parts of the shock polar $I B_1 K$ and $K B_2$. The location of K determines the ratio of the lengths of the faces of the two wedges. In this way one obtains a further series of flows in which the compression shock, causing the transition from supersonic to the subsonic velocity, moves further and further downstream. Further modifications, which then occur, have been described in an article by GUDERLEY [26].

Considering in retrospect the examples discussed thus far it becomes apparent that in all cases a continuous family of flow fields can be found which cover the range between two completely different flow fields. This is confirmed also by further discussions of a similar nature. One is forced, therefore, to regard sudden changes in the behaviour of a flow as improbable also in the transonic regime.

Many of the problems discussed above are naturally only of academic interest. It is, however, also satisfying for a practically inclined engineer when unanswered problems, as, for example, the meaning of CROCCO's point, can be resolved. He knows then how to judge such phenomena physically.

Let us point out one more possibility which has been utilised in the preceding example. It is sometimes possible to formulate a problem in such a manner that eventually, by small changes in the original problem, a discussion with the aid of the hodograph and hence a deeper understanding of certain properties of the flow become possible. We may now mention a few problems which can be treated in this way.

(1) A wedge in an enclosed channel with supersonic flow (GUDERLEY [26]). If the wedge is large, then no solution can be found since the approaching flow cannot pass between the wedge and the wall of the channel. If the wedge is progressively reduced, one obtains first a detached compression shock between the two walls of the channel. Further reduction in the size of the wedge causes the occurence of an attached shock at the wedge and a similar series of results is obtained as in the preceding example.

(2) BUSEMANN's biplane in supersonic flow with wedge-shaped profiles and varying distance between the airfoils (GUDERLEY [26]). This problem corresponds to an experiment of FERRI's. If the two wings are close to one another, a common detached shock arises while, when the distance between the two profiles becomes large, one obtains attached shocks at both leading edges. The flow fields are useful in the analysis of FERRI's experiments. The results are partially altered by boundary layer effects. A theoretical analysis shows further than even without consideration of the changes of entropy and of friction an instability can occur in the flow.

CHAPTER VII

PARTICULAR SOLUTIONS OF TRICOMI'S EQUATION

IN ORDER to gain a deeper understanding of the properties of transonic flows, it becomes necessary to obtain numerical solutions of the boundary value problems in the hodograph plane, or at least to discuss particular methods of solution. Certain families of particular solutions which will be discussed in the present chapter are of considerable help in this respect.

1. Chaplygin's Particular Solutions

TRICOMI's equation

$$\psi_{\eta\eta} - \eta \psi_{\vartheta\vartheta} = 0 \tag{1}$$

was derived in Section V, 7 where we have also discussed expressions which correspond to CHAPLYGIN's particular solutions of the exact hodograph equation. Such solutions occur primarily when a boundary condition $\psi = 0$, or sometimes also $\psi_0 = 0$, is to be satisfied along a line $\vartheta = \Theta_0 = \text{const}$. In view of this we assume a solution to be in the form

$$\psi = g(\eta, m) \sin\left(m\pi \frac{\vartheta}{\Theta_0}\right) \tag{2a}$$

or

$$\psi = g(\eta, m) \cos\left(m\pi \frac{\vartheta}{\Theta_0}\right), \tag{2b}$$

where m is an arbitrary constant which is most frequently an integer or a half integer. Upon substitution into Eq. (1) one obtains the ordinary differential equation

$$g'' + \eta \frac{m^2 \pi^2}{\Theta_0^2} g = 0. \tag{2c}$$

In the supersonic regime the solution of this equation is (cf. e.g. JAHNKE and EMDE [53]).

$$g(\eta, m) = \sqrt{\eta}\left[c_1 J_{1/3}\left(\frac{2}{3}\,\frac{m\pi}{\Theta_0}\,\eta^{3/2}\right) + c_2 J_{-1/3}\left(\frac{2}{3}\,\frac{m\pi}{\Theta_0}\,\eta^{3/2}\right)\right], \tag{3a}$$

while in the subsonic regime the solution is

$$g(\eta, m) = \sqrt{|\eta|}\left[-c_1 e^{\frac{-i\pi}{6}} J_{1/3}\left(e^{\frac{i\pi}{2}} \frac{2}{3}\frac{m\pi}{\Theta_0}|\eta|^{\frac{3}{2}}\right) + \right.$$

$$\left. + c_2 e^{\frac{i\pi}{6}} J_{-1/3}\left(e^{\frac{i\pi}{2}} \frac{2}{3}\frac{m\pi}{\Theta_0}|\eta|^{\frac{3}{2}}\right)\right] .* \tag{3b}$$

$J_{1/3}$ and $J_{-1/3}$ are BESSEL functions of order 1/3 and $-1/3$ respectively. Tables of these functions are listed in the bibliography [12]. The constants c_1 and c_2 are real and arbitrary. It is easy to show that the transition between these solutions at $\eta = 0$ is smooth.

The case of $c_1 = c_2 = 1$ is of particular importance since then, for $\eta \to \infty$, $g \to 0$ [cf. for example Eqs. VII, 7(6) and VII, 7 (9)]. In the subsonic regime this yields

$$g(\eta, m) = \sqrt{|\eta|}\left[-e^{\frac{-i\pi}{6}} J_{1/3}\left(e^{\frac{i\pi}{2}} \frac{2}{3}\frac{m\pi}{\Theta_0}|\eta|^{\frac{3}{2}}\right) + \right.$$

$$\left. + e^{\frac{i\pi}{6}} J_{-1/3}\left(e^{\frac{i\pi}{2}} \frac{2}{3}\frac{m\pi}{\Theta_0}|\eta|^{\frac{3}{2}}\right)\right] \tag{4a}$$

or

$$g(\eta, m) = \frac{\sqrt{3}}{2}\sqrt{|\eta|}\left[e^{\frac{2}{3}\pi i} H^{(1)}_{1/3}\left(e^{\frac{\pi i}{2}} \frac{2}{3}\frac{m\pi}{\Theta_0}|\eta|^{\frac{3}{2}}\right)\right] \quad \text{for} \quad \eta < 0$$

while in the supersonic regime one obtains

$$g(\eta, m) = \sqrt{\eta}\left[J_{-1/3}\left(\frac{2}{3}\frac{m\pi}{\Theta_0}\eta^{3/2}\right) + J_{-1/3}\left(\frac{2}{3}\frac{m\pi}{\Theta_0}\eta^{3/2}\right)\right]. \tag{4b}$$

These expressions are approximations to those exact CHAPLYGIN's solutions whose series expansions commence with a positive power of w (cf. Section V, 6).

Using the series expansion of BESSEL functions Eq. (3) takes at sonic velocity ($\eta = 0$) the form

$$g = c_1\left(\frac{m\pi}{3\Theta_0}\right)^{1/3}\frac{1}{\Gamma(\frac{4}{3})}\eta + c_2\left(\frac{m\pi}{3\Theta_0}\right)^{-1/3}\frac{1}{\Gamma(\frac{2}{3})}. \tag{5}$$

* A somewhat simpler representation of Eq. (3b) is achieved in terms of the modified BESSEL functions $J_{1/3}$ and $J_{-1/3}$ thus

$$g(\eta, m) = \sqrt{|\eta|}\left[-c_1 J_{1/3}\left(\frac{2}{3}\frac{m\pi}{\Theta_0}|\eta|^{\frac{3}{2}}\right) + c_2 J_{-1/3}\left(\frac{2}{3}\frac{m\pi}{\Theta_0}|\eta|^{\frac{3}{2}}\right)\right]$$

(Trans.).

With the aid of Eq. VII, 7 (6) and using the asymptotic expansion of HANKEL functions [Eq. VII, 7 (9)] the functions g, defined by Eq. (3), can for large values of $m\eta^{3/2}$ be approximately expressed by

$$g \sim \eta^{-\frac{1}{4}} \frac{1}{\pi} \sqrt{\frac{3\Theta_0}{m}} \left[c_1 \cos\left(\frac{2}{3} \frac{m\pi}{\Theta_0} \eta^{\frac{3}{2}} - \frac{5}{12}\pi \right) + \right.$$

$$\left. + c_2 \cos\left(\frac{2}{3} \frac{m\pi}{\Theta_0} \eta^{\frac{3}{2}} - \frac{1}{12}\pi \right) \right] \quad \text{for} \quad \eta > 0 \tag{6a}$$

$$g \sim |\eta|^{-\frac{1}{4}} \frac{1}{\pi} \sqrt{\frac{3\Theta_0}{m}} \left[\frac{c_2 - c_1}{2} e^{\frac{3}{2} \frac{m\pi}{\Theta} |\eta|^{3/2}} \right] \quad \text{for} \quad c_1 \neq c_2, \eta < 0 \tag{6b}$$

$$g \sim \sqrt{3}\, |\eta|^{-\frac{1}{4}} \frac{1}{4} \sqrt{\frac{3\Theta_0}{m}} e^{-\frac{2}{3} \frac{m\pi}{\Theta} |\eta|^{3/2}} \qquad c_1 = c_2 = 1, \eta < 0 \tag{6c}$$

If the boundary condition $\psi = 0$ is prescribed for $\vartheta = 0$ and $\vartheta = \Theta_0$ an integer value must be chosen for m. Then, with the aid for a method which will be discussed again in Section VII, 10, it may be shown that in a region $\eta_1 < \eta < \eta_2$, in which TRICOMI's equation and these boundary conditions are everywhere satisfied, the solution can always be expressed as a superposition of these particular solutions

$$\psi = \sum_m \sqrt{\eta} \left[c_{1m} J_{1/3}\left(\frac{2}{3} \frac{m\pi}{\Theta_0} \eta^{3/2} \right) + c_{2m} J_{-1/3}\left(\frac{2}{3} \frac{m\pi}{\Theta_0} \eta^{3/2} \right) \right] \sin \frac{m\pi}{\Theta_0} \vartheta \tag{7}$$

for $\eta > 0$. A similar expression is obtained for $\eta < 0$. Here $c_{1,m}$ and $c_{2,m}$ are appropriate constants.

If a solution in this form and its derivative with respect to η converge at the velocity of sound, then Eq. (5) shows that the series

$$\sum c_{1m} m^{-1/3} \sin \frac{m\pi}{\Theta_0} \vartheta \quad \text{and} \quad \sum c_{2m} m^{1/3} \sin \frac{m\pi}{\Theta_0} \vartheta \tag{8}$$

converge. Introducing now for the supersonic regime the asymptotic expressions of Eq. (6a), the convergence is determined by the following expressions

$$\sum_m c_{1m} m^{-1/2} \sin \frac{m\pi}{\Theta_0} \vartheta \quad \text{and} \quad \sum_m c_{2m} m^{-1/2} \frac{m\pi}{\Theta_0} \vartheta .$$

If the expressions in Eq. (8) converge, then Eq. (7) certainly converges in the supersonic regime. This is important if the boundary conditions are prescribed in the supersonic regime. They can be then satisfied by direct calculation (cf. Section VIII, 4). No corresponding conclusions regarding ψ_η in the supersonic regime can be reached from the convergence of the derivative ψ_η along the sonic line.

If the solution along the sonic line is represented by a convergent series of terms of the form of Eq. (4), then this series converges definitely in the entire subsonic region. This follows from Eq. (6c).

2. Another Type of Particular Solutions

Another class of particular solutions emerges as a result of the following reasoning. In view of the form of TRICOMI's equation the replacement of a known solution η by $\eta\tau^{-1}$ and ϑ by $\vartheta\tau^{-3/2}$ results in a new solution. This follows from the similarity rule. Introducing next a new variable

$$\zeta = \frac{9}{4}\frac{\vartheta^2}{\eta^3}, \tag{1}$$

where the coefficient 9/4 is at present unimportant, then this variable remains unchanged in the above similarity distortion. The parameter τ cancels out of TRICOMI's equation. In view of this, upon transformation to the independent variables ζ and η, the second of these must in each term appear in the same power, including the differentiations with respect to η. This leads to the following assumed form for a particular solution (GUDERLEY [27]).

$$\psi = |\eta|^n f(\zeta, n). \tag{2}$$

In view of the above discussion η must cancel from the differential equation so that an ordinary equation for $f(\zeta, n)$ results*.

To facilitate the substitution of Eq. (2) into TRICOMI's equation we form

$$\frac{\partial \zeta}{\partial \eta} = \frac{-3\zeta}{\eta}; \quad \frac{\partial \zeta}{\partial \vartheta} = \frac{9}{2}\frac{\vartheta}{\eta^3} = 3|\eta|^{-3/2}|\zeta|^{1/2}\operatorname{sgn}(\eta\vartheta),$$

$$\begin{aligned}
\varphi_\eta &= |\eta|^{n-1}(nf - 3\zeta f')\operatorname{sgn}\eta,\\
\varphi_{\eta\eta} &= |\eta|^{n-2}[(n-1)nf - (6n-12)\zeta f' + 9\zeta^2 f''],\\
\varphi_\vartheta &= |\eta|^{n-(3/2)}3|\zeta|^{1/2} f'\operatorname{sgn}(\eta\vartheta),\\
\varphi_{\vartheta\vartheta} &= |\eta|^{n-3}(\tfrac{9}{2}f' + 9\zeta f'')\operatorname{sgn}\eta,
\end{aligned}$$

and obtain the following ordinary differential equation

$$f''\zeta(\zeta-1) + f'\left[\left(\frac{4}{3} - \frac{2}{3}n\right)\zeta - \frac{1}{2}\right] + \frac{(n-1)n}{9}f = 0. \tag{3}$$

This equation is linear, homogeneous and of the second order. The points 0, 1 and ∞ are points of determinateness so that the equation is a hypergeometric

* Instead of starting from TRICOMI's equation one could also transform the exact hodograph equation into the η, ζ plane with the aid of either Eq. V, 7 (3) or Eq. V, 7 (5), where the second form is to be preferred, and restrict oneself to the terms of lowest order in η. This procedure shows that the form of Eq. (2) describes the behaviour of the exact hodograph solutions near the sonic line, which is to be expected.

equation*. A hypergeometric differential equation, and hence the totality of its solutions, are determined by the position of the singular points and by the exponents which occur at these points. Hence the description of the totality of solutions with the aid of RIEMANN's P-function. This function is just a collection of singular points (in the first row) and the appropriate exponents, as well as the independent variables, in the second and third row. In order to determine the P-function the exponents of the singular points must be determined (cf. for example WHITTAKER and WATSON [2; 8] Chapter 10, 3). In this manner one obtains

$$f = P\begin{Bmatrix} \infty & 0 & 1 & \\ -\dfrac{n}{3} & 0 & 0 & \zeta \\ -\dfrac{(n-1)}{3} & \dfrac{1}{2} & \dfrac{4n+1}{6} & \end{Bmatrix}. \tag{4}$$

The lines $\zeta = \text{const}$ in the η, ϑ plane are semi-cubic parabolas. At $\zeta = 0$ one obtains $\vartheta = 0$ while for $\zeta = \infty$ we have $\eta = 0$; this line coincides, therefore, with the sonic line. For $\zeta = 1$ we find $\vartheta = \pm 2/3\, \eta^{3/2}$, i.e. we obtain both the characteristics through the origin (cf. Eq. I, 6 (8)). The variable η is positive in the supersonic and negative in the subsonic regimes, respectively. At points located symmetrically with respect to the axis the same values of ζ are obtained.

The singularity of f at the points $\zeta = 0$ and $\zeta = \infty$ does not imply that the solution ψ must also be singular along these lines in the plane; on the contrary, this would be rather surprising. Information regarding the behaviour of ψ in the vicinity of these lines can be obtained by introducing the first term of a series expansion for f into Eq. (2). This first term is given, except for a coefficient, by the particular exponent of the hypergeometric differential equation. We then obtain for

$$\zeta = 0$$

exponent 0

$$\psi = \eta^n + \cdots$$

exponent $\frac{1}{2}$

$$\psi = \vartheta \eta^{n-3/2} + \cdots$$

for

$$\zeta = \infty$$

exponent $-\frac{n}{3}$

$$\psi = \eta^n \left(\frac{1}{\zeta}\right)^{-n/3} + \cdots = \left(\frac{3}{2}\vartheta\right)^{2n/3} + \cdots,$$

exponent $-\frac{(n-1)}{3}$

$$\psi = \eta \left(\frac{3}{2}\vartheta\right)^{\frac{2(n-1)}{3}} + \cdots.$$

* For the theory and nomenclature regarding hypergeometric differential equations the reader is referred to the literature.

These expressions are evidently free of singularities at all points along th lines considered, with the exception of the origin. Along $\zeta = 1$ this is true fo only one of the linearly independent solutions, while in the other solution a fractional power of $\zeta - 1$ occurs generally. This is understandable. It is know that discontinuities can be propagated along a characteristic. If this happens to be a characteristic passing through the origin, then this fact is expressed by th appropriate particular solution with a singularity. The character of the singula rity is determined by the exponent n. This point will be further discussed i Section X, 2.

It could be contended that because of the choice by the independent variable ζ the assumed form of the solution, Eq. (2), introduces into the differential equa tion for f singularities which are foreign to the solution for ψ. Against this on should point out that this choice of the independent variable leads to a type o differential equation which is known from the technique of the separation o variables. The discussion of the solution is actually facilitated by the fact tha the physically distinctive lines $\vartheta = 0$ and $\eta = 0$ assume a distinctive role als in the differential equation for f.

3. Alternative Form of Solution

The following choice of independent variables is particularly important fo the present discussion

$$\varrho = -\eta^3 + \tfrac{9}{4}\vartheta^2 = \eta^3(\zeta - 1), \qquad (1$$

$$\xi = \frac{\eta}{\left(\frac{3}{2}\vartheta\right)^{3/2}} = \zeta^{-1/3}. \qquad (2$$

The η, ϑ plane with lines of $\xi = \text{const}$ and $\varrho = \text{const}$ is shown in Fig. 65* We assume ψ to be of the form

$$\psi = \varrho^{-(1/12)+\mu} G(\xi, \mu). \qquad (3$$

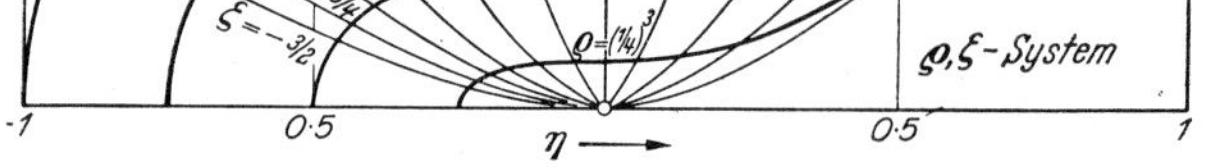

FIG. 65 The η, ϑ plane showing lines of $\varrho = \text{const}$ and $\xi = \text{const}$.

* From this point onwards the symbol ϱ will no longer be used to denote the density.

Replacing in Eq. (3) ϱ by $\eta^3(\zeta - 1)$ one can recognize the close relationship with Eq. VII, 2 (2). A comparison of these two equations yields

$$-\tfrac{1}{4} + 3\mu = n, \tag{4a}$$

$$G(\xi, \mu) = (\xi^{-3} - 1)^{(1/12)-\mu} f(\xi^{-3}, -\tfrac{1}{4} + 3\mu). \tag{4b}$$

The choice of μ in place of n will be found later on to result in simpler expressions. The variable ξ eliminates the singularity occuring on the sonic line. A singularity on the axis $\vartheta = 0$ remains; it is, however, not very disturbing since the solution can be split up into a symmetric and an anti-symmetric part (with respect to the axis) and then the transition through $\vartheta = 0$ need not be discussed.

Rather than derive the differential equation for G directly, we transform first TRICOMI's equation into the ϱ, ξ plane. This yields

$$\frac{(1-\xi^3)^2}{\xi}\psi_{\xi\xi} - \frac{5}{2}\xi(1-\xi^3)\psi_\xi = 9\varrho^2\psi_{\varrho\varrho} + \frac{21}{2}\varrho\psi_\varrho. \tag{5}$$

The following form may frequently be preferred

$$\frac{(1-\xi^3)^{7/6}}{\xi}\left\{\frac{\partial}{\partial\xi}[(1-\xi^3)^{5/6}\psi_\xi]\right\} = 9\varrho^{5/6}\frac{\partial}{\partial\varrho}[\varrho^{7/6}\psi_\varrho]. \tag{5a}$$

Upon substitution of Eq. (3) into these differential equations one obtains an ordinary differential equation for G which can again be written in two forms

$$\frac{d^2G}{d\xi^2} - \frac{5}{2}\frac{\xi^2}{(1-\xi^3)}\frac{dG}{d\xi} + \frac{9\xi}{(1-\xi^3)^2}\left(\frac{1}{144} - \mu^2\right)G = 0, \tag{6a}$$

$$\frac{d}{d\xi}\left[(1-\xi^3)^{5/6}\frac{dG}{d\xi}\right] + \frac{9\xi}{(1-\xi^3)^{7/6}}\left(\frac{1}{144} - \mu^2\right)G = 0. \tag{6b}$$

The principal importance of the form assumed in Eq. (3) lies in the fact that in the above differential equations the parameter μ occurs only in connection with G and not in the coefficients of the derivative G. We obtain thus a differential equation of an eigenvalue problem which permits us to discuss the completeness of a system of solutions to be constructed from particular solutions as given by Eq. (3). This is of primary importance in the discussion of flows in the vicinity of $M = 1$. The introduction of the variable ϱ has the disadvantage that the lines $\varrho = 0$ and $\xi = 1$ coincide. To discuss the solution in the vicinity of the characteristic $\xi = 1$ it is advisable to revert to the variable η.

The coordinates in the physical plane, for these particular solutions, are determined with the aid of Eqs. V, 7 (8) and V, 7 (9) where ϱ^* and w^* can be set equal to one. This yields immediately

$$y = \psi = \varrho^{-(1/12)+\mu} G(\xi, \mu). \tag{7}$$

It is further easy to show that it must be possible to put x in the form

$$x = \varrho^{(1/12)+\mu} K(\xi, \mu). \tag{8}$$

In order to determine the function $K(\xi, x)$ we substitute Eqs. (3) and (8) into Eqs. V, 7 (8)

$$x_\eta = \varrho^{(1/12)+\mu}\left[\frac{\frac{1}{12}+\mu}{\varrho}(-3\eta^2)\,K + \frac{\xi}{\eta}K'\right]$$

$$= (\gamma+1)^{1/3}\,\varrho^{-(1/12)+\mu}\,\eta\left[\frac{-\frac{1}{12}+\mu}{\varrho}\,\frac{9}{2}\vartheta\,G - \frac{2}{3}\,\frac{\xi\,G'}{\vartheta}\right],$$

$$x_\vartheta = \varrho^{(1/12)+\mu}\left[\frac{\frac{1}{12}+\mu}{\varrho}\,\frac{9}{2}\vartheta\,K - \frac{2}{3}\,\frac{\xi}{\vartheta}K'\right]$$

$$= (\gamma+1)^{-1/3}\,\varrho^{(1/12)+\mu}\left[\frac{-\frac{1}{12}+\mu}{\varrho}(-3\eta^2)\,G + \frac{\xi}{\eta}G'\right].$$

Upon substitution for η and ϑ in terms of ϱ and ξ there results

$$\left(\frac{1}{12}+\mu\right)\frac{-3\xi^3}{1-\xi^3}K + \xi K'$$

$$= (\gamma+1)^{1/3}\frac{\xi^2}{(1-\xi^3)^{1/6}}\left[\frac{3\left(-\frac{1}{12}+\mu\right)G}{1-\xi^3} - \xi\,G'\right],$$

$$\left(\frac{1}{12}+\mu\right)\frac{3}{1-\xi^3}K - \xi K'$$

$$= (\gamma+1)^{1/3}\frac{1}{\xi(1-\xi^3)^{1/6}}\left[\frac{-3\left(-\frac{1}{12}+\mu\right)\xi^3 G}{1-\xi^3} + \xi\,G'\right]$$

and hence

$$\left(\frac{1}{12}+\mu\right)3K = (\gamma+1)^{1/3}\,(1-\xi^3)^{5/6}\,G'$$

so that one obtains finally

$$x = \frac{(\gamma+1)^{1/3}}{3}\,\frac{(1-\xi^3)^{5/6}}{\frac{1}{12}+\mu}\,\frac{dG}{d\xi}(\xi,\mu)\,\varrho^{(1/12)+\mu}. \qquad (\text{[illegible]})$$

4. The G Solutions

Since the solutions G can be expressed in terms of f it must, of course, be possible to represent them by means of hypergeometric series. From Eqs. VII, 2 (4) and VII, 3 (4) one finds immediately that the totality of the solutions G is given by

$$G = (1 - \xi^{-3})^{(1/12)-\mu} P \left\{ \begin{matrix} \infty & 0 & 1 & \\ -\mu + \frac{1}{12} & 0 & 0 & \xi^{-3} \\ -\mu + \frac{5}{12} & \frac{1}{2} & 2\mu & \end{matrix} \right\}. \tag{1}$$

To obtain the functions G explicitly we use the following relationships valid generally for hypergeometric differential equations

1. $$P \begin{pmatrix} a & b & c & \\ \alpha & \beta & \gamma & z \\ \alpha' & \beta' & \gamma' & \end{pmatrix} = P \begin{pmatrix} a_1 & b_1 & c_1 & \\ \alpha & \beta & \gamma & z_1 \\ \alpha' & \beta' & \gamma' & \end{pmatrix}, \tag{2}$$

where z_1, a_1, b_1 and c_1 are obtained by the same linear fractional transformation from z, a, b and c. This equation implies that the singular points a, b and c can be transformed into arbitrary prescribed points a_1, b_1 and c_1 and that in this transformation the exponents are unchanged.

2. $$\left(\frac{z-a}{z-b}\right)^k \cdot \left(\frac{z-c}{z-b}\right)^l P \begin{pmatrix} a & b & c & \\ \alpha & \beta & \gamma & z \\ \alpha' & \beta' & \gamma' & \end{pmatrix}$$
$$= P \begin{pmatrix} a & b & c & \\ \alpha + k & \beta - k - l & \gamma + l & z \\ \alpha' + k & \beta' - k - l & \gamma' + l & \end{pmatrix}. \tag{3}$$

This equation becomes clear if one considers that the multiplication of the first P-function by the term in front of it generates a new manifold of solutions which also satisfy a differential equation of the second order with singular points a, b and c where the exponents, however, have been changed by the factor

$$\left(\frac{z-a}{z-b}\right)^k \left(\frac{z-c}{z-b}\right)^l.$$

3. A solution of the manifold given by

$$w = P \begin{pmatrix} \infty & 0 & 1 & \\ a & 0 & 0 & z \\ b & 1-c & c-a-b & \end{pmatrix} \tag{4a}$$

is expressed by the hypergeometric series

$$w = F(a, b, c, z)$$

where

$$F(a, b, c, z) = 1 + \frac{ab}{c\,1!} z + \frac{a(a+1)\,b(b+1)}{c(c+1)\,2!} z^2 +$$

$$+ \frac{a(a+1)\,(a+2)\,b(b+1)\,(b+2)}{c(c+1)\,(c+2)\,3!} z^3 + \cdots. \tag{4b}$$

This could be shown by constructing the differential equation corresponding to this expression and by a subsequent substitution of the series into the equation. The minimum radius of convergence of a hypergeometric series is always 1.

4. The series expansions at the various singular points are linearly related by

$$F(a, b, c, z) = \frac{\Gamma(c)\,\Gamma(c-a-b)}{\Gamma(c-a)\,\Gamma(c-b)} F(a, b, (1+a+b-c), 1-z) +$$

$$+ \frac{\Gamma(c)\,\Gamma(a+b-c)}{\Gamma(a)\,\Gamma(b)} +$$

$$+ (1-z)^{c-a-b} F(c-a, c-b, (1+c-a-b), 1-z) \tag{5a}$$

and

$$\frac{\Gamma(a)\,\Gamma(b)}{\Gamma(c)} F(a, b, c, z)$$

$$= \frac{\Gamma(a)\,\Gamma(b-a)}{\Gamma(c-a)} (-z)^{-a} F(a, (1+a-c), (1+a-b), z^{-1}) +$$

$$+ \frac{\Gamma(b)\,\Gamma(a-b)}{\Gamma(c-b)} (-z)^{-b} F(b, (1+b-c), (1+b-a), z^{-1}). \tag{5b}$$

The reasoning leading to the above equations is quite lengthy.

Equations (2) and (3) are used to obtain a P-function in the form Eq. (4a) and, subsequently, to obtain the solution in series form with the aid of Eq. (4b). The transformation to other series representations is then effected by means of Eq. (5).

The two linearly independent solutions necessary for the complete representation of G should be chosen so that the corresponding solutions for ψ are either symmetric or anti-symmetric with respect to the line $\vartheta = 0$. Depending on which is the case we shall provide the symbol G with a superscript s or a. One must reckon with the possibility that because of the appearance of the singularity at $\xi = 1$ the function G cannot be analytically continued past this point. Two solutions will, therefore, be given separately, one for the region $1 \leq \xi < \infty$ and the second for $-\infty < \xi \leq 1$.

The form of Eq. (1) permits the hypergeometric series to be written down directly. The symmetry of the expression below, with respect to the axis $\vartheta = 0$, follows from the fact the variable $-\xi^3$ can be written as $(9\,\vartheta^2)/(4\,\eta^3)$

$$G^{(s)} = (1 - \xi^{-3})^{(1/12)-\mu} F\left(-\mu + \frac{1}{12}, -\mu + \frac{5}{12}, \frac{1}{2}, \xi^{-3}\right). \tag{6}$$

The radius of convergence of this expression is 1, i.e. the solution converges in the region $1 < \xi < \infty$. In the vicinity of $\xi = 1$ we obtain the following form, with the aid of Eq. (5a)

$$G^{(s)} = (1 - \xi^{-3})^{(1/12)-\mu} \frac{\Gamma\left(\frac{1}{2}\right)\Gamma(2\mu)}{\Gamma\left(\frac{5}{12} + \mu\right)\Gamma\left(\frac{1}{12} + \mu\right)} \times \tag{7}$$

$$\times F\left(-\mu + \frac{1}{12}, -\mu + \frac{5}{12}, 1 - 2\mu, (1 - \xi^{-3})\right) + (1 - \xi^{-3})^{(1/12)+\mu} \times$$

$$\times \frac{\Gamma\left(\frac{1}{2}\right)\Gamma(-2\mu)}{\Gamma\left(\frac{5}{12} - \mu\right)\Gamma\left(\frac{1}{12} - \mu\right)} F\left(\mu + \frac{1}{12}, \mu + \frac{5}{12}, 1 + 2\mu, (1 - \xi^{-3})\right).$$

If in this equation μ is replaced by $-\mu$ the second and third lines are interchanged.

To obtain the solution $G^{(a)}$ from Eq. (1) we must first separate out a factor which is responsible for the anti-symmetric behaviour. In this respect either $(\xi^{-3})^{1/2}$ or $[\zeta^{-3}/(1 - \xi^{-3})]^{1/2}$ can be chosen; in the first case the exponents at the point $\xi^{-3} = 1$ remain unchanged while in the second case this is true of the exponents at $\xi^{-3} = \infty$. We shall only follow the first choice in our presentation, obtaining

$$G^{(a)} = (1 - \xi^{-3})^{(1/12)-\mu} \xi^{-3/2} P \begin{pmatrix} \infty & 0 & 1 & \\ -\mu + \frac{7}{12} & 0 & 0 & \xi^{-3} \\ -\mu + \frac{11}{12} & -\frac{1}{2} & 2\mu & \end{pmatrix}$$

and hence

$$G^{(a)} = (1 - \xi^{-3})^{(1/12)-\mu} \xi^{-3/2} F\left(-\mu + \frac{7}{12}, -\mu + \frac{11}{12}, \frac{3}{2}, \xi^{-3}\right). \tag{8}$$

With the aid of Eq. (5a) we find

$$G^{(a)} = (1 - \xi^{-3})^{(1/12)-\mu} \xi^{-3/2} \frac{\Gamma\left(\frac{3}{2}\right)\Gamma(2\mu)}{\Gamma\left(\frac{11}{12} + \mu\right)\Gamma\left(\frac{7}{12} + \mu\right)} \times$$

$$\times F\left(-\mu + \frac{7}{12}, -\mu + \frac{11}{12}, -2\mu + 1, (1 - \xi^{-3})\right) + (1 - \xi^{-3})^{(1/12)-\mu} \xi^{-3/2} \times$$

$$\times \frac{\Gamma\left(\frac{3}{2}\right)\Gamma(-2\mu)}{\Gamma\left(\frac{11}{12} - \mu\right)\Gamma\left(\frac{7}{12} - \mu\right)} F\left(\mu + \frac{7}{12}, \mu + \frac{11}{12}, 2\mu + 1, (1 - \xi^{-3})\right). \tag{9}$$

The particular solutions

$$(1-\xi^{-3})^{(1/12)-\mu} F\left(-\mu+\frac{1}{12},\ -\mu+\frac{5}{12},\ 1-2\mu,\ (1-\xi^{-3})\right)$$

and

$$(1-\xi^{-3})^{(1/12)-\mu} F\left(\mu+\frac{7}{12},\ \mu+\frac{11}{12},\ 2\mu+1,\ (1-\xi^{-3})\right)$$

occuring in Eqs. (9) and (7) are outwardly different. Since, however, there exist only two linearly independent solutions, and these are already determined by the first exponent of their series expansion, and since in this respect both solutions agree they must represent the same function. This can be verified with the aid of Eqs. (3) and (4).

We require next an expression for $G^{(s)}$ which is valid along the negative part of the ϑ axis ($\xi \to -\infty$). In principle Eq. (1) could be used in this region since it would converge between $\xi^3 = -\infty$ and $\xi^3 = -1$. Better convergence is obtained, however, if the independent variable is subjected to a linear transformation which leaves the origin unchanged and interchanges the points 1 and ∞. To this end we write Eq. (1) in the form

$$G = P\begin{pmatrix} \infty & 0 & 1 & \\ 0 & 0 & \frac{1}{12}-\mu & \xi^{-3} \\ \frac{1}{3} & \frac{1}{2} & \frac{1}{12}+\mu & \end{pmatrix}$$

and introduce as a new variable

$$\frac{-\xi^{-3}}{1-\xi^{-3}} = (1-\xi^3)^{-1}.$$

This yields

$$G = P\begin{pmatrix} \infty & 0 & 1 & \\ \frac{1}{12}-\mu & 0 & 0 & (1-\xi^3)^{-1} \\ \frac{1}{12}+\mu & \frac{1}{2} & \frac{1}{3} & \end{pmatrix}.$$

Hence with the aid of Eq. (4) one obtains easily

$$G^{(s)} = F\left(-\mu+\frac{1}{12},\ \mu+\frac{1}{12},\ \frac{1}{2},\ (1-\xi^3)^{-1}\right). \tag{10}$$

The argument of the function has the value of 1 at $\xi = 0$. Thus with the aid of Eq. (5a) we obtain

$$G^{(s)} = \frac{\Gamma\left(\frac{1}{2}\right)\Gamma\left(\frac{1}{3}\right)}{\Gamma\left(\mu + \frac{5}{12}\right)\Gamma\left(-\mu + \frac{5}{12}\right)} F\left(-\mu + \frac{1}{12}, \mu + \frac{1}{12}, \frac{2}{3}, \frac{\xi^3}{\xi^3 - 1}\right) +$$

$$+ \frac{\Gamma\left(\frac{1}{2}\right)\Gamma\left(-\frac{1}{3}\right)}{\Gamma\left(\mu + \frac{1}{12}\right)\Gamma\left(-\mu + \frac{1}{12}\right)} \frac{\xi}{(\xi^3 - 1)^{1/3}} \times$$

$$\times F\left(\mu + \frac{5}{12}, -\mu + \frac{5}{12}, \frac{4}{3}, \frac{\xi^3}{\xi^3 - 1}\right). \tag{11}$$

This last equation can be used also for positive values of ξ, only however up to $\xi^3/(\xi^3 - 1) = -1$ or $\xi = 2^{-1/3}$. We proceed therefore as follows. The expression

$$F\left(\frac{1}{12} - \mu, \frac{1}{12} + \mu, \frac{2}{3}, \frac{\xi^3}{\xi^3 - 1}\right)$$

is contained in the manifold

$$G = P\left(\begin{array}{cccc} \infty & 0 & 1 & \\ \frac{1}{12} - \mu & 0 & 0 & \frac{\xi^3}{\xi^3 - 1} \\ \frac{1}{12} + \mu & \frac{1}{3} & \frac{1}{2} & \end{array}\right).$$

Hence with the aid of Eq. (2) one obtains

$$G = P\left(\begin{array}{cccc} \infty & 0 & 1 & \\ 0 & 0 & \frac{1}{12} - \mu & \xi^3 \\ \frac{1}{2} & \frac{1}{3} & \frac{1}{12} + \mu & \end{array}\right)$$

$$= (1 - \xi^3)^{(1/12 - \mu)} P\left(\begin{array}{cccc} \infty & 0 & 1 & \\ \frac{1}{12} - \mu & 0 & 0 & \xi^3 \\ \frac{7}{12} - \mu & \frac{1}{3} & 2\mu & \end{array}\right)$$

and finally

$$F\left(-\mu + \frac{1}{12}, \mu + \frac{1}{12}, \frac{2}{3}, \frac{\xi^3}{\xi^3 - 1}\right)$$

$$= (1 - \xi^3)^{(1/12)-\mu} F\left(\frac{1}{12} - \mu, \frac{7}{12} - \mu, \frac{4}{3}, \xi^3\right). \qquad (12)$$

A similar treatment of the second part of Eq. (11) results in

$$\frac{\xi}{(\xi^3 - 1)^{1/3}} F\left(\mu + \frac{5}{12}, -\mu + \frac{5}{12}, \frac{4}{3}, \frac{\xi^3}{\xi^3 - 1}\right)$$

$$= -\xi(1 - \xi^3)^{(1/12)-\mu} F\left(\frac{5}{12} - \mu, \frac{11}{12} - \mu, \frac{4}{3}, \xi^3\right). \qquad (13)$$

With the aid of Eqs. (12) and (13) $G^{(s)}$ can be written

$$G^{(s)} = \frac{\Gamma\left(\frac{1}{2}\right)\Gamma\left(\frac{1}{3}\right)}{\Gamma\left(\mu + \frac{5}{12}\right)\Gamma\left(-\mu + \frac{5}{12}\right)} \times$$

$$\times (1 - \xi^3)^{(1/12)-\mu} F\left(-\mu + \frac{1}{12}, -\mu + \frac{7}{12}, \frac{2}{3}, \xi^3\right) -$$

$$- \frac{\Gamma\left(\frac{1}{2}\right)\Gamma\left(-\frac{1}{3}\right)}{\Gamma\left(\mu + \frac{1}{12}\right)\Gamma\left(-\mu + \frac{1}{12}\right)} \times$$

$$\times \xi(1 - \xi^3)^{(1/12)-\mu} F\left(-\mu + \frac{5}{12}, -\mu + \frac{11}{12}, \frac{4}{3}, \xi^3\right). \qquad (14)$$

To obtain from this expansions valid in the vicinity of $\xi = 1$ it is again ne-necessary to employ Eq. (5a). Although the hypergeometric series which result from the first and from the second part of Eq. (14) appear outwardly to be of a different form, they must represent, however, the same solutions, for reasons which have been discussed above in connection with a similar case. The contribution of the first term of Eq. (14) in the vicinity of $\xi = 1$ is

$$\frac{\Gamma\left(\frac{1}{2}\right)\Gamma\left(\frac{1}{3}\right)}{\Gamma\left(\mu + \frac{5}{12}\right)\Gamma\left(-\mu + \frac{5}{12}\right)} \times$$

$$\times \left\{ \frac{\Gamma\left(\frac{2}{3}\right)\Gamma(2\mu)}{\Gamma\left(\mu + \frac{7}{12}\right)\Gamma\left(\mu + \frac{1}{12}\right)} (1 - \xi^3)^{(1/12)-\mu} \times \right.$$

$$\times F\left(-\mu + \frac{1}{12}, -\mu + \frac{7}{12}, 1 - 2\mu, 1 - \xi^3\right) +$$

$$+ \frac{\Gamma\left(\frac{2}{3}\right)\Gamma(-2\mu)}{\Gamma\left(-\mu + \frac{7}{12}\right)\Gamma\left(-\mu + \frac{1}{12}\right)} \times$$

$$\times (1 - \xi^3)^{(1/12)-\mu} F\left(\mu + \frac{1}{12}, \mu + \frac{7}{12}, 1 + 2\mu, 1 - \xi^3\right)\Bigg\}$$

while the corresponding contribution from the second term of this equation takes the form

$$\frac{-\Gamma\left(\frac{1}{2}\right)\Gamma\left(-\frac{1}{3}\right)}{\Gamma\left(\mu + \frac{1}{12}\right)\Gamma\left(-\mu + \frac{1}{12}\right)} \times$$

$$\times \Bigg\{\frac{\Gamma\left(\frac{4}{3}\right)\Gamma(2\mu)}{\Gamma\left(\mu + \frac{11}{12}\right)\Gamma\left(\mu + \frac{5}{12}\right)} (1 - \xi^3)^{(1/12)-\mu} \times$$

$$\times F\left(-\mu + \frac{1}{12}, -\mu + \frac{7}{12}, 1 - 2\mu, 1 - \xi^3\right) +$$

$$+ \frac{\Gamma\left(\frac{4}{3}\right)\Gamma(-2\mu)}{\Gamma\left(-\mu + \frac{11}{12}\right)\Gamma\left(-\mu + \frac{1}{12}\right)} \times$$

$$\times (1 - \xi^3)^{(1/12)-\mu} F\left(\mu + \frac{1}{12}, \mu + \frac{7}{12}, 1 + 2\mu, 1 - \xi^3\right)\Bigg\}.$$

The first two terms of these two equations can be combined. Let us now recapitulate some properties of the Γ-function which will be used presently.

$$z\Gamma(z) = \Gamma(z + 1), \tag{15a}$$

$$\Gamma(z)\,\Gamma(1 - z) = \frac{\pi}{\sin \pi z}, \tag{15b}$$

$$\Gamma(2z) = \pi^{-1/2}\, 2^{2z-1}\, \Gamma(z)\,\Gamma(z + \tfrac{1}{2}); \quad \Gamma(\tfrac{1}{2}) = \pi^{1/2}, \tag{15c}$$

$$\Gamma(z) \sim e^{-z} z^z \sqrt{\frac{2\pi}{z}} \qquad \text{for} \qquad |z| \gg 1, \quad |\arg z| < \pi. \tag{15d}$$

Hence finally

$$\frac{\Gamma(z+\alpha)}{\Gamma(z)} \sim z^{a} \quad \text{for} \quad |z| \gg 1, \quad |\arg z| < \pi. \tag{15e}$$

Let us temporarily denote the sum of the coefficients of the first hypergeometric function in the preceeding expressions by A. Then

$$A = \frac{\Gamma\left(\frac{1}{2}\right)\Gamma\left(\frac{1}{3}\right)}{\Gamma\left(\mu+\frac{5}{12}\right)\Gamma\left(-\mu+\frac{5}{12}\right)} \frac{\Gamma\left(\frac{2}{3}\right)\Gamma(2\mu)}{\Gamma\left(\mu+\frac{7}{12}\right)\Gamma\left(\mu+\frac{1}{12}\right)} -$$

$$- \frac{\Gamma\left(\frac{1}{2}\right)\Gamma\left(-\frac{1}{3}\right)}{\Gamma\left(\mu+\frac{1}{12}\right)\Gamma\left(-\mu+\frac{1}{12}\right)} \frac{\Gamma\left(\frac{4}{3}\right)\Gamma(2\mu)}{\Gamma\left(\mu+\frac{11}{12}\right)\Gamma\left(\mu+\frac{5}{12}\right)}$$

$$= \frac{\Gamma\left(\frac{1}{2}\right)\Gamma(2\mu)}{\Gamma\left(\mu+\frac{5}{12}\right)\Gamma\left(\mu+\frac{7}{12}\right)} \times$$

$$\times \left\{ \frac{\Gamma\left(\frac{1}{3}\right)\Gamma\left(\frac{2}{3}\right)}{\Gamma\left(-\mu+\frac{5}{12}\right)\Gamma\left(\mu+\frac{7}{12}\right)} - \frac{\Gamma\left(-\frac{1}{3}\right)\Gamma\left(\frac{4}{3}\right)}{\Gamma\left(-\mu+\frac{1}{12}\right)\Gamma\left(\mu+\frac{11}{12}\right)} \right\}$$

and hence with the aid of Eq. (15)

$$A = \frac{\Gamma\left(\frac{1}{2}\right)\Gamma(2\mu)}{\Gamma\left(\mu+\frac{5}{12}\right)\Gamma\left(\mu+\frac{7}{12}\right)} \left\{ \frac{\pi \sin\left[\pi\left(\mu+\frac{7}{12}\right)\right]}{\pi \sin\frac{\pi}{3}} - \frac{\pi \sin \pi\left(\mu+\frac{11}{12}\right)}{\pi \sin\left(-\frac{\pi}{3}\right)} \right\}.$$

The expression in brackets can be put in the form

$$\frac{1}{\sin\frac{\pi}{3}} \left\{ \sin\left[\pi\left(\mu+\frac{3}{4}-\frac{1}{6}\right)\right] + \sin\left[\pi\left(\mu+\frac{3}{4}+\frac{1}{6}\right)\right] = 2\sin\left[\pi\left(\mu+\frac{3}{4}\right)\right] \right\}$$

and thus

$$A = \frac{2\Gamma\left(\frac{1}{2}\right)\Gamma(2\mu)}{\Gamma\left(\mu+\frac{5}{12}\right)\Gamma\left(\mu+\frac{1}{12}\right)} \sin\left[\pi\left(\mu+\frac{3}{4}\right)\right].$$

For the other term it is only necessary to replace μ by $-\mu$, so that finally

$$G^{(s)} = 2\Gamma\left(\frac{1}{2}\right)\left\{\frac{\Gamma(2\mu)\sin\left[\pi\left(\mu+\frac{3}{4}\right)\right]}{\Gamma\left(\mu+\frac{5}{12}\right)\Gamma\left(\mu+\frac{1}{12}\right)}\times\right.$$

$$\times(1-\xi^3)^{(1/12)-\mu}F\left(\frac{1}{12}-\mu,\frac{7}{12}-\mu,1-2\mu,1-\xi^3\right)+ \tag{16}$$

$$+\frac{\Gamma(-2\mu)\sin\left[\pi\left(-\mu+\frac{3}{4}\right)\right]}{\Gamma\left(-\mu+\frac{5}{12}\right)\Gamma\left(-\mu+\frac{1}{12}\right)}\times$$

$$\left.\times(1-\xi^3)^{(1/12)+\mu}F\left(\frac{1}{12}+\mu,\frac{7}{12}+\mu,1+2\mu,1-\xi^3\right)\right\}.$$

Equation (10), (11), (14) and (16) represent $G^{(s)}(\xi,\mu)$ in the interval $-\infty<\xi\leqslant 1$. Whether these equations are actually employed in a numerical calculation of the functions G depends on the available facilities. Using program controlled computers it is more practical to perform directly the numerical integration of the differential equation for G and to use the equations derived above only for the determination of initial values and for checking purposes. From our point of view the importance of these equations lies in the fact that they describe in general terms the behaviour of the function G at $\xi=-\infty$, $\xi=0$ and $\xi=1$, which points have a particular physical meaning.

The corresponding equations for $G^{(a)}$ are

$$G^{(a)}(\xi,\mu)=(1-\xi^3)^{-1/2}F\left(-\mu+\frac{7}{12},\mu+\frac{7}{12},\frac{3}{2},(1-\xi^3)^{-1}\right), \tag{17a}$$

$$G^{(a)}(\xi,\mu)=\frac{\Gamma\left(\frac{1}{3}\right)\Gamma\left(\frac{3}{2}\right)}{\Gamma\left(\mu+\frac{11}{12}\right)\Gamma\left(-\mu+\frac{11}{12}\right)}\times$$

$$\times F\left(-\mu+\frac{1}{12},\mu+\frac{1}{12},\frac{2}{3},\frac{\xi^3}{\xi^3-1}\right)+$$

$$+\frac{\Gamma\left(-\frac{1}{3}\right)\Gamma\left(\frac{3}{2}\right)}{\Gamma\left(\mu+\frac{7}{12}\right)\Gamma\left(-\mu+\frac{7}{12}\right)}\frac{\xi}{(\xi^3-1)^{(1/3)}}\times$$

$$\times F\left(-\mu+\frac{5}{12},\mu+\frac{5}{12},\frac{4}{3},\frac{\xi^3}{\xi^3-1}\right), \tag{17b}$$

$$G^{(a)}(\xi,\mu) = \frac{\Gamma\left(\frac{1}{3}\right)\Gamma\left(\frac{3}{2}\right)}{\Gamma\left(\mu+\frac{11}{12}\right)\Gamma\left(-\mu+\frac{11}{12}\right)}(1-\xi^3)^{(1/12)-\mu}\times$$

$$\times F\left(-\mu+\frac{1}{12},\ -\mu+\frac{7}{12},\ \frac{2}{3},\ \xi^3\right) -$$

$$-\frac{\Gamma\left(-\frac{1}{3}\right)\Gamma\left(\frac{3}{2}\right)}{\Gamma\left(\mu+\frac{7}{12}\right)\Gamma\left(-\mu+\frac{7}{12}\right)}\xi(1-\xi^3)^{(1/12)-\mu}\times$$

$$\times F\left(-\mu+\frac{5}{12},\ -\mu+\frac{11}{12},\ \frac{4}{3},\ \xi^3\right), \tag{17c}$$

$$G^{a}(\xi,\mu) = \Gamma\left(\frac{1}{2}\right)\left\{\frac{\Gamma(2\mu)\sin\left[\pi\left(\mu+\frac{1}{4}\right)\right]}{\Gamma\left(\mu+\frac{11}{12}\right)\Gamma\left(\mu+\frac{7}{12}\right)}(1-\xi^3)^{(1/12)-\mu}\times\right.$$

$$\times F\left(-\mu+\frac{1}{12},\ -\mu+\frac{7}{12},\ -2\mu+1,\ (1-\xi^3)\right)+$$

$$+\frac{\Gamma(-2\mu)\sin\left[\pi\left(-\mu+\frac{1}{4}\right)\right]}{\Gamma\left(-\mu+\frac{11}{12}\right)\Gamma\left(-\mu+\frac{7}{12}\right)}(1-\xi^3)^{(1/12)-\mu}\times$$

$$\left.\times F\left(\mu+\frac{1}{12},\ \mu+\frac{7}{12},\ 2\mu+1,\ (1-\xi^3)\right)\right\}. \tag{17d}$$

Except for the first one, the hypergeometric functions occuring in these equations are, of course, the same ones that occur in the expressions for the $G^{(s)}$.

5. The Special Solutions G

Closed-form solutions are valuable for an initial orientation; they are, however, of special importance also in the applications. These solutions may be obtained easily and systematically with the aid of RIEMANN's P-function. In accordance with Eq. VII, 4 (5b) the hypergeometric series terminates when one of the parameters a or b becomes a negative integer. These parameters constitute, in accordance with Eq. VII, 4 (4a), the exponents of a point at infinity. At the same time it is characteristic for the form of this equation that at both the remaining singular points one of the exponents is zero. Since the singular points can be transformed to an arbitrary location by means of a fractional linear transformation, it is only necessary for the existence of closed-form solutions that one exponent of any two singular points be zero and that the one exponent of the third singular point be a negative integer.

Applying this condition to Eq. VII, 4 (6), one obtains immediately

$$\mu = h + \frac{1}{12} \tag{1}$$

and

$$\mu = h + \frac{5}{12}, \qquad h = 0, 1, 2 \ldots . \tag{2}$$

Putting the second exponent of the point 0 in Eq. VII, 4 (1) equal to zero one obtains

$$(1 - \xi^{-3})^{(1/12)-\mu} P \begin{pmatrix} \infty & 0 & 1 & \\ -\mu + \frac{1}{12} & 0 & 0 & \xi^{-3} \\ -\mu + \frac{5}{12} & \frac{1}{2} & 2\mu & \end{pmatrix} = (1 - \xi^{-3})^{(1/12)-\mu} \times$$

$$\times\, \xi^{-3/2} P \begin{Bmatrix} \infty & 0 & 1 & \\ -\mu + \frac{7}{12} & 0 & 0 & \xi^{-3} \\ -\mu + \frac{11}{12} & -\frac{1}{2} & 2\mu & \end{Bmatrix}$$

from which

$$\mu = h + \frac{7}{12}$$

and

$$\mu = h + \frac{11}{12}.$$

Further transformations of a similar nature yield the same values of μ except for an opposite sign; this is obvious in view of Eq. VII, 3 (6).

A further group of closed-form solutions can be obtained as follows. The exponents at the point $\xi^{-3} = \zeta = 0$ are zero and $\frac{1}{2}$. Introducing a new variable $\zeta^{1/2}$, these exponents become equal to 0 and 1 and the point becomes regular. This transformation, however, moves the singularity from its original location at $\zeta = 1$ to $\zeta^{1/2} = +1$ and $\zeta^{1/2} = -1$. The singularity at infinity remains unaffected except that the exponents there are doubled. One obtains thus again a hypergeometric differential equation. We have therefore the identity

$$(1-\zeta)^{(1/12)-\mu} P \begin{Bmatrix} \infty & 0 & 1 & \\ -\mu+\frac{1}{12} & 0 & 0 & \zeta \\ -\mu+\frac{5}{12} & \frac{1}{2} & 2\mu & \end{Bmatrix} = (1-\zeta)^{(1/12)-\mu} \times$$

$$\times P \begin{pmatrix} \infty & +1 & -1 & \\ -2\mu+\frac{1}{6} & 0 & 0 & \zeta^{1/2} \\ -2\mu+\frac{5}{6} & 2\mu & 2\mu & \end{pmatrix}.$$

In this representation there are actually, as yet, no new closed-form expressions. These are obtained if the points 1 and ∞ are interchanged by a fractional linear transformation, prior to the elimination of the singularity at the origin.

$$G = (1-\zeta)^{(1/12)-\mu} P \begin{pmatrix} \infty & 0 & 1 & \\ -\mu+\frac{1}{12} & 0 & 0 & \zeta \\ -\mu+\frac{5}{12} & \frac{1}{2} & 2\mu & \end{pmatrix}$$

$$= (1-\zeta)^{(1/12)-\mu} P \begin{pmatrix} \infty & 0 & 1 & \\ 0 & 0 & -\mu+\frac{1}{12} & \frac{\zeta}{\zeta-1} \\ 2\mu & \frac{1}{2} & -\mu+\frac{5}{12} & \end{pmatrix}$$

$$= (1-\zeta)^{(1/12)-\mu} P \begin{pmatrix} \infty & -1 & +1 & \\ 0 & -\mu+\frac{1}{12} & -\mu+\frac{5}{12} & \left(\frac{\zeta}{\zeta-1}\right)^{1/2} \\ 4\mu & -\mu+\frac{5}{12} & -\mu+\frac{5}{12} & \end{pmatrix}.$$

A further transformation, which makes the points 0 and 1 singular, must now be applied. This is effected by introducing a new variable

$$\frac{\left(\frac{\zeta}{\zeta-1}\right)^{1/2}-1}{\left(\frac{\zeta}{\zeta-1}\right)^{1/2}+1} = (\sqrt{\zeta}-\sqrt{\zeta-1})^2.$$

As a result of this transformation the point ∞ of the last P-function is transformed into the point 1, the point -1 into 0 and the point $+1$ into ∞. There results then

$$G = (1-\zeta)^{(1/12)-\mu}\left(\sqrt{\zeta}-\sqrt{\zeta-1}\right)^{-2\mu+(1/6)} \times$$

$$\times P\left\{\begin{matrix} 0 & 1 & \infty & \\ 0 & 0 & -2\mu+\dfrac{1}{6} & \left(\sqrt{\zeta}-\sqrt{\zeta-1}\right)^2 \\ \dfrac{1}{3} & 4\mu & -2\mu+\dfrac{1}{2} & \end{matrix}\right\} \tag{3}$$

and hence a new closed-form solution is possible for

$$\mu = \frac{1}{4} + \frac{h}{2}.$$

Let us now recapitulate the closed-form solutions, given above, reverting at the same time to the variables η and ϑ.

The solutions ψ belonging to Eq. VII, 4 (1) may be written in the form

$$\psi = \varrho^{-(1/12)\pm\mu} G = \eta^{-(1/4)\pm 3\mu}(1-\zeta)^{-(1/12)\pm\mu}(1-\zeta)^{(1/12)-\mu} \times$$

$$\times P\begin{pmatrix} \infty & 0 & 1 & \\ -\mu+\dfrac{1}{12} & 0 & 0 & \zeta \\ -\mu+\dfrac{5}{12} & \dfrac{1}{2} & 2\mu & \end{pmatrix},$$

so that there are two solutions

$$\psi = \eta^{-(1/4)+3\mu} P\begin{pmatrix} \infty & 0 & 1 & \\ -\mu+\dfrac{1}{12} & 0 & 0 & \zeta \\ -\mu+\dfrac{5}{12} & \dfrac{1}{2} & 2\mu & \end{pmatrix},$$

and

$$\psi = \eta^{-(1/4)-3\mu}(1-\zeta)^{-2\mu} P\begin{pmatrix} \infty & 0 & 1 & \\ -\mu+\dfrac{1}{12} & 0 & 0 & \zeta \\ -\mu+\dfrac{5}{12} & \dfrac{1}{2} & 2\mu & \end{pmatrix}.$$

We obtain thus for

$$\mu = \frac{1}{12} + h$$

$$\psi = \eta^{3h} F\left(-h,\ -h+\frac{1}{3},\ \frac{1}{2},\ \frac{9}{4}\frac{\vartheta^2}{\eta^2}\right) \tag{4a}$$

and

$$\psi = \eta^{-\frac{1}{2}-3h}\left(1 - \frac{9}{4}\frac{\vartheta^2}{\eta^3}\right)^{-\left(\frac{1}{6}+2h\right)} F\left(-h,\ -h+\frac{1}{3},\ \frac{1}{2},\ \frac{9}{4}\frac{\vartheta^2}{\eta^3}\right), \tag{4b}$$

for

$$\mu = \frac{5}{12} + h$$

$$\psi = \eta^{1+3h} F\left(-\frac{1}{3} - h,\ -h,\ \frac{1}{2},\ \frac{9}{4}\frac{\vartheta^2}{\eta^3}\right) \tag{5a}$$

and

$$\psi = \eta^{-\frac{3}{2}-3h}\left(1 - \frac{9}{4}\frac{\vartheta^2}{\eta^3}\right)^{-\left(\frac{5}{6}+2h\right)} F\left(-\frac{1}{3} - h,\ -h,\ \frac{1}{2},\ \frac{9}{4}\frac{\vartheta^2}{\eta^3}\right), \tag{5b}$$

for

$$\mu = \frac{7}{12} + h$$

$$\psi = \eta^{3h}\left(\frac{3}{2}\vartheta\right) F\left(\frac{1}{3} - h,\ -h,\ \frac{3}{2},\ \frac{9}{4}\frac{\vartheta^2}{\eta^3}\right) \tag{6a}$$

and

$$\psi = \eta^{-\frac{7}{2}-3h}\left(\frac{3}{2}\vartheta\right)\left(1 - \frac{9}{4}\frac{\vartheta^2}{\eta^3}\right)^{-\left(\frac{7}{6}+2h\right)} F\left(\frac{1}{3} - h,\ -h,\ \frac{3}{2},\ \frac{9}{4}\frac{\vartheta^2}{\eta^3}\right), \tag{6b}$$

for

$$\mu = \frac{11}{12} + h$$

$$\psi = \eta^{(1+3h)}\left(\frac{3}{2}\vartheta\right) F\left(-h,\ -\frac{1}{3} - h,\ \frac{3}{2},\ \frac{9}{4}\frac{\vartheta^2}{\eta^3}\right) \tag{7a}$$

and

$$\psi = \eta^{-\frac{9}{2}-3h}\left(\frac{3}{2}\vartheta\right)\left(1 - \frac{9}{4}\frac{\vartheta^2}{\eta^3}\right)^{-\left(\frac{11}{6}+2h\right)} F\left(-h,\ -\frac{1}{3} - h,\ \frac{3}{2},\ \frac{9}{4}\frac{\vartheta^2}{\eta^3}\right), \tag{7b}$$

for

$$\mu = \frac{1}{4} + \frac{h}{2}$$

$$\psi = \eta^{\frac{1}{2}+\frac{3h}{2}}\left(\frac{\frac{3}{2}\vartheta - \sqrt{\frac{9}{4}\vartheta^2 - \eta^3}}{\eta^{3/2}}\right)^{-\frac{1}{3}-h} \times$$

$$\times F\left(-h,\ -\frac{1}{3} - h,\ \frac{2}{3},\ \left[\frac{\frac{3}{2}\vartheta - \sqrt{\frac{9}{4}\vartheta^2 - \eta^3}}{\eta^{3/2}}\right]^2\right) \tag{8a}$$

and

$$\psi = \eta^{-1-\frac{3h}{2}}\left(1 - \frac{9}{4}\frac{\vartheta^2}{\eta^3}\right)^{-\frac{1}{2}-h}\left(\frac{\frac{3}{2}\vartheta - \sqrt{\frac{9}{4}\vartheta^2 - \eta^3}}{\eta^{3/2}}\right)^{-\frac{1}{3}-h} \times$$

$$\times F\left(-h,\ -\frac{1}{3} - h,\ \frac{2}{3},\ \left[\frac{\frac{3}{2}\vartheta - \sqrt{\frac{9}{4}\vartheta^2 - \eta^3}}{\eta^{3/2}}\right]^2\right). \tag{8b}$$

Equations (8a) and (8b) are evidently not symmetrical with respect to the axis $\vartheta = 0$. They can, therefore, be split up into a symmetric and an antisymmetric part, resulting in two linearly independent solutions for the given value of μ. Such a calculation will be found in Section VIII, 3. This procedure does not apply to the remaining expressions, where the calculation of a second solution for the given value of μ requires the evaluation of an integral.

. Relationships Between Solutions for Various Values of μ

The existence of an interrelationship between certain solutions for various values of μ is indicated by the following reasoning: the differentiation with respect to ϑ of a solution of TRICOMI's equations results, evidently, in a new solution since the coefficients of this equation are independent of ϑ. With the aid of Eq. VII, 2 (1) and VII, 2 (2) one obtains as a result of this

$$f\left(\zeta, n - \frac{3}{2}\right) = \zeta^{1/2} f'(\zeta, n),$$

where f denotes a suitably chosen solution of the hypergeometric differential equation VII, 2 (3). Such relationships are known from the theory of the hypergeometric differential equation. The corresponding relationships for the functions G can be derived with the aid of Eqs. VII, 4 (6) and VII, 4 (8).

$$\frac{\partial}{\partial\vartheta}\left[\varrho^{-(1/12)+\mu} G^{(s)}(\xi, \mu)\right] = 6\left(-\mu + \frac{1}{2}\right)\left(-\mu + \frac{5}{12}\right) \times \tag{1}$$

$$\times\, \varrho^{-(1/12)+\mu-(1/2)} G^{(a)}\left(\xi, \mu - \frac{1}{2}\right),$$

$$\frac{\partial}{\partial\vartheta}\left[\varrho^{-(1/12)+\mu} G^{(a)}(\xi, \mu)\right] = \varrho^{-(1/12)+\mu-(1/2)} \frac{3}{2} G^{(s)}\left(\xi, \mu - \frac{1}{2}\right). \tag{2}$$

In these equations the sign of μ in the exponent and of ϱ and in the second argument of G are the same.

. Approximate Expressions for Large Values of $|\mu|$

The expressions for the functions G corresponding to large values of $|\mu|$ are useful both for numerical calculations and for a theoretical analysis of convergence. These expressions could be obtained by means of the saddle point method from the integral representation of hypergeometric functions. This procedure would require a special discussion of the vicinity of the point $\xi = 0$. For this reason the method presented in Section V, 7, in connection with CHAPLYGIN'S differential equation, is to be preferred. There exists an analogy between w and , p and $-\frac{5}{2}\,\xi^2/(1 - \xi^3)$, q and $\xi/(1 - \xi^3)^2$ in the two problems.

Let us denote by $\bar{\xi}$ a variable corresponding to x of the earlier problem. Then from Eq. V, 6 (8)

$$\bar{\xi} = \tilde{\xi}^{2/3}, \tag{1a}$$

where

$$\tilde{\xi} = \int_0^{\xi} \frac{3}{2} \frac{\sqrt{\xi}}{1 - \xi^3} \, d\xi . \tag{1b}$$

Here one selects that branch of the function $\bar{\xi}$ whose expansion at $\xi = 0$ starts with the term ξ in the supersonic as well as the subsonic regime. The integral in Eq. (1b) can be evaluated yielding for $\xi > 0$

$$\tilde{\xi} = \frac{1}{2} \log \frac{1 + \xi^{3/2}}{1 - \xi^{3/2}} , \tag{2a}$$

and for $\xi < 0$

$$\tilde{\xi} = i \arctan (- \xi^{3/2}) \qquad 0 \leqq \frac{\tilde{\xi}}{i} \leqq \frac{\pi}{2} . \tag{2b}$$

The term dx/dw, occurring in our earlier discussion, is now replaced by $d\bar{\xi}/d\xi$ and to this end we calculate

$$\frac{d\tilde{\xi}}{d\xi} = \frac{2}{3} \left(\frac{\xi}{\tilde{\xi}} \right)^{1/2} (1 - \xi^3)^{-1} .$$

Corresponding to h we introduce the quantity h_1 given by

$$h_1 = \left(\frac{\tilde{\xi}}{\xi} \right)^{1/4} (1 - \xi^3)^{1/12} .$$

The assumption of a solution in the form

$$G(\xi) = h_1(\xi) \, \bar{G}(\bar{\xi}, \mu) , \tag{3}$$

in which the function $\bar{G}$ assumes the role of y leads to a differential equation

$$\frac{d^2 \bar{G}}{d\bar{\xi}^2} - \left(9 \mu^2 \bar{\xi} + r(\bar{\xi}) \right) \bar{G} = 0 . \tag{4}$$

The term $r(\bar{\xi})$ is of no particular interest; it is bounded in the region

$$- \left(\frac{\pi}{2} \right)^{2/3} < \bar{\xi} < \infty$$

or $- \infty < \xi < 1$. It can be neglected for large values of $|\mu|$ so that the solutions of Eq. (4) can be given in terms of BESSEL functions of order 1/3*. One obtains thus the following asymptotic expressions for G

$$G \sim \left(\frac{\bar{\xi}}{\xi} \right)^{1/4} (1 - \xi^3)^{1/12} \left| \bar{\xi} \right|^{1/2} J_{\pm 1/3} \left(2 \mu \left| \bar{\xi} \right|^{3/2} \right) \quad \text{for} \quad \xi \leqslant 0$$

* Tables of these functions are listed in the bibliography.

with a similar expression for $\xi \geq 0$. With the aid of Eq. (1a) this may be put in the form

$$G \sim |\tilde{\xi}|^{\frac{1}{2}} \left| \frac{1-\xi^3}{\xi^3} \right|^{\frac{1}{12}} J_{\pm\frac{1}{3}}(2\mu|\tilde{\xi}|) \quad \text{for} \quad \xi \leqslant 0$$

$$G \sim \mp |\tilde{\xi}|^{\frac{1}{2}} \left| \frac{1-\xi^3}{\xi^3} \right|^{\frac{1}{12}} e^{\pm\frac{i\pi}{6}} J_{\pm\frac{1}{3}}\left(2\mu e^{-\frac{i\pi}{6}} |\tilde{\xi}|\right) \quad \text{for} \quad \xi \geqslant 0.$$

For small values of $\xi > 0$ one obtains from Eq. (1)

$$\tilde{\xi} = \xi^{3/2}.$$

Thus at $\xi = 0$ there results, using series expansions of the Bessel functions,

$$|\tilde{\xi}|^{1/2} \left| \frac{1-\xi^3}{\xi^3} \right|^{1/12} J_{+1/3}(2\mu|\tilde{\xi}|) = \frac{\mu^{1/3}}{\frac{1}{3}\Gamma\left(\frac{1}{3}\right)} (-\xi + O(\xi^4)), \tag{5a}$$

$$|\tilde{\xi}|^{1/2} \left| \frac{1-\xi^3}{\xi^3} \right|^{1/12} J_{-1/3}(2\mu|\tilde{\xi}|) = \frac{\mu^{-1/3}}{-\frac{1}{3}\Gamma\left(-\frac{1}{3}\right)} (1 + O(\xi^3)). \tag{5b}$$

If a solution $G^{(a)}$ or $G^{(s)}$ is to be given by a superposition of the two expressions of Eqs. (5) then this must also be true at $\xi = 0$. We thus satisfy a necessary (but not always sufficient) condition by constructing the approximate expressions in such a manner that for large values of $|\mu|$ they agree with the desired functions $G^{(a)}$ and $G^{(s)}$ with respect to both the values of the function and its derivatives at $\xi = 0$. The first and second terms of Eq. VII, 4 (14) correspond to Eqs. (5b) and (5a) respectively, except for suitable multiplying factors. The asymptotic representation of Eq. VII, 4 (14) becomes simpler if similar asymptotic expressions are introduced for the coefficients occuring in the equation. We shall indicate the calculation applicable to the first of the coefficients.

To this end we employ Eq. VII, 4 (15e) derived from Stirling's formula. The negative argument in $\Gamma\left(-\mu + \frac{5}{12}\right)$ is eliminated with the aid of Eq. VII, 4 (15b). This yields

$$\frac{\Gamma\left(\frac{1}{2}\right)\Gamma\left(\frac{1}{3}\right)}{\Gamma\left(\mu+\frac{5}{12}\right)\Gamma\left(-\mu+\frac{5}{12}\right)} = \frac{\Gamma\left(\frac{1}{2}\right)\Gamma\left(\frac{1}{3}\right)}{\Gamma\left(\mu+\frac{5}{12}\right)} \frac{\Gamma\left(\mu+\frac{7}{12}\right)\sin\left[\pi\left(\mu+\frac{7}{12}\right)\right]}{\pi} \sim$$

$$\sim \pi^{-1/2}\,\Gamma\left(\frac{1}{3}\right)\mu^{1/6}\sin\left[\pi\left(\mu+\frac{7}{12}\right)\right].$$

Similarly for the second coefficient in Eq. VII, 4 (14) one obtains

$$\frac{-\Gamma\left(\frac{1}{2}\right)\Gamma\left(-\frac{1}{3}\right)}{\Gamma\left(\mu+\frac{1}{12}\right)\Gamma\left(-\mu+\frac{1}{12}\right)} \sim -\pi^{-1/2}\,\Gamma\left(-\frac{1}{3}\right)\mu^{5/6}\sin\left[\pi\left(\mu+\frac{11}{12}\right)\right].$$

From Eqs. (5a) and (5b) there results

$$G^{(s)} \sim \pi^{-1/2}\left\{\Gamma\left(\frac{1}{3}\right)\mu^{1/6}\sin\left[\pi\left(\mu+\frac{7}{12}\right)\right]\mu^{1/3}\left(-\frac{1}{3}\right)\Gamma\left(-\frac{1}{3}\right)\times\right.$$
$$\times\left|\tilde{\xi}\right|^{1/2}\left|\frac{1-\xi^3}{\xi^3}\right|^{1/12} J_{-1/3}\left(2\mu\left|\tilde{\xi}\right|\right)+\Gamma\left(-\frac{1}{3}\right)\mu^{5/6}\sin\left[\pi\left(\mu+\frac{11}{12}\right)\right]\times$$
$$\left.\times\,\mu^{-1/3}\left(\frac{1}{3}\right)\Gamma\left(\frac{1}{3}\right)\left|\tilde{\xi}\right|^{1/2}\left|\frac{1-\xi^3}{\xi^3}\right|^{1/12} J_{+1/3}\left(2\mu\left|\tilde{\xi}\right|\right)\right\} \quad \text{for} \quad \xi \leqq 0.$$

Further simplification may be effected with the aid of Eqs. VII, 4 (15) for the Γ-function. This results in

$$G^{(s)} \sim \frac{2}{3}\pi^{1/2}(3\mu)^{1/2}\left|\tilde{\xi}\right|^{1/2}\left|\frac{1-\xi^3}{\xi^3}\right|^{1/12}\times$$
$$\times\left\{\sin\left[\pi\left(\mu+\frac{7}{12}\right)\right]J_{-1/3}\left(2\mu\left|\tilde{\xi}\right|\right)-\sin\left[\pi\left(\mu+\frac{11}{12}\right)\right]J_{1/3}\left(2\mu\left|\tilde{\xi}\right|\right)\right\}$$

for $\xi \leq 0$ and

$$G^{(s)} \sim \frac{2}{3}\pi^{\frac{1}{2}}(3\mu)^{\frac{1}{2}}\left|\tilde{\xi}\right|^{\frac{1}{2}}\left|\frac{1-\xi^3}{\xi^3}\right|^{\frac{1}{12}}\left\{\sin\left[\pi\left(\mu+\frac{7}{12}\right)\right]e^{-\frac{i\pi}{6}}\times\right.$$
$$\left.\times J_{-1/3}\left(2\mu e^{-\frac{i\pi}{2}}\left|\tilde{\xi}\right|\right)+\sin\left[\pi\left(\mu+\frac{11}{12}\right)\right]e^{\frac{i\pi}{6}}J_{1/3}\left(2\mu e^{-\frac{i\pi}{2}}\left|\tilde{\xi}\right|\right)\right\}$$

for $\xi \geq 0$.

Similar calculations yield

$$G^{(a)} \sim \pi^{\frac{1}{2}}(3\mu)^{-\frac{1}{2}}\left|\tilde{\xi}\right|^{\frac{1}{2}}\left|\frac{1-\xi^3}{\xi^3}\right|^{\frac{1}{12}}\left\{\sin\left[\pi\left(\mu+\frac{1}{12}\right)\right]\times\right.$$
$$\left.\times J_{-1/3}\left(2\mu\left|\tilde{\xi}\right|\right)-\sin\left[\pi\left(\mu+\frac{5}{12}\right)\right]J_{1/3}\left(2\mu\left|\tilde{\xi}\right|\right)\right\}$$

for $\xi \leq 0$ and

$$G^{(a)} \sim \pi^{\frac{1}{2}}(3\mu)^{-\frac{1}{2}}\left|\tilde{\xi}\right|^{\frac{1}{2}}\left|\frac{1-\xi^3}{\xi^3}\right|^{\frac{1}{12}}\left\{\sin\left[\pi\left(\mu+\frac{1}{12}\right)\right]e^{-\frac{i\pi}{6}}\times\right.$$
$$\left.\times J_{-1/3}\left(2\mu e^{-\frac{i\pi}{2}}\left|\tilde{\xi}\right|\right)+\sin\left[\pi\left(\mu+\frac{5}{12}\right)\right]e^{\frac{i\pi}{6}}J_{1/3}\left(2\mu e^{-\frac{i\pi}{2}}\left|\tilde{\xi}\right|\right)\right\}$$

for $\xi \geq 0$.

Further discussion is facilitated by the introduction of HANKEL functions defined by

$$J_{1/3}(z) = \frac{1}{2}\left(H_{1/3}^{(1)}(z) + H_{1/3}^{(2)}(z)\right), \tag{6a}$$

$$J_{-1/3}(z) = \frac{1}{2}\left(e^{\frac{\pi i}{3}}H_{1/3}^{(1)}(z) + e^{-\frac{\pi i}{3}}H_{1/3}^{(2)}(z)\right). \tag{6b}$$

Substitution into the above expressions yields

$$G^{(s)} \sim -\frac{1}{2}\pi^{\frac{1}{2}}\mu^{\frac{1}{2}}\left|\tilde{\xi}\right|^{\frac{1}{2}}\left|\frac{1-\xi^3}{\xi^2}\right|^{\frac{1}{12}} \times$$

$$\times\left[e^{i\pi\left(\mu+\frac{7}{12}\right)}H_{1/3}^{(2)}(2\mu\left|\tilde{\xi}\right|) + e^{-i\pi\left(\mu+\frac{7}{12}\right)}H_{1/3}^{(1)}(2\mu\left|\tilde{\xi}\right|)\right] \tag{7a}$$

for $\xi \leq 0$

$$G^{(s)} \sim \pi^{\frac{1}{2}}\mu^{\frac{1}{2}}\left|\tilde{\xi}\right|^{\frac{1}{2}}\left|\frac{1-\xi^3}{\xi^3}\right|^{\frac{1}{12}} \times \tag{7b}$$

$$\times\left[\sin\left[\pi\left(\mu+\frac{3}{4}\right)\right]e^{\frac{i\pi}{6}}H_{1/3}^{(1)}\left(2\mu e^{-\frac{i\pi}{2}}\left|\tilde{\xi}\right|\right) + \frac{1}{2}e^{-i\pi\left(\mu+\frac{5}{12}\right)}H_{1/3}^{(2)}\left(2\mu e^{-\frac{i\pi}{2}}\left|\tilde{\xi}\right|\right)\right]$$

for $\xi \geq 0$

$$G^{(a)} \sim -\frac{1}{4}\pi^{\frac{1}{2}}\mu^{-\frac{1}{2}}\left|\tilde{\xi}\right|^{\frac{1}{2}}\left|\frac{1-\xi^3}{\xi^3}\right|^{\frac{1}{12}} \times$$

$$\times\left[e^{i\pi\left(\mu+\frac{1}{12}\right)}H_{1/3}^{(2)}(2\mu\left|\tilde{\xi}\right|) + e^{-i\pi\left(\mu+\frac{1}{12}\right)}H_{1/3}^{(1)}(2\mu\left|\tilde{\xi}\right|)\right] \tag{8a}$$

for $\xi \leq 0$ and

$$G^{(a)} \sim \frac{1}{2}\pi\mu^{-\frac{1}{2}}\left|\tilde{\xi}\right|^{\frac{1}{2}}\left|\frac{1-\xi^3}{\xi^3}\right|^{\frac{1}{12}} \times \tag{8b}$$

$$\times\left[\sin\left[\pi\left(\mu+\frac{1}{4}\right)\right]e^{\frac{i\pi}{6}}H_{1/3}^{(1)}\left(2\mu e^{-\frac{i\pi}{2}}\left|\tilde{\xi}\right|\right) + \frac{1}{2}e^{-i\pi\left(\mu+\frac{1}{12}\right)}H_{1/3}^{(2)}\left(2\mu e^{-\frac{i\pi}{2}}\left|\tilde{\xi}\right|\right)\right]$$

for $\xi \geq 0$.

The asymptotic expressions for HANKEL functions are

$$H_{1/3}^{(1)}(z) \sim \sqrt{\frac{2}{\pi z}}e^{iz-(5/12)i\pi} \quad\text{for}\quad -2\pi < \arg z < \pi, \tag{9a}$$

$$H_{1/3}^{(2)}(z) \sim \sqrt{\frac{2}{\pi z}}e^{-iz+(5/12)i\pi} \quad\text{for}\quad -\pi < \arg z < 2\pi. \tag{9b}$$

These equations indicate that the functions $H_{1/3}^{(1)}$ and $H_{1/3}^{(2)}$ do not approach one another asymptotically for large values of the argument, as has been the case with $J_{1/3}$ and $J_{-1/3}$. The first function tends to infinity for increasing values of z while the second HANKEL function tends to zero. This fact is of importance in the determination of the range validity of the asymptotic representations.

We now introduce Eqs. (9) into Eqs. (7) to compare the behaviour of the latter for $\xi = -\infty$ and for $\xi = 1$ with the exact solutions. After some manipulation one obtains, for large values of the argument of the HANKEL function and for $\xi < 0$,

$$G^{(s)} \sim \left| \frac{1-\xi^3}{\xi^3} \right|^{1/12} \cos\left[2\mu\left(\frac{\pi}{2} - \tilde{\xi}\right)\right]. \qquad (10\text{a})$$

Since in accordance with Eq. (2b) $|\tilde{\xi}| = \pi/2$ at $\xi = -\infty$, the above expression tends asymptotically to the first term of the expansion for $G^{(s)}$ [cf. Eq. VII, 4 (10)].

For $\xi > 0$ one obtains from Eq. (7b)

$$G^{(s)} \sim \left| \frac{1-\xi^3}{\xi^3} \right|^{\frac{1}{12}} \left[\sin\left[\pi\left(\mu + \frac{3}{4}\right)\right] e^{2\mu\tilde{\xi}} + \frac{1}{2} e^{i\pi\left(\frac{1}{4}-\mu\right)} e^{-2\mu\tilde{\xi}} \right]$$

and in view of Eq. (2a) this yields

$$G^{(s)} \sim \left| \frac{1-\xi^3}{\xi^3} \right|^{\frac{1}{12}} \times$$
$$\times \left[\sin\left[\pi\left(\mu + \frac{3}{4}\right)\right] \left(\frac{1+\xi^{3/2}}{1-\xi^{3/2}}\right)^{\mu} + \frac{1}{2} e^{i\pi\left(\frac{1}{4}-\mu\right)} \left(\frac{1-\xi^{3/2}}{1+\xi^{3/2}}\right)^{\mu} \right]. \qquad (10\text{b})$$

When the real part of μ is positive the first term predominates except for the cases in which

$$\sin\left[\pi\left(\mu + \frac{3}{4}\right)\right] = 0,$$

i.e. when

$$\mu = h - \frac{3}{4} \qquad h = 1, 2 \ldots .$$

In these special cases the asymptotic representation takes the form

$$G^{(s)} \sim \frac{1}{2} \left(\frac{1-\xi^3}{\xi^3} \right)^{1/12} (-)^{h+1} \left(\frac{1-\xi^{3/2}}{1+\xi^{3/2}} \right)^{\mu} \quad \text{for} \quad \mu = h - \frac{3}{4}. \qquad (10\text{c})$$

When the imaginary part of μ is positive, Eq. (10b) yields the asymptotic representation

$$G^{(s)} \sim \left| \frac{1-\xi^3}{\xi^3} \right|^{1/12} e^{\pi|\mu|} \cos\left(2|\mu|\tilde{\xi} - \frac{\pi}{4}\right). \qquad (10\text{d})$$

If $1 - \xi \ll 1$, then $\tilde{\xi} \gg 1$ and one obtains the following approximate expressions

$$G^{(s)} \sim \sin\left[\pi\left(\mu + \frac{3}{4}\right)\right] 4^{\mu} (1 - \xi^3)^{(1/12)-\mu} \qquad \mu \neq h - \frac{3}{4}, \tag{11a}$$

$$G^{(s)} \sim \frac{1}{2} (-)^{h+1} 4^{-\mu} (1 - \xi^3)^{(1/12)+\mu} \qquad \mu = h - \frac{3}{4}, \tag{11b}$$

$$G^{(s)} \sim e^{\pi|\mu|} (1 - \xi^3)^{1/12} \cos\left(-|\mu| \log \frac{(1 - \xi^3)}{2} - \frac{\pi}{4}\right) \tag{11c}$$

with μ being a positive imaginary quantity. These expressions can now be compared with Eq. VII, 4 (16), considering $|\mu|$ in the latter equation to be large. For $\mu \neq h - 3/4$ the second term may be neglected and, with the aid of Eqs. VII, 4 (15c) and VII, 4 (15e), one finds

$$\frac{2\Gamma\left(\frac{1}{2}\right)\Gamma(2\mu)}{\Gamma\left(\mu + \frac{5}{12}\right)\Gamma\left(\mu + \frac{1}{12}\right)} = \frac{2\pi^{1/2}\pi^{-1/2}2^{2\mu-1}\Gamma(\mu)\Gamma\left(\mu + \frac{1}{2}\right)}{\Gamma\left(\mu + \frac{5}{12}\right)\Gamma\left(\mu + \frac{1}{12}\right)} \sim 2^{2\mu}$$

for $|\mu| \gg 1$. Thus the agreement between Eqs. (11a) and VII, 4 (16) becomes apparent. The agreement between Eqs. (11b) and VII, 4 (16) for the case $\mu = h - \frac{3}{4}$ is demonstrated in a similar manner.

When μ is purely imaginary, the first and second parts of Eq. VII, 4 (16) are complex conjugate and only twice the real part of these functions has to be determined. Also in this case agreement with the asymptotic formula of Eq. (11c) is established. Thus asymptotic agreement at the points $\xi = 0, -\infty$ and 1 for $\operatorname{Re} \mu \geq 0$ is obtained. Since, however, $G(\xi, \mu) = G(\xi, -\mu)$ the entire domain is included. Actually these considerations do not constitute a proof of the fact that Eq. (7) is an asymptotic representation of $G^{(s)}$. The above results, however, present the functions necessary for such a proof. The corresponding formulae for the antisymmetric particular solutions are

$$G^{(a)} \sim \frac{1}{2\mu}\left|\frac{1 - \xi^3}{\xi^3}\right|^{1/12} \sin\left[2\mu\left(\frac{\pi}{2} - |\tilde{\xi}|\right)\right] \tag{12a}$$

for $\xi < 0$,

$$G^{(a)} \sim \frac{1}{2\mu}\left|\frac{1 - \xi^3}{\xi^3}\right|^{1/12} \sin\left[\pi\left(\mu + \frac{1}{4}\right)\right]\left(\frac{1 + \xi^{3/2}}{1 - \xi^{3/2}}\right)^{\mu} \tag{12b}$$

for $\xi > 0$; $\mu \neq h - \frac{1}{4}$ and

$$G^{(a)} \sim \frac{1}{4\mu}\left|\frac{1 - \xi^3}{\xi^3}\right|^{1/12} (-)^{h+1}\left(\frac{1 - \xi^{3/2}}{1 + \xi^{3/2}}\right)^{\mu} \tag{12c}$$

for $\xi > 0$; $\mu = h - \frac{1}{4}$ and

$$G^{(a)} \sim \frac{1}{2\mu}\left|\frac{1 - \xi^3}{\xi^3}\right|^{1/12} e^{\pi|\mu|} \cos\left[2|\mu|\hat{\xi} - \frac{3}{4}\pi\right] \tag{12d}$$

for positive imaginary values of μ.

Let us denote the following special solution of the equation for G by G_1

$$G_1(\xi, \mu) = (1 - \xi^3)^{(1/12)+\mu} F\left(\mu + \frac{1}{12}, \mu + \frac{7}{12}, 1 + 2\mu, 1 - \xi^3\right). \qquad (13)$$

Equation VII, 4 (16) represents, for example, a linear combination of the expressions $G_1(\xi, \mu)$ and $G_1(\xi, -\mu)$. We note that

$$G_1(\xi, \mu) \mp G_1(\xi, -\mu).$$

The asymptotic expression for G_1 is

$$G_1(\xi, \mu) \sim \left|\frac{1-\xi^3}{\xi^3}\right|^{1/12} \left|\frac{1-\xi^{3/2}}{1+\xi^{3/2}}\right|^{\mu} 2^{2\mu} \quad 0 < \xi \leqq 1, \qquad (14)$$

and it is valid in the entire complex μ plane with the exception of the negative part of the real axis.

8. The Jacobian of the Above Particular Solutions

In Eq. V, 7 (12) the following expression has been obtained for the Jacobian of the hodograph transformation

$$D = -(\gamma + 1)^{2/3} (\psi_\eta^2 - \eta \psi_\Theta^2), \qquad (1)$$

where we have put $\varrho^* w^* = 1$.

For supersonic flow the above expression may be put in the form

$$D = (\gamma + 1)^{2/3} D_1 D_2, \qquad (2a)$$

where

$$D_{1,2} = (\eta^{1/2} \psi_\vartheta \pm \psi_\eta). \qquad (2b)$$

Since both D_1 and D_2 are linear in ψ, the determination of the sign of the Jacobian becomes particularly simple. If ψ is given by

$$\psi = \eta^n f(\zeta, n),$$

one obtains

$$D_{1,2} = \eta^{n-1} \left\{3 \zeta^{1/2} \frac{df'}{d\zeta} \pm (nf - 3\zeta f')\right\}. \qquad (3)$$

If the solutions are superimposed on one another, then a similar superposition takes place in the expressions $D_{1,2}$. It is often sufficient to determine the sign of the Jacobian along $\zeta = 1$ (or $\xi = 1$). In the subsonic regime the Jacobian is always negative; thus if along $\zeta = 1$ a positive value is obtained, then in the intermediate region a change of sign must occur which normally makes the solution unusable. We shall give therefore in the following a few criteria valid for $\zeta = 1$. They apply to the neighbourhood of the origin.

If in an expression

$$\psi = \varrho^{-(1/12+\mu)} G(\xi, \mu)$$

we replace ϱ by $\eta^3(\zeta - 1)$ in accordance with Eq. VII, 3 (1a) there results

$$\psi = \eta^{-(1/4) \pm 3\mu}(\zeta - 1)^{-(1/12) \pm \mu} G(\xi, \mu).$$

From Eq. VII, 4 (7) we can obtain two linearly independent solutions G. Thus a particular solution for ψ takes the form

$$\psi = c_1 \eta^{-(1/4)+3\mu} F\left(-\mu + \frac{1}{12}, -\mu + \frac{5}{12}, 1 - 2\mu, (1 - \zeta)\right) +$$
$$+ c_2 \eta^{-(1/4)+3\mu} |\zeta - 1|^{2\mu} F\left(\mu + \frac{1}{12}, \mu + \frac{5}{12}, 1 + 2\mu, (1 - \zeta)\right) \quad (4)$$

with c_1 and c_2 being arbitrary constants. In a linear combination of such expressions with various values of μ the term corresponding to the lowest value of μ predominates, as far as the first terms of Eq. (4) are concerned, for small values of η and $|\zeta - 1|$. The same is true with respect to the second terms of such a combination. The relationship between the predominating first term and the predominating second term depends on the exponent in $(1 - \zeta)^{2\mu}$ in the second term.

As an example for this discussion let us consider the case in which the exponents of the predominating terms are equal. With the aid of Eq. (3) one finds then in the vicinity of $\zeta = 1$

$$D_1 = \mu^{-(5/4)+3\mu}\left\{c_1\, 3\left(\mu - \frac{1}{12}\right) - \frac{1}{4} c_2 |\zeta - 1|^{2\mu}\right\},$$

$$D_2 = \eta^{-(5/4)+3\mu}\left\{c_1 \frac{1}{2} \frac{\mu - \dfrac{1}{12}}{2\mu - 1} + c_2\, 12\mu \frac{|\zeta - 1|^{2\mu}}{\zeta - 1}\right\}.$$

In these equations the first terms predominate for $\mu > \frac{1}{2}$ so that the Jacobian is positive. For $\mu < 0$ the second terms predominate and then for $\zeta - 1$ or $\xi < 1$ the Jacobian is negative, while for $\zeta < 1$ or $\xi > 1$ it is positive.

When $0 < \mu < \frac{1}{2}$, the first term predominates in D_1, while the second term predominates in D_2. The sign of the Jacobian is therefore the same as that of the product $c_1 c_2(\mu - \frac{1}{12})$. If only the first term appears, then the sign of D is the same as that of $(2\mu - 1)$. On the other hand, if only the second term is present then the sign of D is opposite to that of $(\zeta - 1)$.

If the exponents of the predominating first and of the predominating second term are different, then the sign of the Jacobian may depend on the manner in which η and $\zeta - 1$ tend simultaneously to zero. If one of these criteria yields a positive Jacobian, then the solution should be excluded. Further details of this may be found in an article by GUDERLEY [27]. Here we merely summarize the criteria.

We denote the exponent of the predominating first term by μ_1 and that of the predominating second term by μ_2.

(1) Approach to the origin of the η, ϑ plane along a line $|\zeta - 1| = \text{const} \ll 1$: for $\mu_2 > \mu_1$ or $c_2 = 0$

$$\operatorname{sgn} D = \operatorname{sgn}\left(\mu_1 - \frac{1}{2}\right), \tag{5a}$$

for $\mu_2 < \mu_1$ or $c_1 = 0$

$$\operatorname{sgn} D = \operatorname{sgn}\left(-\mu_2(\zeta - 1)\right), \tag{5b}$$

for $\mu_1 = \mu_2 > \frac{1}{2}$ and $c_1 \neq 0$, $c_2 \neq 0$

$$D > 0, \tag{5c}$$

for $0 < \mu_1 = \mu_2 < \dfrac{1}{2}$ and $c_1 \neq 0$, $c_2 \neq 0$

$$\operatorname{sgn} D = \operatorname{sgn} c_1 c_2 (\zeta - 1)\left(\mu_1 - \frac{1}{12}\right), \tag{5d}$$

for $\mu_1 = \mu_2 < 0$ and $c_1 \neq 0$, $c_2 \neq 0$

$$\operatorname{sgn} D = \operatorname{sgn}(\zeta - 1). \tag{5e}$$

(2) Approach to origin along other lines: for $\mu_2 > \frac{1}{2}$ and $c_1 \neq 0$

$$\operatorname{sgn} D = \operatorname{sgn}\left(\mu_1 - \frac{1}{2}\right), \tag{6a}$$

for $0 < \mu_2 < \frac{1}{2}$ and $c_1 \neq 0$, $c_2 \neq 0$

$$\operatorname{sgn} D = \operatorname{sgn} c_1 c_2 (\zeta - 1)\left(\mu_1 - \frac{1}{12}\right), \tag{6b}$$

for $\mu_2 < 0$ and $c_2 \neq 0$

$$\operatorname{sgn} D = \operatorname{sgn}(\zeta - 1). \tag{6c}$$

9. Systems of Particular Solutions

In the analysis of flow problems one is often confronted by the question of particular solutions which are to be used to describe the flow. Very frequently (cf. for example in the case of flow with $M = 1$ in Chapter VIII) one knows that, for physical reasons, the solutions and their derivatives must be bounded along the characteristic $\xi = 1$ and occasionally the origin must be excluded. This condition dictates the correct choice of the particular solutions. Substituting Eq. VII, 4 (16), which represents the symmetrical particular solutions in the vicinity of $\xi = 1$, into Eq. VII, 4 (3), replacing ϱ by $\eta^3(\zeta - 1)$ with the aid of Eq. VII, 4 (1a), and replacing finally the hypergeometric series by its first term one obtains

$$\psi = 2\Gamma\left(\frac{1}{2}\right)\left(\frac{\eta}{\xi}\right)^{-(1/4)+3\mu} \times \tag{1}$$

$$\times \left\{\frac{\Gamma(2\mu)\sin\left[\pi\left(\mu + \frac{3}{4}\right)\right]}{\Gamma\left(\mu + \frac{5}{12}\right)\Gamma\left(\mu + \frac{1}{12}\right)} + \frac{\Gamma(-2\mu)\sin\left[\pi\left(-\mu + \frac{3}{4}\right)\right]}{\Gamma\left(-\mu + \frac{5}{12}\right)\Gamma\left(-\mu + \frac{1}{12}\right)}(1 - \xi^3)^{2\mu}\right\}.$$

If ψ and its derivatives at $\xi = 1$ are to remain finite, the coefficient of the second term must vanish. The case in which the exponent in the second term is a positive integer must be excluded since then the hypergeometric series for the first term does not exist. This yields the following conditions

$$\sin\left[\pi\left(-\mu + \frac{3}{4}\right)\right] = 0,$$

$$\Gamma\left(-\mu + \frac{5}{12}\right) = \infty,$$

$$\Gamma\left(-\mu + \frac{1}{12}\right) = \infty,$$

and hence

$$\mu = \frac{1}{12} + \frac{h}{3},$$

$$\mu = -\frac{1}{4} - h, \tag{2}$$

where h is a non-negative integer. Similarly for the antisymmetric solutions one obtains from Eq. VII, 4 (17d)

$$\mu = \frac{1}{4} + \frac{h}{3},$$

$$\mu = -\frac{3}{4} - h. \tag{3}$$

These solutions will later play a special role; we shall, therefore, introduce for them a special notation, namely ψ with a subscript which corresponds to the appropriate exponent of ϱ. Whenever it becomes convenient to differentiate between the symmetric and antisymmetric particular solutions these will be denoted by superscripts (s) and (a) respectively. This distinction is not particularly necessary since for a given exponent of ϱ, e.g. $-5/6$, only either the symmetric of the antisymmetric particular solution is finite both as regards its value and as regards its derivative at $\xi = 1$. All these solutions can be expressed in closed form [Eqs. VII, 5 (3) through VII, 5 (8)].

Thus the following selection of solutions is available

$$\psi^{(s)}_{-1/3},\ \psi^{(a)}_{-5/6},\ \psi^{(s)}_{-4/3},\ \psi^{(a)}_{-11/6} \cdots \quad \text{and} \quad \psi^{(s)}_{0},\ \psi^{(a)}_{1/6},\ \psi^{(s)}_{1/3},\ \psi^{(a)}_{1/2} \cdots.$$

We shall on occasion describe these solutions by the common term "natural" particular solutions.

However illuminating the considerations which led to the choice of the particular solutions may have been, they do not constitute a proof of the completeness of this system of solutions. The completeness of another system, determined by an eigenvalue problem, can, however, be demonstrated without difficulty. Apart from the fact that the coefficient of G changes its sign, the differential equation for G [Eq. VII, 3 (6)] is of a form known from classical boundary value problems. If we restrict ourselves to either symmetric or antisymmetric particular solutions, then the condition along $\vartheta = 0$ $(\xi = -\infty)$, namely $G = 0$ or

$$(-\xi)^{-5/2} \frac{\partial G}{\partial \xi} = 0,$$

is also of a form which appears in eigenvalue problems. The boundary condition which we employ for $\xi = 1$ does not, however, fit into this concept. In this respect, the following artifice is helpful: we introduce an upper limit of the domain considered by setting $\xi = c_2 (c_2 < 1)$ and we require that at this limit $G = 0$. We then let c_2 tend to 1.

Next let us consider the case of $c_2 < 1$. To this end we put $\mu^2 = \lambda$. Let G_1 and G_2 be two solutions of the differential equation for G, corresponding to two different values of λ, which we denote by λ_1 and λ_2 respectively. Let G_1 and G_2 satisfy the prescribed condition at $\xi = -\infty$. Integration by parts of

$$\int_{-\infty}^{c_2} \frac{\xi}{(1 - \xi^3)^{1/6}} G_1(\xi)\, G_2(\xi)\, d\xi$$

yields, with the aid of Eq. VII, 3 (6b) for G_1 and G_2, and with the introduction of the boundary condition for $\xi = -\infty$,

$$\int_{-\infty}^{c_2} \frac{\xi}{(1 - \xi^3)^{1/6}} G_1(\xi)\, G_2(\xi)\, d\xi = -\frac{1}{\frac{1}{16} - 9\lambda_1} \int_{-\infty}^{c_2} G_2(\xi) \times$$

$$\times \frac{d}{d\xi}\left[(1 - \xi^3)^{5/6} \frac{dG_1}{d\xi}\right] d\xi = -\frac{1}{\frac{1}{16} - 9\lambda_1} (1 - \xi^3)^{5/6}\, G_2 \frac{dG_1}{d\xi}\Bigg|_{-\infty}^{c_2} +$$

$$+ \frac{1}{\frac{1}{16} - 9\lambda_1} \int_{-\infty}^{c_2} (1 - \xi^3)^{5/6} \frac{dG_2}{d\xi} \frac{dG_1}{d\xi}\, d\xi \tag{4}$$

and

$$\int_{-\infty}^{c_2} \frac{\xi}{(1 - \xi^3)^{1/6}} G_1(\xi)\, G_2(\xi)\, d\xi = -\frac{1}{\frac{1}{16} - 9\lambda_2} (1 - \xi^3)^{5/6}\, G_1 \frac{dG_2}{d\xi}\Bigg|_{-\infty}^{c_2} +$$

$$+ \frac{1}{\frac{1}{16} - 9\lambda_1} \int_{-\infty}^{c_2} (1 - \xi^3)^{5/6} \frac{dG_2}{d\xi} \frac{dG_1}{d\xi}\, d\xi. \tag{5}$$

Hence

$$\int_{-\infty}^{c_2} \frac{\xi}{(1-\xi^3)^{7/6}} G_1(\xi)\, G_2(\xi)\, d\xi = \frac{1}{9(\lambda_1-\lambda_2)} (1-c_2^3)^{5/6} \times$$

$$\times \left(- G_1(c_2) \frac{d G_2}{d\xi}(c_2) + G_2(c_2) \frac{d G_1}{d\xi}(c_2)\right). \quad (6)$$

If the functions G_1 and G_2 satisfy the condition $G = 0$ at $\xi = c_2$, Eqs. (4) and (5) yield the following orthogonality relations

$$\int_{-\infty}^{c_2} \frac{\xi}{(1-\xi^3)^{7/6}} G_1(\xi)\, G_2(\xi)\, d\xi = 0 \quad \text{for} \quad \lambda_1 \neq \lambda_2 \quad (7a)$$

$$\int_{-\infty}^{c_2} (1-\xi^3)^{5/6} \frac{d G_1}{d\xi} \frac{d G_2}{d\xi}\, d\xi = 0 \quad \text{for} \quad \lambda_1 \neq \lambda_2 . \quad (7b)$$

We now consider G in Eq. (6) to be a function of ξ and λ satisfying the boundary conditions for $\xi = -\infty$. The functions G can be considered defined by Eqs. VII, 4 (10), VII, 4 (11), VII, 4 (14) and VII, 4 (16) or VII, 4 (17) with μ replaced by $\sqrt{\lambda}$. When λ_1 and λ_2, and hence also G_1 and G_2, are allowed to approach one another then Eq. (6) yields the following expression which we shall denote by C

$$C = \int_{-\infty}^{c_2} \frac{\xi}{(1-\xi^3)^{1/6}} G^2(\xi, \mu)\, d\xi$$

$$= \frac{(1-c_2^3)^{5/6}}{18\mu} \left(G(c_2, \mu) \frac{\partial^2 G}{\partial \xi\, \partial \mu}(c_2, \mu) - \frac{\partial G}{\partial \xi}(c_2, \mu) \frac{\partial G}{\partial \mu}(c_2, \mu)\right). \quad (8)$$

This formula is of particular importance when G is an eigenfunction; it has been obtained by GUDERLEY [29, 30].

The orthogonality relation, Eq. (7b), indicates that the eigenvalues $\lambda = \mu^2$ must be real. The proof is developed from the classical theory of eigenvalue problems but in the present case, in view of the change of sign of the term $\xi/(1-\xi^3)^{7/6}$ in Eq. (7a) at $\xi = 0$, that equation cannot be used as a starting point. The reasoning is as follows. If a complex eigenvalue $\lambda = \lambda_r + i\lambda_i$ exists, then its complex conjugate $\lambda = \lambda_r - i\lambda_i$ is also an eigenvalue, since the differential Equation VII, 4 (6) has only real coefficients. The corresponding eigenfunctions are also complex conjugate. This may be written as $G^+ = G_r + i G_i$ and $G^- = G_r - i G_i$. Since these eigenvalues are not equal, Eq. (7b) applies. One obtain

$$\int_{-\infty}^{c_2} (1-\xi^3)^{5/6} \left(\frac{\partial G_r}{d\xi} + i \frac{\partial G_i}{\partial \xi}\right)\left(\frac{\partial G_r}{\partial \xi} - i \frac{\partial G_i}{\partial \xi}\right) \partial \xi$$

$$= \int_{-\infty}^{c_2} (1-\xi^3)^{5/6} \left(\left(\frac{\partial G_r}{\partial \xi}\right)^2 + \left(\frac{\partial G_i}{\partial \xi}\right)^2\right) d\xi = 0 .$$

The LHS is always positive which means that the assumption of existence of a complex eigenvalue was false.

The completeness of the system of eigenfunctions can be proved with the aid of HILBERT's theory of the polar integral equation (HAMEL [46]). The classical theory, employing integral equations with a positive definite kernel, fails in view of the change of sign of the "weighting function" $\xi/(1-\xi^3)^{7/6}$ in Eq. (7a).

Let in the following $\xi = c_1$ denote the lower limit of the interval and let either $G = 0$ or $\partial G/\partial \xi = 0$ be satisfied at this limit. If c_1 and c_2 are in the subsonic regime, then $\lambda = \mu^2$ is positive. This is because from $G = 0$ at $\xi = c_1$ and at $\xi = c_2$ it follows that between these points there must occur at least one maximum of the absolute value of G. If G is positive at the point of maximum, then the second derivative is certainly negative (while the first derivative is, of course, zero). The differential equation for G, Eq. VII, 3 (6), indicates that this is only possible for positive values of λ. A similar result is obtained for the boundary condition $G' = 0$ at the two ends of the interval.

If both x_1 and c_2 are in the supersonic regime, then only eigenvalues $\lambda < \frac{1}{12}$ are possible as may be shown by the same reasoning.

If c_1 is located in the subsonic and c_2 in the supersonic regime, then both positive and negative eigenvalues λ are obtained. If λ is negative, then μ is imaginary. Equation (8) applied to an eigenfunction yields, with the aid of Eq. (4)

$$C = \int\limits_{-\infty}^{c_2} \frac{\xi}{(1-\xi^3)^{1/6}} [G(\xi)]^2 \, d\xi = \frac{1}{\frac{1}{16} - 9\lambda} \int\limits_{-\infty}^{c_2} (1-\xi^2)^{5/6} \left(\frac{\partial G}{\partial \xi}\right)^2 d\xi \, .$$

Since the integral on the RHS is always positive, C is always of the same sign as $\frac{1}{16} - 9\lambda$.

The eigenvalues, arranged according to their magnitude, may be denoted as follows

$$\ldots - \lambda_h \ldots \lambda_{-3}\, \lambda_{-2}\, \lambda_{-1}\, \lambda_1\, \lambda_2\, \lambda_3 \ldots \lambda_h \ldots,$$

where the negative and positive subscripts refer respectively to negative and positive eigenvalues. A similar notation will be used for the corresponding values of μ. The corresponding eigenfunctions G are

$$\ldots - G_{-h} \ldots G_{-3}\, G_{-2}\, G_{-1}\, G_1\, G_2\, G_3 \ldots G_h \ldots$$

with a similar notation being employed for the integrals C corresponding to each particular eigenfunction.

Since the system of functions G is complete any function $y(\xi)$ which satisfies certain continuity conditions may be expanded in the form

$$y(\xi) = \sum_{h=1}^{\infty} a_h G_h(\xi) + \sum_{h=1}^{\infty} a_{-h} G_{-h}(\xi) \, . \tag{9}$$

The coefficients $a_{\pm h}$ are found with the aid of Eq. (8), by multiplying the latter by $\xi G_k(\xi)/(1-\xi^3)^{7/6}$ and integrating between the limits of the interval. In view of the orthogonality relation, Eq. (7a), there results

$$a_{\pm k} = (C_{\pm k})^{-1} \int_{-\infty}^{c_2} \frac{\xi}{(1-\xi^3)^{7/6}} y(\xi)\, G_{\pm k}(\xi)\, d\xi . \tag{10}$$

10. The Representation of Appropriate Solutions of Tricomi's Equation by the the Superposition of Particular Solutions Constructed from Eigenfunctions

The completeness of the system of solutions constructed from eigenfunctions follows the completeness of the system of the latter in the following manner. Let us consider a solution of Tricomi's equation, VII, 3 (5a), such that along $\xi = c_1$ and $\xi = c_2$ it satisfies either the boundary condition $\psi = 0$ or the condition $\psi_\xi = 0$. Let the solution be valid for $\varrho_1 < \varrho < \varrho_2$ where ϱ_1 and ϱ_2 are appropriate constants. Then in view of the completeness of the system of the G functions the solution along any line $\varrho = \text{const}$ can be obtained by superposition of these functions in the form

$$\psi = \sum_{h=-\infty}^{h=+\infty} a_h(\varrho)\, G_h(\xi), \tag{1}$$

where $a_{\pm h}(\varrho)$ are suitable functions of ϱ. The differential equation is assumed to be satisfied everywhere in the region considered. Thus the derivatives occurring in the differential equation exist and may be calculated by differentiation under the summation sign in the last equation. In this way one obtains

$$\frac{\partial}{\partial \varrho}(\varrho^{7/6}\psi_\varrho) = \sum_{h=-\infty}^{h=+\infty} \left(\frac{d}{d\varrho}(\varrho^{7/6})\frac{d a_h}{d\varrho}\right) G_h(\xi),$$

$$\frac{\partial}{\partial \xi}(1-\xi^3)^{5/6}\psi_\xi) = \sum_{h=-\infty}^{h=+\infty} a_h(\varrho) \frac{d}{d\xi}\left[(1-\xi^3)^{5/6}\frac{dG_h}{d\xi}\right].$$

Substituting these into Eq. VII, 3 (5a) and using the differential equation VII, 3 (6) for G one obtains the following equations for the coefficients a_h

$$-9\left(\frac{1}{144} - \mu_h^2\right) a_h = 9 \frac{d}{d\varrho}\left[\varrho^{1/6}\frac{d a_h}{d\varrho}\right].$$

Hence the coefficients are of the form

$$a_h(\varrho) = A_{h1}\, \varrho^{-(1/12)+\mu_h} + A_{h2}\, \varrho^{-(1/12)-\mu_h}$$

where $A_{h,1}$ and $A_{h,2}$ are constants. Substituting in Eq. (1) one finds that as a result of Eq. VII, 3 (3) the solution ψ appears in the form of a superposition of particular solutions constructed from eigenfunctions.

11. The Eigenfunctions and Eigenvalues in the Limiting Case of $c_2 \to 1$

From now on we shall again consider the lower limit of the interval to be $c_1 = -\infty$. To determine the eigenvalues for the limiting case $c_2 \to 1$ we start from Eq. VII, 4 (17d). When $\xi = c_2$ is close to 1, the hypergeometric series can be replaced by their first terms and, from the condition $G = 0$, one obtains

$$\frac{\Gamma(2\mu)\sin\left[\pi\left(\mu+\frac{1}{4}\right)\right]}{\Gamma\left(\mu+\frac{11}{12}\right)\Gamma\left(\mu+\frac{7}{12}\right)}(1-c_2^3)^{-\mu+(1/12)} +$$

$$+\frac{\Gamma(-2\mu)\sin\left[\pi\left(-\mu+\frac{1}{4}\right)\right]}{\Gamma\left(-\mu+\frac{11}{12}\right)\Gamma\left(-\mu+\frac{7}{12}\right)}(1-c_2^3)^{\mu+(1/12)} = 0. \tag{1}$$

Since the equation remains unchanged if μ and $-\mu$ are interchanged we can always assume that μ is positive. We divide the equation by $(1-c_2^3)^{-\mu+(1/12)}$ and let c_2 tend to 1. This yields for the antisymmetric particular solutions

$$\sin\left[\pi\left(\mu+\frac{1}{4}\right)\right] = 0,$$

i.e.

$$\mu_h = -\frac{1}{4} + h, \quad h = 1, 2 \ldots \tag{2}$$

and similarly for the symmetrical particular solutions, from Eq. VII, 4 (16)

$$\mu_h = -\frac{3}{4} + h, \quad h = 1, 2 \ldots. \tag{3}$$

The first of the corresponding eigenfunctions are shown in Figs. 66 and 67. It is further necessary to determine the negative eigenvalues. When μ is imaginary both of the terms in Eq. VII, 4 (17d) are complex conjugate. We replace again the hypergeometric series by their first term 1 and introduce

$$\mu = i\nu.$$

We put futher

$$\Gamma\left(\frac{1}{2}\right)\frac{\Gamma(2\mu)\sin\left[\pi\left(\mu+\frac{1}{4}\right)\right]}{\Gamma\left(\mu+\frac{11}{12}\right)\Gamma\left(\mu+\frac{7}{12}\right)} = A(\nu)\,e^{i\sigma(\nu)}, \tag{4}$$

where $A(\nu)$ and $\sigma(\nu)$ are real. There results

$$(1-c_2^3)^{1/12}A(\nu)\,\{e^{i\sigma(\nu)-i\nu\log(1-c_2^3)} + e^{-i\sigma(\nu)+i\nu\log(1-c_2^3)}\} = 0$$

or

$$\cos[\sigma(\nu) - \nu \ln (1 - c_2^3)] = 0.$$

An eigenvalue is obtained when

$$\sigma(\nu) - \nu \ln (1 - c_2^3) = \left(h - \frac{1}{2}\right)\pi, \tag{5}$$

h being an integer. In the limiting case $c_2 \to 1$ the term $\ln(1 - c_2^3)$ tends to $-\infty$ and the difference between two neighbouring eigenvalues becomes infinitesimally small so that a continuous spectrum of negative eigenvalues results. The same situation arises in the case of antisymmetric particular solutions.

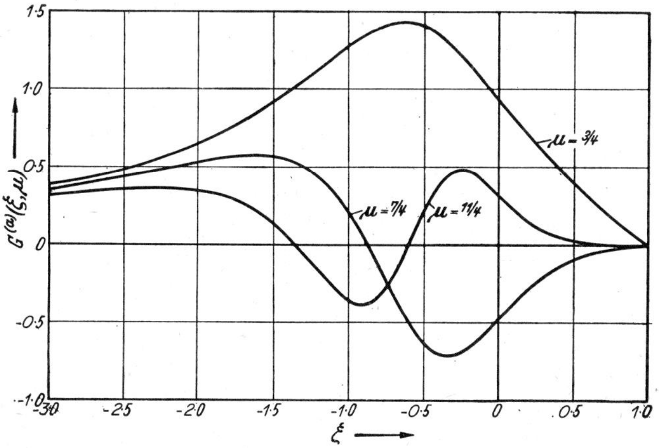

FIG. 66 Some antisymmetric eigenfunctions $G^{(a)}(\xi, \mu)$. $\mu = 3/4$, $\mu = 7/4$, $\mu = 11/4$.

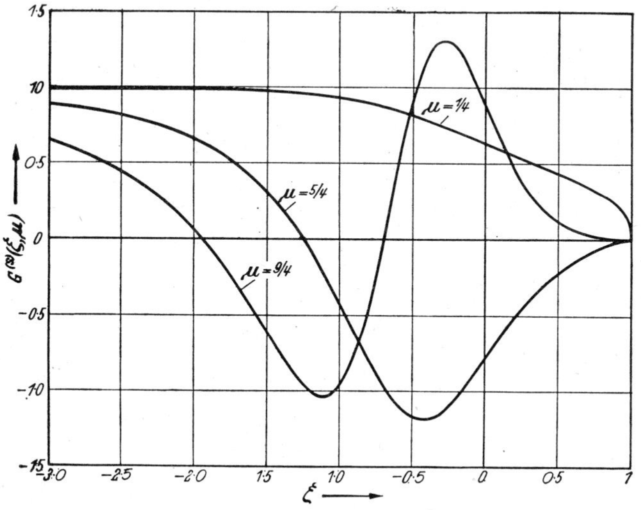

FIG. 67 Some symmetric eigenfunctions $G^{(s)}(\xi, \mu)$. $\mu = 1/4$, $\mu = 5/4$, $\mu = 9/4$.

The particular solutions ψ which can be constructed with the aid of the eigenfunctions, which we have just determined, most frequently do not have the form which could be expected from the physical point of view. The solutions of the form $\psi = G^{(a)}\varrho^{-(1/12)+\mu}$ show a singularity in the higher derivatives, which is propagated along $\xi = 1$, for the positive values of μ found above. The solutions for imaginary values of μ oscillate frequently in the vicinity of $\xi = 1$ and become infinite when $\varrho \to 0$. In Section VII, 13 we shall discuss, however, transformations which result in the expected properties of the function ψ becoming apparent. Temporarily, however, we have to restrict ourselves to the family of particular solutions, just discussed, since only these solutions have been shown to be complete.

12. The Representation of an Arbitrary Function in the Limiting Case $c_2 \to 1$

In view of the occurrence of a continuous spectrum of negative eigenvalues it is not possible to represent an arbitrary function directly with the aid of Eq. VII, 9 (9). The necessary limiting process will be discussed on the example of the antisymmetric solutions. The corresponding formula for the symmetric solutions will be quoted at the end of this discussion.

When $c_2 \to 1$ we find for an arbitrary function, in accordance with Eq. VII, 9 (9),

$$y(\xi) = \sum_{h=1}^{\infty} \frac{G_h(\xi)}{C_h} \int_{-\infty}^{c_2} y(\tau) \frac{\tau}{(1-\tau^3)^{7/6}} G_h(\tau)\, d\tau + \\ + \sum_{h=1}^{\infty} \frac{G_{-h}(\xi)}{C_{-h}} \int_{-\infty}^{c_2} y(\tau) \frac{\tau}{(1-\tau^3)^{7/6}} G_{-h}(\tau)\, d\tau, \tag{1}$$

where the coefficients C_h are defined by

$$C_{\pm h} = \int_{-\infty}^{c_2} G^2_{\pm h}(\tau) \frac{\tau}{(1-\tau^3)^{7/6}}\, d\tau. \tag{2}$$

In order to calculate these coefficients we employ Eq. VII, 9 (8). We put for the sake of brevity

$$B(\mu) = \frac{\Gamma\left(\frac{1}{2}\right)\Gamma(2\mu)}{\Gamma\left(\mu + \frac{11}{12}\right)\Gamma\left(\mu + \frac{7}{12}\right)}, \tag{3}$$

so that the expression for $G^{(a)}$ in the vicinity of $\xi = 1$ may, in accordance with Eq. VII, 4 (17d), be written

$$G^{(a)} = B(\mu)\sin\left[\pi\left(\mu + \frac{1}{4}\right)\right](1-\xi^3)^{(1/12)-\mu} + \\ + B(-\mu)\sin\left[\pi\left(-\mu + \frac{1}{4}\right)\right](1-\xi^3)^{(1/12)+\mu}. \tag{4}$$

Preliminary to calculating C_h we determine

$$\frac{\partial G^{(a)}}{\partial \xi} = B(\mu) \sin\left[\pi\left(\mu + \frac{1}{4}\right)\right](-3)\left(\frac{1}{12} - \mu\right)(1 - \xi^3)^{-(11/12)-\mu} +$$

$$+ B(-\mu) \sin\left[\pi\left(-\mu + \frac{1}{4}\right)\right](-3)\left(\frac{1}{12} + \mu\right)(1 - \xi^3)^{-(11/12)+\mu}. \tag{5}$$

Although the first terms of Eqs. (4) and (5) vanish when μ is an eigenvalue, their contribution to the derivatives with respect to μ is still predominant. Neglecting terms of higher order in $(1 - \xi^3)$ one obtains from Eqs. (4) and (5)

$$\frac{\partial G^{(a)}}{\partial \mu} = \pi B(\mu) \cos\left[\pi\left(\mu + \frac{1}{4}\right)\right](1 - \xi^3)^{(1/12)-\mu},$$

$$\frac{\partial^2 G^{(a)}}{\partial \xi\, \partial \mu} = \pi B(\mu) \cos\left[\pi\left(\mu + \frac{1}{4}\right)\right](-3)\left(\frac{1}{12} - \mu\right)(1 - \xi^3)^{-(11/12)-\mu}$$

with μ being an eigenvalue. Since as a result of Eq. VII, 11 (3),

$$\sin\left[\pi\left(-\mu + \frac{1}{4}\right)\right] = \cos\left[\pi\left(\mu + \frac{1}{4}\right)\right] = \pm 1$$

is satisfied for eigenvalues, there results finally with the aid of Eq. VII, 9 (8)

$$C_h = \frac{\pi}{3} B(\mu_h)\, B(-\mu_h). \tag{6}$$

Here μ is to be obtained from Eq. VII, 11 (3) and B (μ) from Eq. (3).

For negative eigenvalues we introduce again

$$\mu = i\nu \tag{7}$$

and the value of ν corresponding to μ_h will be denoted by ν_h. Hence

$$\frac{d\nu}{d\mu} = -i. \tag{7a}$$

The functions B, A and σ are related by

$$B(i\nu) \sin\left[\pi\left(i\nu + \frac{1}{4}\right)\right] = A(\nu)\, e^{i\sigma(\nu)} \tag{8}$$

in view of the definition in Eq. VII, 11 (4). We calculate next $\partial G/\partial \mu$ and $\partial G/\partial \xi$ for an eigenvalue, i.e. taking into account Eq. VII, 11 (5). The transition to the limit of $c_2 \to 1$ is then carried out in some of the terms. From Eq. (4) one obtains

$$G^{(a)} = (1 - c_2^3)^{1/12} A(\nu) \cos[\sigma(\nu) - \nu \ln(1 - c_2^3)],$$

$$\frac{\partial G^{(a)}}{\partial \mu} = i\, 2A (1 - c_2^3)^{1/12} \times$$
$$\times \sin[\sigma(\nu_h) - \nu_h \ln(1 - c_2^3)] \left(\frac{d\sigma}{d\nu}(\nu_h) - \ln(1 - c_2^3)\right),$$

$$\frac{\partial G}{\partial \xi} = -6A(1 - c_2^3)^{-11/12} \nu_h \sin[\sigma(\nu_h) - \nu_h \ln(1 - c_2^3)].$$

The absolute value of the sine functions occurring here is 1 as a result of Eq. VII, 11 (5). When $\xi = c_2$ then $G = 0$ and Eq. VII, 9 (8) yields

$$C_{-h} = \frac{2}{3} A^2(\nu_h) \left[\frac{d\sigma}{d\nu} - \ln(1 - c_2^3)\right]. \tag{9}$$

so that C_{-h} tends to $+\infty$ when $(1 - c_2^3)$ tends to zero.

It is now necessary to take into account the fact that in this limiting process the negative eigenvalues approach one another. From Eq. VII, 11 (5) one finds

$$\sigma(\nu_h) - \nu_h \ln(1 - c_2^3) = \pi\left(h - \frac{1}{2}\right). \tag{10}$$

For small values of $(1 - c_2^3)$ a unit change in h results in only a small change in $\sigma(\nu_h)$. Denoting the change in ν_h between two successive values of h by $\Delta\nu_h$ the last equation yields

$$\Delta\nu_h \left[\frac{d\sigma}{d\nu}(\nu_h) - \ln(1 - c_2^2)\right] \to \pi \quad \text{for} \quad (1 - c_2^3) \to 0. \tag{11}$$

With the aid of the above equation the second term of Eq. (1) can be transformed from a summation extended over h to one extended over $\Delta\nu_h$. Introducing simultaneously C_{-h} from Eq. (9) one obtains

$$\sum_{h=1}^{\infty} \frac{G_{-h}}{C_{-h}} \int_{-\infty}^{c_2} y(\tau) \frac{\tau}{(1 - \tau^3)^{7/6}} G_{-h}(\tau)\, d\tau$$

$$= \sum_{\Delta\nu_h} \frac{\Delta\nu_h G^{(a)}(\xi, i\nu_h)}{\frac{2}{3}\pi A^2(\nu_h)} \int_{-\infty}^{c_2} y(\tau) \frac{\tau}{(1 - \tau^3)^{7/6}} G^{(a)}(\tau, i\nu_h)\, d\tau.$$

Now the transition to the limit $c_2 \to 1$ can be carried out

$$\lim_{c_2 \to 1} \sum_{h=1}^{\infty} \frac{G_{-h}^{(a)}}{C_{-h}} \int_{-\infty}^{c_2} y(\tau) \frac{\tau}{(1 - \tau^3)^{7/6}} G_{-h}(\tau)\, d\tau$$

$$= \frac{3}{2\pi} \int_0^{\infty} \frac{d\nu\, G^{(a)}(\xi, i\nu)}{A^2(\nu)} \int_{-\infty}^{1} y(\tau) \frac{\tau}{(1 - \tau^3)^{7/6}} G^{(a)}(\tau, i\nu)\, d\tau. \tag{12}$$

These results are introduced in Eq. (1). Expressing C_h with the aid of Eq. (6), the second term of Eq. (1) by means of Eq. (12) and A in terms of B, in accordance with Eq. (8), we replace the integration with respect to ν which occurs in Eq. (12) by an integration with respect to μ along the positive imaginary axis of the complex μ plane and obtain

$$y(\xi) = \frac{3}{\pi}\left\{\sum_{h=1}^{\infty}\left(\frac{G^{(a)}(\xi, \mu_h^{(a)})}{B^{(a)}(\mu_h^{(a)})\, B^{(a)}(-\mu_h^{(a)})} \times \right.\right.$$

$$\left. \times \int_{-\infty}^{1} y(\tau) \frac{\tau}{(1-\tau^3)^{7/6}}\, G^{(a)}(\tau, \mu_h^{(a)})\, d\tau \right) -$$

$$-\frac{i}{2}\int_{\mu=0}^{i\infty}\left(\frac{G^{(a)}(\xi, \mu)}{B^{(a)}(\mu)\, B^{(a)}(-\mu) \sin\Big[\pi + \frac{1}{4}\Big)\Big] \sin\Big[\Big(\pi\Big(-\mu + \frac{1}{4}\Big)\Big]} \times \right.$$

$$\left.\left. \times \int_{-\infty}^{1} y(\tau) \frac{\tau}{(1-\tau^3)^{7/6}}\, G^{(a)}(\tau, \mu)\, d\tau \right) d\mu \right\}, \tag{13}$$

where

$$\mu_h^{(a)} = h - \frac{1}{4} \tag{13a}$$

and

$$B^{(a)}\mu = \frac{\Gamma\left(\frac{1}{2}\right)\Gamma(2\mu)}{\Gamma\left(\mu + \frac{11}{12}\right)\Gamma\left(\mu + \frac{7}{12}\right)}. \tag{13b}$$

The corresponding expression for the symmetric particular solutions is

$$y(\xi) = \frac{3}{\pi}\left\{\sum_{h=1}^{\infty}\left(\frac{G^{(s)}(\xi, \mu_h^{(s)})}{B^{(s)}(\mu_h^{(s)})\, B^{(s)}(-\mu_h^{(s)})} \times \right.\right.$$

$$\left. \times \int_{-\infty}^{1} y(\tau) \frac{\tau}{(1-\tau^3)^{7/6}}\, G^{(s)}(\tau, \mu_h^{(s)})\, d\tau \right) -$$

$$-\frac{i}{2}\int_{\mu=0}^{i\infty}\left(\frac{G^{(s)}(\xi, \mu)}{B^{(s)}(\mu)\, B^{(s)}(-\mu) \sin\left[\pi\left(\mu + \frac{3}{4}\right)\right] \sin\left[\pi\left(-\mu + \frac{3}{4}\right)\right]} \times \right.$$

$$\left.\left. \times \int_{-\infty}^{1} y(\tau) \frac{\tau}{(1-\tau^3)^{7/6}}\, G^{(s)}(\tau, \mu)\, d\tau \right) d\mu \right\}, \tag{14}$$

where

$$B^{(s)}(\mu) = 2\Gamma\left(\frac{1}{2}\right)\frac{\Gamma(2\mu)}{\Gamma\left(\mu+\frac{5}{12}\right)\Gamma\left(\mu+\frac{1}{12}\right)} \tag{14a}$$

and

$$\mu_h^{(s)} = h - \frac{3}{4}\,. \tag{14b}$$

13. The Expansion of a Solution ψ in Terms of Particular Solutions

At the beginning of Section VII, 9 we have derived a system of particular solutions, as a result of certain properties of a solution ψ along a characteristic

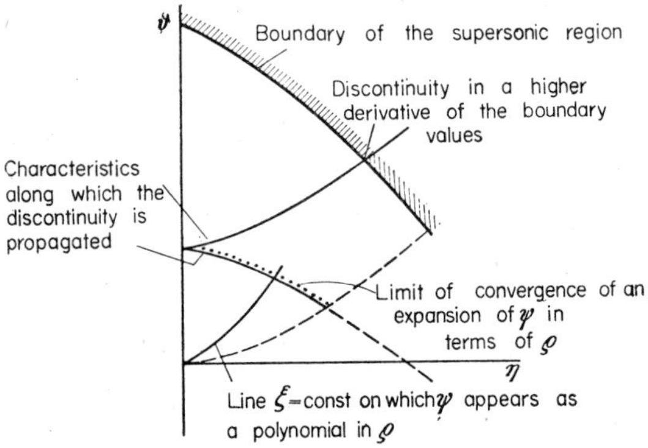

Fig. 68 Illustrating the limitations of an expansion in terms of the "natural" particular solutions.

through the origin. The question as to whether this system of solutions could be used to represent any expression ψ which possesses these properties remained, in any case, open. Such a representation could be of considerable importance. The origin of the η, ϑ plane generally represents infinity in the physical plane. Since these particular solutions are arranged according to the power of ϱ, this yields a particularly clear representation. The fact that along a line ξ = const the solution would then appear in the form of a power series in ϱ indicates, however, the limitations of such a method of representation. It is evidently only applicable as long as the function ψ is regular along a line ξ = const. Such regularity is by no means obvious in the supersonic regime. When, namely, the boundary conditions are not prescribed in terms of regular functions then discontinuities in the higher derivatives of ψ are propagated along certain characteristics in the supersonic regime. Such discontinuities may be very weak; they may, for example, occur in a derivative of a high order; they determine, however, the limit of the region of convergence of the attempted representation (Fig. 68). The question of expansion in terms of such a system of particular solutions has been discussed by GUDERLEY [38]. Here we shall merely reproduce some of the more fundamental ideas and these in only a simplified form. For particulars of the proofs the reader is referred to the original paper.

Let the function ψ, satisfying TRICOMI's equation everywhere in a region such as shown in Fig. 69 and also satisfying TRICOMI's conditions at the origin (cf. Section V, 11), be given. Thus the derivatives ψ_ϱ and ψ_ξ, along a curve C' within the region, are given at least in principle. The function ψ can be reconstructed by an analytical continuation with the aid of the values of ψ and ψ_ϱ along C', at least in the subsonic regime. The desired representation of ψ could, therefore, be obtained by constructing an expression which assumes the required values along C'. If, however, the curve C' satisfies the conditions of TRICOMI's theorem, just the values of ψ are sufficient to determine the function. Thus prescribing the values of the derivatives will, in general, lead to an in-

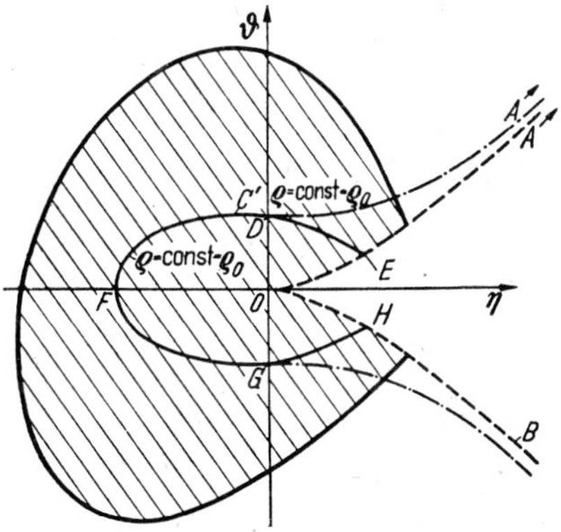

FIG. 69

consistency. The knowledge of the values ψ is unfortunately, however, insufficient if the equations of the preceding section are to be used to obtain an expression for the solution.

We modify, therefore, our problem in the following manner. We consider a function $\bar{\psi}$ which is equal to the original function ψ within the curve C' and such that outside C' $\bar{\psi} \equiv 0$. Thus $\bar{\psi}$ has along C' a discontinuity in its value and in a derivative in a direction different from that of C'. Further, at infinity $\bar{\psi}$ vanishes and at the origin it satisfies TRICOMI's condition. This boundary value problem is completely determined since the difference of two solutions of the problem satisfies TRICOMI's differential equation everywhere to the left of the characteristics OA and OB in Fig. 69 and thus also along C'. Further, the solution vanishes at infinity and satisfies TRICOMI's conditions at the origin. Such a solution is identically equal to zero, as a result of TRICOMI's theorem, when the boundary is allowed to retreat to infinity.

The advantage of this formulation lies in the fact that a solution of the problem can be obtained when along C' the values of ψ and ψ_ϱ (or the jump in $\bar{\psi}$ and in its derivative $\bar{\psi}_\varrho$) are prescribed quite independently. If the prescribed values of the function and of the derivative are not compatible, then the sole result is that outside of C' the solution is non-zero. If one prescribes, on the other hand, along C' values of the function and of the derivative directly, then in general no solution can be obtained.

Prior to carrying out the calculations the solution is split up into a symmetric and antisymmetric part and only the upper half of the η, ϑ plane is considered. We shall restrict ourselves to a discussion of the antisymmetric part. For the sake of simplicity we chose in the present consideration for the curve C' a line $\varrho = \text{const}$. Let this line in the subsonic regime be located wholly within the region G considered. This is impossible in the supersonic regime since then G would extend to infinity. Fortunately, however, only the characteristic DE in

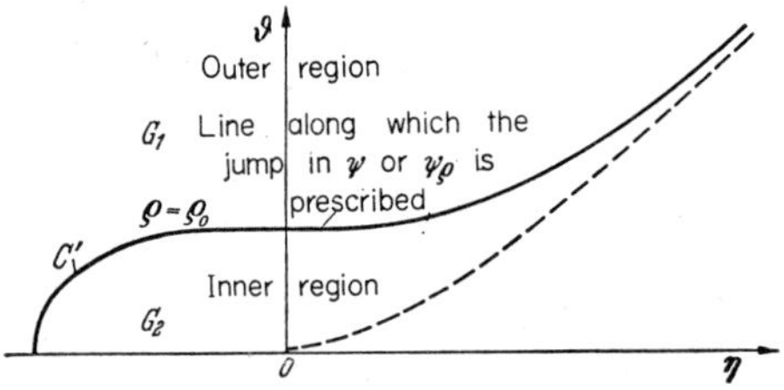

FIG. 70 Division of the η, ϑ plane into an internal and an external region.

Fig. 69, which originates at the intersection of C' with the sonic line, has to lie within G. If, namely, the values of ψ are known on this characteristic, then the solution can be extended up to the original curve $\varrho = \text{const}$ in the following manner. Along the characteristic EA one prescribes arbitrary values of ψ which continuously approach the value of ψ occurring at the point E. The solution is then constructed in the region DEA with the aid of the method of characteristics from the values along DE and EA. Conversely, if we compute a solution which along the line DA ($\varrho = \text{const}$), which is not a characteristic, assumes the just calculated values of $\overline{\psi}$ and its derivative $\overline{\psi}_\varrho$ then this solution agrees in the entire region ADE with that previously obtained in this region. The two solutions agree thus also along the characteristic DE so that the condition for $\overline{\psi}$ along DE is automatically satisfied together with the conditions along DA.

The advantage of this construction lies in a considerable reduction in the analytical effort; it suffers, however, from the disadvantage that the use of the method of characteristics introduces into the investigation an element which cannot immediately be translated into analytical terms. In the article of GUDERLEY this problem does not arise. In what follows, we shall replace $\overline{\psi}$ again by ψ.

We have arrived thus at the following problem. Two functions $f_1(\xi)$ and $f_2(\xi)$ are given. Required is a solution of TRICOMI's equation which vanishes at infinity, satisfies TRICOMI's condition at the origin and, along a line $\varrho = \varrho_0$ exhibits a discontinuity in ψ equal to $f_1(\xi)$ and a discontinuity in ψ_ϱ equal $f_2(\xi)/\varrho_0$, as shown in Fig. 70.

The curve C' divides the η, ϑ plane into two regions, an outer one G_1 ($\varrho > \varrho_0$) and an inner one G_2 ($\varrho < \varrho_0$).

Let the solution in G_1 be represented by

$$\psi_1 = \sum_{h=1}^{\infty} a_h\, G^{(a)}(\xi\,,\, \mu_h^{(a)})\, (\varrho/\varrho_0)^{-(1/12)-\mu_h^{(a)}}\,, \tag{1a}$$

and in G_2 by

$$\psi_2 = \sum_{h=1}^{\infty} b_h\, G^{(a)}(\xi\,,\, \mu_h^{(a)})\, (\varrho/\varrho_0)^{-(1/12)+\mu_h^{(a)}} -$$

$$- \operatorname{Re} \frac{i}{2} \int_{\mu=0}^{i\infty} \beta(\mu)\, G^{(a)}(\xi\,,\, \mu)\, (\varrho/\varrho_0)^{-(1/12)+\mu}\, d\mu\,. \tag{1b}$$

In the above expressions the constants a_h and b_h and the function $\beta(\mu)$ are to be calculated from the conditions prescribed along C'. In the last term it is necessary to specify that only the real part is considered since ϱ/ϱ_0 is raised to a complex power. The assumed form of the solution indicates that the latter tends to zero at infinity. It is not possible to see from this that TRICOMI's condition is satisfied at the origin; the individual particular solutions occurring in the intergral even become infinite at the origin since μ is imaginary. This particular property of the solution will become evident later. The conditions prescribed along C' are

$$\psi_2(\xi\,,\, \varrho_0) - \psi_1(\xi\,,\, \varrho_0) = f_1(\xi)\,, \tag{2a}$$

$$\psi_{2;\,\varrho}(\xi\,,\, \varrho_0) - \psi_{1;\,\varrho}(\xi\,,\, \varrho_0) = \frac{1}{\varrho_0} f_2(\xi)\,. \tag{2b}$$

We expand the functions f_1 and f_2 with the aid of Eq. VII, 12 (13) and substitute Eq. (1) in the conditions given by Eqs. (2).

Making the coefficients of the individual functions on both sides of the resulting equation equal, one obtains

$$b_h - a_h = \left\{\frac{3}{\pi} \int_{-\infty}^{1} \frac{\tau\, f_1(\tau)\, G^{(a)}(\tau\,,\, \mu_h^{(a)})}{(1-\tau^3)^{7/6}}\right\} \Big/ \left(B^{(a)}(\mu_h^{(a)})\, B^{(a)}(-\mu_h^{(a)})\right),$$

$$\left(-\frac{1}{12}\ \mu_h^{(a)}\right) b_h - \left(-\frac{1}{12} - \mu_h^{(a)}\right) a_h$$

$$= \left\{\frac{3}{\pi} \int_{-\infty}^{1} \frac{\tau\, f_2(\tau)\, G^{(a)}(\tau\,,\, \mu_h^{(a)})}{(1-\tau^3)^{7/6}}\, d\tau\right\} \Big/ \left(B^{(a)}(\mu_h^{(a)})\, B^{(a)}(-\mu_h^{(a)})\right),$$

$$\operatorname{Re}\beta(\mu) = \left\{\frac{3}{\pi} \int_{-\infty}^{1} \frac{\tau\, f_1(\tau)\, G^{(a)}(\tau\,,\, \mu)}{(1-\tau^3)^{7/6}}\, d\tau\right\} \Big/ \left\{B^{(a)}(\mu)\, B^{(a)}(-\mu)\, \times \right.$$

$$\left. \times \sin\left[\pi\left(\mu + \frac{1}{4}\right)\right] \sin\left[\pi\left(-\mu + \frac{1}{4}\right)\right]\right\},$$

$$\operatorname{Re}\left(-\frac{1}{12} + \mu\right)\beta(\mu) = \left\{\frac{3}{\pi} \int_{-\infty}^{1} \frac{\tau\, f_2(\tau)\, G^{(a)}(\tau\,,\, \mu)}{(1-\tau^3)^{7/6}}\, d\tau\right\} \Big/ \left\{B^{(a)}(\mu)\, B^{(a)}(-\mu)\, \times \right.$$

$$\left. \times \sin\left[\pi\left(\mu + \frac{1}{4}\right)\right] \sin\left[\pi\left(-\mu + \frac{1}{4}\right)\right]\right\},$$

and hence

$$a_h = \frac{3}{\pi} I(-\mu_h^{(a)}) \frac{1}{2\mu_h^{(a)}} \Big/ \{B^{(a)}(\mu_h^{(a)})\, B^{(a)}(-\mu_h^{(a)})\}, \tag{3a}$$

$$b_h = \frac{3}{\pi} I(+\mu_h^{(a)}) \frac{1}{2\mu_h^{(a)}} \Big/ \{B^{(a)}(\mu_h^{(a)})\, B^{(a)}(-\mu_h^{(a)})\}, \tag{3b}$$

$$\beta = \frac{3}{\pi} I(\mu) \frac{1}{\mu} \Big/ \left\{B^{(a)}(\mu)^{(a)} B^{(a)}(-\mu) \sin\left[\pi\left(\mu + \frac{1}{4}\right)\right] \sin\left[\pi\left(-\mu + \frac{1}{4}\right)\right]\right\}, \tag{3c}$$

where

$$I(\mu) = \int_{-\infty}^{1} \left[f_1(\tau)\left(\mu + \frac{1}{12}\right) + f_2(\tau)\right] \frac{\tau}{(1-\tau^3)^{7/6}} G^a(\tau, \mu)\, d\tau \tag{4}$$

and in accordance with Eq. VII, 12 (13a)

$$\mu_h^{(a)} = h - \frac{1}{4}. \tag{5}$$

Thus the solution in the outer region G_1 is

$$\psi_1 = \frac{3}{\pi} \sum_{h=1}^{\infty} \frac{G^{(a)}(\xi, \mu_h^{(a)})}{B^{(a)}(\mu_h^{(a)}) B^{(a)}(-\mu_h^{(a)})} \frac{1}{2\mu_h^{(a)}} I(-\mu_h^{(a)}) \left(\frac{\varrho}{\varrho_0}\right)^{-(1/12)-\mu_h^{(a)}}, \tag{6a}$$

and in the inner region G_2

$$\psi_2 = \frac{3}{\pi} \left\{ \sum_{h=1}^{\infty} \frac{G^{(a)}(\xi, \mu_h^{(a)})}{B^{(a)}(\mu_h^{(a)}) B^{(a)}(-\mu_h^{(a)})} \frac{1}{2\mu_h^{(a)}} I(\mu_h^{(a)}) \left(\frac{\varrho}{\varrho_0}\right)^{-(1/12)+\mu_h^{(a)}} - \right.$$

$$- \operatorname{Re} i \int_0^{i\infty} \frac{G^{(a)}(\xi, \mu)\, I(\mu)}{B^{(a)}(\mu)\, B^{(a)}(-\mu)\, 2\mu \sin\left[\pi\left(\mu + \frac{1}{4}\right)\right] \sin\left[\pi\left(-\mu + \frac{1}{4}\right)\right]} \times$$

$$\left. \times \left(\frac{\varrho}{\varrho_0}\right)^{-(1/12)+\mu} d\mu \right\}. \tag{6b}$$

Two facts are important for the further development; they will, however, be stated without proof. (1) The function I defined by Eq. (4) is a single-valued analytic function of μ. (2) When $|\mu|$ tends to infinity in the first quadrant of the complex μ plane, the integrand occurring in the second part of Eq. (6) decreases in a region of the ϱ, ξ plane, in such a manner that a deformation of the integration path from the imaginary to the real μ axis is possible.

We assume, in addition, that the function $I(\mu)$ has no poles in the first quadrant. This will be discussed more fully later.

Let us consider the second term in Eq. (6b). Under the above assumptions the singularities of the integrand are given by the singularities of the expression

$$G^{(a)}(\xi, \mu) \left(\frac{\varrho}{\varrho_0}\right)^{-(1/12)+\mu} \times$$

$$\times \left\{B^{(a)}(\mu)\, B^{(a)}(-\mu) \sin\left[\pi\left(\mu + \frac{1}{4}\right)\right] \sin\left[\pi\left(-\mu + \frac{1}{4}\right)\right]\right\}^{-1}.$$

Excluding $\xi = 1$ from our consideration, the function $G^{(a)}(\xi, \mu)$ is regular for all values of μ, since it is determined by a linear differential equation and an initial condition (at $\xi = -\infty$) which does not contain μ. Singularities of the solution can occur only at points at which the differential equation is singular. No such singularities exist, however, for $\xi \neq 1$. We have to consider, therefore, only the poles of

$$\left\{B^{(a)}(\mu)\, B^{(a)}(-\mu) \sin\left[\pi\left(\mu + \frac{1}{4}\right)\right] \sin\left[\pi\left(-\mu + \frac{1}{4}\right)\right]\right\}^{-1}. \tag{7}$$

Some of the poles, namely the zeros of the trigonometric functions, can be found immediately. The poles due to the vanishing of $\sin[\pi(\mu + \frac{1}{4})]$ occur exactly at those values of $\mu_h^{(a)}$ which occur in the first sum in Eq. (6b). These poles are considered separately since they exactly cancel this sum. The residues at these points are given by

$$\frac{G^{(a)}(\xi, \mu_h^{(a)}) \left(\dfrac{\varrho}{\varrho_0}\right)^{-(1/12) + \mu_h^{(a)}}}{B^{(a)}(\mu_h^{(a)})\, B^{(a)}(-\mu_h^{(a)})\, \pi\, 2\mu_h^{(a)}}\, I(\mu_h).$$

In order to analyze the other poles, the explicit expressions for $B^{(a)}$ or Eq. VII, 12 (13) are introduced and the Γ functions occurring in them are transformed with the aid of Eq. VII, 7 (15) yielding

$$[B^{(a)}(\mu)\, B^{(a)}(-\mu)]^{-1}$$

$$= \frac{\Gamma\left(\mu + \frac{11}{12}\right)\Gamma\left(\mu + \frac{7}{12}\right)\Gamma\left(-\mu + \frac{11}{12}\right)\Gamma\left(-\mu + \frac{7}{12}\right)}{\pi\, \Gamma(2\mu)\, \Gamma(-2\mu)},$$

$$= \frac{-2\mu \sin(2\pi\mu)\, \Gamma\left(\mu + \frac{11}{12}\right)\Gamma\left(\mu + \frac{7}{12}\right)}{\sin\left[\pi\left(\mu + \frac{1}{12}\right)\right]\sin\left[\pi\left(\mu + \frac{5}{12}\right)\right]\Gamma\left(\mu + \frac{1}{12}\right)\Gamma\left(\mu + \frac{5}{12}\right)}.$$

Hence, in conjunction with Eq. (7), one finds that poles occur at the points

$$\mu = \frac{1}{4} + \frac{h}{3} \qquad h = 0, 1, 2, 3 \ldots \tag{8}$$

and the corresponding residues are

$$G^{(a)}\left(\xi, \frac{1}{4} + \frac{h}{3}\right)\left(\frac{\varrho}{\varrho_0}\right)^{(1/6) + (h/3)} \times$$

$$\times \frac{4}{3\pi} \frac{\Gamma\left(\frac{7}{6} + \frac{h}{3}\right)\Gamma\left(\frac{5}{6} + \frac{h}{3}\right)}{\Gamma\left(\frac{1}{3} + \frac{h}{3}\right)\Gamma\left(\frac{2}{3} + \frac{h}{3}\right)}\, I\left(\frac{1}{4} + \frac{h}{3}\right) \qquad h = 0, 1, 2 \ldots. \tag{9}$$

After deformation, the path of integration follows the real μ axis and goes in small semicircles around the poles located on the real axis, as shown in Fig. 71. On the real axis the integrand is obviously real. Because of the factor i in front of the integral in Eq. (6b) the real part of this contribution is zero. On the other hand the semicircles, describing the poles, produce imaginary contributions to the integral, namely each particular residue multiplied by $-i\pi$. The negative sign indicates that the poles are described in a negative (clockwise) sense. Thus the real part of the entire expression is the sum of the residues multiplied by π. One notices that the residues at the points $\mu_h^{(a)}$ cancel the sum occurring in Eq. (6b). One obtains thus

$$\psi_2 = -\frac{4}{\pi}\sum_{h=0}^{\infty} G^{(a)}\left(\xi, \frac{1}{4}+\frac{h}{3}\right)\left(\frac{\varrho}{\varrho_0}\right)^{(1/6)+(h/3)} \times$$

$$\times \frac{\Gamma\left(\frac{7}{6}+\frac{h}{3}\right)\Gamma\left(\frac{5}{6}+\frac{h}{3}\right)}{\Gamma\left(\frac{1}{3}+\frac{h}{3}\right)\Gamma\left(\frac{2}{3}+\frac{h}{3}\right)} I\left(\frac{1}{4}+\frac{h}{3}\right). \tag{10}$$

This expression is in fact a superposition of particular solutions with positive exponents of ϱ which we have obtained in Section VII, 9 [cf. Eq. VII, 9 (3)]. It cannot, however, be always considered as a full representation of the solution ψ_2. The definition of I, as given by Eq. (4), indicates that as long as f_1 and f_2 are bounded (which is always assumed to be the case) and as long as G is also bounded, I converges uniformly and is therefore an analytic function of μ and one which has no poles in the complex μ plane. The behaviour of $G(\tau, \mu)$ for $\tau = -\infty$ is such that no difficulties arise on this account. One should note, however, that in general for $\tau \to 1$ the function G becomes infinite. [Compare the asymptotic representation Eq. VII, 7 (12b)]. The function I is certainly analytic when in the vicinity of $\tau = 1$, for example for $\xi_1 < \tau < 1$, where ξ_1 is a suitable constant, the functions f_1 and f_2 are identically zero.

We shall assume now that the above condition is satisfied. The location of the point ξ_1 influences the boundary of the region in which the above transformations are permissible. This region is determined by the condition that the integrand in Eq. (6b) should tend to zero sufficiently fast when $|\mu|$ in a complex plane tends to infinity. This depends also, however, on I and therefore on ξ_1. A more exact investigation yields as a region of validity of Eq. (10) the shaded figure in Fig. 72. Through the point $\xi = \xi_1$ of the line C' we draw a characteristic with a positive slope and through the intersection G of the latter with the sonic line we draw the line $\varrho = \text{const}$ (GK) and also the characteristic with the negative slope GH. These last two lines are both boundaries of the region of validity. Equation (10) cannot, in general, converge outside of this region. One cannot, namely, exclude the possibility that a discontinuity is propagated along a characteristic FG. This would be reflected at the sonic line and result in a discontinuity along GH. Since, as mentioned before, the representation of ψ_2 along a line $\xi = \text{const}$ by Eq. (10) is a power series in $\varrho^{1/3}$, the region of convergence does not extend beyond the next discontinuity, i.e. beyond the line GH. The effect of this on the subsonic regime can be obtained from the asymptotic representation of G.

As ξ tends to 1 the region of convergence becomes progressively smaller so that Eq. (10) apparently loses its value. This demands a more refined expression for the function I, so that the region in the vicinity of $\xi = 1$ can be included in our considerations. In any case, in accordance with our above discussion, no singularities in the functions f_1 and f_2 can occur in the vicinity of $\xi = 1$. At the point $\xi = 1$ itself, however, singularities in the higher derivatives are possible. It is thus natural to demand that in the vicinity of $\xi = 1$ the functions f_1 and f_2 are to be analytic in ξ. Thus in the vicinity of $\xi = 1$ these functions are defined also in the complex ξ plane. They are, in general, multivalued functions

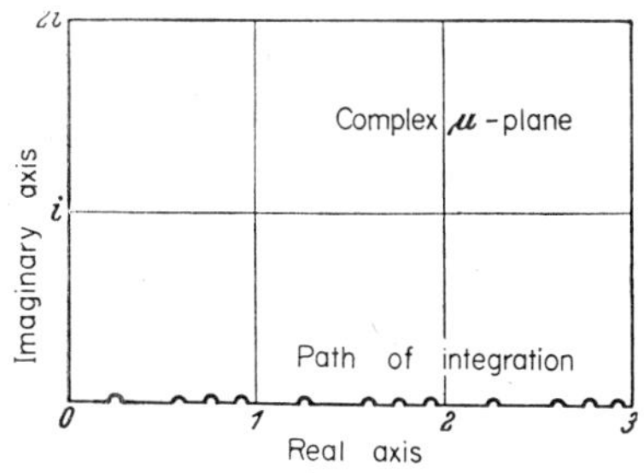

FIG. 71
Path of integration in the complex μ plane.

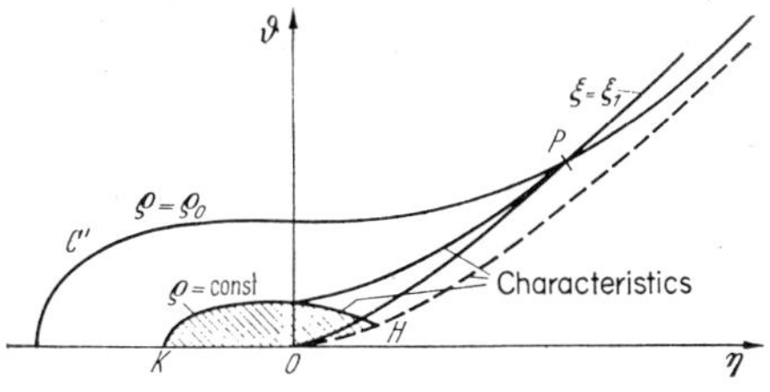

FIG. 72 Region of convergence of a representation of ψ in terms of "natural" particular solutions.

whose branch points are at $\xi = 1$. It is in fact not possible, without a definition of this kind, to determine the function I for large values of the real part of μ since the integral occurring in Eq. (4) would then diverge.

If a discontinuity is propagated along $\xi = 1$ this may be seen from the behaviour of f_1 and f_2 in the vicinity of $\xi = 1$. Such a discontinuity can be fully identified. Equation (10) can evidently be only used when we demand, in addition, of the functions f_1 and f_2 that they do not cause a discontinuity to be propagated along $\xi = 1$. This, however, prescribes for these power series a definite form at $\xi = 1$. If this requirement is not satisfied, then additional poles result in the complex μ plane and additional expressions describing the propagation of discontinuities are introduced in Eq. (10) (cf. GUDERLEY [38]).

The above is, however, the only restriction as to the applicability of Eq. (10). The region of convergence is always of the form shown in Fig. 72; the exact position of the boundaries depends, however, on the behaviour of f_1 and f_2 in the complex ξ plane. The behaviour for real values of ξ does not, in this respect, provide a sufficient criterion.

In the above-mentioned article GUDERLEY analyzes these problems in detail and, in particular, the choice of the contour C' is more general. In most cases one would assume this curve to coincide with the contour of the region considered.

The results of this work can be utilized in order to obtain the coefficients of the expansion in Eq. (10) for a solution, which was obtained numerically, by means of integrals.

Similar considerations can be applied to a region whose contour corresponds to that in Fig. 73. The contour of the original region is $ABDEFGH$. Within this region, one choses the two curves C' and C'' in the subsonic regime; these are lines $\varrho =$ const. Then the curve C' is continued as the characteristic LM. By assuming suitable boundary values along the characteristic MK, a continuation of the solution in the region MKL can be found. From this continuation one then obtains the values of ψ and ψ_ϱ on the curves $C'(ILK)$ and $C''(NPK)$. The procedure described above yields then a solution for the region located between C' and C''. In this region the contributions of C' and C'' are simply

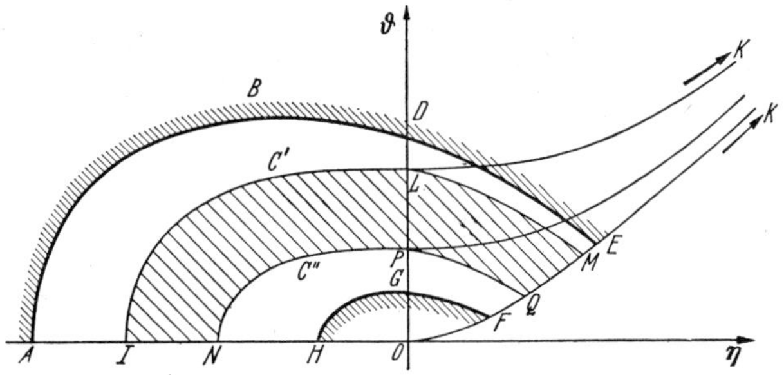

FIG. 73 Region of convergence of a representation of ψ in terms of "natural" particular solutions

added to one another. The contribution due to C'' has the form of Eq. (6a) and no further transformations are necessary. This part of the solution converges not only outside of C'' but even outside the line NPQ. This may best be shown with the aid of the asymptotic representation of the corresponding functions G. The contribution due to C' is transformed as described above. As far as the limit of convergence of the transformed expression is concerned, our considerations on the preceding pages are valid. In the subsonic regime this limit takes the form of a line $\varrho =$ const which continues in the supersonic regime as a characteristic with a negative slope. For certain boundary values in the supersonic regime this limit of convergence could coincide with the line ILM. The common region of convergence of the contributions due to C' and C'', respectively, is then as represented by the shaded area in Fig. 73. With the notation of Section VII, 9 the resulting solution contains both terms $\psi_{-(5/6)-h}$ and terms $\psi_{(1/6)+(h/3)}$. In the most general case one should add to this also the symmetric particular solutions $\psi_{-(1/3)-h}$ and $\psi_{h/3}$.

14. The Particular Solutions of Tamada and Tomotika

The particular solutions of Tamada and Tomotika, and the particular solutions of Falkowich, to be discussed in the next Section, both yield singularities in the subsonic regime. They are convenient for the calculation of flow problems in which the approaching flow is subsonic or in discussing details of the flow fields described in Chapter VI.

The fundamental points of the analysis of TAMADA and TOMOTIKA are as follows. TRICOMI's differential equation contains ϑ only in the derivatives of ψ and not in the coefficients. This is due to the fact that no characteristic direction of velocity exists in the hodograph. This means that from a given solution ψ one can obtain new solutions by changing all the values of ϑ by a constant ϑ_0. This is true also if an imaginary constant $i\vartheta_0$ is added to all values of ϑ. Since the coefficients in TRICOMI's equation are real, both the real and the imaginary parts of the solution obtained in this manner are each separately a solution of TRICOMI's equation. Applying this to the particular solutions

$$\psi = \varrho^{-(1/12)+\mu} G(\xi, \mu) \tag{1}$$

one obtains

$$\varrho = -\eta^3 + \frac{9}{4}(\vartheta + i\vartheta_0)^2, \tag{2a}$$

$$\xi = \frac{\eta}{\left(\frac{3}{2}(\vartheta + i\vartheta_0)\right)^{2/3}}. \tag{2b}$$

The function G is determined by a linear differential equation with singular points at $\xi = \sqrt[3]{1}$ and $\xi = \infty$. For finite values of η and ϑ, ξ can never be infinite. At the singular point $\xi = \sqrt[3]{1}$ one obtains from Eq. (2b)

$$\eta^3 = \frac{9}{4}(\vartheta^2 - \vartheta_0^2) - 2\,\frac{9}{4}\,i\,\vartheta\,\vartheta_0 = 0$$

and since both the real and imaginary parts must vanish, there results

$$\vartheta = 0,$$

$$\eta = -\left(\frac{2}{3}\vartheta_0\right)^{2/3}.$$

This is the only point of the η, ϑ plane in which the solution can become singular. The solution G at this point takes the form of a superposition of two linearly independent expressions which, in accordance with Eq. VII, 4 (16), can be written

$$(1-\xi^3)^{-\mu+(1/12)} F\left(\frac{1}{12}-\mu, \frac{7}{12}-\mu, 1-2\mu, 1-\xi^3\right)$$

and

$$(1-\xi^3)^{\mu+(1/12)} F\left(\frac{1}{12}+\mu, \frac{7}{12}+\mu, 1+2\mu, 1-\xi^3\right).$$

The behaviour at $\vartheta = 0$, $\eta = -\left(\frac{2}{3}\vartheta_0\right)^{2/3}$ is controlled by the first term of these series. Upon transformation to the variables η and ϑ, Eq. (1) yields

$$\psi = \left[\frac{3}{2}(\vartheta + i\,\vartheta_0)^2\right]^{(1/2)-\mu}$$

or

$$\psi = \left[\frac{3}{2} (\vartheta + i\,\vartheta_0)^2\right]^{(1/12)+\mu} \left(-\eta^3 + \frac{9}{4} (\vartheta + i\,\vartheta_0)\right)^{2\mu}.$$

In the first expression $\vartheta = 0$, $\eta = \left(-\frac{2}{3}\,\vartheta_0\right)^{2/3}$ is a regular point. The second term, however, is singular and the character of the singularity is determined by the exponent 2μ. To obtain, for example, a branch point so that the η, ϑ plane has two RIEMANN sheets, one must put

$$\mu = \frac{1}{4}.$$

To determine the flow field the function G must be calculated for complex values of the argument. It is useful, in this connection, that for $\mu = \frac{1}{4}$ the closed form expression for the solution [cf. Eq. VII, 5 (8a)] is available. An application of these particular solutions can be found in the original paper by TAMADA and TOMOTIKA.

15. The Particular Solutions of FALKOWICH

Another representation which yields singularities in the subsonic regime is due to FALKOWICH. In this case the solution is also assumed to be in the form of a product but the variables occurring in the solution are real in the η, ϑ plane so that the resulting functions need only be evaluated for real values of the arguments. We shall now show how the results of FALKOWICH are obtained.

To start with, TRICOMI's differential equation is put in a form which is as similar as possible to LAPLACE's differential equation. To this end we put

$$s = \frac{2}{3} (-\eta)^{3/2} \tag{1a}$$

and

$$\psi = (-\eta)^{\alpha}\, \Psi(s, \vartheta), \tag{1b}$$

whence

$$\frac{\partial \psi}{\partial \eta} = -\alpha (-\eta)^{\alpha-1}\, \Psi - (-\eta)^{\alpha+(1/2)}\, \Psi_s,$$

$$\frac{\partial^2 \psi}{\partial \eta^2} = \alpha(\alpha - 1)(-\eta)^{\alpha-2}\, \Psi + \left(2\alpha + \frac{1}{2}\right)(-\eta)^{\alpha-(1/2)}\, \Psi_s + (-\eta)^{\alpha+1}\, \Psi_{ss}.$$

Substitution of the above in TRICOMI's equation yields

$$(-\eta)^{\alpha+1}\, \Psi_{ss} + \left(2\alpha + \frac{1}{2}\right)(-\eta)^{\alpha-(1/2)}\, \Psi_s + $$
$$+ \alpha(\alpha - 1)(-\eta)^{\alpha-2}\, \Psi + (-\eta)^{\alpha+1}\, \Psi_{\vartheta\vartheta} = 0.$$

If we now put $\alpha = -\frac{1}{4}$ the derivative Ψ_s is eliminated, yielding the following differential equation

$$\Psi_{ss} + \Psi_{\vartheta\vartheta} + \frac{5}{36 s^2}\Psi = 0. \tag{2}$$

The variable s is real in the subsonic regime and imaginary in the supersonic regime. This fact should be carefully considered when a solution obtained in the subsonic regime is to be extended into the supersonic one.

The principal idea involved in the particular solutions of FALKOWICH is the introduction of bi-polar coordinates in the s, ϑ plane. The necessary transformations are particularly simple if complex variables are employed. Let

$$z = s + i\vartheta, \tag{3a}$$

$$\bar{z} = s - i\vartheta, \tag{3b}$$

$$\Psi(s, \vartheta) = \tilde{\Psi}(z, \bar{z}), \tag{4}$$

where z and $\bar{z}$ are to be considered independent of one another. This implies that one is not restricted to real values of s and ϑ. Constructing the partial derivatives with respect to z and $\bar{z}$ one finds

$$\Psi_s = \tilde{\Psi}_z + \tilde{\Psi}_{\bar{z}}, \qquad \Psi_\vartheta = i\tilde{\Psi}_z - i\tilde{\Psi}_{\bar{z}},$$

$$\Psi_{ss} = \tilde{\Psi}_{zz} + 2\tilde{\Psi}_{z\bar{z}} + \tilde{\Psi}_{\bar{z}\bar{z}}, \qquad \Psi_{\vartheta\vartheta} = -\tilde{\Psi}_{zz} + 2\tilde{\Psi}_{z\bar{z}} - \tilde{\Psi}_{\bar{z}\bar{z}},$$

so that Eq. (2) yields

$$\tilde{\Psi}_{z\bar{z}} + \frac{5}{36}(z + \bar{z})^{-2}\tilde{\Psi} = 0. \tag{5}$$

We now introduce a new independent variable $\zeta = h(z)$ where $h(z)$ is an analytic function of z which is real for real values of the argument. For complex conjugate values of z the Schwartz principle of reflection yields complex conjugate values of h, i.e. when

$$\zeta = h(z) \tag{6a}$$

we have

$$\bar{\zeta} = h(\bar{z}). \tag{6b}$$

In these equations, as in Eq. (3), the bar denotes complex conjugate functions. Let further

$$\tilde{\Psi}(z, \bar{z}) = \psi^*(\zeta, \bar{\zeta}), \tag{6c}$$

so that

$$\tilde{\Psi}_{z\bar{z}} = \psi^*_{\zeta\bar{\zeta}}\, h'(z)\, h'(\bar{z}),$$

and one obtains finally a new differential equation

$$\psi^*_{\zeta\bar{\zeta}}\, h'(z)\, h(\bar{z}) + \frac{5}{36}(z + \bar{z})^{-2}\psi^* = 0. \tag{7}$$

Now the functions of z and $\bar{z}$ must be expressed in terms of ζ and $\bar{\zeta}$. The introduction of z and $\bar{z}$ or ζ and $\bar{\zeta}$ is particularly useful since then the differential equation contains only the mixed second derivative as the highest order derivative.

For the function $h(z)$ FALKOWICH selects

$$\zeta = h(z) = \ln \frac{z + s_0}{z - s_0}, \tag{8}$$

where s_0 is a constant. This yields

$$e^{\zeta} = \frac{z + s_0}{z - s_0}, \qquad \frac{z}{s_0} = \frac{e^{\zeta} + 1}{e^{\zeta} - 1},$$

$$\frac{dz}{d\zeta} = \frac{-2 s_0 e^{\zeta}}{(e^{\zeta} - 1)^2}, \qquad h' = \frac{(e^{\zeta} - 1)^2}{-2 s_0 e^{\zeta}},$$

and the differential equation for ψ^* takes the form

$$\psi^*_{\zeta\bar{\zeta}} \left(e^{\frac{\zeta + \bar{\zeta}}{2}} - e^{-\frac{\zeta + \bar{\zeta}}{2}}\right)^2 + \frac{5}{36} \psi^* = 0. \tag{9}$$

It is now convenient to revert to real independent variables. Putting

$$\left.\begin{aligned} \zeta &= \alpha + i\beta \\ \bar{\zeta} &= \alpha - i\beta \end{aligned}\right\} \tag{10}$$

or

$$\alpha = \frac{\zeta + \bar{\zeta}}{2},$$

$$\beta = i \frac{\bar{\zeta} - \zeta}{2}$$

and if

$$\psi^*(\bar{\zeta}, \zeta) = \tilde{\tilde{\psi}}(\alpha, \beta), \tag{10a}$$

one obtains

$$\psi^*_{\zeta\bar{\zeta}} = \frac{1}{4}(\tilde{\tilde{\psi}}_{\alpha\alpha} + \tilde{\tilde{\psi}}_{\beta\beta})$$

and the differential equation in terms of the independent variables α and β takes the form

$$(\tilde{\tilde{\psi}}_{\alpha\alpha} + \tilde{\tilde{\psi}}_{\beta\beta}) \left(\frac{e^{\alpha} - e^{-\alpha}}{2}\right)^2 + \frac{5}{36} \tilde{\tilde{\psi}} = 0. \tag{11}$$

This equation may be solved by separation of variables

$$\tilde{\tilde{\psi}} = f(\alpha) \begin{matrix}\sin \\ \cos\end{matrix} (m\beta), \tag{12}$$

resulting in the following ordinary differential equation

$$(f'' - m^2 f)\left(\frac{e^{\alpha} - e^{-\alpha}}{2}\right)^2 + \frac{5}{36} f = 0. \tag{13}$$

The coefficients of this differential equation are rational if one puts

$$e^{\alpha} = t, \quad f(\alpha) = g(t).$$

This yields

$$g'' + \frac{g'}{t} + \frac{5}{9}\,\frac{g}{(t^2-1)^2} = 0.$$

The above equation has singular points at $t = 0$, $t = \infty$, $t = +1$ and $t = -1$. The exponents at 0 and ∞, and at $+1$ and -1 are equal. A considerable simplification, namely a reduction in the number of singular points, results from a transformation which causes singular points with equal exponents to coalesce. This may be effected in several ways; we chose, however, the transformation given originally by FALKOWICH

$$u = \left(\frac{t + t^{-1}}{2}\right)^2. \tag{14}$$

This transformation reduces the singular points 0 and ∞ to the single point $u = \infty$, while the points $t = +1$ and $t = -1$ are transformed into the point $u = 1$. The one-to-one correspondence between the u and t planes is disturbed when du/dt vanishes. At those points new singularities can occur. This situation arises when $t = \pm 1$ and $t = \pm i$. Points $t = \pm 1$ were already singular in the original differential equation so that this does not introduce new singularities in the transformed equation. At $t = \pm i$ one obtains, however, a new singular point, namely at $u = 0$. Thus, the differential equation resulting from the transformation of Eq. (14) has three singular points and it is easy to show that these are regular singular points of the equation. Putting

$$g(t) = k(u), \tag{15}$$

one obtains, after some algebraic transformations, the following hypergeometric differential equation

$$\frac{d^2k}{du^2} + \frac{dk}{du}\left(\frac{1}{2u} + \frac{1}{2(u-1)}\right) + k\left(\frac{-m^2}{u(u-1)} + \frac{5}{144}\,\frac{1}{u(u-1)^2}\right) = 0. \tag{16}$$

With the aid of RIEMANN's P-function (cf. Section VII, 4) its solution takes the form

$$k = P\begin{Bmatrix} \infty & 0 & 1 & \\ \frac{m}{2} & 0 & \frac{5}{12} & u \\ -\frac{m}{2} & \frac{1}{2} & \frac{1}{12} & \end{Bmatrix}. \tag{17}$$

It is now necessary to express the variable u in terms of the original variables s and ϑ. From Eqs. (3a), (8a) and (10) one obtains

$$e^{\alpha + i\beta} = \frac{s + i\vartheta + s_0}{s + i\vartheta - s_0},$$

$$e^{\alpha - i\beta} = \frac{s - i\vartheta + s_0}{s - i\vartheta - s_0},$$

$$t^2 = e^{2\alpha}\frac{(s + s_0)^2 + \vartheta^2}{(s - s_0)^2 + \vartheta^2},$$

$$u = \frac{1}{4}(t^2 + 2 + t^{-2}) = \frac{[s^2 + s_0^2 + \vartheta^2]^2}{[(s - s_0)^2 + \vartheta^2]\,[(s + s_0)^2 + \vartheta^2]}. \tag{18}$$

while Eq. (17) yields

$$\tan\beta = \frac{\operatorname{Im}\left\{\dfrac{s + i\vartheta + s_0}{s + i\vartheta - s_0}\right\}}{\operatorname{Re}\left\{\dfrac{s + i\vartheta + s_0}{s + i\vartheta - s_0}\right\}} = -\frac{2\vartheta s_0}{s^2 - s_0^2 + \vartheta^2}. \tag{19}$$

When $s = s_0$ and $\vartheta = 0$, $u = \infty$
When s $= 0$ $u = 1$.

If for $s = 0$ the value of ϑ varies from 0 to s_0, then $\tan\beta$ varies from 0 to ∞, while if ϑ varies from s_0 to $+\infty$, then $\tan\beta$ varies from $-\infty$ and 0. This means that β assumes values between 0 and π on the upper half of the sonic line. Actually the entire upper half of the subsonic regime is covered by the curves $\beta =$ const; the value of the constant varying between 0 and ∞. From the above considerations one finds easily that a possible representation for k is

$$k = \left(\frac{u-1}{u}\right)^{1/12}\left(\frac{1}{u}\right)^{m/2} F\left(\frac{m}{2} + \frac{1}{12}, \frac{m}{2} + \frac{7}{12}, 1 + m, u^{-1}\right),$$

$$k = \left(\frac{u-1}{u}\right)^{1/12}\left(\frac{1}{u}\right)^{-m/2} F\left(-\frac{m}{2} + \frac{1}{12}, -\frac{m}{2} + \frac{7}{12}, 1 - m, u^{-1}\right). \tag{20}$$

If necessary, a representation for k in the vicinity of the sonic line can be obtained with the aid of Eq. VII, 4 (5a). With the aid of this equation a continuation into the supersonic regime can be obtained.

Collecting together all the transformations one obtains the following form of the particular solutions

$$\psi = (\eta)^{-1/4} k(u) \begin{matrix}\sin\\ \cos\end{matrix} (m\beta), \tag{21}$$

where u and β in Eqs. (18) and (19) have been expressed in terms of s and ϑ and

$$s = \frac{2}{3}(-\eta)^{3/2}. \tag{21a}$$

The choice of m is determined by the character of the singularity which is to be represented. In the original work of FALKOWICH $m = 0$ was chosen, for example, resulting in a singularity corresponding to the imaginary part of a logarithm in incompressible flow.

For a general application of the particular solutions it is important to note that along a line $t =$ const or $u =$ const the solution is represented by a sine or a cosine of β. It is therefore easy to give a complete system of particular solutions with the aid of which a general function, which at the point $s = s_0, \vartheta = 0$ has a branch point with prescribed properties, can be represented.

If s_0 is allowed to become infinite then the lines $t =$ const evidently transform into lines $\eta =$ const, while the lines $\beta =$ const transform into lines $\vartheta =$ const. Thus the form of solution of FALKOWICH represents a generalization of CHAPLYGIN's particular solutions. The limiting process illustrates the transition from a hypergeometric series to a BESSEL function which is, of course, a confluent hypergeometric series.

Since the number of applications in which the above considerations can be of use is not particularly large, we shall not discuss this present matter any further. In view of their generality, as well as simplicity, these particular solutions can be very useful in special cases.

CHAPTER VIII

FLOWS WITH $M = 1$

1. General Considerations

The representation of a flow with a Mach number of unity around a body of finite thickness provides, at first, certain difficulties. The mass flow density has a maximum at $M = 1$ [Eq. I, 2 (10a)]; this means that the mass flow rate across a given cross section area is smaller at any other Mach number than at $M = 1$. When we talk about an obstacle in parallel flow we assume tacitly that, with increasing distances from the obstacle, the streamlines deviate less and less from parallel straight lines. Thus one is led to the conclusion that the cross-section at the point in which the obstacle is located cannot be sufficient to permit the passage of the approaching mass flow.

On the other hand we can devise experiments in reasoning which show that it is possible to approach a Mach number of unity as closely as we please. Consider, for example, a nozzle in a closed-circuit wind tunnel operating under choking conditions, i.e. at the highest possible subsonic Mach number. If the flow is continued beyond the walls of the tunnel by reflection, then the walls can be omitted (Fig. 74). If, in the resulting field, we pick out two streamlines, which correspond to the lines of symmetry of two neighbouring walls and follow respectively the upper and lower contour of each, then we obtain the flow in a De Laval nozzle. An example of such a flow has been shown already in Fig. 16; it may be considered as typical.

We expect that the sonic line, which occurs in the De Laval nozzle, originates at a point upstream of the main cross-section. The sonic line runs in general across the streamlines; it is at the same time always inclined in a downstream direction when one is moving along it away from a model. This is due to the fact that the Mach lines originating at the model terminate at the sonic line. The flow upstream and downstream of the sonic line is respectively subsonic and supersonic. To determine the flow field in the subsonic region, the boundary of the nozzle (i.e. the surface of the profile) must be known also in a part of the supersonic field. In order to pinpoint this part of the supersonic field more exactly, let us consider the Mach lines originating from the boundary of the De Laval nozzle. Some of these Mach lines terminate at the sonic line, while those originating further downstream terminate at the opposite wall. For the determination of the subsonic field we must, obviously, know that part of the profile of the nozzle which emits Mach waves terminating at the sonic line. The last of these MACH lines is the so-called limiting characteristic. Since the velocity vector on this characteristic is horizontal on the sonic line and because all MACH lines which intersect this characteristic represent compression waves (since they originate from the sonic line; cf. Section VI, 1), the slope of the contour of the lower half of the nozzle, at the point from which the limiting characteristic originates, is positive. This point, therefore, is located upstream of the throat of the nozzle or, as far as our profile is concerned, upstream of the maximum thickness.

If the shape of the model is maintained constant, and the width of the tunnel is allowed to become infinite, while the latter still operates at a choking MACH number, then the general form of the flow field is preserved. The choking MACH

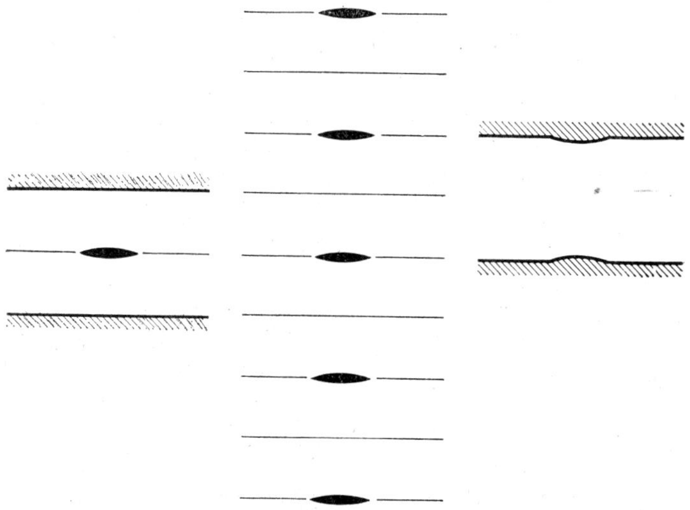

FIG. 74 Equivalence of a flow in a DE LAVAL nozzle and through a cascade of profiles in a duct.

number, as well as the MACH number along the walls of the tunnel, gradually approach unity. In this manner one can visualize the form of such a flow field. At the end of the next section we shall discuss the extent to which the difficulty, mentioned at the beginning of this chapter, actually applies.

2. The Hodograph Representation

To the calculation of a hodograph solution it is important that all the streamlines at infinity of the physical plane form a parallel flow with sonic velocity. This means that all the streamlines in the hodograph plane originate from the same point on the sonic line. At this point a singularity is obtained and the considerations of the preceding chapter may be applied to it.

If the characteristics originating at the body are described in terms of their intersections with the sonic line, then the limiting characteristic is obtained when this intersection point approaches infinity. In the η, ϑ plane, therefore, this characteristic passes through the origin. As shown above, the limiting characteristic originates at a point on the body upstream of the point of maximum thickness; the entire characteristic therefore can certainly not be mapped into infinity.

It is possible, but very unlikely, that the profile considered has, at the point at which the characteristic originates, a discontinuity in the profile (e.g. a finite change in the curvature). Such cases will be excluded from our consideration.

We consider next a body which is symmetric with respect to the x axis (Fig. 75). The stream function in the hodograph plane is then antisymmetric with respect to the η axis. For ψ to become infinite at the origin of the η, ϑ plane, the exponent of ϱ in Eq. VII, 3 (3) must be negative. An antisymmetric particular solution of the form of Eq. VII, 3 (3) can, in the vicinity of the limiting

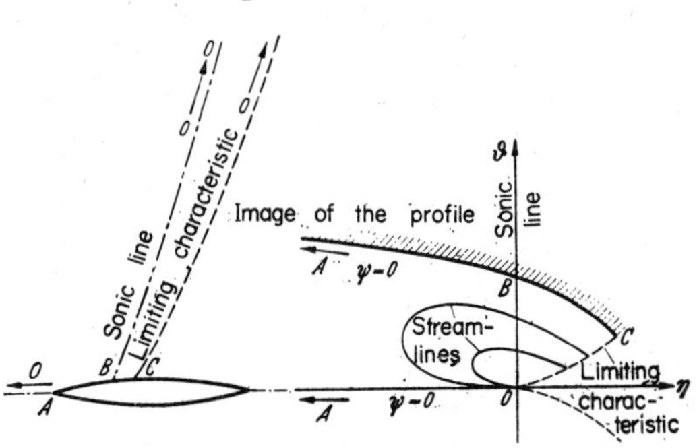

FIG. 75 Sonic flow past a profile and its representation in the η, ϑ plane. (According to GUDERLEY [26]).

characteristic, i.e. of the line $\xi = 1$, be represented by Eq. VII, 9 (1). If the entire limiting characteristic is not to be mapped into infinity, the coefficient of the second term must vanish. This condition expresses at the same time the requirement that for positive μ no discontinuity should be propagated along $\xi = 1$. Hence one obtains the values introduced in Eq. VII, 9 (3)

$$\mu = -\frac{1}{12} + \frac{h}{3},$$

$$\mu = -\frac{3}{4} - h.$$

These particular solutions can be written down in closed form (cf. p. 173).

In order to select from the infinite number of negative values of μ, which we have obtained thus far, that particular one which yields the characteristic singularity for a flow at $M = 1$, the functions G must be considered in detail. The first of these functions are shown in Fig. 66. Only the function $G(\xi, -\frac{3}{4})$ has no zeros between $\xi = -\infty$ and $\xi = 1$; every other G-function has one additional zero. For a solution, as given by Eq. VII, 3 (3), each line $\xi =$ const maps into a generalized parabola in the physical plane. This becomes apparent when ϱ is eliminated from the appropriate equations for x and y. When the hodograph plane is generated by lines of ξ = const, the physical plane is at the same time generated by the corresponding generalized parabolas. The Jacobians of the solutions, considered here, do not vanish anywhere in the subsonic region. If one did vanish at any given point, it would also have to do so along the entire line ξ = const passing through this point. It could be shown then, however, that the solution is identically equal to zero. Thus a one-to-one mapping exists between the physical and the hodograph planes.

Let the line $\xi = -\infty$ be mapped into the negative x axis. Then the line ξ = const which corresponds to the next zero of G must map into the positive x axis. Thus the region between $\xi = -\infty$ and the first zero of G covers already the entire upper half of the physical plane. If ξ were allowed to increase above this first zero, for example up to 1, then additional sheets would be obtained in the physical plane. Besides, in view of the special behaviour of ϱ and ξ at $\xi = 1$, the line $\xi = 1$ does not map into the x axis although G vanishes there also. As a result of this discussion we find that only that G function which has no zeros between $\xi = -\infty$ and $\xi = 1$ can be used to represent infinity in a flow at $M = 1$. This means that the singularity occurring at the origin is given by

$$\psi_{-5/6} = \varrho^{-5/6}\, G^{(a)}\left(\xi, \frac{3}{4}\right). \tag{1}$$

A general description of the hodograph plane is now comparatively simple (Fig. 75). Let us continue to consider a symmetrical profile. Moving along the streamline of symmetry, from infinity towards the profile, the velocity decreases. At the leading edge of the profile the velocity is either zero or has some subsonic value depending on whether the included angle at the leading edge is zero or not. Both in the physical plane and in the hodograph plane this streamline divides at the leading edge. The direction of the velocity vector changes and, in general, the velocity along the surface of the body increases. Even before the point of maximum thickness is reached the velocity becomes sonic and subsequently supersonic.

Along the image of the surface of the body the stream function has the value zero (or, more generally, it is constant). On the singular expression $\psi_{-5/6}$, multiplied by a constant depending on the size of the body, there must be superimposed an expression which is not singular at O, so that along the hodograph image of the contour of the profile $\psi = 0$. For a given contour in the hodograph plane one could probably devise a systematic procedure for this superposition; there is, however, no great practical need for it since the contour in the hodograph plane cannot, in general, be determined directly from the shape of the profile in the physical plane.

In accordance with the discussion in Section VII, 12, the solution in the vicinity of the point 0 can be obtained by superposition of the "natural" particular solutions. The appropriate coefficients are determined by the shape and size of the body.

The behaviour of the solutions at infinity is determined solely by $\psi_{-5/6}$. From Eqs. VII, 3 (7) and VII, 3 (9) x and y are given by

$$x = \varrho^{-4/6} f_1(\xi), \tag{2a}$$

$$y = \varrho^{-5/6} f_2(\xi), \tag{2b}$$

where $f_1(\xi)$ and $f_2(\xi)$ can be expressed in terms of $G^{(a)}(\xi, 3/4)$. Elimination of ϱ yields

$$\frac{x^{5/4}}{y} = \frac{f_1(\xi)^{5/4}}{f_2(\xi)} = f_3(\xi). \tag{3}$$

This equation expresses the already mentioned fact that the lines $\xi = \text{const}$ map, in the physical plane, into generalized parabolas. The sonic line and the limiting characteristic are included in these parabolas. The distance measured in the x direction between these curves evidently increases with y. In order to calculate the shape of the streamlines, i.e. their deviation from lines $y = \text{const}$ which describe the streamlines of the undisturbed flow, we must calculate

$$\tilde{y} = \int_{\xi=-\infty}^{\xi} \vartheta(\xi)\, d(x(\xi)) \qquad \text{for } y = \text{const}.$$

From Eq. VII, 3 (1a)

$$\varrho = \frac{9}{4}\vartheta^2 (1 - \xi^3)$$

or

$$\vartheta = \varrho^{1/2} f_4(\xi). \tag{4}$$

With the aid of Eq. (2b) there results

$$\vartheta = y^{-3/5} f_5(\xi),$$

and further from Eq. (3)

$$x = y^{4/5} f_6(\xi).$$

Thus

$$\tilde{y} = y^{1/5} \int_{-\infty}^{\xi} f_7(\xi)\, d\xi .$$

This expression shows that the displacement of the streamline from its original position increases with y. As $y \to \infty$ the displacement also tends to infinity. This answers the question how the approaching flow at $M = 1$ finds room to flow past the model. It should be stressed that the velocity vector approaches, with increasing y, a parallel flow with critical velocity. That the displacement becomes infinite follows from the integration of the slope of the streamline in the x direction. These discussions were first presented by Frankl [19] and by Guderley [27].

3. An Example of Flow with $M = 1$

Let us first describe the notation which will be used in the analysis to follow. We shall frequently encounter solutions which are singular at the origin of the hodograph plane and which otherwise satisfy the boundary conditions prescribed along the hodograph image of a profile. When the coefficient of the term, which is singular at the origin, is not determined by the profile it will be put equal to 1. Such solutions will be denoted by ψ with a superscript corresponding to the subscript of the predominant singularity. A function ψ occurring in such solutions and satisfying TRICOMI's condition at O would be denoted by $\tilde{\psi}$ with a corresponding subscript. The same notation will be used for the transformed potential φ.

A first example (GUDERLEY [27]) of a flow with $M = 1$ is obtained by putting

$$\Psi^{-5/6} = c_1 \psi_{-5/6} + c_2 \psi_{1/6}. \tag{1}$$

The choice of the constants c_1 and c_2, except for their sign, is unimportant. This is because a multiplication of the entire expression by a constant multiplies all the corresponding values of x and y by the same constant so that merely a change in the scale in the physical plane takes place. An application of the similarity rule for transonic flows leaves the coordinates unchanged while each ϱ becomes multiplied by a factor τ^3. Since both terms of the last equation contain different powers of ϱ the factors τ in the two terms are different.

To determine the shape of a body in the physical plane one must determine first the zero streamline and then the x coordinates corresponding to it. The shape of the body is then obtained by integration of the slope of this streamline with respect to x.

If this calculation is carried out in general terms, its details are quite laborious but the result is very simple. The most important steps involved will be reproduced here. The necessary particular solutions $\psi_{-5/6}$ and $\psi_{1/6}$ are obtained with the aid of Eq. VII, 5 (3) with $\mu = 3/4$ and $\mu = 1/4$. Thus

$$G\left(\xi, \frac{1}{4}\right) = (1 - \zeta)^{-1/6} \left(\sqrt{\zeta} - \sqrt{\zeta - 1}\right)^{-1/3}, \tag{2a}$$

$$G\left(\xi, \frac{3}{4}\right) = (1 - \zeta)^{-2/3} \left(\sqrt{\zeta} - \sqrt{\zeta - 1}\right)^{-4/3} \left[1 - 2 \left(\sqrt{\zeta} - \sqrt{\zeta - 1}\right)^2\right], \tag{2b}$$

where

$$\zeta = \xi^3.$$

These expressions represent the solutions of the equation for G but not, directly, the expressions for $G^{(a)}$ which we require. Since these functions are defined by their behaviour for large negative values of ξ, i.e. for small negative values of ζ, we multiply Eqs. (2a) and (2b) by suitable constants and write them in such a form that they are real for negative values of ζ

$$G\left(\xi, \frac{1}{4}\right) = (1 - \zeta)^{-1/6} \left(\sqrt{-\zeta} - \sqrt{1 - \zeta}\right)^{-1/3},$$

$$G\left(\xi, \frac{3}{4}\right) = (1 - \zeta)^{-2/3} \left(\sqrt{-\zeta} - \sqrt{1 - \zeta}\right)^{-4/3} \left[1 - 2 \left(\sqrt{-\zeta} - \sqrt{1 - \zeta}\right)^2\right].$$

For $(-\zeta) = 0$ one obtains the following expansions

$$G\left(\xi, \frac{1}{4}\right) = -1 + \frac{1}{3}\sqrt{-\zeta} + \cdots,$$

$$G\left(\xi, \frac{3}{4}\right) = -1 + \frac{8}{3}\sqrt{-\zeta} + \cdots.$$

The desired solutions $G^{(a)}$ have, as a first term in this expansion, $\sqrt{(-\zeta)}$. Further solutions for G are obtained by replacing $\sqrt{(-\zeta)}$ by $-\sqrt{(-\zeta)}$. The functions $G^{(a)}$ are obtained, in principle, as the difference between the original expressions and the solutions which are obtained by a change of sign

$$G^{(a)}\left(\xi, \frac{1}{4}\right) = \frac{3}{2}(1-\zeta)^{-1/6} \times$$
$$\times \left\{\left(\sqrt{-\zeta} - \sqrt{1-\zeta}\right)^{-1/3} - \left(-\sqrt{-\zeta} - \sqrt{1-\zeta}\right)^{-1/3}\right\}, \tag{3a}$$

$$G^{(a)}\left(\xi, \frac{3}{4}\right) = \frac{3}{16}(1-\zeta)^{-2/3} \times$$
$$\times \left\{\left(\sqrt{-\zeta} - \sqrt{1-\zeta}\right)^{-4/3} - 2\left(\sqrt{-\zeta} - \sqrt{1-\zeta}\right)^{2/3} - \right.$$
$$\left. - \left(-\sqrt{-\zeta} - \sqrt{1-\zeta}\right)^{-4/3} + 2\left(-\sqrt{-\zeta} - \sqrt{1-\zeta}\right)^{2/3}\right\}. \tag{3b}$$

Next a new independent variable is introduced

$$\left(\sqrt{-\zeta} - \sqrt{1-\zeta}\right)^{1/3} = u, \tag{4}$$

and then

$$\left.\begin{aligned}
\left(-\sqrt{-\zeta} - \sqrt{1-\zeta}\right)^{1/3} &= u^{-1} \\
(1-\zeta) &= \frac{1}{4}(u^3 + u^{-3})^2 \\
-\zeta &= \frac{1}{4}(u^3 - u^{-3})^2 \\
1 - \xi^3 = \frac{1-\zeta}{-\zeta} &= \frac{(u^3 + u^{-3})^2}{(u^3 - u^{-3})^2} \\
\frac{du}{d\zeta} &= -\frac{2}{3}\,\frac{u}{u^6 - u^{-6}}, \\
\frac{du}{d\xi} = -\frac{du}{d\zeta}\,3\,\zeta^{4/3} &= \frac{2^{-5/3}\,u\,(u^3 - u^{-3})^{8/3}}{u^6 - u^{-6}}.
\end{aligned}\right\} \tag{5}$$

With the aid of Eq. VII, 3 (1) there results further

$$\eta = -\varrho^{1/3}(1-\zeta)^{-1/3} = -\varrho^{1/3}\,2^{2/3}(u^3 + u^{-3})^{-2/3}. \tag{6}$$

The two required solutions ψ appear thus in the form

$$\psi_{1/6} = \varrho^{1/6} \frac{3}{2} 3^{1/3} [u^3 + u^{-3}]^{-1/3} [u^{-1} - u],$$

$$\psi_{-5/6} = \varrho^{-5/6} \frac{3}{16} 2^{4/3} [u^3 + u^{-3}]^{-4/3} \{u^{-4} - 2u^2 - u^4 + 2u^2\} \tag{7a}$$

or

$$\psi_{-5/6} = -\varrho^{-5/6} \frac{3}{16} 2^{4/3} [u^3 + u^{-3}]^{-4/3} \{(u + u^{-1})^3 (u - u^{-1})\}. \tag{7b}$$

If in Eq. (1) the constants c_1 and c_2 are put equal to 1, one obtains

$$\Psi_{-5/6} = -\varrho^{-5/6} \frac{3}{16} 2^{4/3} (u^3 + u^{-3})]^{-4/3} [u + u^{-1}]^3 [u - u^{-1}] -$$
$$- \varrho^{1/6} \frac{3}{2} 2^{1/3} [u^3 + u^{-3}]^{-1/3} [u - u^{-1}]. \tag{8}$$

Equating this expression to zero yields the zero streamline.

To calculate the x coordinates we employ Eq. VII, 3 (9). It is convenient to put x in the form $x = \eta f(u)$. With the aid of Eqs. (5) and (6) there results

$$x = (\gamma + 1)^{1/3} [-\eta \varrho^{-1/3} \cdot 2^{-2/3} (u^3 + u^{-3})^{2/3}] \times$$
$$\times \frac{(u^3 + u^{-3})^{5/3}}{(u^3 - u^{-3})^{5/3}} 2^{-5/3} \frac{u(u^3 - u^{-3})^{8/3}}{u^6 - u^{-6}} \times$$
$$\times \left[\varrho^{1/6} \left(-\frac{1}{2}\right) \frac{d}{du} \left\{-\frac{3}{16} 2^{4/3} \varrho^{-5/6} [u^3 + u^{-3}]^{-4/3} (u + u^{-1})^3 (u - u^{-1})\right\} + \right.$$
$$\left. + \varrho^{1/6} \frac{d}{du} \left\{-\frac{3}{2} 2^{1/3} \varrho^{1/6} [u^3 + u^{-3}]^{-1/3} (u - u^{-1})\right\}\right].$$

The condition that $\psi^{-5/6}$ is equal to zero makes both the brackets in the last equation, which are to be differentiated with respect to u, equal except for their sign. This permits the following transformation

$$x = (\gamma + 1)^{1/3} [-\eta \varrho^{-1/3} 2^{-2/3} (u^3 + u^{-3})^{2/3}] \frac{(u^3 + u^{-3})^{5/3}}{(u^3 - u^{-3})^{5/3}} \times$$
$$\times 2^{-5/3} \frac{u(u^3 - u^{-3})^{8/3}}{u^6 - u^{-6}} \varrho^{1/6} \left(-\frac{3}{2}\right) 2^{1/3} \varrho^{1/6} [u^3 + u^{-3}]^{-1/3} (u - u^{-1}) \times$$
$$\times \left\{\frac{d}{du} \left[\frac{1}{2} \ln [(u^3 + u^{-3})^{-4/3} (u + u^{-1})^3 (u - u^{-1})]\right] + \right.$$
$$\left. + \frac{d}{du} \ln [(u^3 + u^{-3})^{-1/3} (u - u^{-1})]\right\}.$$

Hence by direct calculation we find

$$x = (\gamma + 1)^{1/3} \frac{9}{4} \eta. \tag{9}$$

The shape of the profile is obtained by calculating $\int \vartheta \, dx$ for the zero streamline. In view of the proportionality between η and x [Eq. (9)], we express all quantities here in terms of η. Next, from Eq. (8) ϱ is expressed as a function of u

$$\varrho = \frac{1}{4} \frac{(u + u^{-1})^3}{u^3 + u^{-3}}. \tag{10}$$

From Eq. VII, 3 (1a)

$$\varrho = \eta^3 (\zeta - 1).$$

So that, with the aid of Eq. (5),

$$\varrho = -\frac{\eta^3}{4} (u^3 + u^{-3})^2,$$

and hence, using Eq. (10),

$$\frac{1}{\eta} = -(u^2 - 1 + u^2). \tag{11}$$

Further, in accordance with Eqs. VII, 3 (1b) and (5),

$$\vartheta = \frac{2}{3} (-\eta)^{3/2} \sqrt{-\zeta} = \frac{1}{3} (-\eta)^{3/2} (u^2 + 1 + u^{-2}) (u - u^{-1}).$$

In this expression u can be expressed in terms of η, with the aid of Eq. (5)

$$u^2 + 1 + u^{-2} = 2 - \frac{1}{\eta},$$

$$u - u^{-1} = \sqrt{-1 - \frac{1}{\eta}},$$

$$\vartheta = \frac{1}{3} (-2\eta + 1) \sqrt{1 + \eta}. \tag{12}$$

The branch point of the zero streamline is located on the η axis. There $\zeta = 0$ and, in accordance with Eq. (4), $u = -1$. Thus, in view of Eq. (11), at this point $\eta = -1$. This value provides the lower limit of integration for the calculation of the contour of the profile. Using our previous results one finds

$$\tilde{y} = \int \vartheta \, dx = (\gamma + 1)^{1/3} \frac{3}{4} \int_{-1}^{\eta} \sqrt{1 + \eta} \, (-2\eta + 1) \, d\eta,$$

$$\tilde{y} = (\gamma + 1)^{1/3} \frac{3}{2} (1 - \eta)^{3/2} \left(\frac{3}{5} - \frac{2}{5} \eta \right). \tag{13}$$

Substitution of Eq. (9) yields

$$\tilde{y} = (\gamma + 1)^{1/3} [9 + 4x (\gamma + 1)^{-1/3}]^{3/2} [27 - 8x (\gamma + 1)^{-1/3}], \tag{14}$$

$\tilde{y}$ vanishes for

$$x = -\left(\frac{9}{4}\right) (\gamma + 1)^{1/3} \quad \text{and} \quad x = \left(\frac{27}{8}\right) (\gamma + 1)^{1/3}.$$

Equations (14) and (9) give the contour of the profile and the distribution of η from which the pressure distribution can be calculated in accordance with Eq. V, 7 (11). The shape of the profile, $\tilde{y} = \tilde{y}(x)$, and the points at which the sonic line and the limiting characteristic originate are shown in Fig. 76. Downstream of the limiting characteristic the flow field presents a purely supersonic problem. It is possible in this region to distort the contour without affecting the

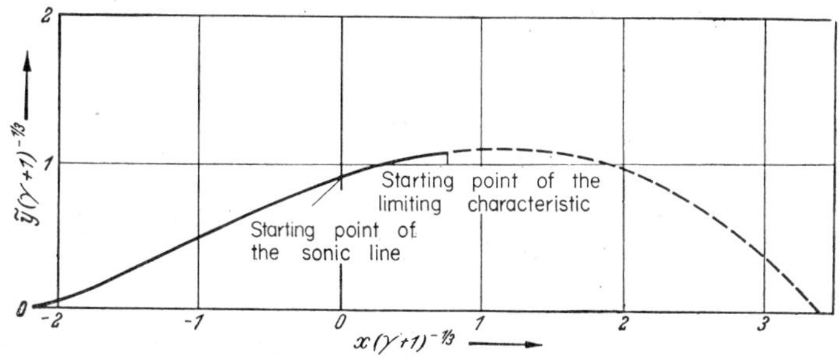

FIG. 76 A profile for which the flow at $M = 1$ is given by a simple analytical expression. (According to GUDERLEY [26]).

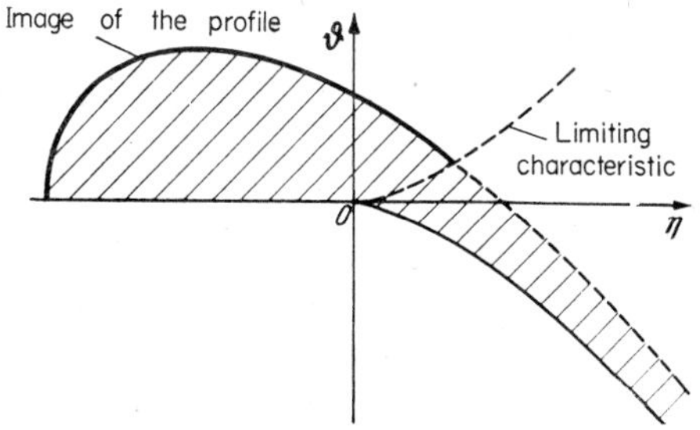

FIG. 77 Representation of the flow of Fig. 76 in the η, ϑ plane. (According to GUDERLEY [26]).

flow upstream of the point of distortion. This is the reason why the profile can be terminated at the point $x = \dfrac{27}{8}(\gamma + 1)^{1/3}$ where y becomes equal to zero.

Figure 77 shows the profile in the η, ϑ plane, for the upper half of the physical plane. The region corresponding to the physical plane is shaded. In the downstream part of the profile the slope of the streamlines is negative so that the image of the profile extends into the region below the η axis. If the lower half of the physical plane were also represented in the hodograph plane, then the region between the characteristics through O would be covered twice. Only that part of the contour shown by a solid line in the η, ϑ plane is necessary for the determination of the subsonic flow region. This part of the contour terminates at a characteristic going through the origin, i.e. at the limiting characteristic.

The functions G can, on the sonic line, be represented with the aid of Eq. VII, 4 (17b) by

$$G^{(a)}\left(\xi, \frac{1}{4}\right) = \frac{\Gamma\left(\frac{1}{3}\right)\Gamma\left(\frac{3}{2}\right)}{\Gamma\left(\frac{7}{6}\right)\Gamma\left(\frac{2}{3}\right)} - \frac{\Gamma\left(-\frac{1}{3}\right)\Gamma\left(\frac{3}{2}\right)}{\Gamma\left(\frac{5}{6}\right)\Gamma\left(\frac{1}{3}\right)}\,\xi,$$

$$G^{(a)}\left(\xi, \frac{3}{4}\right) = \frac{\Gamma\left(\frac{1}{3}\right)\Gamma\left(\frac{3}{2}\right)}{\Gamma\left(\frac{5}{3}\right)\Gamma\left(\frac{1}{6}\right)} - \frac{\Gamma\left(-\frac{1}{3}\right)\Gamma\left(\frac{3}{2}\right)}{\Gamma\left(\frac{4}{3}\right)\Gamma\left(-\frac{1}{6}\right)}\,\xi.$$

Equations (3) would yield, of course, the same result. The Γ functions can be transformed with the aid of Eqs. VII, 4 (15), yielding

$$G^{(a)}\left(\xi, \frac{1}{4}\right) = \frac{3}{2}\left(2^{1/3} - 2^{-1/3}\,\xi\right),$$

$$G^{(a)}\left(\xi, \frac{3}{4}\right) = \frac{3}{2}\left(2^{-5/3} - 2^{-4/3}\,\xi\right).$$

Then, with the aid of Eqs. VII, 3 (7) and VII, 3 (9) one obtains

$$y = \frac{3}{2}\,2^{-5/3}\left(\frac{3}{2}\,\vartheta\right)^{-5/3} + \frac{3}{2}\,2^{1/3}\left(\frac{3}{2}\,\vartheta\right)^{1/3},$$

$$(\gamma + 1)^{-1/3}\,x = \frac{1}{2}\,\frac{3}{2}\,2^{-4/3}\left(\frac{3}{2}\,\vartheta\right)^{-4/3} + \frac{3}{2}\,2^{-1/3}\left(\frac{3}{2}\,\vartheta\right)^{2/3}.$$

For the limiting characteristic $\xi = 1$ there results

$$G^{(a)}\left(\xi, \frac{1}{4}\right) = \frac{\Gamma\left(\frac{1}{2}\right)}{\Gamma\left(\frac{7}{6}\right)\Gamma\left(\frac{5}{6}\right)}\,(1 - \xi^3)^{-1/6} = \frac{3}{\sqrt{\pi}}\,(1 - \xi^3)^{-1/6},$$

$$G^{(a)}\left(\xi, \frac{3}{4}\right) = \frac{-\Gamma\left(-\frac{3}{2}\right)}{\Gamma\left(\frac{1}{6}\right)\Gamma\left(-\frac{1}{6}\right)}\,(1 - \xi^3)^{5/6} = \frac{4}{\sqrt{\pi}}\,(1 - \xi^3)^{5/6},$$

and hence

$$y = \frac{4}{\sqrt{\pi}}\left(\frac{9}{4}\,\vartheta^2\right)^{-5/6} + \frac{3}{\sqrt{\pi}}\left(\frac{9}{4}\,\vartheta^2\right)^{1/6},$$

$$(\gamma + 1)^{-1/3}\,x = \frac{5}{\sqrt{\pi}}\left(\frac{9}{4}\,\vartheta^2\right)^{-2/3} + \frac{3}{2\sqrt{\pi}}\left(\frac{9}{4}\,\vartheta^2\right)^{1/3}.$$

Downstream of the limiting characteristic the shape of the body can be altered at will, as long as this does not introduce compression waves which reach the sonic line and hence influence the subsonic flow field. It is possible, for example, to choose the downstream part of the profile in such a manner that, with a given upstream part and the same chord length, a minimum drag is obtained. A drag is obtained in any case; only for a semi-infinite body can the downstream flow be converted into a parallel flow with sonic velocity without losses. The construction of the tail of the profile, which offers a minimum drag, can be found in an article by GUDERLEY [27]. One finds that downstream of the expansion fan,

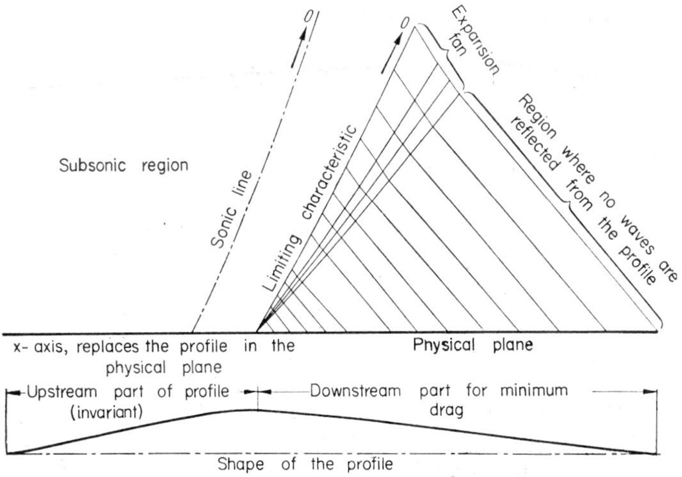

FIG. 78 Construction of the downstream part of a profile which offers a minimum drag for a given chord and a given form of the upstream part of the profile.

which must be located at the intersection of the contour with the limiting characteristic and whose extent determines the chord of the profile, the contour must be shaped in such a manner that no MACH waves are reflected from it (Fig. 78). In the physical plane, for $\tau \to 0$, the profile appears as a section of a straight line $y = 0$. For this reason the shape of the profile is shown below the diagram of the flow. The corresponding pressure distribution is shown in Fig. 79. Further profiles which can be arrived at in this manner are shown in Fig. 80.

All these profiles can be transformed to the same thickness ratio with the aid of the similarity rule. In this manner one obtains a series of profiles in which the position of the point of maximum thickness and the form of the upstream part of the profile vary and which are obtained from one another by an affine distortion (Fig. 81). In this manner one obtains theoretical values of the drag in a flow approaching with $M = 1$ and, at the same time, a relationship between the drag and the position of the point of maximum thickness. This is shown in Fig. 82. In the same figure there is shown the corresponding curve for a wedge-shaped upstream part of the profile as well as the drag coefficient for a rhombic

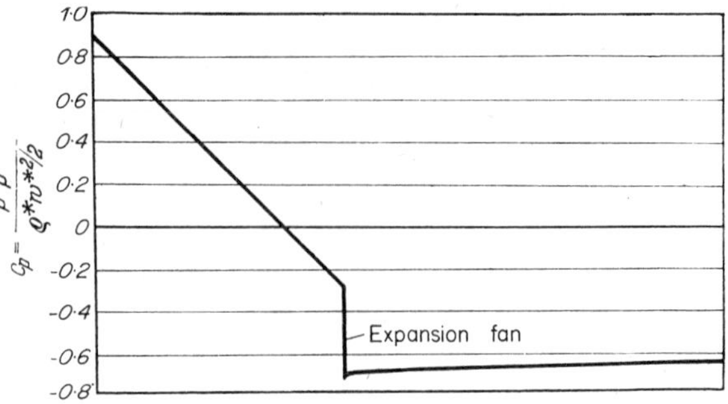

FIG. 79 Pressure distribution of the profile shown in Fig. 78.

FIG. 80 Profiles of various lengths with a common upstream part. Each afterbody offers minimum drag for the given chord. (According to GUDERLEY [27]).

profile. All the results apply to a thickness ratio of 10 %. For affine profiles the drag coefficient is proportional to the $\frac{5}{3}$ power of the thickness ratio, in accordance with the similarity rule.

Since it is impossible, with the aid of the hodograph method, to calculate directly flows around arbitrarily prescribed profiles, it appears indicated to extend the inverse procedure, just described, by the addition of further "natural" particular solutions in a systematic manner, and in this way to obtain a catalog of profiles and the flows around them. In this manner, however, one would never obtain profiles whose slope at the leading edge is other than zero.

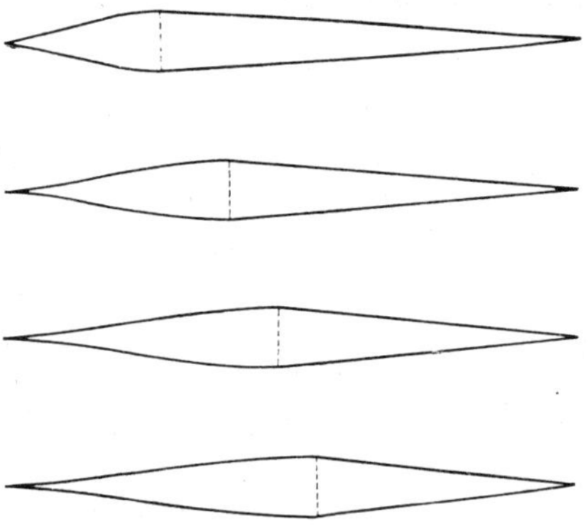

FIG. 81 Profiles with varying positions of the point of maximum thickness. The upstream parts are related by an affine distortion. For each upstream part the profile offers minimum drag. (According to GUDERLEY [27]).

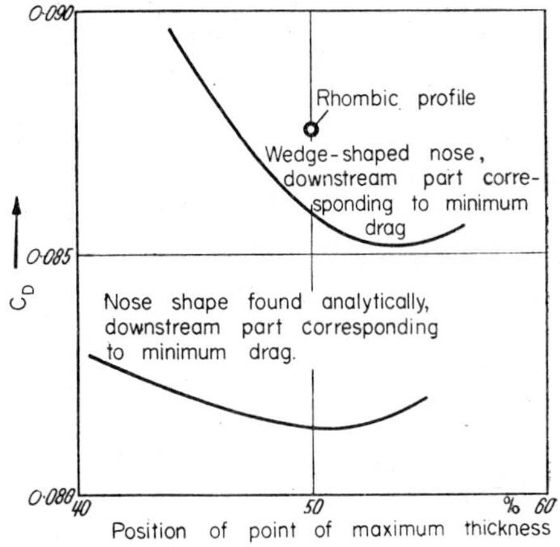

FIG. 82 Variation of the drag coefficient with the position of the point of maximum thickness for a thickness ratio of 10%. (According to GUDERLEY [27]).

4. Sonic Flow Past a Wedge

The hodograph image of the faces of a wedge is known in advance and the boundary value problem in the hodograph plane can be completely formulated. The engineering importance of the wedge profile is, of course, limited; for theoretical discussions, however, it is particularly useful because of the simplicity of the calculations involved. In addition, a wedge-shaped model is easy to manufacture, so that a comparison with experimental results is fairly simple.

The hodograph image is obtained by allowing the shock polar in Fig. 45c to contract to zero and by introducing at the origin the singularity characteristic of $M = 1$ (Fig. 83). The coefficient by which this singularity is multiplied is, of

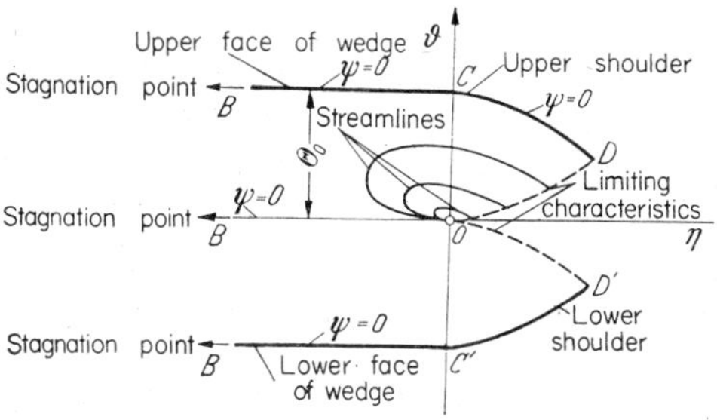

FIG. 83 The boundary values problem for a wedge in the η, ϑ plane.

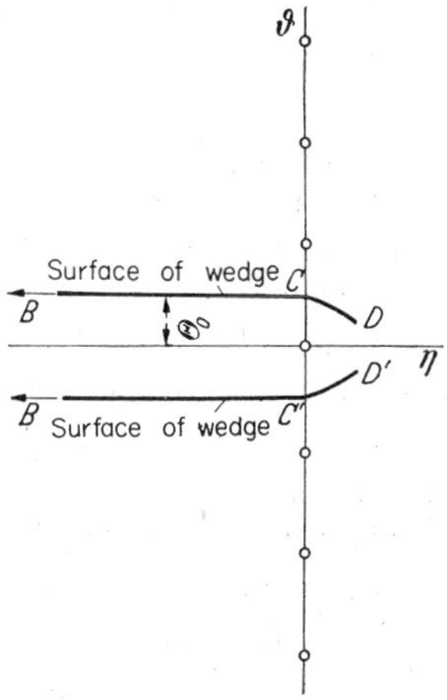

FIG. 84 Arrangement of singularities along the ϑ axis.

course, determined by the size of the wedge. Conversely, the dimensions of the wedge are determined by a choice of the coefficient. Let us, initially, chose for this coefficient the value 1.

First we obtain a function which satisfies the condition $\psi = 0$ on the faces of the wedge (Fig. 84). Let this be denoted by ψ_1. We obtain this expression by the reflection of a singular solution. If the half-angle of the wedge is given by ϑ_0, and if we use the notation

$$\psi_{-5/6}\,(\varrho, \xi) = \overline{\psi}_{-5/6}\,(\eta, \vartheta), \tag{1}$$

then this part of the solution can be written in the form

$$\psi_1 = \sum_{h=-\infty}^{h=+\infty} \overline{\psi}_{-5/6}\,(\eta, \vartheta - 2h\,\theta_0)\,. \tag{2}$$

The solution $\overline{\psi}^{-5/6}$ was defined by Eq. (1) and the transition from the variables ϱ and ξ to η and ϑ is effected with the aid of Eq. VII, 3 (1). In order to satisfy the boundary condition $\psi = 0$ along the characteristic CD, we employ CHAPLYGIN's particular solutions given by Eq. VII, 1 (2a). The term $g(\eta, m)$, occurring there, is expressed with the aid of Eq. VII, 1 (4a)

$$\psi_2 = \sum_{h=1}^{\infty} a_h g\left(\eta, \frac{h\pi}{\theta_0}\right) \sin\left[h \frac{\pi\vartheta}{\theta_0}\right]. \tag{3}$$

This evidently also satisfies the boundary condition $\psi = 0$ on the faces of the wedge. The solution ψ_2 is to be determined in such a way that $\psi_1 + \psi_2 = 0$ on the characteristics CD and $C'D'$. Thus ψ_2 is determined by a boundary value problem of TRICOMI's type. Along the sonic line ψ_2 is bounded so that the expression in Eq. (2) converges at least on the average*. According to the remarks at the end of Section VII, 1, convergence along the sonic line implies also that ψ_2 converges in the supersonic flow region. In Section VII, 1 the question of completeness of the system of particular solutions, employed to obtain ψ_2, was also answered. From the practical point of view the solution, as given by Eq. (3) would be considered satisfactory if only, as a result of the calculation, one would find that the desired boundary conditions are satisfied with sufficient accuracy

Since convergence is assured in the supersonic region, it is possible to determine the coefficients a_h by requiring directly that the boundary conditions along the characteristic CD be satisfied. This reduces to a numerical calculation. In an article of MARSCHNER [60], in which a similar problem arose, the boundary conditions were approached by using the first ten terms of Eq. (2). To this end the values of CHAPLYGIN's solutions, and the boundary values to be satisfied along the characteristic CD, were calculated at 40 points. The coefficients a_h were determined so that the sum of the squares of the deviations of the approximate solution from the exact boundary values was a minimum.

The solution of our problem is thus given by

$$\psi = \psi_1 + \psi_2 .$$

This solution is important for the region $BCDOD'C''$ in Fig. 83. It is meaningless between the characteristics OD and OD'. The continuation of the solution past the limiting characteristic is best determined with the aid of the method of characteristics, after the position of the limiting characteristic in the physical plane has been established. In order to transform the solution from the hodograph plane to the physical plane, we use Eqs. V, 7 (8) and V, 7 (9). If only the pressure distribution along the wedge is desired, it is sufficient to determine the x coordinates of the faces of the wedge. As a result of the differential equation for g [Eq. VII, 1 (2c)] one finds for ψ_2 [Eq. (3)]

$$x_2 = -(\gamma + 1)^{1/3} \sum_{h=1}^{\infty} a_h \frac{\theta_0}{h\pi} \frac{dg}{d\eta}\left(\eta, \frac{h\pi}{\theta_0}\right) \cos\left[\frac{h\pi\vartheta}{\theta_0}\right]. \tag{4}$$

* The behaviour of ψ_2 in the vicinity of the point O has been discussed in Section VII, 13. In accordance with that discussion ψ_2 can be represented by a superposition of the "natural" particular solutions $\psi_{1/6}$, $\psi_{1/2}$, $\psi_{5/6}$ ....

Another possibility, which occurs, for example, in an article by GUDERLEY and YOSHIHARA [43], is that one first calculates φ from ψ, using Eq. V, 7 (7), and then obtains x with the aid of Eq. V, 7 (10).

In order to calculate the limiting MACH line, which is required for the calculation of the flow over the downstream part of the body, one only needs to obtain its y coordinate as a function of η, since the values of x follow from the equation of the characteristic

$$\frac{dy}{dx} = (\gamma + 1)^{-1/3} \eta^{-1/2}.$$

Starting with the limiting characteristic the flow over the downstream part of the profile can be computed using the method of characteristics.

For practical calculation it is best to chose ϑ/θ_0 and $\eta \Big/ \left(\frac{3}{2}\,\theta_0\right)^{2/3}$ as independent variables. It may be noted from Eq. VII, 1 (3a) that Eq. (3) appears already in this form. It is easy to show that

$$\psi_{-5/6} = \varrho^{-5/6}\, G^{(a)}\left(\xi, \frac{3}{4}\right)$$

can be put in the form

$$\overline{\psi}_{-5/6} = \theta_0^{-5/3}\, \overline{\overline{\psi}} \left(\frac{\eta}{\left(\frac{3}{2}\,\theta_0\right)^{2/3}}, \frac{\vartheta}{\theta_0} \right).$$

This shows that the factor $\theta_0^{-5/3}$ occurs also in ψ_2,

$$\psi_2 = \theta_0^{-5/3} \sum_{h=1}^{\infty} \bar{a}_h\, g\left(\eta, \frac{h\pi}{\theta_0}\right) \sin\left[\frac{h\pi\vartheta}{\theta_0}\right].$$

Here the modified coefficients $\bar{a}_h$ are independent of θ_0. From Eqs. V, 7 (8) and V, 7 (9), one finds then that the corresponding values of y and x are respectively proportional to $\theta_0^{-5/3}$ and to $\theta_0^{-4/3}$. The values of η and ϑ at the corresponding points are, of course (because of the present choice of the independent variables), proportional to $\theta_0^{2/3}$ and θ_0, respectively.

The pressure distribution for a rhombic profile is shown by the solid line in Fig. 85. This result can be put in the form

$$c_p = -2(\gamma + 1)^{-1/3}\, \eta = -2(\gamma + 1)^{-1/3}\, \theta_0^{2/3}\, g\left(\frac{x}{L}\right). \tag{5}$$

If L denotes the overall length of the profile, then the corresponding expression $\Psi^{-5/6}$ is given by

$$\Psi^{-5/6} = \frac{L}{2\,47} \left(\frac{3}{2}\,\theta_0\right)^{4/3} (\gamma + 1)^{-1/3}\, (\psi_1 + \psi_2). \tag{6}$$

The notation $\Psi^{-5/6}$ was explained at the beginning of the previous section. The factor $\theta_0^{4/3}$ becomes clear in view of the above remarks. It should be remembered that the coefficient of the term $\psi_{-5/6}$, which occurs in Eq. (6), is equal to 1 because of Eq. (2). These results have been repeatedly confirmed by actual measurements*.

By using for the hodograph plane an approximate equation different from TRICOMI's equation, LIGER [57] has succeeded in expressing a flow past a wedge in closed form.

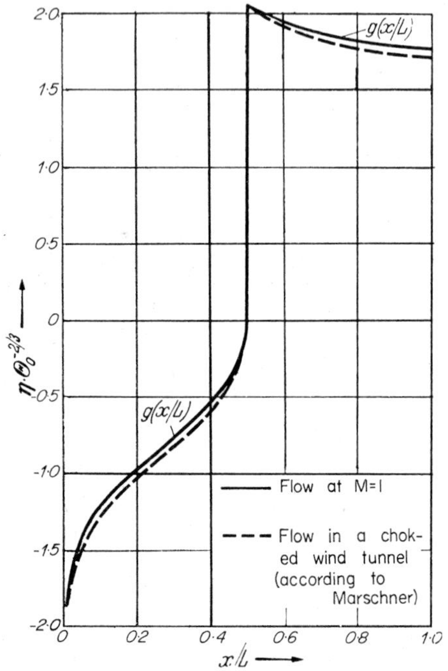

FIG. 85 Distribution of η for a rhombic profile in a choked wind tunnel with an approaching flow at $M = 1$. Θ_0 is the half-angle of the upstream wedge and the thickness ratio of the profile. For this example the thickness ratio is 10% and the chord is equal to 13% of the width of the tunnel. The choking MACH number is equal to 0.86. (According to GUDERLEY and YOSHIHARA [43] and MARSCHNER [60]).

The calculation procedure which was used here to determine ψ_2 can be extended to the boundary value problems for free jets, formulated in Figs. 50 and 51. It is questionable, however, if such an investigation is worth the effort.

5. The Interpretation of Certain Solutions Corresponding to Other Values of μ

The singularity, which occurs at the point O in a flow with $M = 1$, was found to be represented by $\psi_{-5/6}$. In this Section we shall discuss the physical meaning of other antisymmetric particular solutions which map the point O into infinity and for which the power of ϱ is lower than $-\frac{5}{6}$. We consider an antisymmetric

* The good agreement between theory and experiment has increased the confidence in both the experimental methods and in the theory.

particular solution $\psi = \varrho^{-(1/12)-\mu} G^{(a)} (\xi, \mu)$. The first zero of the function G occurring here, reckoned from $\xi = -\infty$, is at $\xi = c_1$. In the physical plane one evidently obtains at infinity a parallel flow with sonic velocity. The negative η axis maps into the negative x axis. There $\vartheta = 0$. The line $\xi = c_1$ yields then the positive x axis. There, however, the slope of the streamlines is different from zero. By integrating the slope of the streamlines one can calculate the shape of a body which fits this flow. Let G' be the derivative of G with respect to ξ at $\xi = c_1$. A point on the line $\xi = c_1$, characterized by a given value of ϱ, maps, in accordance with Eqs. VII, 3 (7) and VII, 3 (9) into a point whose coordinates are

$$y = 0, \tag{1a}$$

$$x = (\gamma + 1)^{1/3} \frac{(1 - c_1^3)^{5/6}}{3\left(\frac{1}{12} - \mu\right)} G' \varrho^{(1/12)-\mu}. \tag{1b}$$

The corresponding values of ϑ are, in accordance with Eq. VII, 3 (1),

$$\vartheta = \frac{2}{3} \frac{\sqrt{\varrho}}{(1 - c_1^3)^{1/2}}.$$

Elimination of ϱ with the aid of Eq. (1b) yields

$$\vartheta = \frac{2}{3}\left[3\left(\frac{1}{12} - \mu\right)\right]^{\frac{1}{(1/6)-2\mu}} (\gamma + 1)^{-\frac{1}{3[(1/12)-\mu]}} (1 - c_1^3)^{-\frac{1}{2}-\frac{5}{12}\frac{1}{(1/12)-\mu}} \times$$

$$\times [G']^{-\frac{1}{(1/6)-2\mu}} x^{\frac{1}{(1/6)-2\mu}} = \text{const}\, x^{\frac{1}{(1/6)-2\mu}},$$

and hence

$$\tilde{y} = \int \vartheta \, dx = \text{const} \frac{\frac{1}{6} - 2\mu}{\frac{7}{6} - 2\mu} x^{\frac{(7/6)-2\mu}{(1/6)-2\mu}}.$$

Thus one obtains the flow past a half-body whose profile is given by a generalised parabola. Along the contour the velocity is either supersonic or subsonic, depending on whether c_1 is positive or negative. In the first case, the sonic line originates from the tip of the profile. The simplified hodograph equation is, of course, not applicable there. The transition between the two cases occurs at $\mu = 11/12$. Then $c_1 = 0$ and $\tilde{y} \sim x^{0.4}$. The sonic line and the positive x axis coalesce. These flow fields can be interpreted as approximations to the flow in the vicinity of the nose of a profile. If the profile is pointed, then the nose lies in the region of subsonic velocities. When $\tilde{y} = x^{0.4}$ the entire profile is at sonic velocity. For lower powers of x the supersonic region begins, in this approximation, immediately at the leading edge. This is, however, so blunt that the subsonic regime approaches it very closely. The sonic line extends from the leading edge to infinity.

6. Unsymmetrical Profiles at $M = 1$

The hodograph image of infinity represents, also in the case of unsymmetrical profiles, a singular point. Of the solutions occurring at such a point one must again require that the MACH lines $\xi = 1$ should not map into infinity and that no discontinuities should be propagated along these lines. With this condition one obtains, in addition to those solutions which were found for symmetrical profiles, further solutions which are determined by Eq. VII, 9 (2). These are the particular solutions

$$\psi^{(s)}_{h/3} \tag{1a}$$

and

$$\psi^{(s)}_{-(1/3)-h}. \tag{1b}$$

Apart from certain coefficients, the corresponding transformed potentials are $\varphi^{(a)}_{(1/2)+(h/3)}$ and $\varphi^{(a)}_{(1/6)-h}$. Since the position vector in the physical plane is determined by the gradient of the transformed potential, and since for the two above potentials $\varphi_\eta = 0$ along the negative η axis, this line maps into the y axis. It represents then the axis of symmetry of the required flow field. The two characteristics through the origin, which must represent the limiting characteristics of the flow, will thus be symmetric with respect to the y axis. This contradicts, of course, our notions regarding the form of the flow field. Thus none of the particular solutions, listed above, can alone represent the flow field past a non-symmetrical body at infinity of the physical plane.

One should note, further, that all the particular solutions $\psi^{(s)}_{-(1/3)-h}$, except the first one, tend to infinity faster, as the origin is approached, then the particular solution $\psi^{(a)}_{-5/6}$. This last solution describes the behaviour of the flow at infinity for a symmetrical body. A linear combination, therefore, of a solution $\psi^{(s)}_{-(4/3)-h}$ and $\psi^{(a)}_{-5/6}$ would, in the vicinity of the origin, be still dominated by the term $\psi^{(s)}_{-(4/3)-h}$. Thus the solution at the origin can only be given by a linear combination of the solutions $\psi^{(a)}_{-5/6}$ and $\psi^{(s)}_{-1/3}$. For the LEGENDRE potential one obtains correspondingly $\varphi^{(s)}_{-1/3}$ and $\varphi^{(a)}_{1/6}$. In this case, however, only the first of these would be considered singular in the sense of TRICOMI's discussion. In the solution for a given profile there are, in addition, superimposed the particular solutions $\psi^{(s)}_{h/3}$ and $\psi^{(a)}_{(1/6)+(h/3)}$ or $\varphi^{(s)}_{h/3}$ and $\varphi^{(a)}_{(1/2)+(h/3)}$, which satisfy TRICOMI's conditions at the origin. The region of convergence of such a representation does not generally extend right up to the profile.

7. The Flow Past an Inclined Wedge

It is reasonable for symmetrical profiles to start with a hodograph solution which is simple to calculate and subsequently to determine the profile in the physical plane. Such a procedure for profiles inclined to the flow is hardly of any interest since the principal objective of the analysis would always be a comparison with a corresponding profile at zero angle of attack so that definite conclusions regarding the lift can be reached. This requires, however, that the form of the profile should remain constant while the angle of attack is changed.

As a first example we will consider an inclined wedge. This flow field is not entirely satisfactory since the flow past the leading edge has a local supersonic region. It would be better, from this point of view, to consider a profile with a rounded leading edge. A more detailed discussion will show that for small angles of attack, the influence of the local supersonic region is negligible (GUDERLEY and YOSHIHARA [45]).

If this local supersonic region is ignored, then the hodograph representation of the flow is as shown in Fig. 86. When in the process of inclining the profile, the direction of flow is maintained constant; the position of the origin remains unchanged while the faces of the wedge become displaced by the angle of attack. The boundary condition along the surface of the wedge is $\psi = 0$. The solution contains now two arbitrary constants, namely the coefficients of the singular expressions $\psi^{(a)}_{-5/6}$ and $\psi^{(s)}_{-1/3}$. As in the case of a wedge parallel to the flow, where, however, only one constant occurred, these coefficients are determined by the dimensions of the faces of the wedge. Let us assume temporarily that the coefficient of $\psi_{-1/3}$ is arbitrarily put equal to zero. Because of the asymmetry of the hodograph boundary with respect to the origin, one obtains an unsymmetric hodograph solution and, in the physical plane, a wedge whose faces are of different lengths. By a proper adjustment of the coefficient of $\psi_{-1/3}$ the faces of the wedge can be made equal.

As mentioned above, in view of the flow around the leading edge, a local supersonic region is to be expected. To what extent does the present hodograph representation indicate that such a region is necessary? In the case of a symmetric wedge it was obvious that a branch point of the streamlines must occur at the stagnation point, i.e. when $\eta \to -\infty$. It cannot be expected that this is also the case in an asymmetrical flow, namely for the following reasons. For negative values of η the solution can be expanded in terms of CHAPLYGIN's particular solutions. Using the asymptotic forms of HANKEL functions, given by Eq. VII, 7 (9a) one obtains, as the predominant particular solutions for $\eta \to -\infty$

$$|\eta|^{-1/4}\, e^{-(2/3)\,|\eta|^{3/2}\,\pi/(2\,\theta_0)} \cos\left[\frac{\vartheta}{\theta_0}\,\frac{\pi}{2}\right]$$

and

$$|\eta|^{-1/4}\, e^{-(2/3)\,|\eta|^{3/2}\,\pi/\theta_0} \sin\left[\frac{\vartheta}{\theta_0}\,\pi\right].$$

The first of the above expressions decreases much more slowly than the second and is therefore predominant as $\eta \to -\infty$. Since this first expression has no zeros between $-\theta_0$ and $+\theta_0$, the streamline pattern in the η, ϑ plane is largely similar to that shown in Fig. 32, although there a different system of coordinates was employed. Only when the coefficient of this particular solution vanishes can the branch point of the streamlines occur when $\eta \to -\infty$. In general, one must expect a hodograph picture as shown in Fig. 86.

Although a local supersonic region (such as shown in Fig. 87) would allow a modification of the hodograph image of the flow, such that the stagnation point again becomes a branch point of the streamlines; practically however it is hardly possible to calculate this region. Even if it were possible, the result would hardly be realistic since one would have to reckon with separation occurring in the flow. A similar supersonic region occurs also on an inclined plate. GUDERLEY and YOSHIHARA estimated the influence of the local supersonic region in the following manner. To the hodograph image in Fig. 88 there corresponds a flow past a wedge provided with a flap at the leading edge. The branch point occurs at the foremost edge of this flap. As may be seen from the hodograph both branches of the streamline have the same direction after the branch point, they differ only in the velocity. At zero velocity there results a concave corner. The length of the flap, and the force transmitted by it, tend to zero when the angle of attack tends to zero. It is plausible that the influence of the flap on total lift is of the

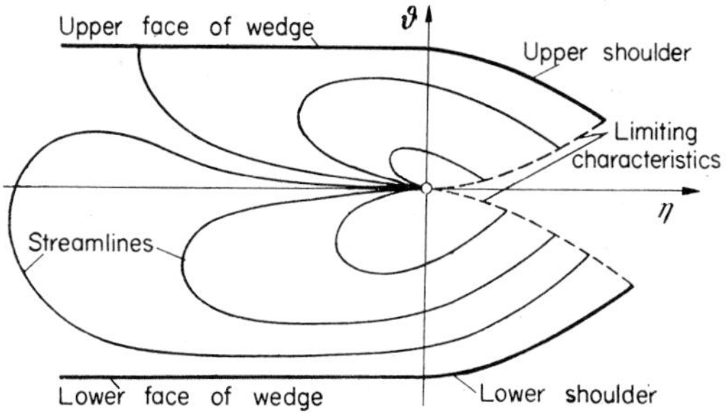

FIF. 86 The hodograph for an inclined wedge. (According to GUDERLEY and YOSHIHARA [45]).

order of magnitude of the force exerted on the flap. An estimate of this force shows that it decreases with the angle of attack faster than the lift so that it becomes negligible for sufficiently small angles of attack.

The details of the calculation of GUDERLEY and YOSHIHARA are based on the following considerations. Up to now the change in the angle of attack was expressed by a displacement of the hodograph image of the profile in the direction of ϑ. The same result is obtained if the image of the profile remains stationary and the singular point O is displaced in the opposite direction. This displacement is considered to be small. The flow past the wedge at zero angle of attack is considered as the base flow and it was calculated on p. 225. At the origin this flow contains the term $\psi_{-5/6}$. The same singularity at a point $\eta = 0$, $\vartheta = \alpha$ (where α represents the angle of attack) is given by

$$\psi_{-5/6}(\eta, \vartheta - \alpha).$$

This last expression can be expanded in terms of α and one obtains with the aid of Eq. VII, 6 (2)

$$\begin{aligned}\psi_{-5/6}(\eta, \vartheta - \alpha) &= \psi_{-5/6}(\eta, \vartheta) - \alpha \frac{\partial \psi_{-5/6}(\eta, \vartheta)}{\partial \vartheta} \\ &= \psi_{-5/6}(\eta, \vartheta) - \alpha \frac{3}{2} \psi_{-4/3}(\eta, \vartheta).\end{aligned}$$

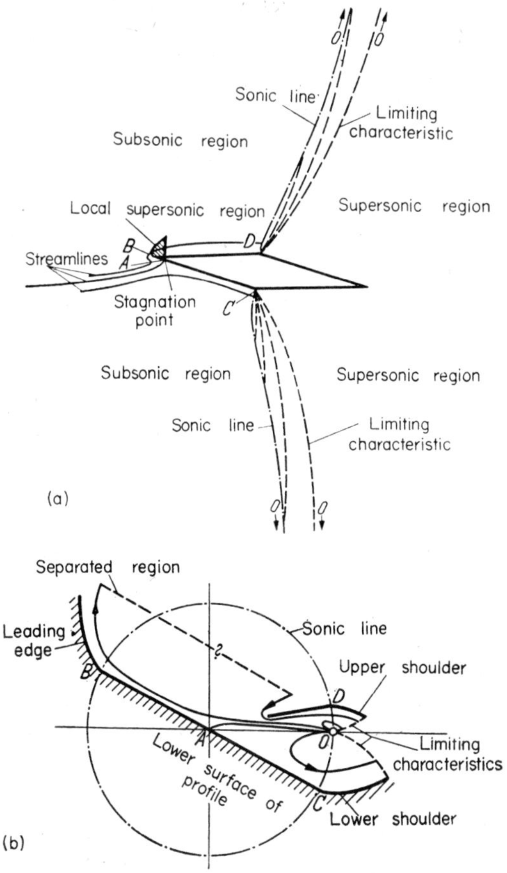

FIG. 87 (a) The flow past an inclined wedge.
(b) Hodograph of the flow past an inclined wedge.

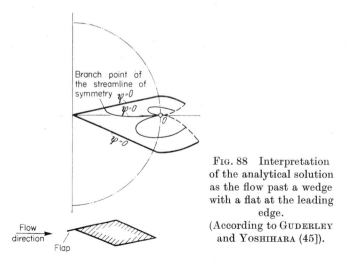

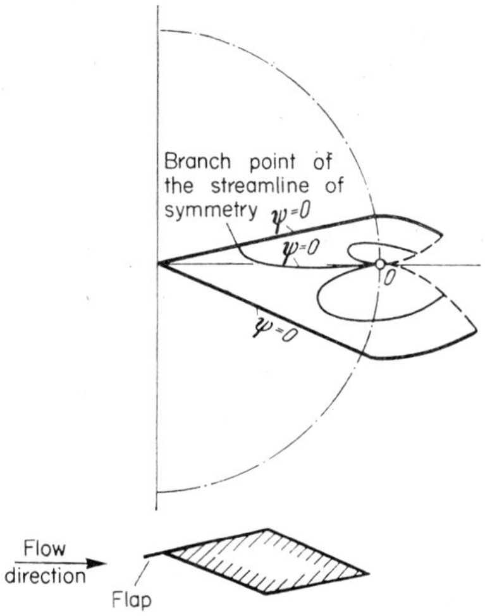

FIG. 88 Interpretation of the analytical solution as the flow past a wedge with a flat at the leading edge.
(According to GUDERLEY and YOSHIHARA (45]).

Thus the displacement of the singular term $\psi_{-5/6}$ from the point $\eta = 0$, $\vartheta = 0$ to $\eta = 0$, $\vartheta = \alpha$ is, in the first approximation, equivalent to a superposition of a term $-\alpha\frac{3}{2}\psi_{-4/3}(\eta, \vartheta)$ onto the original singularity. Let us temporarily ignore the coefficient $-\frac{3}{2}\alpha$. Onto $\psi_{-4/3}(\eta, \vartheta)$ one must superimpose a solution $\tilde{\psi}$ which satisfies TRICOMI's conditions and is so chosen that the resulting sum satisfies the boundary condition $\psi = 0$ along the image of the contour of the profile. This is done, as on p. 225, by a reflection of the singularity at the images of the faces of the wedge and by the addition of CHAPLYGIN's particular solutions. The solution found in this manner (including $\psi_{-4/3}$) is denoted by ψ_{I}. When ψ_{I} is superimposed on the base flow, there results a solution which, in the first approximation, is equivalent to that for a problem which has a singularity $\psi_{-5/6}$ at $\eta = 0$, $\vartheta = \alpha$ and includes a condition $\psi = 0$ along the faces of the wedge.

In the next step one must find a solution which at $\eta = 0$, $\vartheta = \alpha$ has the singularity $\psi_{-1/3}$ and for which, along the image of the faces, $\psi = 0$. In a consistent approximation the singularity at the above point can be replaced by the same singularity at $\eta = 0$ and $\vartheta = 0$. The calculation procedure is, of course, the same as before. This solution is denoted by ψ_{II}. Now we seek such a combination $\psi_{\mathrm{I}} + \text{const}\,\psi_{\mathrm{II}}$ which yields no contribution to the length of the faces of the wedge. To this end we determine, for the solutions ψ_{I} and ψ_{II}, the values of x at the shoulder of the wedge, choosing $x = 0$ at the leading edge ($\eta = -\infty$). The coefficient of ψ_{II} must be chosen such that the value of x at the shoulder, for ψ_{II}, is equal and opposite to the corresponding value of x for the solution ψ_{I}. Since the contribution to x of each solution is the same for the upper and lower faces, except for an opposite sign, the above condition has to be satisfied only for one face. The resulting solution, which does not change the shape of the wedge upon superposition on the base flow, is denoted by

$$\Psi^{-4/3} = \psi_{\mathrm{I}} + \text{const}\,\psi_{\mathrm{II}}.$$

The form of this solution is in principle

$$\Psi^{-4/3} = \psi_{-4/3} + \alpha_{-1/3}^{-4/3}\,\psi_{-1/3} + \tilde{\psi}^{-4/3}, \tag{1}$$

where $\alpha_{-1/3}^{-4/3}$ is a constant and $\tilde{\psi}^{-4/3}$ satisfies TRICOMI's conditions. The notation is that introduced at the beginning of Section VIII, 3.

Let the solution for a wedge at zero angle of attack be given by

$$\Psi^{-5/6} = \alpha_{-5/6}^{-5/6}\,\psi_{-5/6} + \tilde{\psi}^{-5/6},$$

where $\alpha_{-5/6}^{-5/6}$ is a constant determined by the dimensions of the wedge and which can be calculated from Eq. VIII, 4 (6). The influence of a small angle of attack is obtained by the superposition of an expression which in the subsequent calculation is denoted by $\overline{\psi}$

$$\overline{\psi} = -\left(\frac{3}{2}\alpha\right)\alpha_{-5/6}^{-5/6}\,\Psi^{-4/3}. \tag{2}$$

Here α is the angle of attack, as before.

If another solution is added to the base flow in the hodograph plane, a point at which a given velocity vector occurs in the physical plane is displaced by an amount given by the superimposed solution. We are, of course, interested primarily in the change in the pressure (or in a change in η) at a given point. To find this we must perform a linearisation. It implies no added restriction, since a linearisation was already introduced in the expansion in terms of the angle of attack.

The values of x and y calculated for the base flow are denoted by $x_0(\eta, \vartheta)$ and $y_0(\eta, \vartheta)$. The corresponding values calculated for the superimposed flow $\overline{\psi}$ are denoted by $\bar{x}(\eta, \vartheta)$ and $\bar{y}(\eta, \vartheta)$. One obtains as a result

$$x = x_0(\eta, \vartheta) + \bar{x}(\eta, \vartheta),$$

$$y = y_0(\eta, \vartheta) + \bar{y}(\eta, \vartheta).$$

When $\overline{\psi}$ is superimposed on the base flow and η and ϑ are simultaneously changed by $\Delta\eta$ and $\Delta\vartheta$ respectively then, under the assumption that $\overline{\psi}$ is a small quantity of first order, the resulting changes in x and y are

$$\Delta x = \bar{x}(\eta, \vartheta) + \frac{\partial x_0}{\partial \eta}\Delta\eta + \frac{\partial x_0}{\partial \vartheta}\Delta\vartheta,$$

$$\Delta y = \bar{y}(\eta, \vartheta) + \frac{\partial y_0}{\partial \eta}\Delta\eta + \frac{\partial y_0}{\partial \vartheta}\Delta\vartheta.$$

We now determine $\Delta\eta$ and $\Delta\vartheta$ such that Δx and Δy vanish. Then $\eta + \Delta\eta$, $\vartheta + \Delta\vartheta$ represents a velocity vector which in the superposition of $\overline{\psi}$ is mapped into a point at which, in the base flow, the values of η and ϑ occurred. Thus the local changes of η and ϑ are

$$\Delta\eta = \frac{-\bar{x}\dfrac{\partial y_0}{\partial \vartheta} + \bar{y}\dfrac{\partial x_0}{\partial \vartheta}}{\dfrac{\partial x_0}{\partial \eta}\dfrac{\partial y_0}{\partial \vartheta} - \dfrac{\partial x_0}{\partial \vartheta}\dfrac{\partial y_0}{\partial \eta}}, \tag{3a}$$

$$\Delta\vartheta = \frac{\bar{x}\dfrac{\partial y_0}{\partial \eta} - \bar{y}\dfrac{\partial x_0}{\partial \eta}}{\dfrac{\partial x_0}{\partial \eta}\dfrac{\partial y_0}{\partial \vartheta} - \dfrac{\partial x_0}{\partial \vartheta}\dfrac{\partial y_0}{\partial \eta}}. \tag{3b}$$

Naturally at the surface of the profile $y_0 = 0$. Since the faces of a wedge are lines of $\vartheta = \text{const}$, along these faces $\partial y_0/\partial\eta = 0$. At the profile of a wedge $\bar{y} = 0$. Thus for the surface of the wedge there results

$$\Delta\eta = \frac{-\bar{x}}{\partial x_0/\partial\eta}; \quad \Delta\eta = 0. \tag{4}$$

From this the change in the pressure can be found with the aid of Eq. V, 7 (11).

In supersonic flow the solution $\overline{\psi}$ can be found with the aid of the method of characteristics. The following considerations are helpful in this respect. If the solution is expressed in terms of the transformed potential, then

$$\bar{x} = (\gamma + 1)^{1/3}\, \overline{\varphi}_\eta,$$

$$\bar{y} = \overline{\varphi}_\vartheta.$$

The characteristics of TRICOMI's equation are given by

$$\frac{d\eta}{d\vartheta} = \pm\eta^{-1/2}$$

and the compatibility condition is

$$d\overline{\varphi}_\eta \mp \sqrt{\eta}\, d\overline{\varphi}_\vartheta = 0,$$

or

$$\frac{d\bar{x}}{d\bar{y}} = \pm(\gamma + 1)^{1/3}\sqrt{\eta}.$$

Thus the compatibility condition, for the characteristics in the hodograph plane, determines the characteristic directions in the physical plane. The determination of the transformed potential in the hodograph plane can, therefore, be interpreted as a construction of the characteristic net in the physical plane. For the base flow this is trivial. It is valid, however, also for the superimposed flow alone. As regards the boundary conditions for the superimposed solution $\overline{\psi}$ the following may be stated: along the downstream part of a rhombic profile, which in the present approximation maps into $\bar{y} = 0$, we have $\vartheta = -\vartheta_0$. We have, therefore, as a boundary condition in the hodograph plane $\bar{y} = 0$ for $\vartheta = -\vartheta_0$. In the $\bar{x}, \bar{y}$ plane the condition is: $\vartheta = -\vartheta_0$ at $\bar{y} = 0$. The coordinates $\bar{x}$ and $\bar{y}$ are determined as follows. One calculates first, along the limiting characteristic, and for the same values of η and ϑ which were used for the base flow, the values of $\bar{x}$ and $\bar{y}$ corresponding to the superimposed solution $\overline{\psi}$. Then the characteristic net is constructed in an $\bar{x}$, $\bar{y}$ diagram in the usual manner. The boundary condition is $\vartheta = -\vartheta_0$ for $\bar{y} = 0$. In order to determine the changes in the pressure distribution, caused by $\overline{\psi}$, one obtains from this field the intersections of the same characteristics of the hodograph plane, which were drawn in the base flow, i.e. for the same values of η and ϑ, the values of $\bar{x}$ and $\bar{y}$. These are then introduced into Eqs. (3a) and (3b) or, at the profile, into Eq. (4).

The result of this calculation is shown in Fig. 89, in which the dimensionless change in η per unit of angle of attack is plotted for a rhombic profile. At the nose of the profile, this curve can be compared with the differential change in the pressure distribution on a wedge when the angle of the latter is increased by a small amount. Since in accordance with Eq. VIII, 4 (5)

$$\eta = g\left(\frac{x}{L}\right)\theta_0^{2/3},$$

one obtains, as a result of a change of the angle of the wedge by $\Delta\theta_0$,

$$\Delta\eta = \frac{2}{3}\,\theta_0^{-1/3}\, g\left(\frac{x}{L}\right) \Delta\theta_0 .$$

This last equation is shown by the dotted line in Fig. 89. The influence of the change in the angle of attack is comparable in magnitude to that of a simple change in the angle of the wedge, but is generally larger.

Integration yields $dc_L/d\alpha$. For $\gamma = 1{\cdot}4$

$$\frac{dc_L}{d\alpha} = 2{\cdot}49\ \theta_0^{-1/3}.$$

The center of pressure is located at 29·4 % of the chord of the rhombic profile.

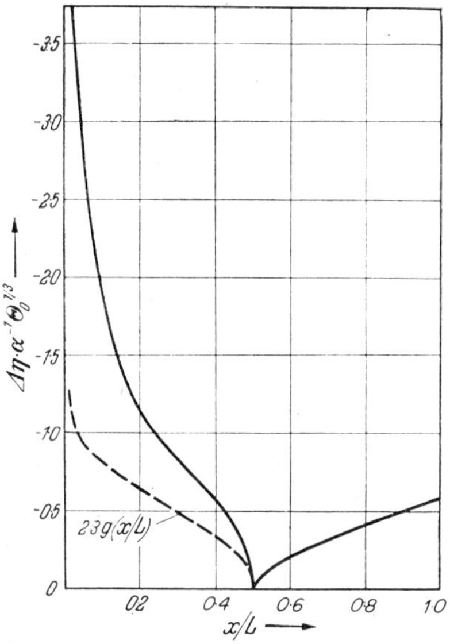

FIG. 89 ——— The variation of η for an inclined rhombic profile. – – – – — The variation of η for a wedge whose angle is increased by α. Θ_0 is the half-angle of the foremost wedge and the thickness ratio, α is the angle of attack. (According to GUDERLEY and YOSHIHARA [45]).

It is noteworthy that $dc_L/d\alpha$ depends on the thickness ratio θ_0. This is not true of linearized subsonic or supersonic flow. Another noticeable feature is shown in Fig. 105 where $dc_L/d\alpha$ is plotted in terms of the MACH number of the approaching flow. The right-hand part of the curve represents the conditions in purely supersonic flow. It can be determined by performing the well-known supersonic flow calculations with the requisite simplifications for the region in the vicinity of $M = 1$. The lift coefficient in this region is considerably higher than that indicated by the beginning of the left hand part of the curve at $M = 1$. A later discussion will show that the curve on the left has a horizontal tangent at $M = 1$ ($\eta = 0$) and that its curvature at that point vanishes. Between the MACH number of unity and a purely supersonic flow the lift coefficient must, therefore, behave in a really remarkable manner. This state of affairs caused VINCENTI and WAGONER [80] to investigate the intermediate points both theoretically and experimentally. The left curve shows VINCENTI's points. With regard to the details of the technique, the reader is referred to the original article. The problem of an attached shock, behind which a supersonic region occurs, was discussed in connection with Fig. 53. An analytical solution for that case is given by YOSHIHARA [85]. Some remarks regarding his calculation will be found on p. 289. The results of this investigation are shown by the dotted part of the curve in Fig. 105.

8. The Boundary Value Problem for an Arbitrarily Shaped Profile at a Small Angle of Attack and Related Problems

Let the flow at $M = 1$, and hence also the corresponding hodograph image (Fig. 90), be known for an arbitrary profile. To this solution we assign a zero

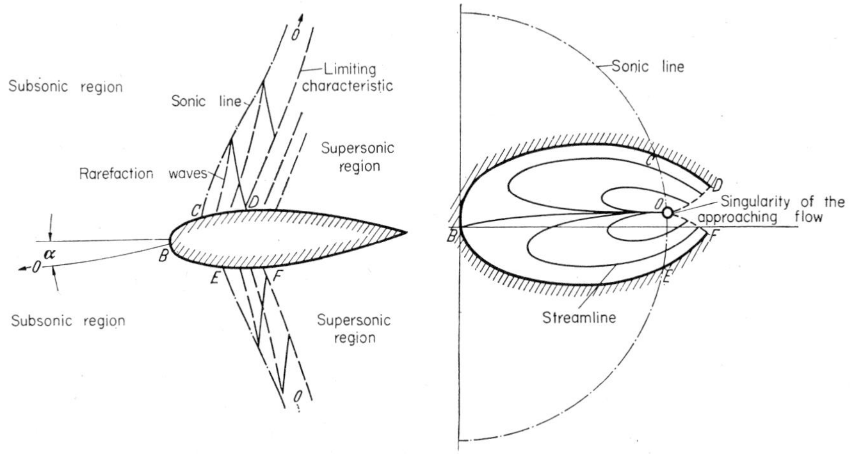

FIG. 90 The physical and hodograph planes for a body of general form at $M = 1$.

angle of attack. The hodograph solution is denoted by $\Psi^{-5/6}$. We are interested in the change in the pressure distribution, resulting from a small change in the angle of attack. As in the preceding section, the change in the angle of attack is represented by a displacement of that point of the hodograph which represents infinity of the physical plane. In accordance with the discussion in Section VIII, 7 this displacement is effected by a superposition on $\Psi^{-5/6}$ of a solution in which, at the origin, the singular term $\psi_{-4/3}$ predominates. This solution must satisfy the boundary conditions which express the fact that the profile of the body does not change. Later we shall require solutions which satisfy the same boundary conditions, which however at the origin possess singularities given by $\psi_{-(4/3)-(h/2)}$. The following discussion includes this more general case.

The boundary conditions on the surface of the profile are most simply expressed in terms of the transformed potential φ, which also satisfies TRICOMI's differential equation. The boundary condition which expresses the invariance of the contour in the physical plane takes, in accordance with Section V, 11, the form

$$L(\varphi) = \varphi_\eta + \varphi_\vartheta \, \eta_0 \frac{d\eta_0}{d\vartheta} = 0. \tag{1}$$

Here $\eta = \eta_0(\vartheta)$ is the hodograph contour of the base flow. With the aid of the equation $\psi = \varphi_\vartheta$, which relates the stream function to the transformed potential and which was derived in Section V, 7, and with the aid of Eqs. VII, 6 (1) and VII, 6 (2) one finds that to $\psi_{-(5/6)\mp h}$ and $\psi_{-(4/3)\mp h}$ there correspond $[6(\frac{1}{3} \pm \pm h)(\frac{2}{3} \pm h)]^{-1} \varphi_{-(1/3)\mp h}$ and $\frac{2}{3}\, \varphi_{-(5/6)\mp h}$ respectively when the transformed potential is employed. The term $\psi_{-1/3}$, which evidently does not satisfy TRICOMI's condition, changes in this process, except for a coefficient, into a term $\varphi_{1/6}$ to which TRICOMI's conditions apply. When the boundary value problem can be formulated in terms of ψ, the coefficient of $\psi_{-1/3}$ is, however, determined (cf. p. 240).

Thus we have to find a solution φ of TRICOMI's equation which, along the profile, satisfies the condition of Eq. (1) and which, at the origin, has the predominant singularity $\varphi_{-(5/6)-(h/2)}$.

Here the following train of thought may be followed; in a flow with a MACH number of unity, a singular expression $\varphi_{-1/3}$ occurs at the origin, multiplied by a coefficient which is determined by the dimensions of the body. If the body is unsymmetric with respect to the direction of the approaching flow, then one should assume that this coefficient changes with the angle of attack. (For reasons of symmetry this coefficient must have a stationary value in the case of a symmetric body.) One expects, of course, that the flow is unique, i.e. that this change of the coefficient is determined by the boundary value problem. The displacement of the origin is expressed by the superposition of the solution $\varphi_{-5/6}$. If the coefficient of $\varphi_{-1/3}$ changes simultaneously in the complete solution, then in the superimposed solution there will occur a term $\varphi_{-1/3}$ (multiplied by a factor determined by the change of the coefficient). The superimposed solution thus contains two terms which are singular at the origin but it must still be unique. One may ask how this property of the solution of a boundary value problem can be expressed mathematically. A complete treatment of the boundary value problem of the second kind is, as yet, not available. The following plausibility argument shows, however, that in this case an additional condition must be included in the boundary values, also for TRICOMI's equation. This condition is similar to those known from potential theory. If this were not the case, then for a known flow with $M = 1$ a solution of TRICOMI's equation in the form

$$\varphi = \varphi_{-1/3} + \tilde{\varphi}$$

could be found which, upon superposition on the base flow, would not affect the contour in the physical plane. (In accordance with the notation described in the beginning of Section VIII, 3, $\tilde{\varphi}$ always denotes a solution which satisfies TRICOMI's conditions.) By superimposing such a solution onto the base flow further solutions, for the same profile with $M = 1$, could be obtained so that the flow with a MACH number of unity would not be unique.

This discussion shows also that when the term $L(\varphi)$, defined by Eq. (1), is formed for $\varphi_{-1/3}$, in order to obtain the boundary conditions for the function $\tilde{\varphi}$ in the last equation, this term can never satisfy the additional conditions which must be prescribed for a boundary value problem of the second kind. (This is remarkable in so far as the details of this condition are not known.) It follows thus, however, that the boundary value problem of the second kind can be made soluble by allowing the presence of a term $\varphi_{-1/3}$ multiplied by a suitable factor.

Thus we come to the conclusion that the boundary value problem for φ, which we have formulated at the beginning, has a solution in the form

$$\Phi^{-(5/6)-(h/2)} = \varphi_{-(5/6)-(h/2)} + \alpha_{-(1/3)}^{-(5/6)-(h/2)} \varphi_{-1/3} + \tilde{\varphi}^{-(5/6)-(h/2)} . \tag{2}$$

In the vicinity of the origin the solution $\tilde{\varphi}^{-(5/6)-(h/2)}$ is expressed as a superposition of the "natural" particular solutions $\varphi_{(1/6)+(h/6)}$. The boundary value problem for $\tilde{\varphi}^{-(5/6)-(h/2)}$, to which we are led in this manner, can be solved by introducing a distribution of singularities along the hodograph image of the contour. These singularities are analogous to a distribution of sources in an incompressible flow. In order to satisfy the boundary conditions it would then be necessary to solve an integral equation. Such a procedure has, as yet, not been carried out.

If we change from φ to ψ, Eq. (2) takes the form

$$\Psi^{-(4/3)-(h/2)} = \psi_{-(4/3)-(h/2)} + \alpha_{-(5/6)}^{-(4/3)-(h/2)} \psi_{-5/6} + \alpha_{-1/3}^{-(4/3)-(h/2)} \times$$
$$\times \psi_{-1/3} + \tilde{\psi}^{-(4/3)-(h/2)} . \tag{3}$$

Obviously the coefficients α are different in Eqs. (2) and (3). In addition, the singular term $\psi_{-1/3}$, which was included in $\tilde{\varphi}$ in Eq. (2), occurs here.

The calculation of these particular solutions for the wedge is more lucid, since there the boundary conditions can be immediately given. Both for the base flow and for the superimposed solutions $\psi = 0$ along the image of the faces of the wedge. Solutions which satisfy this boundary condition need contain only *one* singularity $\psi_{-1/3}$ or $\psi_{-(5/6)-(h/2)}$ at the origin. Such solutions contribute, however, in general to the length of the faces of the wedge and therefore, upon superposition on a base flow, do not leave the profile of the body unchanged. If the solution ψ is antisymmetric (h even), then these contributions to the length of the faces have the same sign. If the solution ψ is symmetric (h odd), then one of the faces is lengthened while the other shortened, as we have seen in our calculation of an inclined wedge. In order to obtain solutions which leave the length of the faces of the wedge invariant, further terms must be superimposed. For even h one uses the solution which has $\psi_{-5/6}$ as the singular component, i.e. the solution for $M = 1$. For odd h one uses the solution containing the singularity $\psi_{-1/3}$. Thus the form of the desired particular solutions is

$$\Psi^{-(5/6)-h} = \psi_{-(5/6)-h} + \alpha_{-5/6}^{-(5/6)-h} \psi_{-5/6} + \tilde{\psi}^{-(5/6)-h} \qquad h = 1, 2 \ldots \tag{4}$$

and

$$\Psi^{-(4/3)-h} = \psi_{-(4/3)-h} + \alpha_{-1/3}^{-(4/3)-h}\, \psi_{-1/3} + \tilde{\psi}^{-(4/3)-h} \quad h = 0, 1, 2 \ldots. \tag{5}$$

Apart from the fact that, because of the symmetry properties of the problem, certain terms do not occur, Eqs. (4) and (5) agree with Eq. (3).

9. The Inclined Flat Plate at $M = 1$

The solution for the inclined plate at $M = 1$ is particularly interesting because of its simplicity. It can be interpreted as the limiting case of a slender wedge whose angle of attack is large compared with the wedge angle.

The pattern of the flow field is shown in Fig. 91. This is obtained by considering first the plate in a tunnel with plane walls and operated at a choking MACH number. In this manner one obtains two minimum cross-sections, one between the leading edge and the upper wall, the other between the trailing edge and the

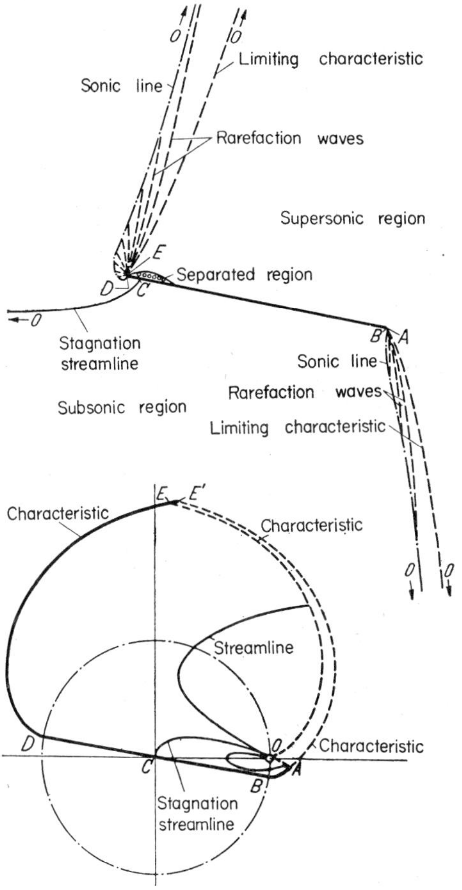

FIG. 91 The flow past an inclined plate at $M = 1$.

lower wall. One should expect, therefore, that a sonic line runs from the leading edge towards the upper wall, while a similar sonic line runs from the trailing edge to the lower wall. As always in subsonic flow there exists a stagnation point in the vicinity of the leading edge. The streamlines immediately below the stagnation point streamline are always oriented in the direction of the approaching flow. Streamlines immediately above the stagnation streamline run, shortly after the stagnation point, in an almost opposite direction to the approaching flow. Around the leading edge, therefore, we have a rapid expansion. The sonic line, originating at the leading edge, starts out normal to the plate in a downward direction. It is caused by the expansion cone which occurs at that point. The sonic line then changes its direction by almost 180°, so that it finally runs towards the upper wall. The flow in the vicinity of the trailing edge is quite similar to that which occurs at the shoulder of a wedge.

Theoretically the expansion around the leading edge involves the occurrence of absolute vacuum, followed by a pressure increase generated by the compression waves which originate at the sonic line. In practice a local separation region occurs. The slope of the upper surface of the plate is such that it lies completely in the supersonic regime.

Having thus gained a picture of the flow in a tunnel, we can obtain the flow at $M = 1$ by allowing the walls to recede to infinity. In the case of an inclined wedge we have found that, in the vicinity of the leading edge, a local supersonic region is obtained. In the present case this region extends over the entire upper surface of the plate.

After this description no further explanation of the hodograph image (Fig. 91) is necessary. It is only uncertain how the condition for the region of expansion at the leading edge should be formulated. If we limit ourselves to small angles of attack, the point O is located very close to the image of the lower face of the wedge. If the hodograph image is now distorted in accordance with the similarity rule, in such a manner that the location of the origin with respect to the face of the wedge is unchanged, i.e. by the introduction of new variables

$$\tilde{\eta} = \frac{\eta}{\tau}, \quad \tilde{\vartheta} = \frac{\vartheta}{\tau^{3/2}},$$

where the angle of attack is also proportional to $\tau^{3/2}$, then in the limit as $\tau \to 0$ the part of the $\tilde{\eta}$, $\tilde{\vartheta}$ plane representing the flow around the leading edge moves to infinity. This boundary condition becomes, therefore, unimportant (Fig. 92). The solution must satisfy $\psi = 0$ along ABC and at infinity. The singularity at O must appear as a superposition of $\psi_{-5/6}$ and $\psi_{-1/3}$. As a further condition one finds that for $\tau \to \infty$ the streamlines must branch and that the solution must yield the prescribed value L for the length of the plate. These two conditions determine the two free parameters of the problems, namely the coefficients of the two particular solutions $\psi_{-5/6}$ and $\psi_{-1/3}$.

In the following calculations we shall write η and ϑ in place of $\tilde{\eta}$ and $\tilde{\vartheta}$. The solution may be guessed in view of the form which it must assume at the point

B and at infinity (GUDERLEY [36]). We choose B as the origin of the η, ϑ system of coordinates. As a result of the boundary condition $\psi = 0$ along CB and BA, one finds that the solution at B can be represented as a superposition of the particular solutions $\psi^a_{(2/3)+h}$. Along the line BC these solutions appear in the form

$$\psi = (-\xi)^{-3/2}\, \varrho^{(2/3)+h},$$

so that the entire solution is given by

$$\psi = (-\xi)^{-3/2}\, \varrho^{2/3}\, P(\varrho), \tag{1}$$

where $P(\varrho)$ represents a temporarily unknown power series in ϱ. In order to determine the behaviour of this solution at infinity, we imagine next that the solution is extended past the characteristic OD up to the characteristic AE. To this end

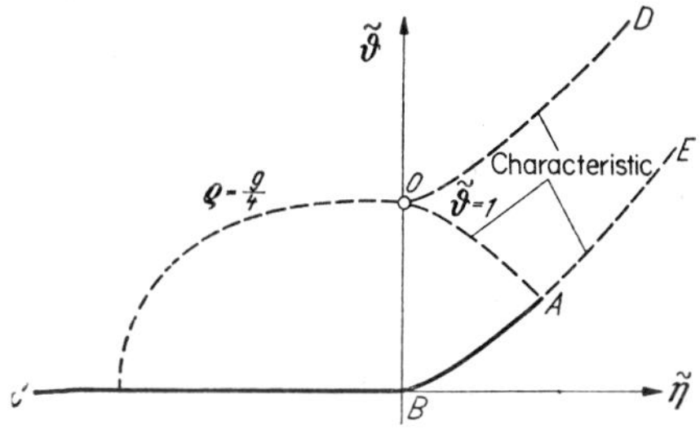

FIG. 92 The $\tilde{\eta}$, $\tilde{\vartheta}$ plane for the flow past a plate inclined at a small angle.

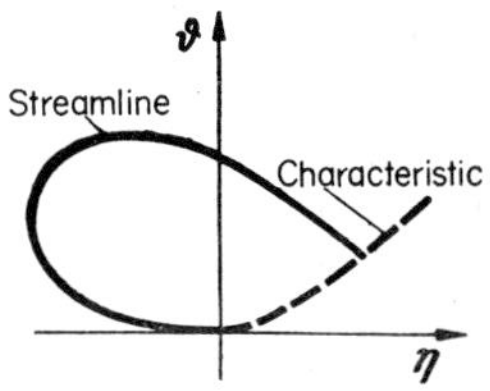

FIG. 93 Typical for of a streamline for a solution $\psi^a_{-5/6}$.

one would utilize the values of ψ obtained along the characteristic OD and the condition $\psi = 0$ at infinity. The characteristic AE is one of the MACH lines belonging to the expansion fan attached to the leading edge of the plate. It can therefore not be permitted to map into infinity in the physical plane. Particular solutions which for $\varrho \to \infty$ tend to zero, for which $\psi = 0$ along $\xi = -\infty$ and whose characteristic $\xi = 1$ does not map into infinity, are given by

$$\psi^a_{-5/6}, \tag{2a}$$

and

$$\psi^a_{-(5/6)-h} \qquad h = 1, 2 \ldots. \tag{2b}$$

The function $G^{(a)}$ appropriate to the first particular solution has no zeros between $\xi = -\infty$ and $\xi = 1$. The pattern of the streamlines corresponds approximately to Fig. 93, i.e. this solution has no branch point at infinity. Since this solution occurs with the least possible negative exponent of ϱ it would predominate for $\varrho \to \infty$ and there would determine the behaviour of the solution. Therefore, the condition that infinity represents a branch point of the streamlines excludes the occurence of the particular solution given by Eq. (2a). For large values of ϱ and $\xi = -\infty$ the solution, therefore, takes the form

$$\psi = (-\xi)^{-3/2}\, \varrho^{-1/16}\, P(\varrho^{-1}).$$

Let ϱ_0 denote the value corresponding to the velocity of approach. If θ_0 is the angle of attack then

$$\varrho_0 = \frac{9}{4}\,\theta_0^2. \tag{3}$$

We now try to represent the solution along $\xi = -\infty$ in the form

$$\psi = (-\xi)^{-3/2}\left(\frac{\varrho}{\varrho_0}\right)^{2/3}\left(1 + \frac{\varrho}{\varrho_0}\right)^{-5/2} \tag{4}$$

which is certainly of the correct form for $\varrho \to \infty$ and for $\varrho = 0$. From this the entire flow field can be determined by an analytical continuation. It is necessary to prove that in the entire flow field, except for the origin, there exist no singularities and that the singularity at O has the desired character. With a view to our later discussions let us consider here the more general expression, namely

$$\psi^{m,n} = (-\xi)^{-3/2}\left(\frac{\varrho}{\varrho_0}\right)^{(2/3)+m}\left(1 + \frac{\varrho}{\varrho_0}\right)^{-(5/2)-n}, \tag{5}$$

where m and n are integers. The binomial expansions of this equation with respect to ϱ/ϱ_0 and $(\varrho/\varrho_0)^{-1}$ are given by

$$\psi^{m,n} = (-\xi)^{-3/2}\sum_{h=0}^{\infty}(-)^h \frac{\Gamma\left(\frac{5}{2}+n+h\right)}{\Gamma\left(\frac{5}{2}+n\right)\Gamma(h+1)}\left(\frac{\varrho}{\varrho_0}\right)^{(2/3)+m+h}$$

and

$$\psi^{m,n} = (-\xi)^{-3/2}\sum_{h=0}^{\infty}(-)^h \frac{\Gamma\left(\frac{5}{2}+n+h\right)}{\Gamma\left(\frac{5}{2}+n\right)\Gamma(h+1)}\left(\frac{\varrho}{\varrho_0}\right)^{-(11/6)+m-n-h}.$$

Hence, as an analytic continuation of the solution, one obtains

$$\psi^{m,n} = \sum_{h=0}^{\infty}(-)^h \frac{\Gamma\left(\frac{5}{2}+n+h\right)}{\Gamma\left(\frac{5}{2}+n\right)\Gamma(h+1)}\, G^{(a)}\left[\xi, \left(\frac{3}{4}+m+h\right)\right]\left(\frac{\varrho}{\varrho_0}\right)^{(2/3)+m+h} \tag{6a}$$

and

$$\psi^{m,n} = \sum_{h=0}^{\infty}(-)^h \frac{\Gamma\left(\frac{5}{2}+n+h\right)}{\Gamma\left(\frac{5}{2}+n\right)\Gamma(h+1)}\times$$

$$\times\, G^{(a)}\left[\xi, \left(\frac{3}{4}+1+n-m+h\right)\right]\left(\frac{\varrho}{\varrho_0}\right)^{-(11/6)+m-n-h}. \tag{6b}$$

If we introduce here the corresponding asymptotic forms of $G^{(a)}(\xi, \mu)$, (cf. p. 181), we find that the first expression converges for $\varrho/\varrho_0 < 1$ while the second converges for $\varrho/\varrho_0 > 1$. With the aid of Eq. VII, 4 (17b) there results along the sonic line

$$\psi^{m,n} = (-)^m \frac{3}{8} \times$$
$$\times \left\{ 2^{1/3} \sum_{h=0}^{\infty} \left(\frac{\varrho}{\varrho_0}\right)^{(2/3)+m+h} \frac{\Gamma\left(\frac{5}{2}+n+h\right)\Gamma\left(\frac{5}{6}+m+h\right)\Gamma\left(\frac{5}{3}\right)}{\Gamma\left(\frac{5}{2}+n\right)\Gamma(h+1)\,\Gamma\left(\frac{5}{6}\right)\Gamma\left(\frac{5}{3}+m+h\right)} - \right.$$
$$\left. - 2^{2/3}\,\xi \sum_{h=0}^{\infty} \left(\frac{\varrho}{\varrho_0}\right)^{(2/3)+m+h} \frac{\Gamma\left(\frac{5}{2}+n+h\right)\Gamma\left(\frac{7}{6}+m+h\right)\Gamma\left(\frac{4}{3}\right)}{\Gamma\left(\frac{5}{2}+n\right)\Gamma(h+1)\,\Gamma\left(\frac{7}{6}\right)\Gamma\left(\frac{4}{3}+m+h\right)} \right\} \tag{7a}$$

$$\psi^{m,n} = (-)^{n+m+1} \frac{3}{8} \left\{ 2^{1/3} \sum_{h=0}^{\infty} \left(\frac{\varrho}{\varrho_0}\right)^{-(11/6)+m-n-h} \times \right.$$
$$\times \frac{\Gamma\left(\frac{5}{2}+n+h\right)\Gamma\left(\frac{11}{6}+n-m+h\right)\Gamma\left(\frac{5}{3}\right)}{\Gamma\left(\frac{5}{2}+n\right)\Gamma(h+1)\,\Gamma\left(\frac{5}{6}\right)\Gamma\left(\frac{8}{3}+n-m+h\right)} -$$
$$- 2^{2/3}\,\xi \sum_{h=0}^{\infty} \left(\frac{\varrho}{\varrho_0}\right)^{-(11/6)+m-n-h} \times$$
$$\left. \times \frac{\Gamma\left(\frac{5}{2}+n+h\right)\Gamma\left(\frac{13}{6}+n-m+h\right)\Gamma\left(\frac{4}{3}\right)}{\Gamma\left(\frac{5}{2}+n\right)\Gamma(h+1)\,\Gamma\left(\frac{7}{6}\right)\Gamma\left(\frac{6}{3}+n-m+h\right)} \right\}. \tag{7b}$$

These equations can also be rewritten in the form

$$\psi^{m,n} = (-)^n \frac{3}{8} \left(\frac{\varrho}{\varrho_0}\right)^{(2/3)+m} \times$$
$$\times \left\{ 2^{1/3} \frac{\Gamma\left(\frac{5}{6}+m\right)\Gamma\left(\frac{5}{3}\right)}{\Gamma\left(\frac{5}{6}\right)\Gamma\left(\frac{5}{3}+m\right)} F\left(\frac{5}{2}+n,\ \frac{5}{6}+m,\ \frac{5}{3}+m,\ \frac{\varrho}{\varrho_0}\right) - \right.$$
$$\left. - 2^{2/3}\,\xi \frac{\Gamma\left(\frac{7}{6}+m\right)\Gamma\left(\frac{4}{3}\right)}{\Gamma\left(\frac{7}{6}\right)\Gamma\left(\frac{4}{3}+m\right)} F\left(\frac{5}{2}+n,\ \frac{7}{6}+m,\ \frac{4}{3}+m,\ \frac{\varrho}{\varrho_0}\right) \right\}. \tag{8a}$$

and

$$\psi^{m,n} = (-)^{n+m+1}\frac{3}{8}\left(\frac{\varrho}{\varrho_0}\right)^{(11/6)+m-n} \times$$

$$\times \left\{ 2^{1/3}\frac{\Gamma\left(\frac{11}{6}+n-m\right)\Gamma\left(\frac{5}{3}\right)}{\Gamma\left(\frac{5}{6}\right)\Gamma\left(\frac{8}{3}+n-m\right)} \times \right.$$

$$\times F\left(\frac{5}{2}+n, \frac{11}{6}+n-m, \frac{8}{3}+n-m, \left(\frac{\varrho}{\varrho_0}\right)^{-1}\right) -$$

$$- 2^{2/3}\,\xi\,\frac{\Gamma\left(\frac{13}{6}+n-m\right)\Gamma\left(\frac{4}{3}\right)}{\Gamma\left(\frac{7}{6}\right)\Gamma\left(\frac{7}{3}+n-m\right)} \times$$

$$\left. \times F\left(\frac{5}{2}+n, \frac{13}{6}+n-m, \frac{7}{3}+n-m, \left(\frac{\varrho}{\varrho_0}\right)^{-1}\right)\right\}. \tag{8b}$$

Hence we can determine the behaviour in the vicinity of the singular point $O(\varrho/\varrho_0 = 1)$. First we find that the hypergeometric functions, which occur in the first terms of Eqs. (8a) and (8b), satisfy the same hypergeometric differential equation. The same is true of the hypergeometric functions occurring in the second terms of the two equations. Therefore Eqs. (8a) and (8b), when expanded with the aid of Eq. VII, 4 (5a) at $\varrho/\varrho_0 = 1$, yield linear combinations of the same hypergeometric functions.

In order to show that the two expressions, given by Eq. (8), match at O, it is only therefore necessary to investigate the coefficients by which the hypergeometric functions are multiplied. Such an analysis yields then, of course, also the expansion of the solution at the point O. Regarding the details of this calculation the reader is referred to an article by GUDERLEY [36, 37]. The result can be expressed as follows. Let $\bar{\varrho}$ and $\bar{\xi}$ be the values of ϱ and ξ when the point O is chosen as the origin of the η, ϑ system of coordinates. The solution along the sonic line for $\vartheta < \theta_0$ is given by

$$\psi^{m,n} = \sum_{k=0}^{\infty} a_k^0 \left(\frac{\bar{\varrho}}{\varrho_0}\right)^{k/2} + \left(\frac{\bar{\varrho}}{\varrho_0}\right)^{-(5/6)-(n/2)} \sum_{k=0}^{\infty} a_k^{-(5/3)-n}\left(\frac{\bar{\varrho}}{\varrho_0}\right)^{k/2} +$$

$$+ \bar{\xi}\left(\frac{\bar{\varrho}}{\varrho_0}\right)^{1/3} \sum_{k=0}^{\infty} b_k^0 \left(\frac{\bar{\varrho}}{\varrho_0}\right)^{k/2} +$$

$$+ \bar{\xi}\left(\frac{\bar{\varrho}}{\varrho_0}\right)^{-(5/6)-(n/2)} \sum_{k=0}^{\infty} b_k^{-(7/2)-n}\left(\frac{\bar{\varrho}}{\varrho_0}\right)^{k/2}. \tag{9}$$

The first coefficients a_0^0; $a_0^{-(5/3)-n}$; b_0^0 and $b_0^{-(7/2)-n}$ of the series involved are

$$\left.\begin{aligned} a_0^0 &= (-)^m \frac{3}{8} 2^{1/3} \frac{\Gamma\left(\frac{5}{3}\right)\Gamma\left(\frac{5}{6}+m\right)\Gamma\left(-\frac{5}{3}-n\right)}{\Gamma\left(\frac{5}{6}\right)^2\Gamma\left(-\frac{5}{2}+m-n\right)}, \\ a_0^{-(5/3)-n} &= (-)^m 2^{-(5/3)-n} \frac{3}{8} 2^{1/3} \frac{\Gamma\left(\frac{5}{3}\right)\Gamma\left(\frac{5}{3}+n\right)}{\Gamma\left(\frac{5}{6}\right)\Gamma\left(\frac{5}{2}+n\right)}, \end{aligned}\right\} \quad (10\text{a})$$

$$\left.\begin{aligned} b_0^0 &= (-)^{m+1} \frac{3}{8} 2^{2/3} \frac{\Gamma\left(\frac{4}{3}\right)\Gamma\left(\frac{7}{6}+m\right)\Gamma\left(-\frac{7}{3}-n\right)}{\Gamma\left(\frac{7}{6}\right)\Gamma\left(\frac{1}{6}\right)\Gamma\left(-\frac{7}{6}+m-n\right)}, \\ b_0^{-(7/3)-n} &= (-)^{m+1} 2^{-(7/3)-n} \frac{3}{8} 2^{2/3} \frac{\Gamma\left(\frac{4}{3}\right)\Gamma\left(\frac{7}{3}+n\right)}{\Gamma\left(\frac{7}{6}\right)\Gamma\left(\frac{5}{2}+n\right)}. \end{aligned}\right\} \quad (10\text{b})$$

Further coefficients are calculated with the aid of the following recurrence formulas

$$\begin{aligned} & a_k^\nu (k+\nu)\left[-2(k+\nu) - 2n - \frac{10}{3}\right] + \\ & + a_{k-1}^\nu \left\{3\left[k+\nu+\frac{1}{6}+\left(\frac{2}{3}\right)(n-m)^2\right] - \right. \\ & \left. - \frac{103}{36} - 4(n-m) - \left(\frac{4}{3}\right)(n-m)^2\right\} - \\ & - a_{k-2}^\nu \left(k+\nu-\frac{5}{3}\right)\left[k+\nu+\frac{5}{3}+2(n-m)\right] = 0, \quad (11\text{a}) \end{aligned}$$

$$\begin{aligned} & b_{k-1}^\mu (k+\mu)\left[-2(k+\mu) - 2n - \frac{14}{3}\right] + \\ & + b_{k-1}^\mu \left\{3\left[k+\mu+\frac{5}{6}+\left(\frac{2}{3}\right)(n-m)^2\right] - \right. \\ & \left. - \frac{103}{36} - 4(n-m) - \left(\frac{4}{3}\right)(n-m)^2\right\} - \\ & - b_{k-2}^\mu \left(k+\mu-\frac{1}{3}\right)\left[k+\mu+\frac{7}{3}+2(n-m)\right] = 0. \quad (11\text{b}) \end{aligned}$$

In accordance with Eq. (9) the solutions can, in the vicinity of a point O, be expressed as a superposition of particular solutions of the form $\bar{\varrho}^{-(1/12)\pm\mu}\, G(\bar{\xi}, \mu)$. If the exponent of $\bar{\varrho}$ is negative then the corresponding particular solution is singular at O; there is always only a limited number of such terms present. Let us now give the explicit forms of the first terms of the expansions for $\psi^{0,0}$, $\psi^{1,1}$ and $\psi^{2,2}$ which will be required later. For $\vartheta < \theta_0$ there results

$$\psi^{0,0} = \frac{1}{9\sqrt{3}}\, 2^{1/3}\left[\left(\frac{\bar{\varrho}}{\varrho_0}\right)^{-5/6} + \frac{19}{12}\left(\frac{\bar{\varrho}}{\varrho_0}\right)^{-1/3} + \cdots\right], \tag{12a}$$

$$\psi^{1,1} = \frac{1}{9\sqrt{3}}\, 2^{1/3}\left[-\frac{1}{3}\left(\frac{\bar{\varrho}}{\varrho_0}\right)^{-4/3} + \cdots\right], \tag{12b}$$

$$\psi^{2,2} = \frac{1}{9\sqrt{3}}\, 2^{1/3}\left[\frac{8}{63}\left(\frac{\bar{\varrho}}{\varrho_0}\right)^{-11/6} - \frac{143}{378}\left(\frac{\bar{\varrho}}{\varrho_0}\right)^{-4/3} + \cdots\right]. \tag{12c}$$

From these the coefficients of the corresponding singular particular solutions $\psi_{-1/3}$, $\psi_{-5/6}$ etc. can be calculated. One obtains

$$\psi^{0,0} = -\frac{8}{27\sqrt{3}}\, \varrho_0^{5/6}\psi_{-5/6}(\bar{\varrho}, \bar{\xi}) + \frac{19}{54\sqrt{3}}\, \varrho_0^{1/3}\psi_{-1/3}(\bar{\varrho}, \bar{\xi}) + \cdots, \tag{13a}$$

$$\psi^{1,1} = \frac{8}{135\sqrt{3}}\, \varrho_0^{4/3}\psi_{-4/3}(\bar{\varrho}, \bar{\xi}) + \cdots, \tag{13b}$$

$$\psi^{2,2} = \frac{128}{27\cdot 63\sqrt{3}}\, \varrho_0^{11/6}\psi_{-11/6}(\bar{\varrho}, \bar{\xi}) + \frac{143\cdot 8}{378\cdot 45\sqrt{3}}\, \varrho_0^{4/3}\psi_{-4/3}(\bar{\varrho}, \bar{\xi}) \cdots. \tag{13c}$$

This provides a sufficient description of the desired solutions in the hodograph plane. In particular $\psi^{0,0}$ represents, except for a multiplying factor which depends on the length of the plate L, the solution for an inclined plate.

Next we must transform the solution into the physical plane and, in particular, determine the distribution of η along the plate. From Eq. (4) and with the aid of Eq. V, 7 (8) one obtains

$$\frac{\partial x^{n,n}}{\partial \eta} = -(\gamma+1)^{-1/3}\left(\frac{3}{2}\right)\left(\frac{3}{2}\theta_0\right)^{-1/3} \times$$
$$\times \left(\frac{-\eta}{\left(\frac{3}{2}\theta_0\right)^{2/3}}\right)^{(3/2)+3n}\left[1 + \left(\frac{-\eta}{\left(\frac{3}{2}\theta_0\right)^{2/3}}\right)^{3}\right]^{-(5/2)-n}, \tag{14}$$

where $x^{n,n}$ denotes that value of x along the plate which corresponds to the solution $\psi^{n,n}$. At this point it is convenient to introduce a new variable

$$\bar{\bar{\eta}} = \frac{\eta}{\left(\frac{3}{2}\theta_0\right)^{2/3}}. \tag{15}$$

One obtains then

$$x^{n,n} = \left\{(\gamma + 1)^{1/3} \left(\frac{3}{2}\right)^{4/3} \theta_0^{1/3}\right\} \int\limits_{\infty}^{-\bar{\bar{\eta}}} u^{(3/2)+3n} (1 + u^3)^{-(5/2)-n} \, du$$

$$(\bar{\bar{\eta}} \leqq 0) \tag{16}$$

where u is a dummy variable. Let $l^{n,n}$ be defined by

$$l^{n,n} = \int\limits_{\infty}^{0} u^{(3/2)+3n} (1 + u^3)^{-(5/2)-n} \, du. \tag{17}$$

Introducing

$$u^3 = \frac{v}{1 - v},$$

Eq. (17) transforms into a B function so that

$$l^{n,n} = -\frac{1}{3} \frac{\Gamma\left(\frac{5}{6} + n\right) \Gamma\left(\frac{5}{3}\right)}{\Gamma\left(\frac{5}{2} + n\right)}.$$

In particular

$$l^{0,0} = -\frac{1}{3} \frac{\Gamma\left(\frac{5}{6}\right) \Gamma\left(\frac{5}{3}\right)}{\Gamma\left(\frac{5}{2}\right)}, \tag{18a}$$

$$l^{1,1} = \frac{1}{3} l^{0,0}, \tag{18b}$$

$$l^{2,2} = \frac{11}{63} l^{0,0}. \tag{18c}$$

Thus the solution for the flow past an inclined plate of length L, at a MACH number of unity, is finally given by

$$\Psi_{-5/6} = -\left\{(\gamma + 1)^{1/3} \left(\frac{3}{2}\right)^{4/3} \vartheta_0^{1/3}\right\}^{-1} \frac{3\,\Gamma\left(\frac{5}{2}\right)}{\Gamma\left(\frac{5}{6}\right) \Gamma\left(\frac{5}{3}\right)} L \psi^{0,0}. \tag{19}$$

The coefficients of the particular solutions $\psi_{-5/6}$ and $\psi_{-1/3}$ in the above equation are given by

$$\alpha_{-5/6}^{-5/6} = \left\{(\gamma + 1)^{1/3} \left(\frac{3}{2}\right)^{4/3} \theta_0^{1/3}\right\}^{-1} \frac{\Gamma\left(\frac{5}{2}\right)}{\Gamma\left(\frac{5}{6}\right) \Gamma\left(\frac{5}{3}\right)} \frac{8}{9\sqrt{3}} L \varrho_0^{5/6}, \tag{20a}$$

$$\alpha_{-1/3}^{-5/6} = -\left\{(\gamma + 1)^{1/3} \left(\frac{3}{2}\right)^{4/3} \theta_0^{1/3}\right\}^{-1} \frac{\Gamma\left(\frac{5}{2}\right)}{\Gamma\left(\frac{5}{6}\right) \Gamma\left(\frac{5}{3}\right)} \frac{19}{18\sqrt{3}} L \varrho_0^{1/3}. \tag{20b}$$

Expressing ϱ_0 in terms of θ_0 with the aid of Eq. (3) there results

$$\alpha_{-5/6}^{-5/6} = (\gamma + 1)^{-1/3} \frac{\Gamma\left(\frac{5}{2}\right) 12^{-1/6} \cdot 8}{\Gamma\left(\frac{5}{6}\right) \Gamma\left(\frac{5}{3}\right) 9} L \theta_0^{4/3}, \tag{20c}$$

$$\alpha_{-1/3}^{-5/6} = -(\gamma + 1)^{-1/3} \frac{\Gamma\left(\frac{5}{2}\right) 12^{-1/6}}{\Gamma\left(\frac{5}{6}\right) \Gamma\left(\frac{5}{3}\right)} \frac{19}{27} L \theta_0^{1/3}. \tag{20d}$$

The following equation expresses x/L as a function of $\bar{\bar{\eta}}$. The pressure distribution along the pressure side of the plate can be calculated from this equation. Since x belongs to the solution $\Psi^{-5/6}$, we shall apply the notation $x^{-5/6}$

$$\frac{x^{-5/6}}{L} = \frac{3\Gamma\left(\frac{5}{2}\right)}{\Gamma\left(\frac{5}{6}\right) \Gamma\left(\frac{5}{3}\right)} \bar{\bar{x}}^{-5/6} (\bar{\bar{\eta}}), \tag{21}$$

where

$$\bar{\bar{x}}^{-5/6} = \int_{-\bar{\bar{\eta}}}^{\infty} u^{3/2} (1 + u^3)^{-5/2} \, du. \tag{21a}$$

Since $\bar{\bar{\eta}}$ is always negative the lower limit of the integral is always positive.

The pressure distribution on the suction side can be found by means of the method of characteristics. The problem of flow separation at the leading edge occurs here again. The region of separation obviously becomes smaller as the angle of attack tends to zero and its influence on the pressure distribution can then be neglected. Further, at each point in the field, with the exception of the leading edge, the deviation of the velocity vector from the sonic velocity is decreased so that one is justified, at least formally, in employing the approximate equations of transonic flow. One calculates first the location of the MACH line OD (or of another line which can be easily calculated from the preceding results) and from this line the remaining flow field is determined by means of the method of characteristics for transonic flows. When the compression waves, originating at the sonic line, are reflected at the surface of the plate they result in a shock which emanates from the leading edge. The construction of the flow shows, however, that the pressure on the suction side is quite well represented by an analytical continuation of the solution for the pressure distribution on the pressure side. Thus for the x coordinate on the suction side there results

$$\frac{x}{L} = \frac{3\Gamma\left(\frac{5}{2}\right)}{\Gamma\left(\frac{5}{6}\right) \Gamma\left(\frac{5}{3}\right)} \int_{\bar{\bar{\eta}}}^{\infty} u^{3/2} (u^3 - 1)^{-5/2} \, du \quad \bar{\bar{\eta}} > 1. \tag{22}$$

This result is plotted in Fig. 94. As in the case of a wedge, it can be written in the form

$$\eta = \theta_0^{2/3}\, g\left(\frac{x}{L}\right)$$

or

$$c_p = -2(\gamma + 1)^{-1/3}\, \theta_0^{2/3} g\left(\frac{x}{L}\right). \tag{23}$$

The function $g(x/L)$ is, of course, different on the upper and lower sides of the plate. For purposes of comparison the pressure coefficient, which results when a

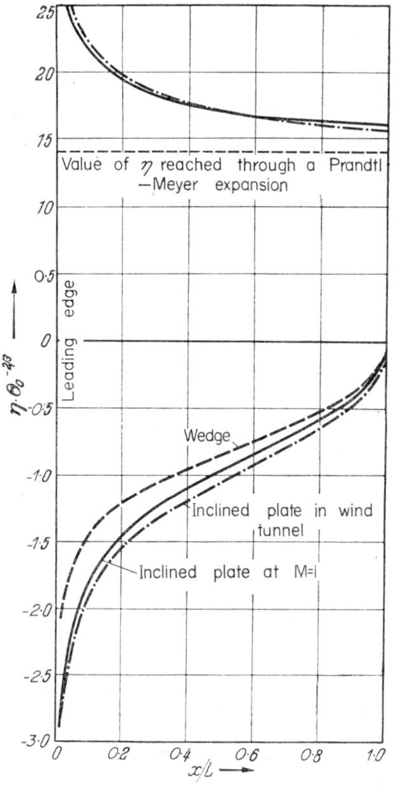

FIG. 94

——— Values of η for an inclined plate at $M = 1$.
-·-·-· Values of η for an inclined plate in a choked wind tunnel.
– – – – Values of η for a wedge.
Θ_0 angle of attack or half-angle of the wedge. The curves for the plate in a wind tunnel were calculated for an angle of attack or 0.1 (5.7°) and a length L equal to one-tenth of the width of the tunnel. (According to GUDERLEY [26]).

parallel sonic flow is deflected through a PRANDTL-MEYER expansion cone by an angle equal to the angle of attack of the plate, is included in Fig. 94. This pressure coefficient would be obtained if the upper side of the plate were not influenced by the lower side of the plate. Figure 94 includes also the pressure distribution for a wedge whose half angle is equal to the angle of attack of the plate. The conditions at the shoulder of the wedge are the same as those at the trailing edge of the plate. The difference in the pressure distribution is due to the different flow around the leading edge. From these curves one can conclude that the mutual influence of the lower side on the upper side of the plate, and vice versa, is not very pronounced. The total lift of the plate is somewhat larger than double the value which would be obtained by an expansion of the type described above. The center of pressure is located at 46 % of the chord, measured from the leading edge. The meaning of the third curve will be discussed later. An exact calculation of this flow in the hodograph plane (Fig. 30) is due to VINCENTI *et al.* [81].

We shall later require the particular solutions $\Psi^{-4/3}$ and $\Psi^{-11/6}$ or, more generally, $\Psi^{-(4/3)-(h/2)}$, which can be described as follows:

(1) The dominating singularity at the point 0 is $\psi_{-(4/3)-(h/2)}$; it occurs multiplied by the coefficient 1. Apart from this singular term the solutions contain only $\psi_{-5/6}$ and $\psi_{-1/3}$.

(2) Along the image of the surface of the plate $\psi = 0$.

(3) When $\varrho \to \infty$ the streamlines have a branch point.

(4) The contribution of these solutions to the total length of the plate is zero.

Such solutions can be found from Eqs. (13) and (18) without difficulty. We write them in the form

$$\Psi^{-4/3} = \varrho_0^{-4/3}\, \overline{\overline{\psi}}^{-4/3}, \tag{24a}$$

$$\Psi^{-11/6} = \varrho_0^{-11/6}\, \overline{\overline{\psi}}^{-11/6}, \tag{24b}$$

where

$$\overline{\overline{\psi}}^{-4/3} = 5 \cdot 3^{7/2} \cdot 2^{-3} \left(\psi^{1,1} - \frac{1}{3}\, \psi^{0,0} \right), \tag{24c}$$

$$\overline{\overline{\psi}}^{-11/6} = 3^{11/2} \cdot 7 \cdot 2^{-7} \left(\psi^{2,2} - \frac{143}{126}\, \psi^{1,1} + \frac{11}{54}\, \psi^{0,0} \right). \tag{24d}$$

Finally let us summarise the corresponding expressions for x calculated along the plate, using again with x a superscript corresponding to that of Ψ. One obtains

$$x^{-4/3} = \varrho_0^{-4/3} \left\{ (\gamma + 1)^{1/3} \left(\frac{3}{2} \right)^{4/3} \theta_0^{1/3} \right\} \overline{\overline{x}}^{-4/3}, \tag{25a}$$

$$x^{-11/6} = \varrho_0^{-11/6} \left\{ (\gamma + 1)^{1/3} \left(\frac{3}{2} \right)^{4/3} \theta_0^{1/3} \right\} \overline{\overline{x}}^{-11/6}, \tag{25b}$$

where

$$\overline{\overline{x}}^{-4/3} = -\frac{9}{4} \sqrt{3}\, (-\overline{\overline{\eta}})^{5/2} (1 + (-\overline{\overline{\eta}})^3)^{-5/2}, \tag{25c}$$

$$\overline{\overline{x}}^{-11/6} = 3^{11/2} \cdot 7 \cdot 2^{-7} (-\overline{\overline{\eta}})^{5/2} (1 + (-\overline{\overline{\eta}})^3)^{-5/2} \times \left\{ \frac{11}{135} - \frac{2}{21}\, \frac{(-\overline{\overline{\eta}})^3}{1 + (-\overline{\overline{\eta}})^3} \right\}. \tag{25d}$$

The following expressions are quoted because of their extreme simplicity

$$\frac{\bar{\bar{x}}^{-4/3}}{\dfrac{d}{d\bar{\bar{\eta}}}(\bar{\bar{x}}^{-5/6})} = -\frac{9}{4}\sqrt{3}\,(-\bar{\bar{\eta}}), \tag{26a}$$

$$\frac{\bar{\bar{x}}^{-11/6}}{\dfrac{d}{d\bar{\bar{\eta}}}(\bar{\bar{x}}^{-5/6})} = 3^{11/2}\cdot 7\cdot 2^{-7}\,(-\bar{\bar{\eta}})\left(\frac{11}{135} - \frac{2}{21}\,\frac{(-\bar{\bar{\eta}})^3}{1+(-\bar{\bar{\eta}})^3}\right). \tag{26b}$$

10. Particular Solutions which can be Calculated by Similar Methods

Here we shall indicate some additional applications of the calculation procedure for the solutions ψ, which was described in the preceding section. These results will be required later.

For the calculation of the flow past an unsymmetric obstacle in a choked wind tunnel, one requires a solution which has a branch point of the second order at the point O in Fig. 95. One is tempted at first to use the solutions of FALKOWICH (cf. p. 206). They are in this connection unsuitable, however, for the following reason: the analysis in which these solutions occur expands the flow field in terms of a parameter which describes the distance of the point Q from the sonic velocity. The solutions must therefore also be usable when the point Q reaches the sonic velocity. This requires that, also in this case, the MACH lines through the origin should not map into infinity in the physical plane nor should they behave in a singular manner with respect to the curvature of the streamlines. This is neither true of the solutions of FALKOWICH nor of those of TAMADA and TOMOTIKA. Actually not only is the limiting case, when the point Q becomes identical with the point O, critical, but considerable difficulties in the calculation would already result when the point Q approaches the origin.

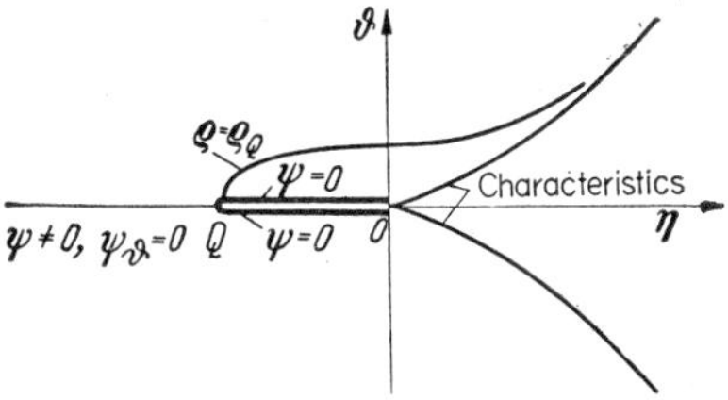

FIG. 95 Boundary conditions for a branch point of the second order.

The solutions which will be derived here utilize the superposition of "natural" particular solutions and therefore these difficulties do not occur.

The particular solutions to be considered are symmetric with respect to the line $\bar{\xi} = -\infty$ and satisfy $\psi = 0$ along the line OQ (Fig. 95). We try to represent the solution along $\bar{\xi} = -\infty$ for $\bar{\varrho} > \bar{\varrho}_Q$ by

$$\psi = \left(\frac{\bar{\varrho}}{\bar{\varrho}_Q}\right)^{-1/3}\left(1 - \left(\frac{\bar{\varrho}}{\bar{\varrho}_Q}\right)^{-1}\right)^{-(1/2)-k}, \tag{1}$$

where k is an integer. This expression is subsequently expanded in terms of $(\bar{\varrho}/\bar{\varrho}_Q)^{-1}$. Starting with this expansion, a continuation of the solution in the region $\bar{\varrho}/\bar{\varrho}_Q > 1$ can then be found, with the aid of the particular solutions $\psi^{(s)}_{-(1/3)-k}$. Along the sonic line one obtains

$$\psi = \frac{1}{2}\left(\frac{\bar{\varrho}}{\bar{\varrho}_Q}\right)^{-1/3}\left\{2^{1/3} F\left(\frac{1}{2}+k, \frac{5}{6}, \frac{2}{3}, \left(\frac{-\bar{\varrho}}{\bar{\varrho}_Q}\right)^{-1}\right) - \right.$$

$$\left. - \bar{\xi}\, 2^{-1/3} F\left(\frac{1}{2}+k, \frac{7}{6}, \frac{1}{3}, \left(\frac{-\bar{\varrho}}{\bar{\varrho}_Q}\right)^{-1}\right)\right\}.$$

In this form one notices already a continuation of the solution for the entire sonic line and not only for $\bar{\varrho} > \bar{\varrho}_Q$. If one expands the solution, obtained along the sonic line, in terms of the particular solutions with imaginary values of μ, one finds that the function ψ has no singularities in the subsonic region except along the line $\bar{\xi} = -\infty$. The hypergeometric functions representing ψ along the sonic line can now be written as a series in $\bar{\varrho}/\bar{\varrho}_Q$. This expansion forms the starting point for the following representation of ψ in the region $\bar{\varrho} < \bar{\varrho}_Q$.

$$\psi = 2^{-2/3}\left\{\left(\frac{\bar{\varrho}}{\bar{\varrho}_Q}\right)^{(1/6)+k} \frac{\Gamma\left(\frac{1}{3}-k\right)\Gamma\left(\frac{2}{3}\right)}{\Gamma\left(\frac{1}{6}-k\right)\Gamma\left(\frac{5}{6}\right)} F\left(\frac{1}{2}+k, \frac{5}{6}+k, \frac{2}{3}+k, \left(\frac{-\bar{\varrho}}{\bar{\varrho}_Q}\right)\right) - \right.$$

$$\left. - \left(\frac{\bar{\varrho}}{\bar{\varrho}_Q}\right)^{1/2} \frac{\Gamma\left(k-\frac{1}{3}\right)\Gamma\left(\frac{2}{3}\right)}{\Gamma\left(\frac{1}{2}+k\right)\Gamma\left(-\frac{1}{6}\right)} F\left(\frac{5}{6}, \frac{7}{6}, \frac{4}{3}-k, \left(\frac{-\bar{\varrho}}{\bar{\varrho}_Q}\right)\right)\right\} -$$

$$- \bar{\xi}\, 2^{-4/3}\left\{\left(\frac{\bar{\varrho}}{\bar{\varrho}_Q}\right)^{(1/6)+k} \frac{\Gamma\left(\frac{2}{3}-k\right)\Gamma\left(\frac{1}{3}\right)}{\Gamma\left(-\frac{1}{6}-k\right)\Gamma\left(\frac{7}{6}\right)} F\left(\frac{1}{2}+k, \frac{7}{6}+k, \frac{1}{3}+k, \left(\frac{-\bar{\varrho}}{\bar{\varrho}_Q}\right)\right) + \right.$$

$$\left. + \left(\frac{\bar{\varrho}}{\bar{\varrho}_Q}\right)^{1/2} \frac{\Gamma\left(k-\frac{2}{3}\right)\Gamma\left(\frac{1}{3}\right)}{\Gamma\left(-\frac{5}{6}\right)\Gamma\left(\frac{1}{2}+k\right)} F\left(\frac{7}{6}, \frac{11}{6}, \frac{5}{3}-k, \left(\frac{-\bar{\varrho}}{\bar{\varrho}_Q}\right)\right)\right\}.$$

With the aid of this series expansion and of the asymptotic expressions for G, it may be shown that no singularities occur for $\bar{\varrho} < \bar{\varrho}_Q$. The exponents of $\bar{\varrho}$ occurring here correspond to the antisymmetric "natural" particular solutions. The coefficients of these particular solutions can be calculated with the aid of the last equation and one actually finds that $\psi = 0$ for $\bar{\xi} = -\infty$ and $\bar{\varrho} < \bar{\varrho}_Q$.

The solutions, which have a branch point of second order at the point Q, satisfy the condition $\psi = 0$ for $\bar{\xi} = -\infty$ and $\bar{\varrho} < \bar{\varrho}_Q$, and which tend to infinity n the prescribed manner when $\bar{\varrho} \to \infty$ are also of interest. Here one starts with he equation

$$\psi = \left(\frac{\bar{\varrho}}{\bar{\varrho}_Q}\right)^h \int \left(\frac{\bar{\varrho}}{\bar{\varrho}_Q}\right)^{-h-1} \hat{\psi}\, d\left(\frac{\bar{\varrho}}{\bar{\varrho}_Q}\right)$$

$$= \left(\frac{\bar{\varrho}}{\bar{\varrho}_Q}\right)^h \int \left(\frac{\bar{\varrho}}{\bar{\varrho}_Q}\right)^{-(1/3)-h-1} \left(1 - \left(\frac{\bar{\varrho}}{\bar{\varrho}_Q}\right)^{-1}\right)^{-1/2} d\left(\frac{\bar{\varrho}}{\bar{\varrho}_Q}\right), \tag{2}$$

where $\hat{\psi}$ is the term given by Eq. (1) for $k = 0$, and h is arbitrary. A comprehensive discussion which agrees with the above example in many details is found n an article by GUDERLEY [37]. An important question which we have not, so far, encountered concerns the determination of the integration constant in Eq. (2). As a result one obtains the following series expansion in the region $\bar{\varrho} > \bar{\varrho}_Q$

$$\psi = \frac{\Gamma\left(\frac{1}{3} + h\right)}{\Gamma\left(\frac{5}{6} + h\right)} \pi^{1/2} \left(\frac{\bar{\varrho}}{\bar{\varrho}_Q}\right)^h G^{(s)}\left(\xi, h + \frac{1}{12}\right) -$$

$$- \frac{2}{\sqrt{3}} \pi^{1/2} \frac{\Gamma\left(\frac{1}{2} - 3h\right)}{\Gamma(-3h)} \left(\frac{\bar{\varrho}}{\bar{\varrho}_Q}\right)^h G^{(a)}\left(\xi, h + \frac{1}{12}\right) + \tag{3}$$

$$+ \left(\frac{\bar{\varrho}}{\bar{\varrho}_Q}\right)^{-1/3} \sum_{k=0}^{\infty} \frac{\Gamma\left(\frac{1}{2} + k\right)}{\Gamma\left(\frac{1}{2}\right) \Gamma(k+1)\, \Gamma\left(-\frac{1}{3} - k\right)} \left(\frac{\bar{\varrho}}{\bar{\varrho}_Q}\right)^{-k} G^{(s)}\left(\xi, \frac{1}{4} + k\right).$$

The flow in a free jet with sonic velocity, which will be discussed later, leads to he boundary value problem shown in Fig. 96. The η, ϑ plane is divided into an nternal and an external region by the line $\varrho =$ const, indicated in the figure. In he inner region there occurs a superposition of

$$\psi = \varrho^{5/6+h} G^{(a)}\left(\xi, \frac{11}{12} + h\right)$$

nd, because of $\psi =$ const for $\xi = 0$,

$$\psi = G^{(a)}\left(\xi, \frac{1}{12}\right). \tag{4}$$

n the external region one obtains a superposition of particular solutions

$$\psi = \varrho^{-(5/6)-h} G^{(a)}\left(\xi, \frac{3}{4} + h\right).$$

n the solution for the inner region, the expression given in Eq. (4) is inconenient. Therefore we find first, in place of the solution ψ, its derivative with espect to ϱ to which the term given by Eq. (4) does not contribute. Let

$$\chi(\xi, \varrho) = \psi_\varrho(\xi, \varrho).$$

For a function χ one obtains the boundary conditions shown in Fig. 96. For $\varrho = \varrho_0$ the function χ is expressed as a superposition of terms

$$\varrho^{-(1/6)+h}\, G^{(a)}\left(\xi,\ \frac{11}{12}+h\right)$$

while for the external region one obtains the terms

$$\varrho^{-(11/6)-h}\, G^{(a)}\left(\xi,\ \frac{3}{4}+h\right).$$

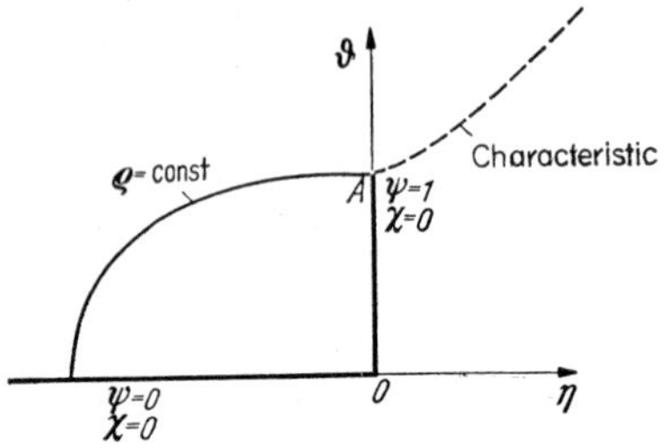

FIG. 96

We try to represent the solution, for $\xi = -\infty$, in the form

$$\chi = \left(\frac{\varrho}{\varrho_0}\right)^{-1/6}\left(1+\frac{\varrho}{\varrho_0}\right)^{-5/3}(-\xi)^{-3/2}. \tag{5}$$

It may be shown, as before, that in the entire subsonic region no singularities occur. In particular one obtains the following results

$$\chi = \sum_{h=0}^{\infty} \frac{\Gamma\left(\frac{5}{3}+h\right)}{\Gamma\left(\frac{5}{3}\right)\Gamma(h+1)}(-)^h G^{(a)}\left(\xi,\ \frac{11}{12}+h\right)\left(\frac{\varrho}{\varrho_0}\right)^{-(1/6)+h} \tag{6a}$$

for $\varrho < \varrho_0$, and

$$\chi = \sum_{h=0}^{\infty} \frac{\Gamma\left(\frac{5}{3}+h\right)}{\Gamma\left(\frac{5}{3}\right)\Gamma(h+1)}(-)^h G^{(a)}\left(\xi,\ \frac{3}{4}+h\right)\left(\frac{\varrho}{\varrho_0}\right)^{-(11/6)-h} \tag{6b}$$

for $\varrho > \varrho_0$.

Along the sonic line there results

$$\chi = -\xi\left(\frac{\varrho}{\varrho_0}\right)^{-1/6} F\left(\frac{5}{3},\ \frac{4}{3},\ \frac{3}{2},\ \frac{\varrho}{\varrho_0}\right)$$

for $\varrho < \varrho_0$, and

$$\chi = \frac{3}{4}\,2^{-2/3}\left(\frac{\varrho}{\varrho_0}\right)^{-11/6}\left(1-\frac{\varrho_0}{\varrho}\right)^{-5/6} - \frac{3}{4}\,2^{-1/3}\,\xi\left(\frac{\varrho}{\varrho_0}\right)^{-11/6}\times$$
$$\times F\left(\frac{5}{3},\ \frac{7}{6},\ \frac{2}{3},\ \left(\frac{\varrho}{\varrho_0}\right)^{-1}\right)$$

for $\varrho > \varrho_0$.

Thus the behaviour of the solution in the vicinity of the point A can be analysed and it may be shown that it is as expected.

Now it is necessary to perform the transformation from χ to ψ and, in particular, the value of ψ along the line OA is required. In accordance with the conditions of the problem, at infinity $\psi = 0$. Next for $\xi = -\infty$

$$\psi_\varrho = \left(\frac{\varrho}{\varrho_0}\right)^{-1/6}\left(1+\frac{\varrho}{\varrho_0}\right)^{-5/3}(-\xi)^{-3/2},$$

and hence by integration

$$\psi = \varrho_0(-\xi)^{-3,2}\int\limits_{\infty}^{\varrho/\varrho_0}\left(\frac{\varrho}{\varrho_0}\right)^{-1/6}\left(1+\frac{\varrho}{\varrho_0}\right)^{-5/3} d\left(\frac{\varrho}{\varrho_0}\right).$$

At the origin this expression can be evaluated as a B-integral; one obtains

$$\psi = -\varrho_0(-\xi)^{-3/2}\frac{\Gamma^2\left(\frac{5}{6}\right)}{\Gamma\left(\frac{5}{3}\right)}. \tag{7}$$

Further terms of the expansion of ψ at the origin are obtained by a term-by-term integration of Eq. (6a). The last equation yields the integration constant. Equation (7) defines the coefficient of the particular solution $G^{(a)}(\xi, \frac{1}{12})$. Then, with the aid of Eq. VII, 4 (17b), along the sonic line

$$\psi = -\varrho_0\frac{3}{4}2^{1/3}.$$

Thus the function arising from Eq. (5) must be divided by this quantity, in order to obtain the solution which satisfies the boundary condition $\psi = 1$ along the line OA in Fig. 96. We need, for later use, the first terms of the expansion at infinity. For these one finds

$$\psi = \frac{8}{5}2^{-1/3}\pi^{-1}\left(\frac{\varrho}{\varrho_0}\right)^{-5,6}G^{(a)}\left(\xi, \frac{3}{4}\right) - \frac{40}{33}2^{-1/3}\pi^{-1}\left(\frac{\varrho}{\varrho_0}\right)^{-11/6}G^{(a)}\left(\xi, \frac{7}{4}\right).$$

CHAPTER IX

FLOW FIELDS WHICH DEVIATE ONLY SLIGHTLY FROM FLOWS WITH MACH NUMBERS OF UNITY

1. Introductory Discussion

In the preceding chapter, a discussion of the singularities suitable for the representation of the flow at infinity in the case of a symmetrical obstacle, at an approach MACH number of unity, has led us to an infinite number of particular solutions, namely $\psi_{-5/6}$, $\psi_{-11/6}$, etc. All of these satisfy the condition which must be demanded of MACH lines passing through the origin. A single expression was obtained only by requiring further that the physical plane should consist of a single sheet. Since an infinite number of particular solutions was obtained, one is led to suppose that, by a superposition of such particular solutions, one could represent flow fields which, at a large distance from the obstacle, satisfy different conditions.

The meaning of the above statement will be explained by means of an analogy. The complex potential of an incompressible source at a point $z = 1$ is given by

$$\varphi = \operatorname{Re} \ln (z - 1),$$

where $z = x + iy$. This can be expanded for large values of z yielding

$$\varphi = \operatorname{Re}\left[\ln z + \ln\left(1 - \frac{1}{z}\right)\right] = \operatorname{Re}\left[\ln z - \frac{1}{z} - \frac{1}{2}\frac{1}{z^2} - \frac{1}{3}\frac{1}{z^3}\cdots\right]$$

$$= \ln r - r^{-1}\cos\nu - \frac{1}{2} r^{-2}\cos 2\nu - \frac{1}{3} r^{-3}\cos 3\nu \ldots,$$

where

$$r = \sqrt{x^2 + y^2}$$

and

$$\nu = \arctan\left(\frac{y}{x}\right).$$

The analogy mentioned above exists between the following quantities:

complex z plane	η, ϑ plane
$z = 0$	point O
ν	ξ
r	ϱ
Particular solutions $r^{-m}\cos m\xi$	Particular solutions $\psi_{-(5/6)-h}$
Singularity at $z = 1$	Singularity in the subsonic region.

Actually more than one singularity can be present; an analytic function can always be expressed in terms of a LAURENT series independently of the properties of the function within the circle of convergence. It may be expected therefore that by superposition of the functions $\psi_{-(5/6)-h}$ such solutions of TRICOMI's equations which within a given curve $\varrho =$ const are of a quite complicated form can also be represented. This curve $\varrho =$ const plays, in this connection, the role of a circle of convergence. For example, within this curve there could be gaps, such as occur in the hodograph plane because of the presence of shocks.

We shall put our above speculation on a more solid foundation using the methods of Chapter VII (GUDERLEY [29]).

2. Examples of Flows which Deviate Only Slightly From a Flow with Mach Number of Unity

In the first place one thinks in this connection of flows whose velocity of approach is nearly sonic. Here we shall, however, extend this concept to include also such fields in which the deviation from the original flow (with $M = 1$) is caused by the boundary conditions prescribed at a large distance from the immersed body. Particularly instructive are such examples for which the hodograph can easily be constructed. Among these we have the flow past an obstacle in a choked, closed-circuit wind tunnel, the flow past an obstacle in a free sonic jet and the flow past an obstacle, with a supersonic MACH number. The flow at a high subsonic MACH number is too complicated to be followed in detail. A qualitative description will be found on p. 329 *ff*.

We have met a flow with a supersonic MACH number already in Fig. 45, where the obstacle was chosen in the form of a wedge. In the present connection it will be assumed that the deviation from $M = 1$ in the approaching flow is very small so that the shock polar lies in the immediate vicinity of the origin. In the flow past a body in a choked wind tunnel (Fig. 97) all the streamlines originate from the point P, located in the subsonic region, which indicates the choking MACH number. The upper wall of the tunnel maps into the line PO which represents a part of the upper boundary of the cut OQ. The lower wall is represented by the contour PQO, where PQ lies along the upper edge and QO along the lower edge of the cut. The point Q indicates the minimum value of the velocity occurring along the lower wall. It should be noted that for an unsymmetrical flow field the point P does not have to lie at the end of the line OQ. For a symmetric flow field the points P and Q are, of course, identical. Along the lines PO and PQO we have to prescribe the values of the stream function which occur at the wall. For a tunnel whose width is W, $\psi = W/2$ along PO and $\psi = -W/2$ along PQO when the mass flow density $\varrho^* w^*$ is put equal to 1.

In the case of flow in a parallel sonic jet (Fig. 98) the streamlines originate from a point on the sonic line (point O). Along the boundary streamlines of the jet the velocity is sonic everywhere but its direction changes. In the hodograph these boundaries are mapped, therefore, into the sonic line. For an unsymmetrical flow field the images OE and OE' of the boundaries of the jet are of different lengths. The boundary conditions on the surface of the immersed body require no further explanation.

These boundary value problems contain, in general, two free parameters. In the case of flow in a choked tunnel (Fig. 97), for example, the choking MACH number and the minimum velocity of the wall, i.e. the positions of the points P and Q, are not directly determined by the geometrical data of the flow field. A similar situation arises in Fig. 98 with respect to the position of the points E

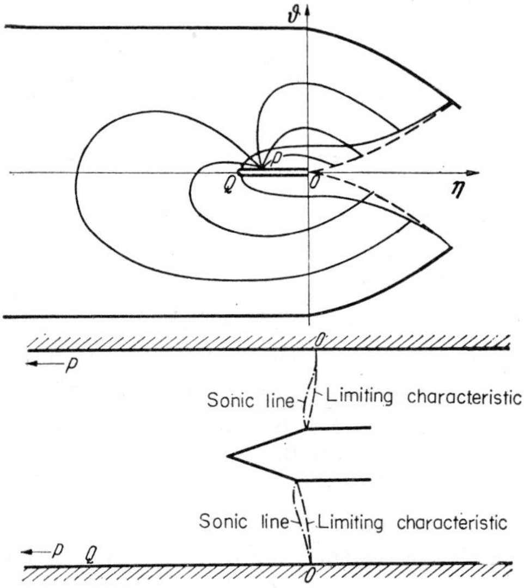

FIG. 97. Unsymmetric flow in a choked wind tunnel. (According to GUDERLEY [29]).

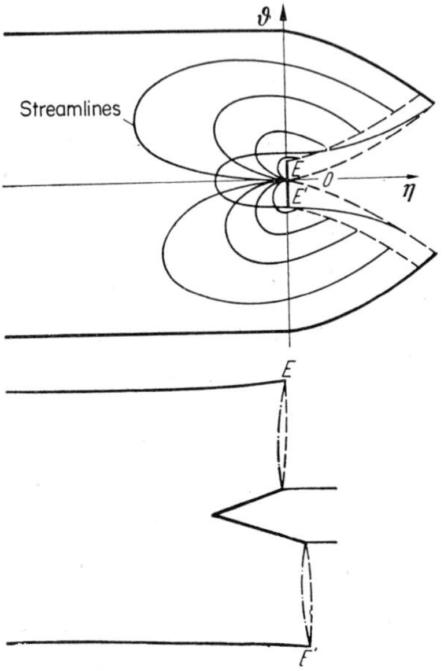

FIG. 98 Unsymmetric flow in a sonic jet. (According to GUDERLEY [29]).

and E'. For a unique determination of the flow problem, formulated in Fig. 45, it is necessary to prescribe the values of ψ at E and at the point located symmetrically with respect to E. For calculation purposes we shall introduce, however, different and less artificial quantities.

It may easily be seen by the example of an unsymmetric wedge that the desired flow field results only when these parameters are chosen in the correct manner According to TRICOMI's theorem, the solution of the hodograph problem, formulated in Fig. 97, is uniquely determined when the positions of the points P and Q are given. This means that the length of the faces of the wedge is also determined. Only for a definite choice of the points P and Q does one obtain a prescribed shape of the wedge. We shall see later that even in more general cases these parameters are obtained simultaneously with a solution of the boundary value problem.

In treating these problems one determines first a family of solutions which satisfy the boundary conditions at the profile but not the boundary conditions in the vicinity of O. At the point O the solutions are singular; they satisfy, however, TRICOMI's differential equation everywhere in the region of the hodograph plane bounded by the image of the profile of the body and by the characteristics through the origin. The desired solution for flows in the vicinity of $M = 1$ can always be obtained as a superposition of the solutions just described. The boundary conditions, prescribed in the vicinity of O, yield an infinite system of equations for the coefficients of solutions which take part in the superposition. The solution of this system of equations is obtained in the form of a series expansion in terms of a parameter which describes the deviation of the desired flow from the original one with $M = 1$.

3. Solutions which Satisfy the Boundary Conditions at the Surface of the Body

The determination of solutions which satisfy the boundary conditions at the surface of the body was described already in Section VIII, 6, in connection with the flow past an arbitrary profile at a small angle of attack. Here we shall merely summarize these results, and the notation, and we shall show that each solution which satisfies these boundary conditions can be represented by a superposition of such expressions.

We assume that the flow at $M = 1$ is known. In accordance with the discussion in the previous chapter it is always of the form

$$\Psi^{-5/6} = \alpha_{-5/6}^{-5/6}\,\psi_{-5/6} + \alpha_{-1/3}^{-5/6}\,\psi_{-1/3} + \tilde{\psi}^{-5/6}. \tag{1a}$$

The notation used is that introduced at the beginning of Section VIII, 3. The function $\tilde{\psi}^{-5/6}$ can, in an appropriate region, always be expanded in terms of the "natural" particular solutions

$$\tilde{\psi}^{-5/6} = \sum_{0}^{\infty} \alpha_{k/6}^{-5/6}\,\psi_{h/6}. \tag{1b}$$

The coefficients α occurring on the RHS's of Eq. (1) are determined by the shape of the body. Their superscripts correspond to that of the functions Ψ, in whose representation the coefficients occur, while the subscripts correspond to the "natural" particular solutions $\psi_{-5/6}$, $\psi_{-1/3}$ or $\psi_{h/6}$, to which the appropriate coefficients belong. The superscripts of the functions $\tilde{\psi}$ correspond to those of the functions Ψ.

In accordance with Section VIII, 6 the particular solutions which, upon superposition on a base flow, leave the contour of the body unchanged are of the form

$$\Psi^{-(4/3)-(h/2)} = \psi_{-(4/3)-(h/2)} + \alpha_{-5/6}^{-(4/3)-(h/2)}\,\psi^{-5/6} +$$
$$+ \alpha_{-1/3}^{-(4/3)-(h/2)}\,\psi_{-1/3} + \tilde{\psi}^{-(4/3)-(h/2)}. \tag{2}$$

Here the function $\tilde{\psi}^{-(4/3)-(h/2)}$ can be expressed by

$$\tilde{\psi}^{-(4/3)-(h/2)} = \sum_{k=0}^{\infty} \alpha_{k/6}^{-(4/3)-(h/2)} \psi_{k/6}. \tag{2a}$$

In order to show that all the particular solutions, which upon superposition onto a flow at $M = 1$ leave the contour of the body in the physical plane unchanged, can in a suitable region be expressed by an infinite series of the particular solutions given by Eq. (2), we must revert to the transformed potential. The form of the particular solutions, Eq. (2), is then given by Eq. VIII, 8 (2).

$$\Phi^{-(5/6)-(h/2)} = \varphi_{-(5/6)-(h/2)} + \alpha_{-1/3}^{-(5/6)-(h/2)} \varphi_{-1/3} + \tilde{\varphi}^{-(5/6)-(h/2)}.$$

Let the hodograph image of the profile in the original flow at $M = 1$ be denoted by K. The region bounded by K and by the characteristics through O shall be denoted by G. The fact that in the superposition of a solution $\bar{\varphi}$ the profile in the physical plane remains unchanged is expressed by a boundary condition of the second kind. With the notation introduced in Eq. VIII, 8 (1) we have

$$L(\bar{\varphi}) = 0. \tag{3}$$

Let such a solution $\bar{\varphi}$ satisfy TRICOMI's equation everywhere in G except for the immediate vicinity of the point O. This vicinity represents a region in which further boundary conditions are prescribed (cf. Figs. 97 and 98). In an appropriate part of G, an expansion in terms of the "natural" particular solutions is possible (cf. Section VII, 13 and Fig. 73). In this expansion let $\beta_{-(5/6)-(h/2)}$ be the coefficients of the particular solutions $\psi_{-(5/6)-(h/2)}$. Let us now consider the expression

$$\bar{\bar{\varphi}} = \sum_{h=0}^{\infty} \beta_{-(5/6)-(h/2)} \Phi^{-(5/6)-(h/2)} \tag{4}$$

and determine its region of convergence, i.e. the region in which the function $\bar{\bar{\varphi}}$ is really defined by Eq. (4). First we consider only the first terms of the functions $\Phi^{-(5/6)-(a/2)}$, i.e. the expression

$$\sum_{h=0}^{\infty} \beta_{-(5/6)-(h/2)} \varphi_{-(5/6)-(h/2)}.$$

This is that part of the function $\bar{\varphi}$ (expanded in the above named part of G) whose terms increase as the origin is approached. This expression converges, in accordance with Section VII, 13, in this part of G and also for larger values of ϱ since no functions which increase with ϱ occur in it. In particular, both this expression and its derivative converge along the image of the profile K. Thus

$$\sum_{h=0}^{\infty} L(\beta_{-(5/6)-(h/2)} \varphi_{-(5/6)-(h/2)})$$

converges also. More correctly we should say that the sums

$$\sum_{h=0}^{\infty} L(\beta_{-(5/6)-(h/2)} \varphi_{-(5/6)-(h/2)})$$

converge as $N \to \infty$. Since in accordance with our assumptions

$$L(\Phi^{-(5/6)-(h/2)}) = 0,$$

we have

$$\sum_{h=0}^{N} L(\beta_{-(5/6)-(h/2)}\, \Phi^{-(5/6)-(h/2)}) = 0$$

or

$$\sum_{h=0}^{N} L(\beta_{-(5/6)-(h/2)}\, (\alpha_{-1/3}^{-(5/6)-(h/2)}\, \varphi_{-1/3} + \tilde{\varphi}^{-(5/6)-(h/2)})) = -\sum_{h=0}^{N} \beta_{-(5/6)-(h/2)}\, \varphi_{-(5/6)-(h/2)}\,. \tag{5}$$

This means that the expressions

$$\sum_{h=0}^{N} \beta_{-(5/6)-(h/2)}\, (\alpha_{-1/3}^{-(5/6)-(h/2)}\, \varphi_{-1/3} + \tilde{\varphi}^{-5/6-h/2})$$

satisfy the boundary value problem of a second kind when the boundary values are given by the RHS of Eq. (5). Since, however, in a well-formulated boundary value problem the solution is a continuous function of the boundary values and since it is probable that the present boundary value problem is so formulated, the convergence of

$$\sum_{h=0}^{N} \beta_{-(5/6)-(h/2)}\, (\alpha_{-1/3}^{-(5/6)-(h/2)}\, \varphi_{-1/3} + \tilde{\varphi}^{-(5/6)-(h/2)})$$

in the entire region G follows from the convergence of the RHS of Eq. (5) for $N \to \infty$.

Having thus determined that $\overline{\overline{\varphi}}$ converges along K it is convenient to show next that the difference $\overline{\varphi} - \overline{\overline{\varphi}}$ satisfies the boundary condition

$$L(\overline{\varphi} - \overline{\overline{\varphi}}) = 0 \tag{6}$$

along K. In addition the function $\overline{\varphi} - \overline{\overline{\varphi}}$ can, in the region G, be expanded in terms of the "natural" particular solutions. In view of the construction of $\overline{\overline{\varphi}}$ this expansion contains no terms of the form $\varphi_{-(5/6)-(h/2)}$. For this reason, if the term $\varphi_{-1/3}$ is ignored, the expansion converges up to the point O.

The difference $\overline{\varphi} - \overline{\overline{\varphi}}$ thus represents in the region G a function satisfying Tricomi's condition and whose only singular component is the function $\varphi_{-1/3}$. Further, this difference satisfies the boundary condition, Eq. (6). Thus, in accordance with the arguments of Section VIII, 8, it is equal to zero so that $\overline{\overline{\varphi}}$, as given by Eq. (4), is the desired representation of the function $\overline{\varphi}$.

4. The Boundary Conditions in the Vicinity of the Point O

The examples in Section IX, 2 show that the boundary conditions, applicable in the vicinity of O, assume quite varied forms. These boundary conditions can be linear and homogeneous or non-homogeneous. They can depend on parameters which are either given within the problem itself (e.g. the values of ψ along the wall of the tunnel) or which are determined simultaneously with the solution (e.g. the position of the points P and Q in Fig. 97). Non-linear boundary conditions can also occur.

All the boundary conditions have one thing in common in that they provide relations which determine those quantities which are as yet unknown. If we revert to ψ, and include the initial flow in the solution, then each solution which satisfies the boundary conditions at the profile can be written in the form

$$\psi = \Psi^{-5/6} + \sum_{h=0}^{\infty} B_{-(4/3)-(h/2)} \Psi^{-(4/3)-(h/2)}. \tag{1}$$

Here the functions Ψ are given by Eqs. IX, 3 (1) and IX, 3 (2). The constants $B_{-(4/3)-(h/2)}$ occur in place of the constants $\beta_{-(5/6)-(h/2)}$ of Eq. IX, 3 (4). Thus the boundary conditions in the vicinity of O must yield equations for the constants $B_{-(4/3)-(h/2)}$.

The solution can, in an appropriate part of G, be expanded in terms of the "natural" particular solutions

$$\psi = B_{-5/6}\,\Psi_{-5/6} + B_{-1/3}\,\psi_{-1/3} + \sum_{h=0}^{\infty} B_{-(4/3)-(h/2)}\,\psi_{-(4/3)-(h/2)} + \sum_{h=0}^{\infty} A_{h/6}\,\psi_{h/6}. \tag{2}$$

This form is more suitable for the expression of the boundary conditions in the vicinity of O than Eq. (1), since it is independent of the particular shape of the immersed body. We expect that the boundary conditions in the vicinity of O yield equations of the form

$$B_{-(4/3)-(h/2)} = F^{-(4/3)-(h/2)}\,(B_{-5/6}, B_{-1/3}, A_0, A_{1/3} \ldots A_{k/3} \ldots). \tag{3}$$

Here the functions F are known and, in general, non-linear in the arguments indicated. The quantities $A_{k/6}$ as well as $B_{-5/6}$ and $B_{-1/3}$ can be expressed in terms of the, thus far unknown, quantities $B_{-(4/3)-(h/2)}$ with the aid of Eqs. (1), IX, 3 (1), and IX, 3 (2)

$$\left.\begin{aligned} B_{-5/6} &= \alpha_{-5/6}^{-5/6} + \sum_{k=0}^{\infty} B_{-(4/3)-(k/2)}\,\alpha_{-5/6}^{-(4/3)-(k/2)}, \\ B_{-1/6} &= \alpha_{-1/3}^{-5/6} + \sum_{k=0}^{\infty} B_{-(4/3)-(k/2)}\,\alpha_{-1/3}^{-(4/3)-(k/2)}, \\ A_{h/6} &= \alpha_{h/6}^{-5/6} + \sum_{k=0}^{\infty} B_{-(4/3)-(k/2)}\,\alpha_{h/6}^{-(4/3)-(k/2)}. \end{aligned}\right\} \tag{4}$$

If these quantities are introduced in Eq. (3) one obtains a system of equations for the quantities $B_{-(4/3)-(h/2)}$. This system is best solved by an iteration procedure. As a first approximation we take an initial flow with $M = 1$. Here

$$B_{-(4/3)-(h/2)} = 0.$$

Then from Eqs. (4)

$$B_{-5/6} = \alpha_{-5/6}^{-5/6},$$
$$B_{-1/3} = \alpha_{-1/3}^{-5/6},$$
$$A_{h/3} = \alpha_{h/3}^{-5/6}.$$

Introducing these into Eq. (3) one obtains approximations for the quantities B, namely

$$B_{-(4/3)-(h/2)} = F^{-(4/3)-(h/2)}\,(\alpha_{-5/6}^{-5/6}, \alpha_{-5/6}^{-5/6}, \alpha_0^{-5/6}, \alpha_{1/6}^{-5/6} \ldots \alpha_{k/3}^{-5/6} \ldots).$$

Using these values the results can be further improved.

Our examples show that the boundary conditions can contain free parameters which become determined in the process of calculation. Equations (3) assume that these parameters have been eliminated. It is most often convenient to leave these parameters in the boundary conditions. One obtains then additional equations equal in number to that of the parameters. Such equations are obtained most naturally for $B_{-1/3}$ and $B_{-5/6}$.

These free parameters can have the character of ϱ, e.g. if the positions of the points P and Q in Fig. 97 are determined by the prescribed values of ϱ at these points, or they can represent values of the stream function. In accordance with their character they are denoted by ϱ_1 and ϱ_2 or by ψ_1 and ψ_2. Further, in the formulation of non-homogeneous boundary conditions there occur quantities which, although they are determined by the flow field, are still best included as parameters in the boundary conditions. The same notation will be employed for these quantities. Thus the boundary conditions in the vicinity of O can be expressed by the following equations

$$B_{-(1/3)-(h/2)} = \bar{F}^{-(1/3)-(h/2)}\,(\psi_1, \psi_2, \varrho_1, \varrho_2, A_0, A_{1/6}, A_{1/3} \ldots A_{k/3} \ldots), \tag{5}$$

where it is assumed that of the four parameters occurring here two have the character of ψ and two the character of ϱ. Two of these parameters are to be considered known.

Because of the form of TRICOMI's equation and the simplified shock conditions, the hodograph solutions remain valid when (a) the scale of ϱ is changed and (b) the solution is multiplied by a constant. The first of these changes represents a distortion of the flow field, in accordance with the similarity rule, while the second represents a simple change of scale in the physical plane. To show the effect of this on the form of Eq. (4) we re-write Eq. (2) in such a manner that it remains invariant under the above transformations.

$$\psi = \psi_0 \Big[b_{-5/6}(\varrho_0^{5/6}\psi_{-5/6}) + b_{-1/3}(\varrho_0^{1/3}\psi_{1/3}) + \\ + \sum_{h=0}^{\infty} b_{-(4/3)-(h/2)}\,(\varrho_0^{(4/3)+(h/2)}\psi_{-(4/3)-(h/2)}) + \sum_{h=0}^{\infty} a_{h/6}(\varrho_0^{-h/6}\,\psi_{h/6})\Big]. \tag{6}$$

Here ψ_0 and ϱ_0 are characteristic values of ψ and ϱ for the given problem, while a and b are new coefficients in the expansion. By comparison with Eq. (2) one obtains

$$\left.\begin{aligned} B_{-(1/3)-(h/2)} &= \psi_0 \varrho_0^{(1/3)+(h/2)} b_{-(1/3)-(h/2)}, \\ A_{h/6} &= \psi_0 \varrho_0^{-h/6} a_{h/6}. \end{aligned}\right\} \tag{7}$$

The boundary conditions corresponding to Eq. (5) appear now in the form of relations between the coefficients a and the coefficients b

$$b_{-(1/3)-(h/2)} = \bar{R}^{-(1/3)-(h/2)}\left(\frac{\psi_1}{\psi_0}, \frac{\psi_2}{\psi_0}, \frac{\varrho_1}{\varrho_0}, \frac{\varrho_2}{\varrho_0}, a_0, a_{1/6}, \ldots, a_{k/3} \ldots\right).$$

Here the $\bar{R}$'s are functions determined by the boundary conditions in the vicinity of O. Introducing Eq. (7) in the above one obtains as a more specific formulation of Eq. (5)

$$B_{-(1/3)-(h/2)} = \psi_0 \varrho_0^{(1/3)+(h/2)} \times$$
$$\times \bar{R}^{-(1/3)-(h/2)}\left(\frac{\psi_1}{\psi_0}, \frac{\psi_2}{\psi_0}, \frac{\varrho_1}{\varrho_0}, \frac{\varrho_2}{\varrho_0}, \ldots \frac{A_{k/6}\varrho_0^{k/6}}{\psi_0} \ldots\right).$$

The characteristic quantities ψ_0 and ϱ_0 will, of course, be equated to parameters which are already present in the boundary conditions, e.g. to ψ_1 and ϱ_1. Then the boundary conditions become independent of these parameters. The remaining parameters are best chosen such that they vanish for a flow field antisymmetric in ψ and, further, that the expansion of the functions R in terms of these parameters starts with a linear term. Whether this is the case can be only discovered when the boundary conditions for a specific situation are investigated. In the flow in a closed-circuit tunnel three parameters occur, in accordance with the formulation in Section IX, 2, namely the value of ψ at the wall (this will be chosen as the quantity ψ_1) and the values of ϱ at the points P and Q denoted respectively by ϱ_P and ϱ_Q. For the parameter ϱ_1 the value of ϱ_Q is suitable. In order for an antisymmetric flow field to correspond to a zero value of the second parameter, we chose the latter to be equal to $\varrho_Q - \varrho_P$. We shall see later that the expansion of the boundary conditions in terms of this parameter starts with the term $(\varrho_Q - \varrho_P)^{1/2}$. It is, therefore, more convenient to introduce $p_1 = [(\varrho_Q - \varrho_P)/\varrho_Q]^{1/2}$. Another parameter, when applicable, might also be chosen in this manner. Thus one obtains finally a simplified form of the last equation, namely

$$B^{-(1/3)-(h/2)} = \psi_1 \varrho_1^{(1/3)+(h/2)} \times$$
$$\times R^{-(1/3)-(h/2)}\left(p_1, p_2, \frac{A_0}{\psi_1} \ldots \frac{A_{k/6}\varrho_1^{k/6}}{\psi_1} \ldots\right). \tag{8}$$

If the functions R are to be determined for given boundary conditions characterised by ψ_1, ψ_2, ϱ_1, and ϱ_2, in the vicinity of O, one must obtain a solution of TRICOMI's equation which satisfies these boundary conditions. In addition, the expansion of this solution in terms of the "natural" particular solutions for a positive exponent of ϱ must have the form

$$\sum_{k=0}^{\infty} A_{k/6}\psi_{k/6}$$

Then in this solution the quantities $B_{-(1/3)-(h/2)}$ are the coefficients of the "natural" particular solutions for negative exponents of ϱ. Returning, with the aid of Eq. (8), to the functions R these are found to depend only on the arguments indicated in that equation. Thus the calculation has to be performed only for a single choice of the parameters ψ_1 and ϱ_1, e.g. $\psi_1 = 1$ and $\varrho_1 = 1$. Examples of such an analysis will be shown later.

5. Flows which are Antisymmetric in ψ with Respect to the x Axis

The objective of the following analysis is to find an expansion of the solution, as given by Eq. IX, 4 (1), in terms of a parameter describing the deviation of the flow field from the base flow at $M = 1$. We shall always confine ourselves to the determination of terms of lowest order.

The parameters p_1 and p_2 are zero for an antisymmetric flow field. Further, the coefficients $A_{h/3}$ and $B_{-(1/3)-h}$ do not occur. Equations IX, 4 (8) appear, therefore, in the simpler form

$$B_{-(5/6)-h} = \psi_1 \varrho_1^{(5/6)+h} R^{-(5/6)-h}\left(\dots \frac{A_{(1/6)+(k/3)}\, \varrho_1^{(1/6)+(k/3)}}{\psi_1} \dots\right).$$

All the functions R, occurring in this section, belong to the antisymmetric particular solutions. If the deviation from the base flow is small, then ϱ_1 is small. Thus if the deviations from the base flow tend to zero, the arguments of the functions R vanish. Then as the term of lowest order in an expansion for B one obtains

$$B_{-(5/6)-h} = \psi_1 \varrho_1^{(5/6)+h} R^{-(5/6)-h}(0, 0, \dots). \tag{1}$$

The power of ϱ, which appears as a factor in B, increases with h. From Eq. IX, 4 (4) we find, considering only the lowest power of ϱ

$$B_{-5/6} = \alpha_{-5/6}^{-5/6}.$$

Substitution of the above into Eq. (1) yields

$$\alpha_{-5/6}^{-5/6} = \psi_1 \varrho_1^{5/6} R^{-5/6}(0, 0 \dots). \tag{2}$$

Here $\alpha_{-5/6}^{-5/6}$, $R^{-5/6}$ and either ϱ_1 or ψ_1 are known. This equation, therefore, establishes a relationship between the known and the unknown parameters. Substitution of this last equation in Eq. (1) yields

$$B_{-(5/6)-h} = \varrho_1^h \alpha_{-5/6}^{-5/6} \frac{R^{-(5/6)\ h}(0, 0 \dots)}{R^{-5/6}(0, 0 \dots)}. \tag{3}$$

Thus, from Eq. IX, 4 (1), and considering again only the lowest power of ϱ_1, we find

$$\psi = \Psi^{-5/6} + \varrho_1 \alpha_{-5/6}^{-5/6} \frac{R^{-11/6}(0, 0 \dots)}{R^{-5/6}(0, 0 \dots)} \Psi^{-11/6}. \tag{4}$$

It may be shown subsequently, with the aid of Eq. IX, 4 (4), that the quantities A are actually of order 1 and that, therefore, the arguments of R really do tend to zero with ϱ_1. If the terms of higher order in Eq. (4) were to be calculated, one would also have to consider the fact that the boundary conditions at the profile were linearised. An exception to this is offered by the flow past a wedge.

The functions Ψ depend only on the shape of the body while the quantities R and ϱ_1 depend only on the boundary conditions in the vicinity of the point O. In accordance with Eq. (4) the deviation from the base flow is represented by $\Psi^{-11/6}$ except for a multiplying factor. This function is, in the first approximation, independent of the boundary conditions prescribed in the vicinity of O.

From Eq. (4) we can, of course, directly determine the changes in the pressure and velocity distributions in the physical plane, using Eqs. VIII, 7 (3) and VIII, 7 (4).

6. Unsymmetric Flow Fields

A lack of symmetry can be introduced into a flow field both by the shape of the profile and by the conditions in the vicinity of the point O. As an example of the second situation one may consider a profile situated not quite in the center of a tunnel. The parameter describing the departure from symmetry can be considered known. Let this parameter be always so small that the boundary conditions can be expanded in terms of it. No such parameter occurs in unbounded flows.

The boundary conditions in the vicinity of O contain a further parameter which may cause a deviation from symmetry. In Fig. 97 this was the location of the point P. This parameter is determined only in the course of the calculation of the solution and depends principally on the lack of symmetry of the profile.

Certain symmetry properties of the functions $R^{-(1/3)-(h/2)}$ are important for our further analysis. These properties arise from the fact that $B_{-(5/6)-h}$ and $A_{(1/6)+(h/3)}$ are the coefficients of antisymmetric particular solutions, while $B_{-(1/3)-h}$ and $A_{h/3}$ are the coefficients of symmetric particular solutions. If p_1 and p_2 are both equal to zero the boundary conditions are purely antisymmetric.

To bring out these symmetry properties let us consider two solutions which can be obtained from one another by a reflection on the axis and a simultaneous change of sign. In these solutions the coefficients of the antisymmetric particular solutions $\varphi_{(1/6)+(h/3)}$ and $\varphi_{-(5/6)-h}$, i.e. the quantities $A_{(1/6)+(h/3)}$ and $R^{-(5/6)-h}$ have the same sign. The coefficients of the symmetric particular solutions $A_{h/3}$ and $R^{-(1/3)-h}$, as well as the parameters p_1 and p_2 which describe the deviation from a purely antisymmetric solution, have opposite signs. In what follows, the change of sign which occurs in the transition from the first to the second solution, will always be accounted for by a change of sign in the second solution. The boundary conditions in the vicinity of the point O, which are expressed by the functions R, are always satisfied in the reflection process described above. Then in the first case we have, in accordance with Eq. IX, 4 (8),

$$B_{-(5/6)-h} = \psi_1 \varrho_1^{(5/6)+h} \times$$
$$\times R^{-(5/6)-h}\left(p_1, p_2, \frac{A_0}{\psi_1}, \frac{A_{1/6}\varrho_1^{1/6}}{\psi_1} \cdots \frac{A_{k/3}\varrho_1^{k/3}}{\psi_1}, \frac{A_{(1/6)+(k/3)}\varrho_1^{(1/6)+(k/3)}}{\psi_1} \cdots\right),$$

while in the second case

$$B_{-(5/6)-h} = \psi_1 \varrho_1^{(5/6)+h} \times$$
$$\times R^{-(5/6)-h}\left(-p_1, -p_2, \frac{-A_0}{\psi_1}, \frac{A_{1/6}\varrho_1^{1/6}}{\psi_1} \cdots \frac{-A_{k/3}\varrho_1^{k/3}}{\psi_1}, \frac{A_{(1/6)+(k/3)}\varrho_1^{(1/6)+(k/3)}}{\psi_1} \cdots\right).$$

Hence

$$R^{-(5/6)-h}\left(p_1, p_2, \frac{A_0}{\psi_1}, \frac{A_{1/6}\varrho_1^{1/6}}{\psi_1}, \cdots \frac{A_{k/3}\varrho_1^{k/3}}{\psi_1}, \frac{A_{(1/6)+(k/3)}\varrho_1^{(k/6)+(k/3)}}{\psi_1} \cdots\right)$$
$$= R^{-(5/6)-h}\left(-p_1, -p_2, \frac{-A_0}{\psi_1}, \frac{A_{1/6}\varrho_1^{1/6}}{\psi_1} \cdots \cdots \frac{-A_{k/3}\varrho_1^{k/3}}{\psi_1}, \frac{A_{(1/6)+(k/3)}\varrho_1^{(1/6)+(k/3)}}{\psi_1} \cdots\right). \tag{1}$$

Similarly

$$R^{-(1/3)-h}\left(p_1, p_2, \cdots \frac{A_{k/3}\varrho_1^{k/3}}{\psi_1}, \frac{A_{(1/6)+(k/3)}\varrho_1^{(1/6)+(k/3)}}{\psi_1} \cdots\right)$$
$$= -R^{-(1/3)-h}\left(-p_1, -p_2, \cdots -\frac{A_{k/3}\varrho_1^{k/3}}{\psi_1}, \frac{A_{(1/6)+(k/3)}\varrho_1^{(1/6)+(k/3)}}{\psi_1} \cdots\right). \tag{2}$$

If one assumes that the functions R are differentiable with respect to their arguments, there follows

$$R^{-(1/3)-h}\left(0, 0, \ldots 0, \frac{A_{(1/6)+(k/3)}\varrho_1^{(1/6)+(k/3)}}{\psi_1}, 0 \ldots\right) = 0 \tag{3a}$$

$$h = 0, 1, 2 \ldots, \quad k = 0, 1, 2 \ldots,$$

$$\frac{\partial}{\partial p_{1,2}} R^{-(5/6)-h}\left(0, 0, \ldots 0, \frac{A_{(1/6)+(k/3)}\varrho_1^{(1/6)+(k/3)}}{\psi_1}, 0 \ldots\right) = 0, \tag{3b}$$

$$\frac{\partial}{\partial A_{m/3}} R^{-(5/6)-h}\left(0, 0, \ldots 0, \frac{A_{(1/6)+(k/3)}\varrho_1^{(1/6)+(k/3)}}{\psi_1}, 0 \ldots\right) = 0 \tag{3c}$$

$$h = 0, 1, 2 \ldots, \quad k = 0, 1, 2 \ldots, \quad m = 0, 1, 2 \ldots.$$

In a flow with $M = 1$ the antisymmetric term $\psi_{-5/6}$ predominates in the vicinity of O over the symmetric term $\psi_{1/3}$. This means that the further one moves away from the profile in the physical plane, or the closer one approaches the point O in the hodograph plane, the more does the flow field approximate a form antisymmetric in ψ. One must presume, therefore, that the parameter which is not given in advance, and which describes the deviations of the boundary conditions from their antisymmetric form, tends to zero as ϱ_1 tends to zero, i.e. when the deviation of the flow field from the base flow becomes smaller and smaller.

All the remaining arguments of the functions R tend, further, to zero with ϱ_1. We now determine the terms of lowest order in ϱ_1 in the quantities $B_{-(1/3)-(h/2)}$. For the coefficients $B_{-(5/6)-h}$, which belong to the antisymmetric particular solution, one finds

$$B_{-(5/6)-h} = \psi_1 \varrho_1^{(5/6)+h} R^{-(5/6)-h}(0, 0, \ldots). \tag{4}$$

For the coefficients $B_{-(1/3)-h}$ of the symmetric particular solutions an expansion in terms of the parameters p_1 and p_2 is necessary, in accordance with Eq. (3a). The remaining arguments are small and of higher order in ϱ_1. One obtains the equations

$$B_{-(1/3)-h} = \psi_1 \varrho_1^{(1/3)+h} \times$$
$$\times \left\{ p_1 \frac{\partial}{\partial p_1} (R^{-(1/3)-h}(0, 0, \ldots)) + p_2 \frac{\partial}{\partial p_2} (R^{-(1/3)-h}(0, 0, \ldots)) \right\}. \tag{5}$$

Now, from Eq. IX, 4 (4), retaining only the lowest power of ϱ_1, we obtain

$$B_{-5/6} = \alpha_{-5/6}^{-5/6} \quad \text{and} \quad B_{-1/3} = \alpha_{-1/3}^{-5/6}.$$

Substitution in Eq. IX, 4 (8) yields

$$\alpha_{-5/6}^{-5/6} = \psi_1 \varrho_1^{5/6} R^{-5/6}(0, 0, \ldots) \tag{6}$$

and

$$\alpha_{-1/3}^{-5/6} = \psi_1 \varrho_1^{1/3} \times$$
$$\times \left\{ p_1 \frac{\partial}{\partial p_1} (R^{-1/3}(0, 0, \ldots)) + p_2 \frac{\partial}{\partial p_2} (R^{-1/3}(0, 0, \ldots)) \right\}. \tag{7}$$

As for a flow field antisymmetric in ψ, one finds from Eqs. (6) and (4)

$$B_{-(5/6)-h} = \varrho_1^h \alpha_{-5/6}^{-5/6} \frac{R^{-(5/6)-h}(0, 0 \ldots)}{R^{-(5/6)}(0, 0 \ldots)}. \tag{8}$$

A parameter p, say p_1, is to be considered known in Eq. (7). Then the other parameter can be calculated with the aid of Eq. (6)

$$p_2 = \varrho_1^{1/2} \frac{R^{-5/6}(0, 0, \ldots)}{\alpha_{-5/6}^{-5/6}} \alpha_{-1/3}^{-5/6} \frac{1}{\frac{\partial}{\partial p_2}(R^{-1/3}(0, 0, \ldots))} - p_1 \frac{\frac{\partial}{\partial p_1}(R^{-1/3}(0, 0, \ldots))}{\frac{\partial}{\partial p_2}(R^{-1/3}(0, 0, \ldots))}.$$

From this, and with the aid of Eq. (6), one obtains from Eq. (5)

$$B_{-(1/3)-h} = \varrho_1^h \frac{\frac{\partial}{\partial p_2}(R^{-(1/3)-h}(0, 0, \ldots))}{\frac{\partial}{\partial p_2}(R^{-1/3}(0, 0, \ldots))} \alpha_{-1/3}^{-5/6} +$$
$$+ \varrho_1^{-(1/2)+h} p_1 \frac{\alpha_{-5/6}^{-5/6}}{R^{-5/6}(0, 0, \ldots)} \left\{ \frac{\partial}{\partial p_1}(R^{-(1/3)-h}(0, 0, \ldots)) - \right.$$
$$\left. - \frac{\partial}{\partial p_2}(R^{-(1/3)-h}(0, 0, \ldots)) \frac{\frac{\partial}{\partial p_1}(R^{-1/3}(0, 0, \ldots))}{\frac{\partial}{\partial p_2}(R^{-1/3}(0, 0, \ldots))} \right\}. \tag{9}$$

The first term is due to the non-symmetry of the profile, as expressed by $\alpha_{-1/3}^{-5/6}$. The second term describes the asymmetry due to the boundary conditions in the vicinity of O, as expressed by p_1.

Omitting the second term and restricting ourselves to terms of lowest order in ϱ_1 we obtain from Eq. IX, 4 (1)

$$\psi = \Psi^{-5/6} + \\ + \varrho_1 \left[\alpha_{-5/6}^{-5/6} \frac{R^{-11/6}(0,0,\ldots)}{R^{-5/6}(0,0,\ldots)} \Psi^{-11/6} + \alpha_{-1/3}^{-5/6} \frac{\frac{\partial}{\partial p_2}(R^{-4/3}(0,0,\ldots))}{\frac{\partial}{\partial p_2}(R^{-1/3}(0,0,\ldots))} \Psi^{-4/3} \right]. \quad (10)$$

This formula shows that the coefficients of $\Psi^{-11/6}$ and $\Psi^{-4/3}$ are of the same order in ϱ_1. If ϱ_1 is not given directly, it may be calculated from ψ_1 with the aid of Eq. (6). The dependence of the correction terms on ϱ_1 forms the most important general result of the present analysis.

7. The Expansion of a Flow Field in Terms of the Deviation of the Undisturbed Flow Mach Number from Unity

In both the transformations which in Section V, 7 led from the exact hodograph equation to TRICOMI's equation, ϱ_1 is, in the first approximation, proportional to $(M - 1)^3$, where M is a MACH number characterised by ϱ_1. For example in the case of supersonic upstream flow M is the MACH number of the approaching flow, while in the case of flow in a choked wind tunnel M is the choking MACH number. If TRICOMI's equation were identical with the hodograph equation, it would follow that the changes in the flow field, resulting from the deviation of this characteristic MACH number from unity, would be proportional to $(M - 1)^3$. Since TRICOMI's equation is only an approximation to the exact hodograph equation, we can at first conclude only that this is true when the approximation is valid, namely for small values of the parameter τ in Eq. V, 7 (3), in other words for the limiting case of slender bodies.

Actually this result is true quite generally; the solutions of TRICOMI's equation can namely be interpreted as approximations to the solutions of the exact hodograph equation, valid in the vicinity of the origin. This point will be discussed in a little more detail in the following paragraphs.

Let us revert to Eq. V, 7 (2) and let us omit the function $h(w)$ in Eq. V, 7 (1) since it appears as a universal factor in all particular solutions. The exact solutions of Eq. V, 7 (2) must take into account the expression on the RHS of the equation. For all finite values of η, in particular also for $\eta = 0$, $r(\eta)$ is a regular function. Because of this term the solutions of TRICOMI's equation require correction terms. On the whole, as particular solutions corresponding to Eqs. VII, 3 (3) we obtain expressions of the form $\varrho^{-(1/12)+\mu}\, G(\xi, \mu)\,(1 + 0(\eta^2))$. We now form particular solutions of the hodograph equation which satisfy the boundary conditions at the surface of the profile and which are singular at the point O. In each such particular solution the term predominating at the origin is the same as that in the solution of TRICOMI's equation. In deriving the results of the preceding section only the term predominating at the origin was, however, utilised. Thus also in the case of the exact hodograph equation the term of lowest order in an expansion in terms of $(M - 1)$ is proportional to $(M - 1)^3$.

If from the expressions Ψ in the hodograph plane we go over to the velocity changes in the physical plane then these are, of course, also proportional to $(M - 1)^3$, when the stagnation pressure (i.e. the constant in BERNOULLI's equation) is held constant. The same is true of the local changes in the MACH number and the local pressure changes at a constant stagnation pressure. The conclusion does not apply to the pressure coefficients. In terms of the usual definition

$$c_p = \frac{p - p_\infty}{\frac{1}{2}\varrho_\infty w_\infty^2}.$$

The subscript ∞ in this connection denotes the condition in the approaching flow. In this equation the quantities dependent on the approaching flow vary, in the first approximation, with $(M - 1)$. This influence exceeds that of the changes in the pressure. This point will now be considered in more detail. As a result of the present analysis we have found

$$\frac{p}{p^*} = \left(\frac{p}{p^*}\right)_{M_\infty = 1} + \frac{\Delta p}{p^*}, \tag{1}$$

where

$$\frac{\Delta p}{p^*} = O\left((M_\infty - 1)^3\right). \tag{1a}$$

Let c_p^* denote the pressure coefficient at $M = 1$

$$c_p^* = \frac{p - p^*}{\frac{1}{2}\varrho^* w^{*2}}. \tag{2}$$

A similar notation will later be used for the lift and drag coefficients. For any other MACH number we have then

$$c_p = \frac{p - p_\infty}{\frac{1}{2}\varrho_\infty w_\infty^2} = \frac{p - p^*}{\frac{1}{2}\varrho^* w^{*2}} \frac{\varrho^* w^{*2}}{\varrho_\infty w_\infty^2} - \frac{p_\infty - p^*}{\frac{1}{2}\varrho_\infty w_\infty^2} = c_p^* \frac{\varrho^* w^{*2}}{\varrho_\infty w_\infty^2} - \frac{p_\infty - p^*}{\frac{1}{2}\varrho_\infty w_\infty^2}.$$

Expansion of this in terms of $(M_\infty - 1)$ yields

$$c_p = c_p^* \left\{1 - \frac{2}{\gamma + 1}(M_\infty - 1) + \frac{5\gamma + 1}{(\gamma + 1)^2}(M_\infty - 1)^2\right\} + \\ + \frac{4}{\gamma + 1}(M_\infty - 1) + \frac{2(3\gamma + 1)}{(\gamma + 1)^2}(M_\infty - 1)^2 + O[(M_\infty - 1)^3]. \tag{3}$$

Here only the first and last terms are related to the pressure distribution on the surface of the body. All the other terms are due to a change of state at infinity, resulting from a change in the MACH number. They are cancelled out when the forces on a closed contour, as for example the lift and the drag, are being determined. For the lift and drag coefficients the corresponding equations take the form

$$c_L = c_L^* \left\{1 - \frac{2}{\gamma + 1} (M_\infty - 1) + \frac{5\gamma + 1}{(\gamma + 1)^2} (M_\infty - 1)^2 + O([M_\infty - 1]^3)\right\} \quad (4)$$

with a similar equation for c_D. First order changes in c_L are due only to the definition of c_L; only in the third order does a real physical effect appear. From the physical point of view it is, therefore, preferable to use p/p^*, c_p^*, c_L^*, c_D^* and the local MACH numbers in order to describe the flow. For engineering applications one would, of course, use the normal definitions c_p, c_L and c_D.

Occasionally one finds drag coefficients referred only to the nose of an obstacle in the flow and to the pressure at infinity as a reference pressure. In such cases the dominant change in the vicinity of $M = 1$ is given by the term $[4/(\gamma + 1)] (M_\infty - 1)$ of Eq. (3). Such a representation gives one the impression that in two-dimensional flow the drag coefficient increases with the MACH number while, in accordance with Eq. (4), it should decrease.

The slight dependence of the drag coefficient on the MACH number, found here, applies also to a body with a blunt tail, since the pressure at the base is determined by the flow past the obstacle.

We shall show later that a similar behaviour is found in the case of axisymmetric flows, but the influence of a change in the MACH number is considerably stronger, namely proportional to $(M_\infty - 1)^{5/3}$ *.

* Occasionally, under the heading "the correspondence principle", the above result is obtained from the following argument: the MACH numbers before and after a normal shock deviate from unity, in the first approximation, by equal amounts except, of course, for a different sign. Therefore a profile, in an approaching supersonic flow, before which a detached shock exists is, as it were, in a subsonic flow field. From this it is concluded that the resulting flow agrees quite closely with a subsonic flow whose MACH number is equal to that reached after the shock. If one assumes further, usually tacitly, that the pressure curve during the transition through $M = 1$ can be differentiated twice, one actually finds that the curve of the local MACH number, plotted versus the velocity of the approaching flow, has a horizontal tangent for an approaching flow at $M = 1$. This argument cannot be considered rigorous. Immediately after the shock there occur all the velocities between that corresponding to a normal shock and the velocity of the approaching flow. Thus the velocity corresponding to the normal shock is not really a characteristic one. We know further that in the transonic region disturbances are propagated mainly at right angles to the flow; it is doubtful, therefore, whether the velocity occurring upstream of the model, at the shock, can control the flow field around the profile. Also the shock polar, with the corresponding streamline directions (Fig. 44), does not suggest the point corresponding to a normal shock as a possible common origin of the streamlines. A point within the shock polar would be more likely. Finally the assumption that the transition through $M = 1$ is described by a twice-differentiable function does not appear probable *a priori*; one should only consider that in not such a distant past the existence of a flow with M = 1 was doubted. In the axisymmetric case this assumption is certainly false.

In the above discussions we have formed a fairly clear picture of flows in the vicinity of $M = 1$. What range should be regarded as the vicinity of $M = 1$ depends on the thickness ratio of the profile. If one treats, for example, a supersonic flow in the manner outlined in the preceding sections, then one must assume that the shock polar, corresponding to the MACH number of the approaching flow, is small in comparison with the other dimensions of the hodograph plane. If, at a given constant supersonic MACH number, the wedge angle is gradually reduced then this assumption becomes, in the end, no longer applicable, and the methods, just described, cannot be used.

8. The Flow past a Rhombic Profile in a Choked Closed-Circuit Wind Tunnel

The flows to be considered in this section and in the subsequent one are of practical interest since they illustrate the influence of the walls on wind tunnel measurements in the vicinity of $M = 1$. The flow in a closed-circuit wind tunnel and in a free jet at $M = 1$ was calculated by MARSCHNER [60] for a rhombic profile.

Since the flow fields are antisymmetric in ψ, only the functions $\Psi^{-5/6}$ and $\Psi^{-11/6}$ are, in accordance with the considerations of Section IX, 5, necessary in order to determine, in the first approximation, the changes in the pressure distribution at the profile. The calculation procedure leading to these solutions was given already in Sections VIII, 4, VIII, 6 and VIII, 8. In the calculation of $\Psi^{-5/6}$ (i.e. of the flow with an approach MACH number of 1) we obtain the following quantity necessary in the evaluation of Eq. IX, 5 (2) [cf. Eq. VIII, 4 (6)]

$$\alpha_{-5/6}^{-5/6} = \frac{L}{2{,}47}\left(\frac{3}{2}\,\theta_0\right)^{4/3} (\gamma + 1)^{-1/3}. \qquad (1)$$

In accordance with Eq. IX, 5 (4) one requires, further, the quantities $R^{-5/6}(0, 0, \ldots)$ and $R^{-11/6}(0, 0, \ldots)$. The arguments of these functions are all zero, i.e. we are concerned here with a calculation of that portion which satisfies the inhomogeneous boundary conditions in the vicinity of O and vanishes at infinity of the η, ϑ plane. The constants ψ_1 and ϱ_1 can be put equal to 1, as was shown at the end of Section IX, 4. The particular boundary conditions to be satisfied can be obtained from Fig. 97, and in the case of later examples, from Figs. 98 and 45. In the present case the flow field is antisymmetric in ψ, i.e. the points P and Q in Fig. 97 coincide and one obtains the boundary conditions shown in Fig. 99. In view of the requirement of antisymmetry, Fig. 98 yields the boundary value problem represented in Fig. 96. The conditions at a shock polar which have to be satisfied in accordance with Fig. 45, require no simplification.

To obtain explicitly the conditions for a closed-circuit wind tunnel we divide the region of the η, ϑ plane into two parts by the line $\varrho = 1$ through the point Q (Fig. 99). We choose initially an expression which in the inner region satisfies TRICOMI's differential equation and the inhomogeneous boundary conditions such as for example $\psi = 1$. Somewhat more tractable is an expression $H(\xi$

which has the following characteristics: it satisfies Eq. VII, 3 (6b), when in the latter we put $\mu = \frac{1}{12}$, i.e.

$$\frac{d}{d\xi}\left[(1-\xi^3)^{5/6}\frac{dH}{d\xi}\right] = 0. \tag{2}$$

It satisfies, further, the boundary conditions

$$H(-\infty) = 1,$$
$$H(1) = 0. \tag{2a}$$

The function consists, of course, of a linear combination of particular solutions $G^{(a)}(\xi, \frac{1}{12})$ and $G^{(s)}(\xi, \frac{1}{12})$. This function tends to zero as $\xi \to 1$ which saves some discussion of convergence.

Outside of the line $\varrho = 1$, the desired solution is represented only by the particular solutions $\psi_{-5/6-h}$. Within this line we have, in addition to the function

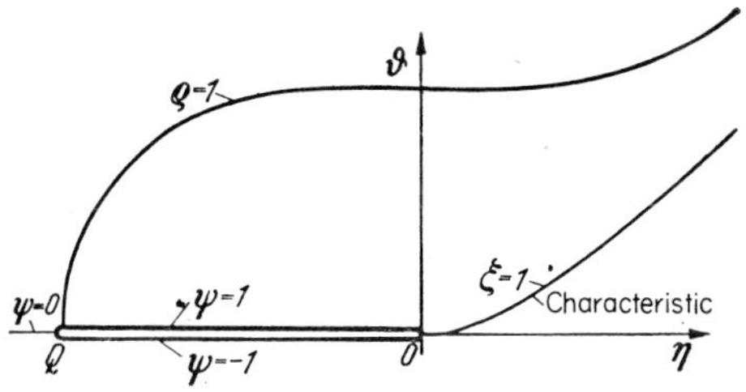

FIG. 99

H, also a term which satisfies TRICOMI's conditions. If the quantity $H(\xi)$ is ignored then the remaining part of ψ (denoted by $\hat{\psi}$) can be described as follows: at $\xi = -\infty$, and also at infinity of the η, ϑ plane, we have $\hat{\psi} = 0$. Further $\hat{\psi}$ satisfies at the origin TRICOMI's conditions and exhibits along $\varrho = 1$ a discontinuity in the value of the function, the magnitude of the discontinuity being given by $H(\xi)$. This problem was discussed in Section VII, 13. In Eq. VII, 13 (2) we must put

$$f_1(\xi) = H(\xi),$$
$$f_2(\xi) = 0.$$

We are next interested in an expansion in the external region. There $H(\xi)$ does not occur and ψ is identical with $\hat{\psi}$. The solution is given directly by Eq. VII, 13 (3a), where the quantity $B^{(a)}$ is defined by Eq. VII, 12 (13b). One obtains

$$a_h = \left[\frac{3}{\pi}\int_{-\infty}^{1} H(\xi)\left(-\mu_h + \frac{1}{12}\right)\frac{1}{2\mu_h}\frac{\tau}{(1-\tau^3)^{7/6}} G^{(a)}(\tau, \mu_h)\, d\tau\right] \times$$
$$\times \left[\frac{\Gamma\left(\mu_h + \frac{11}{12}\right)\Gamma\left(\mu_h + \frac{7}{12}\right)\Gamma\left(-\mu_h + \frac{11}{12}\right)\Gamma\left(-\mu_h + \frac{7}{12}\right)}{\Gamma\left(\frac{1}{2}\right)\Gamma(2\mu_h)\,\Gamma\left(\frac{1}{2}\right)\Gamma(-2\mu_h)}\right], \tag{3}$$

where

$$\mu_h = h - \frac{1}{4}.$$

The integral in Eq. (3) can be evaluated by parts, with the aid of Eqs. (2) and VII, 3 (6b),

$$\int_{-\infty}^{1} H(\xi) \frac{\tau}{(1-\tau^3)^{7/6}} G^{(a)}(\tau, \mu_h)\, d\tau = \frac{1}{6\left(\frac{1}{144} - \mu_h^2\right)}.$$

Introducing this in Eq. (3) one obtains

$$a_h = \frac{2}{\pi\sqrt{3}} \frac{\dfrac{\Gamma\left(h+\frac{2}{3}\right)}{\Gamma\left(\frac{2}{3}\right)} \dfrac{\Gamma\left(h+\frac{1}{3}\right)}{\Gamma\left(\frac{1}{3}\right)}}{\dfrac{\Gamma\left(h+\frac{5}{6}\right)}{\Gamma\left(\frac{5}{6}\right)} \dfrac{\Gamma\left(h+\frac{1}{6}\right)}{\Gamma\left(\frac{1}{6}\right)}}.$$

a_1 is the coefficient of the solution $\psi_{-5/6}$, a_2 is the coefficient of $\psi_{-11/6}$, so that these quantities represent the desired values of R

$$R^{-5/6}(0, 0, \ldots) = \frac{16}{5\pi\sqrt{3}} = 0{\cdot}588, \tag{4a}$$

$$R^{-11/6}(0, 0, \ldots) = \frac{16}{5\pi\sqrt{3}} \frac{\frac{5}{3}\,\frac{4}{4}}{\frac{11}{6}\,\frac{7}{6}} = 0{\cdot}612. \tag{4b}$$

For the boundary conditions just discussed the functions R, incidentally, do not depend on the coefficients $A_{(1/6)+(h/3)}$, since the particular solutions belonging to the quantities A contribute nothing to the values of ψ along the line $\xi = -\infty$, and therefore do not alter the boundary conditions prescribed there. For a wedge no linearisation of the boundary conditions at the image of the profile is necessary; the entire solution can, therefore, be given without difficulty as long as the functions $\Psi^{-(5/6)-h}$ are known.

Using the values found above, one determines next ψ_1 from Eq. IX, 5 (2). The parameter ψ_1 is given by the value of the stream function at the upper wall of the tunnel. If the width of the tunnel is W there results

$$\psi_1 = \frac{W}{2}.$$

Hence

$$\varrho_1 = \left[\frac{2}{W}\frac{\alpha_{-5/6}^{-5/6}}{0{\cdot}588}\right]^{6/5}. \tag{5}$$

Thus all the quantities occurring in Eq. IX, 5 (4) can be considered known. We now move immediately to the changes in the pressure distribution along the surface of the wedge. Let $x^{-5/6}$ and $x^{-11/6}$ be the values of x calculated along the image of the surface of the wedge for the solutions $\Psi^{-5/6}$ and $\Psi^{-11/6}$. These quantities are, of course, functions of η. By a process quite analogous to that which led finally to Eqs. VIII, 7 (3) and (4), we find the change in η at a given fixed point along the surface to be given by

$$\Delta\eta = -\varrho_1 \frac{R^{-11/6}(0, 0, \ldots)}{R^{-5/6}(0, 0, \ldots)} \times \times \left[\frac{\alpha_{-5/6}^{-5/6} x^{-11/6}}{\dfrac{\partial x^{-5,6}}{\partial\eta}}\right]_{\text{Profile}}.$$

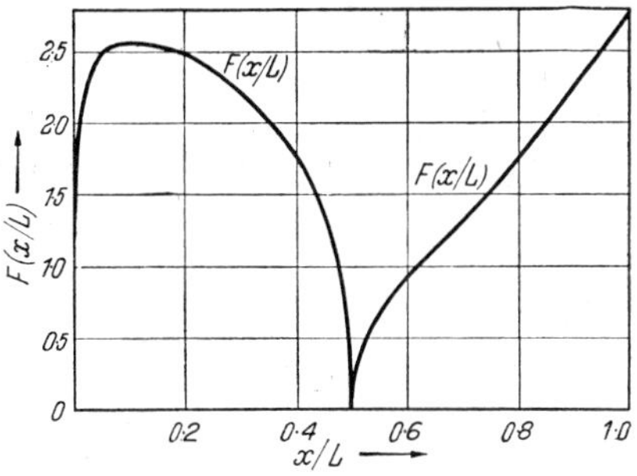

FIG. 100 The function $F(x/L)$ for a rhombic profile. (According to MARSCHNER [60]).

The quantity $\alpha_{-5/6}^{-5/6}$, which occurs in the solution $\Psi^{-5/6}$, and therefore in $x^{-5/6}$, as a factor, is determined by the dimensions of the profile. When x/L is chosen as an independent variable this quantity must cancel out. This is actually the case in the expression

$$\left[\frac{\alpha_{-5/6}^{-5/6} x^{-11/6}}{\dfrac{\partial x^{-5/6}}{\partial\eta}}\right].$$

The functions $\Psi^{-5/6}$ and $\Psi^{-11/6}$, and therefore also $x^{-5/6}$ and $x^{-11/6}$, depend further on the angle of the wedge. If we consider a series of flows related to one another simply by a change in θ_0 then a discussion, similar to that in Section VIII, 4, shows that a corresponding points of these flow fields $x^{5\,6}$ is proportional to $\theta_0^{-4/3}$ and $x^{-11/6}$ is proportional to $\theta_0^{-10/3}$. In accordance with the definition, η is at such points proportional to $\theta_0^{2/3}$ and ϑ to θ_0. Therefore the term

$$\left[\frac{\alpha_{-5/6}^{-5/6} x^{-11/6}}{\dfrac{\partial x^{-5/6}}{\partial\eta}}\right]$$

is proportional to $\theta_0^{4/3}$. This term may be put in the form

$$\frac{\alpha_{-5/6}^{-5/6} x^{-11/6}}{\dfrac{\partial x^{-5/6}}{\partial\eta}} = F\left(\frac{x}{L}\right)\left(\frac{3}{2}\theta_0\right)^{-4/3}. \tag{6}$$

The function $F(x/L)$ is shown in Fig. 100. One obtains

$$\Delta\eta = -\varrho_1 \frac{R^{-11/6}(0,0,\ldots)}{R^{-5/6}(0,0,\ldots)} F\left(\frac{x}{L}\right)\left(\frac{3}{2}\theta_0\right)^{-4/3} = -\varrho_1 \frac{80}{77} F\left(\frac{x}{L}\right)\left(\frac{3}{2}\theta_0\right)^{-4/3} \quad (7)$$

or

$$\Delta\eta = -\left(\frac{L}{W}\right)^{6/5} \theta_0^{4/15}(\gamma+1)^{-2/5}\, 1{\cdot}70\, F\left(\frac{x}{L}\right). \quad (8)$$

when Eqs. (1) and (5) are introduced. From Eq. V, 7 (23) the change in the pressure coefficient is given by

$$\Delta c_p^* = -2(\gamma+1)^{-1/3}\Delta\eta. \quad (8a)$$

The choking MACH number can be determined from Eq. (5), with the aid of Eq. V, 7 (23). Introducing Eq. (1) there results

$$1 - M_{\text{choked}} = \left(\frac{L}{W}\right)^{2/5} \theta_0^{8/15}(\gamma+1)^{8/15}\, 0{\cdot}705,$$

and, in particular, for $\gamma = \frac{1}{4}$

$$1 - M_{\text{choked}} = \left(\frac{L}{W}\right)^{2/5} \theta_0^{8/15}\, 1{\cdot}127. \quad (9)$$

This last equation shows that the choking MACH number is not only a function of the cross-section available for the flow but also of the chord of the profile. The minimum cross-section available between the wedge and the wall is not fully utilized, since the streamlines are not normal to this cross-section and since the mass flow density is not a maximum there. The fact that both L and θ_0 do not occur raised to the $\frac{1}{2}$ power in Eq. (9) shows that for a sufficiently wide wind tunnel the choking MACH number is not determined by the minimum cross-section.

We shall later compare the choking MACH number for a rhombic profile with that corresponding to a flat inclined plate. To this end the following equation is useful. Let L_s be the length of the rhombic profile from the leading edge to the widest point. Then $L = 2L_s$ and one obtains

$$1 - M_{\text{choked}} = 1{\cdot}488\left(\frac{L_s}{W}\right)^{2/5} \theta_0^{8/15}. \quad (9a)$$

The pressure distribution at $M = 1$ was expressed in Eq. VIII, 4 (5) by

$$c_p = -2(\gamma+1)^{-1/3}\theta_0^{2/3} g\left(\frac{x}{L}\right).$$

Introducing the correction, which we have just calculated, there results for the pressure distribution in a choked tunnel

$$c_p^* = -2(\gamma+1)^{-1/3}\theta_0^{2/3}\left\{g\left(\frac{x}{L}\right) - (\gamma+1)^{-2/5}\, 1{\cdot}70\left(\frac{L}{W}\right)^{6/5}\theta_0^{-2/5} F\left(\frac{x}{L}\right)\right\}. \quad (10)$$

A comparison of the solid and dotted lines in Fig. 85 shows the difference in the pressure distribution for a wedge, with 10% thickness ratio, in a choked wind tunnel and in an unbounded air stream, at $M = 1$. In this example the chord is equal to 13% of the width of the tunnel. The choking MACH number is 0·86. The effect of a change in θ_0 and in the width of the tunnel on this result can be found with the aid of Eqs. (9) and (10). The relative error in the pressure distribution is, for a given chord, smaller in the case of the body with a larger thickness ratio θ_0. This was already derived qualitatively in Section II, 7 as an application of the similarity rule.

Our present analysis shows that the choking MACH number does not offer a suitable criterion for assessing the accuracy of a wind tunnel measurement. A change in the choking MACH number from 0·9 to 0·95 reduces the deviations of the pressure distribution to one-eighth of their original values. In general it may be said that in a choked wind tunnel one can obtain experimental data which do not differ by very much from those obtained in an unbounded flow at $M = 1$.

The pressure distribution at the wall of the tunnel (GUDERLEY [35]) which may be of interest in the evaluation of the experiments, requires for its determination the calculation of the solution in the region as < 1 in Fig. 99. To this end we use Eq. VII, 13 (10), in which ϱ_0 is replaced by ϱ_1. The function I is given by Eq. VII, 13 (4), i.e. by

$$I(\mu_h) = \int_{-\infty}^{1} H(\tau)\left(\mu_h + \frac{1}{12}\right)\frac{\tau}{(1-\tau^3)^{7/6}}\, G^{(a)}(\tau, \mu_h)\, d\tau .$$

The calculation is quite similar to that involved in Eq. (3) and one finds

$$I(\mu_h) = -\frac{1}{6}\,\frac{1}{\left(\mu_h - \frac{1}{12}\right)} .$$

Equation VII, 13 (10) gives the solution of the problem, considered in that section, for the case in which no discontinuities are propagated along $\xi = 1$. The discontinuities are distinguished by the character of the functions f_1 and f_2, which describe the jump along $\varrho = \varrho_0 = \varrho_1$, i.e. in the present case by the character of $H(\xi)$. The function $H(\xi)$ is in fact such that a discontinuity is propagated along $\xi = 1$ and therefore in the function $\hat{\varphi}$, to be superimposed, there occurs a corresponding term. This just cancels the discontinuity in $H(\xi)$.

We transform immediately from the expression for ψ, which results from Eq. VII, 13 (10), to one for x and obtain with the aid of Eq. VII, 3 (9)

$$x = -\frac{W}{2}(\gamma+1)^{1/3}\varrho_1^{1/6}\,\frac{1}{3\pi}\sum_{h=0}^{\infty}\frac{\Gamma\left(\frac{h}{3}+\frac{1}{6}\right)\Gamma\left(\frac{h}{3}+\frac{5}{6}\right)}{\Gamma\left(\frac{h}{3}+\frac{4}{3}\right)\Gamma\left(\frac{h}{3}+\frac{2}{3}\right)}\left(\frac{\varrho}{\varrho_1}\right)^{(1/3)+(h/3)} . \qquad (11)$$

ϱ_1 corresponds to the choking MACH number. In view of Eq. V, 7 (11), one obtains

$$\frac{\varrho}{\varrho_1} = \left(\frac{1 - M}{1 - M_{\text{choked}}}\right)^3.$$

We denote the sum in Eq. (11) by

$$E\left(\frac{1 - M}{1 - M_{\text{choked}}}\right) = \sum_{h=0}^{\infty} \frac{\Gamma\left(\frac{h}{3} + \frac{1}{6}\right)\Gamma\left(\frac{h}{3} + \frac{5}{6}\right)}{\Gamma\left(\frac{h}{3} + \frac{4}{3}\right)\Gamma\left(\frac{h}{3} + \frac{2}{3}\right)} \left(\frac{1 - M}{1 - M_{\text{choked}}}\right)^{1+h}.$$

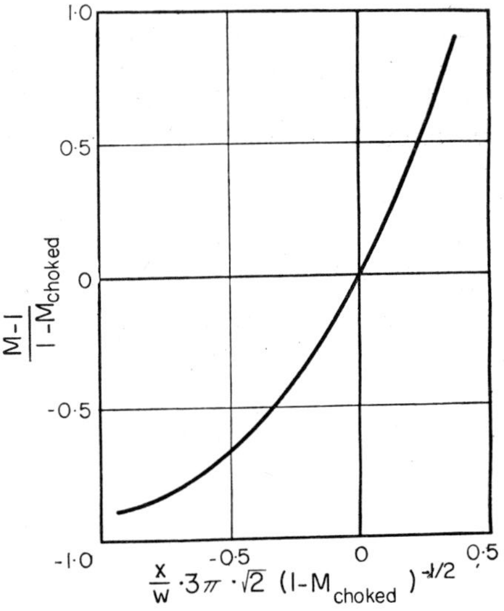

FIG. 101 The pressure distribution on the wall of a choked wind tunnel. (According to GUDERLEY [35]).

Let the negative inverse function be

$$-\frac{1 - M}{1 - M_{\text{choked}}} = \frac{M - 1}{1 - M_{\text{choked}}} = F(E).$$

Replacing, in accordance with Eq. V, 7 (11), the quantity $\varrho_1^{1/6}$ in Eq. (11) by

$$(1 - M_{\text{choked}})^{1/2} (\gamma + 1)^{-1/3}\, 2^{1/2},$$

one obtains

$$\frac{M - 1}{1 - M_{\text{choked}}} = F\left(\frac{x}{W}\, 3\pi \cdot 2^{1/2}\, (1 - M_{\text{choked}})^{-1/2}\right).$$

This result is shown in Fig. 101. The last equation contains the width of the tunnel W and choking MACH number as parameters. In this form it is valid (for a sufficiently wide tunnel) independently of the shape of the profile. For a rhombic profile the choking MACH number is related to the dimensions of the tunnel, and to those of the model, by Eq. (9).

9. The Flow past a Rhombic Profile in a Free Jet at Critical Velocity and the Flow in a Supersonic Unbounded Air Stream

The search for the coefficients $R^{-5/6}(0, 0, \ldots)$ and $R^{-11/6}(0, 0, \ldots)$ for a free jet at critical velocity leads to a boundary value problem which was already discussed in Section VIII, 10. We have

$$R^{-5/6}(0, 0, \ldots) = \frac{8}{5} 2^{-1/3} \pi^{-1} = 0{\cdot}403,$$

$$R^{-11/6}(0, 0, \ldots) = \frac{-40}{33} 2^{-1/3} \pi^{-1} = 0{\cdot}306.$$

Thus as a counterpart of Eq. IX, 8 (10) we obtain

$$c_p^* = -2(\gamma + 1)^{-1/3} \theta_0^{2/3} \left\{ g\left(\frac{x}{L}\right) + (\gamma + 1)^{-2/5} 1{\cdot}943 \left(\frac{L}{W}\right)^{6/5} \theta_0^{-2/5} F\left(\frac{x}{L}\right) \right\}.$$

The influence of the boundary of the jet is some 14% larger than that of the wall of a closed-circuit tunnel, and it is of opposite sign. From the point of view of corrections for a wind tunnel the free jet offers, therefore, no advantages.

The solution to a problem corresponding to an approaching supersonic flow may be found in an article by GUDERLEY [33]. The limit of convergence of an infinite series of particular solutions $\psi^{-(5\,6)-h}$ is a line $\varrho = \text{const}$. The shock polar does not deviate very much from such a line. One attempts, therefore, to satisfy the boundary conditions along a shock polar directly by a finite number of terms $\psi^{-(5/6)-h}$. One could presume at first that the accuracy cannot be increased arbitrarily by increasing the number of terms. Even this restriction, however, need not apply, as follows from an analysis by BERGMANN [6] which, however, refers to boundary conditions of a different kind.

The numerical results are not very satisfactory; even with eight free functions the shock conditions cannot be accurately satisfied. In spite of this the following values appear to be quite reliable

$$R^{-5/6}(0, 0, \ldots) = 1^*,$$

$$R^{-11/6}(0, 0, \ldots) = -1{\cdot}67.$$

In analogy with Eq. IX, 8 (7) this leads to the following expression

$$\Delta\eta = \varrho_1 \, 1{\cdot}67 \, F\left(\frac{x}{L}\right) \left(\frac{3}{2} \theta_0\right)^{-4/3}.$$

Here ϱ_1 is that value of ϱ which is reached from the velocity of approach through a normal shock. If η_I is the value of η before the shock then the value of η after the shock is $-\eta_I$ [Eq. II, 4 (5)] and $\varrho_1 = \eta_I^3$. If M_I is the MACH number of the approaching flow then with the aid of Eq. V, 7 (11)

$$\varrho_1 = 8(\gamma + 1)^{-2} (M - 1)^3$$

* The first of these values may be prescribed.

and

$$\Delta\eta = 8(\gamma + 1)^{-2}(M - 1)^3\, 1{\cdot}67\left(\frac{3}{2}\,\theta_0\right)^{-4/3} F\left(\frac{x}{L}\right),$$

$$\Delta c_p^* = -16(\gamma + 1)^{-7/3}(M - 1)^3\, 1{\cdot}67\left(\frac{3}{2}\,\theta_0\right)^{-4/3} F\left(\frac{x}{L}\right).$$

Since the sign of the perturbation term Δc_p^* is the same in a free jet with a critical velocity and for a supersonic MACH number, the flow in the jet can, in this approximation, be considered equivalent to a flow at a supersonic MACH number. The correspondence between the two flows is, however, very difficult to illustrate. An attempt in this direction may be found in an article by GUDERLEY [33]. In the same article there is given the asymptotic form of the shock wave for MACH numbers in the vicinity of 1.

10. The Flat Plate in a Choked, Closed-Circuit Wind Tunnel

The influence of the walls resulting for an unsymmetric body in a choked closed-circuit wind tunnel can be illustrated on the example of an inclined plate (GUDERLEY [31]). Figure 102 shows the physical plane, the hodograph plane and, for the limiting case of small angles of attack, the boundary value problem in the η, ϑ plane. The notation is the same as in Section VIII, 9, i.e. the point B is the origin of the η, ϑ system of coordinates in which the quantities ϱ and ξ are defined. An auxiliary system of coordinates has its origin at O. The values of ϑ, measured from O, are denoted by $\bar{\vartheta}$ and the corresponding quantities ϱ and ξ are denoted by $\bar{\varrho}$ and $\bar{\xi}$.

In accordance with Eq. IX, 6 (10) we require, in addition to the base flow $\Psi^{-5/6}$, the terms $\Psi^{-4/3}$ and $\Psi^{-11/6}$. These were already given in Eqs. VIII, 9 (19) and VIII, 9 (24). The expression given by Eq. IX, 6 (10), which we have to calculate, contains the constants $\alpha_{-5/6}^{-5/6}$ and $\alpha_{-1/3}^{-5/6}$. These are given by Eqs. VIII, 9 (20)

$$\alpha_{-5/6}^{-5/6} = \left\{(\gamma + 1)^{1/3}\left(\frac{3}{2}\right)^{4/3}\theta_0^{-1/3}\right\}^{-1} \frac{\Gamma\left(\frac{5}{2}\right)}{\Gamma\left(\frac{5}{6}\right)\Gamma\left(\frac{2}{3}\right)}\,\frac{8}{9\sqrt{3}}\,L\varrho_0^{5/6}. \tag{1a}$$

$$\alpha_{-1/3}^{-5/6} = -\left\{(\gamma + 1)^{1/3}\left(\frac{3}{2}\right)^{4/3}\theta_0^{-1/3}\right\}^{-1} \frac{\Gamma\left(\frac{5}{2}\right)}{\Gamma\left(\frac{5}{6}\right)\Gamma\left(\frac{5}{3}\right)}\,\frac{19}{18\sqrt{3}}\,L\varrho_0^{1/3}. \tag{1b}$$

We require, further, the quantities

$R^{-11/6}(0, 0, \ldots)$, $R^{-5/6}(0, 0, \ldots)$, $\partial R^{-4/3}(0, 0, \ldots)/\partial p_2$ and $\partial R^{-1/3}(0, 0, \ldots)/\partial p_2$.

These are obtained from the boundary conditions in the vicinity of the point O. The constants $R^{-11/6}(0, 0, \ldots)$ and $R^{-5/6}(0, 0, \ldots)$ are the same as those in an antisymmetric flow field since the parameters which express the deviation from antisymmetry are zero. These constants were found in connection with the flow past a symmetric model in a choked wind tunnel [Eq. IX, 8 (4)]

$$R^{-5/6}(0, 0, \ldots) = \frac{16}{5\pi\sqrt{3}} = 0{\cdot}588, \tag{2a}$$

$$R^{-11/6}(0, 0, \ldots) = \frac{16}{5\pi\sqrt{3}} \cdot \frac{\Gamma\left(\frac{5}{3}\right)\Gamma\left(\frac{4}{3}\right)}{\Gamma\left(\frac{11}{6}\right)\Gamma\left(\frac{7}{6}\right)} = 0{\cdot}612. \tag{2b}$$

To find the derivatives $\partial(R^{-1/3})/\partial p_2$ and $\partial(R^{-4/3})/\partial p_2$ we must take into account the asymmetry in the boundary conditions. This asymmetry is due to the fact

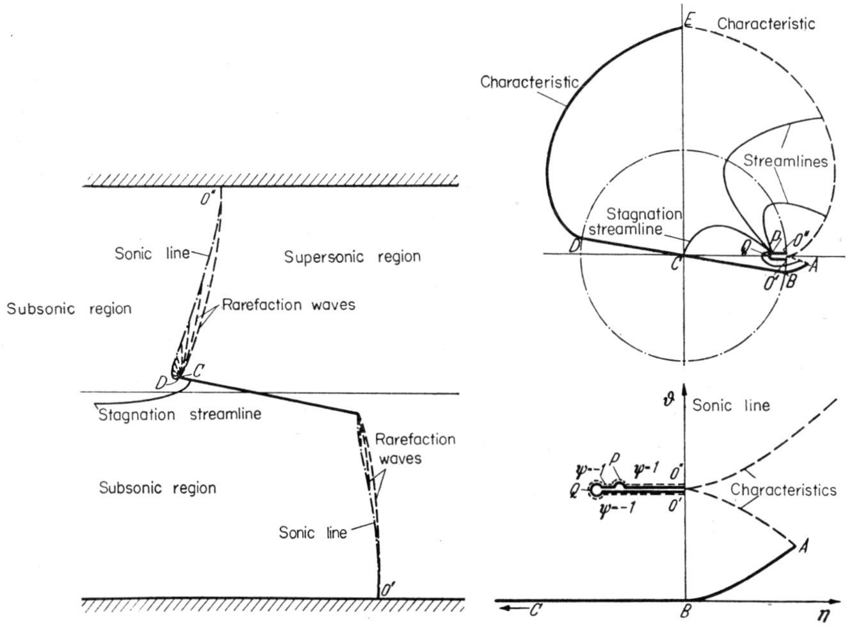

FIG. 102 Flow past an inclined plate in a choked wind tunnel. (According to GUDERLEY [37]).

that the points P and Q in Fig. 102c do not coincide. For a wide tunnel this deviation is small and its influence can be described by the first term of an expansion.

TRICOMI's equation in the immediate vicinity of the point Q can be simplified to

$$\psi_{\eta\eta} + |\eta_Q|\,\psi_{\vartheta\vartheta} = 0.$$

Here η_Q is the value of η at Q. Within the region, in which this approximation is valid, we obtain for ψ

$$\psi = 1 - \frac{2}{\pi} \operatorname{Im} \ln \left\{\sqrt{[\eta + i\bar{\vartheta}|\eta_Q|^{-1/2}] + |\eta_Q|} - \sqrt{|\eta_Q| - |\eta_P|}\right\}. \quad (3)$$

Here η_P is the value of η at P. The second root is always positive; the first is positive in the region $O''PQ$ (Fig. 102c). Between O'' and P we have to form the logarithm of a positive number so that the imaginary part is zero. When one follows the path shown in the figure around the point P, the argument of the function whose logarithm is to be determined changes by π. Therefore along $O''P$ we have $\psi = 1$ and along PQ $\psi = -1$. In going around the point Q the sign of the first root changes but we still have to form the logarithm of a negative quantity so that ψ retains the value -1. Expanding Eq. (3) in terms of $(|\eta_Q| - |\eta_P|)^{1/2}$ one obtains

$$\psi = 1 - \frac{1}{\pi} \operatorname{Im} \log [(\eta + i\bar{\vartheta}|\eta_Q|^{-1/2}) + |\eta_Q|] -$$

$$- \frac{2}{\pi}\sqrt{|\eta_Q| - |\eta_P|} \operatorname{Im} [(\eta + i\bar{\vartheta}|\eta_Q|^{-1/2}) + |\eta_Q|]^{-1/2}. \quad (4)$$

In accordance with this, at a sufficient distance from Q, the behaviour of ψ, as given by Eq. (3), can be expressed by a superposition of a logarithmic singularity, characteristic of antisymmetric boundary conditions, and of a function which has a branch point of the second order at Q. The singularity of the antisymmetric boundary conditions was discussed before. The solution which has a branch point of the second order at Q is obtained by putting $k = 0$ in Eq. VIII, 10 (1). The resulting expression can be rewritten in the form

$$\psi = \left(\frac{\bar{\varrho}}{\bar{\varrho}_Q}\right)^{1/6} \left(\frac{\bar{\varrho}}{\bar{\varrho}_Q} - 1\right)^{-1/2} \sim 3^{-1/2}\left(\frac{\eta}{\eta_Q} - 1\right)^{-1/2} \quad \text{for} \quad \bar{\vartheta} = 0,\ \frac{\eta}{\eta_Q} \sim 1.$$

For $\bar{\vartheta} = 0$ and $(\eta/\eta_Q) > 1$ the second part of Eq. (4) can be written in the form

$$-\frac{2}{\pi}\sqrt{\frac{|\eta_Q| - |\eta_P|}{|\eta_Q|}}\left(\frac{\eta}{\eta_Q} - 1\right)^{-1/2}.$$

We identify the quantity

$$-\frac{2}{\pi}\sqrt{\frac{|\eta_Q| - |\eta_P|}{|\eta_Q|}} \cdot 3$$

with the parameter p_2, occurring in Eq. IX, 6 (10), and put $p_1 = 0$. The parameter p_1 would be different from O if the model were not located in the center of the tunnel. Then the expression

$$p_2(\bar{\varrho}/\bar{\varrho}_Q)^{-1/3}\,[1 - (\bar{\varrho}/\bar{\varrho}_Q)^{-1}]^{-1/2}$$

corresponds to the second part of Eq. (4). Expanding this expression in terms of $(\bar{\varrho}/\bar{\varrho}_Q)^{-1}$ and using the individual terms as coefficients of the particular solutions $\Psi^{-(1/3)-h}$ one obtains

$$\frac{\partial}{\partial p_2} R^{-1/3}(0, 0, \ldots) = 1. \tag{4a}$$

$$\frac{\partial}{\partial p_2} R^{-4/3}(0, 0, \ldots) = \frac{1}{2}. \tag{4b}$$

The parameter ψ_1 is given by the value of ψ along the wall of the tunnel

$$\psi_1 = \frac{W}{2}.$$

The quantity $\bar{\varrho}_Q$ corresponds now to ϱ_1 in Eq. IX, 6 (10).

All the quantities required for the evaluation of Eq. IX, 6 (10) are now known. Equation IX, 6 (6) yields

$$\varrho_1 = \left[\frac{\alpha_{-5/6}^{-5/6}}{\psi_1} \frac{1}{R^{-5/6}(0, 0, \ldots)}\right]^{6/5} =$$

$$= \left(\frac{L}{W}\right)^{6/5} (\gamma + 1)^{-2/5} \theta_0^{8/5} \left[\frac{5\pi}{9} \frac{\Gamma\left(\frac{5}{2}\right)}{\Gamma\left(\frac{5}{6}\right)\Gamma\left(\frac{5}{3}\right)}\right]^{6/5} \left(\frac{3}{2}\right)^{2/5}$$

or

$$\frac{\bar{\varrho}_Q}{\varrho_0} = \left(\frac{L}{W}\right)^{6/5} \theta_0^{-2/5} (\gamma + 1)^{-2/5} \left[\frac{5\pi}{9} \frac{\Gamma\left(\frac{5}{2}\right)}{\Gamma\left(\frac{5}{2}\right)\Gamma\left(\frac{5}{3}\right)}\right]^{6/5} \left(\frac{3}{2}\right)^{-8/5}. \tag{5}$$

With the aid of Eq. VIII, 9 (3) one obtains for the choking MACH number

$$1 - M_{\text{choked}} = \left(\frac{L}{W}\right)^{2/5} \theta_0^{8/15} [\gamma + 1]^{8/15} \left[\frac{5\pi}{9} \frac{\Gamma\left(\frac{5}{2}\right)}{\Gamma\left(\frac{5}{6}\right)\Gamma\left(\frac{5}{3}\right)}\right]^{2/5} \frac{1}{2}\left[\frac{3}{2}\right]^{2/15}.$$

and hence for $\gamma = 1{\cdot}4$

$$1 - M_{\text{choked}} = 1{\cdot}170\, \theta_0^{8/15} \left(\frac{L}{W}\right)^{2/5}. \tag{6}$$

If in Eq. IX, 6 (10) we transform the values of ψ to the values of x along the plane, with the aid of Eq. VIII, 9 (25) we obtain

$$x = L \frac{\Gamma\left(\frac{5}{2}\right)}{\Gamma\left(\frac{5}{6}\right)\Gamma\left(\frac{5}{3}\right)} \left[3\, \bar{\bar{x}}^{5/6} + \frac{\bar{\varrho}_Q}{\varrho_0} \frac{8}{9\sqrt{3}} \frac{80}{77} \bar{\bar{x}}^{-11/6} - \frac{19}{36\sqrt{3}} \bar{\bar{x}}^{-4/3}\right].$$

The first term in the bracket originates from the flow in an unbounded region. The second term indicates the influence of the walls of the tunnel. At a constant value of x this term introduces a change in η, and hence with the aid of the definition given by Eq. VIII, 9 (15), in $\bar{\bar{\eta}}$, which can be established on the basis of the discussion in Section VIII, 7. One obtains

$$\Delta\bar{\bar{\eta}} = -\frac{\bar{\varrho}_Q}{\varrho_0}\left[\frac{8}{9\sqrt{3}}\,\frac{80}{77}\,\bar{\bar{x}}^{-11/6} - \frac{19}{36\sqrt{3}}\,\bar{\bar{x}}^{-4/3}\right]\left[3\,\frac{d\bar{\bar{x}}^{-5/6}}{d\bar{\bar{\eta}}}\right]^{-1}.$$

Hence, with the aid of Eq. VIII, 9 (26),

$$\Delta\bar{\bar{\eta}} = \frac{\bar{\varrho}_Q}{\varrho_0}\,\bar{\bar{\eta}}\left[\frac{35}{48} + \frac{30}{77}\,\frac{\bar{\bar{\eta}}^3}{1-\bar{\bar{\eta}}^3}\right]. \tag{7}$$

In Eq. VIII, 9 (23) η is expressed as

$$\eta = \theta_0^{2/3}\, g\left(\frac{x}{L}\right),$$

and hence

$$\bar{\bar{\eta}} = g\left(\frac{x}{L}\right)\left(\frac{3}{2}\right)^{-2/3}.$$

The complete equation for the distribution of η along the plate in the tunnel is then given by

$$\eta = \theta_0^{2/3}\, g\left(\frac{x}{L}\right)\left[1 + \frac{\bar{\varrho}_Q}{\varrho_0}\left[\frac{35}{49} + \frac{30}{77}\right]\frac{\frac{4}{9}\, g\left(\frac{x}{L}\right)^3}{1 - \frac{4}{9}\, g\left(\frac{x}{L}\right)^3}\right]. \tag{8}$$

In view of our experience in the case of a plate at $M = 1$, the pressure distribution on the suction side can be approximately obtained by an analytic continuation. This results simply in the same expression, except with the values of $g(x/L)$ corresponding to the suction side.

The dotted line in Fig. 94 represents the pressure distribution on a plate in a choked tunnel. The length of the plate is equal to 0·1 times the width of the tunnel, the angle of attack is 0·1 (5·7°). A comparison with the other curves in this figure shows that even in this case the influence of the walls is rather small.

The influence of the angle of attack on the length of the plate is expressed in the solution by the quantity $\bar{\varrho}_Q/\varrho_0$ [Eq. (5)]. It is evident that an increase in the length of the plate increases the relative influence of the wall. The fact that a decrease in the angle of attack has the same effect may at first appear surprising; it is, however, a result of the similarity rule.

The equation for the choking Mach number is of the same form as for a rhombic profile in a wind tunnel [Eq. IX, 8 (9a)]. Even the coefficients in Eqs. IX, 8 (9a) and IX, 10 (6) are not very different from one another. The boundary condition on the pressure side of the trailing edge of the plate agrees with the boundary condition at the shoulder of a wedge. There are differences, however, in the flow fields near the leading edge of a wedge and of a plate, respectively.

GUDERLEY [37] has further indicated that, in the present approximation, a displacement of the plate off the centerline of the tunnel is exactly equivalent to a change in the angle of attack. The effect, however, is very small.

It may be said, in general, that the influence of boundary conditions at a large distance from an immersed body is of a uniform character even in the case of unsymmetric flows. This influence is expressed by two functions determined by the shape of the body. The boundary conditions determine the coefficients of these functions. If we should desire to identify the measurements in a tunnel with a different flow, e.g. with a flow at a high subsonic MACH number, then it would be necessary to make both these coefficients identical in the two flows. One of the parameters which can be matched in subsonic flow is the MACH number of the approaching flow, the other is the angle of attack. It is important here that the solution $\Psi^{-4/3}$, also in the case of a body of general form, describes the effect of a change in the angle of attack (cf. Section VIII, 8). Thus, in the present approximation, the measurement in a tunnel is equivalent to a measurement in an unbounded air stream at a suitable MACH number of the approaching flow and with a different angle of attack.

This discussion illustrates the influence of the disturbances introduced at a large distance from an immersed body, in particular the influence of the walls of the wind tunnel. The fact that in the cases considered the influence of the walls is very small and does not, in the first approximation, depend on the type of boundary conditions permits us to conclude that in the transonic region it is also possible to introduce corrections for the influence of the walls of a tunnel. This is true also for nearly choked flow; as well as for wind tunnels with perforated walls. This idea was further developed by GUDERLEY [31]. The corrections have to be found by systematic measurements. They take the form of a relationship between the pressure distribution at the wall, the effective MACH number, and the effective angle of attack. The number of required measurements can be reduced by the application of the similarity rule. This is possible because of the fact that the form of the immersed body need not be taken into account.

11. Further Cases of Two-Dimensional Flow Fields

At the end of Section IX, 7 we have already indicated that when the angle of the wedge or, more generally, the thickness ratio become sufficiently small, at any constant MACH number of the approaching flow, the analysis of the preceding Sections is no longer applicable. This need not, however, contradict the application of the potential equation simplified for the transonic region.

Solutions of the boundary value problems for such cases are due to VINCENTI and WAGONER [79]. The boundary value problem for a wedge was already formulated in Fig. 45. One could attempt to solve this problem analytically by determining the particular solutions which satisfy the boundary conditions at the surface of the wedge and which have a logarithmic singularity at one point of the shock polar. The complete solution could be represented as a distribution of such singularities along the shock polar. The properties of these singularities could probably be arranged in such a manner that an integral equation of the second kind would result. This could then be solved numerically.

VINCENTI and WAGONER [79] use a direct numerical procedure. They establish a network in the η, ϑ plane and approximate the derivatives in TRICOMI's equation by the differences in the values of the stream function at the nodes of the network. Since the original differential equation and the boundary conditions

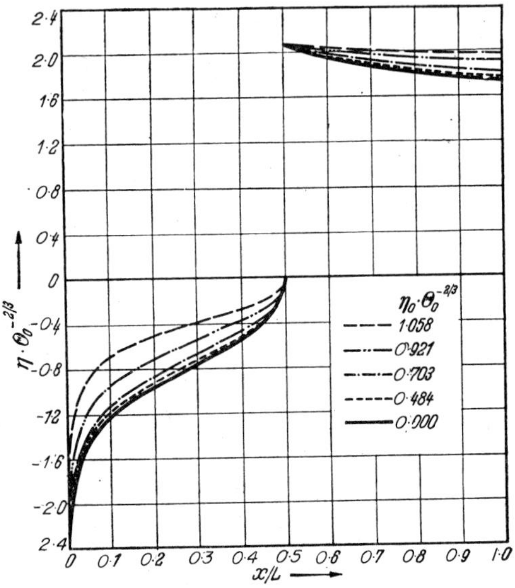

FIG. 103

Distribution of η for a rhombic profile at sonic velocity and with a supersonic approaching flow. (According to VINCENTI and WAGONER [79, 80]). η_0 is the value of η for the approaching flow; Θ_0 is the half-angle of the wedge and the thickness ratio of the profile.

are linear, one obtains in this manner a system of linear equations. The chief difficulty of the technique lies in the solution of this system of equations. VINCENTI and WAGONER employ relaxation methods. It would be of little value to describe the details of the calculation procedure, since for a practical application of the method it would always be useful to refer to the original article in order to become acquainted with the special steps which have been found convenient.

Figure 103 shows the quantities $\eta/\theta_0^{2/3}$ for a rhombic profile and for various values of the MACH number of the approaching flow, as described by the corresponding quantities $\eta_0/\theta_0^{2/3}$. It is easy, of course, to obtain from this the pressure distribution. The variable $\eta/\theta_0^{2/3}$, represented in this figure, is identical with the velocity function ξ introduced by VINCENTI and WAGONER. The same variable occurs also in Fig. 85.

Figure 104 shows the drag coefficient for a rhombic profile. The quantity plotted is $c_D(\gamma + 1)^{1/3}\theta_0^{-5/3}$. In order to obtain this curve from the results given above, it is necessary to express the pressure in the terms of Eq. V, 7 (11). The stagnation pressure is here expressed by $\varrho^* w^{*2}/2$. The smooth transition through $M = 1$ is apparent. The result can be considered accurate for thin profiles and consequently for MACH numbers very close to 1. It is not easy to say how these results could be extended to thicker profiles and larger deviations of the MACH number from unity. A recommendation in this respect is given by SPREITER [71].

The same procedure was used to investigate the influence of the angle of attack at supersonic MACH numbers. In Section VIII, 7 the influence of the angle of attack at $M = 1$, for a rhombic profile, was analyzed. The result of this investigation was that the value of $dc_L/d\alpha$ is considerably lower than in a purely supersonic flow. Intermediate points for a detached shock were found by

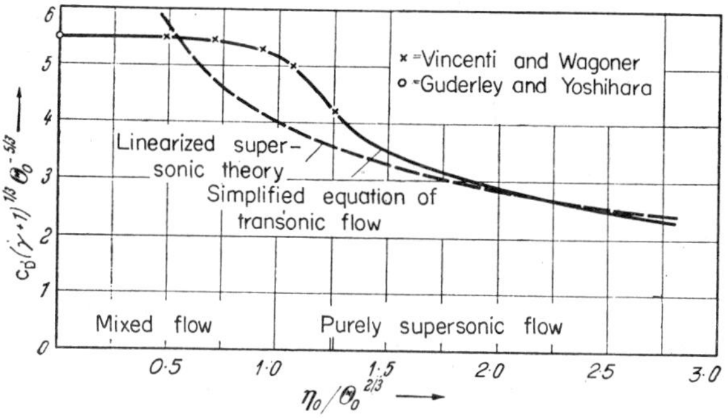

FIG. 104 Variation of the drag coefficient for a rhombic profile with η_0, at sonic and supersonic velocities. (According to VINCENTI and WAGONER [79, 80]), η_0 is the value of η for the approaching flow; Θ_0 is the half-angle of the wedge and the thickness ratio of the profile.

VINCENTI and WAGONER [80] (cf. Fig. 105). These values were verified experimentally for small angles of attack at which no flow separation occurs. One cannot assume that for other profiles a similarly surprising behaviour would occur.

The points corresponding to a shock attached to the leading edge of the wedge, with a subsonic velocity downstream of the shock, were investigated by YOSHIHARA [85]. In this case the upper and lower surfaces of the profile are independent of one another: the flow fields over the upper and lower faces depend only on the angle between the respective face and the direction of the approaching flow. The boundary value problem was illustrated in Fig. 53 and is shown again in Fig. 106. YOSHIHARA starts with the particular solutions

$$\psi^{(a)}_{(2/3)+h}$$

which satisfy the boundary conditions on the face OF and along the characteristic OA. The shock conditions are then approximately satisfied by a superposition of these particular solutions. It would be rather difficult to increase the accuracy of the results using this procedure; the accuracy appears, however, satisfactory for practical purposes. A differentiation of the results with respect to the wedge angle yields the lift coefficient. These results are included in Fig. 105.

YOSHIHARA [87] has also given an example of a flow at a high subsonic velocity.

VINCENTI, WAGONER and FISHER [81] have, further, investigated the flow past an inclined plate at $M = 1$, using the exact hodograph equation. Such an analysis illustrates the influence of the terms of the hodograph equation which are neglected in TRICOMI's equation. The result is shown in Fig. 30.

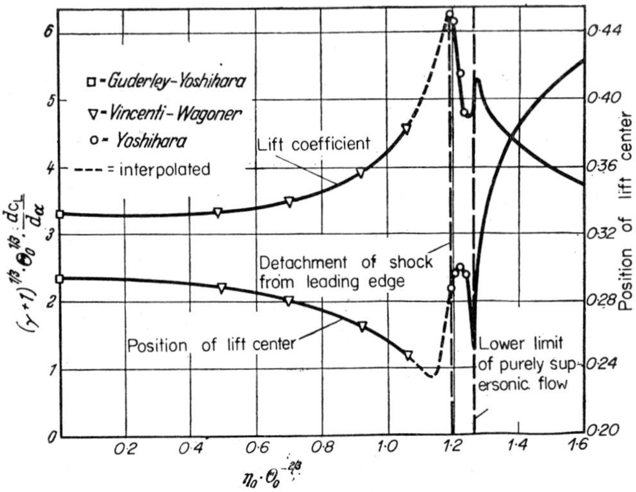

FIG. 105 Lift coefficient and the position of the lift center for a rhombic profile in supersonic flow. (According to VINCENT and WAGONER [79, 80] and YOSHIHARA [85]).

Θ_0 is the half-angle of the foremost wedge and the thickness ratio of the profile; α is the angle of attack and η_0 the value of η corresponding to the approaching flow.

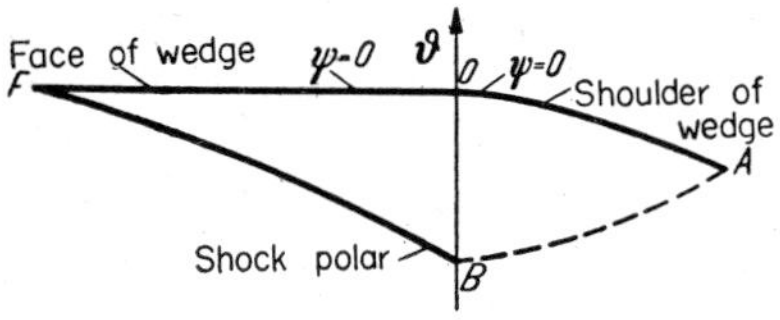

FIG. 106 The hodograph for a shock attached to the leading edge of a wedge.

One would expect that two-dimensional flow fields represent an approximation to wings of large aspect ratios. The question as to how the pressure distribution on the cross section of the wing approximates to that corresponding to two-dimensional flow, with an increasing aspect ratio, is discussed in an article by GUDERLEY [39]. The deviations from the pressure distribution in a two-dimensional flow are proportional to the aspect ratio, raised to the $-1{\cdot}2$ power. They can be interpreted as the superposition of a change in the MACH number, a change in the pressure level and, for inclined profiles, in the angle of attack. The details of this investigation are not included here for reasons of brevity.

CHAPTER X

SPECIAL CASES IN WHICH THE PARTICULAR SOLUTIONS GIVEN BY EQ. VII, 3 (3) ARE EMPLOYED

PARTICULAR solutions of the form of Eq. VII, 3 (3) are occasionally useful in the discussion of special problems, for example when it is desired to investigate the mathematical properties of mixed subsonic-supersonic flows on the basis of examples. This may be of considerable importance since a mathematical theory, leading to the desired conclusions, may not always be available. Investigations of this kind will be discussed in this chapter.

1. The Hodograph Solution at an Non-Degenerate Point on the Sonic Line

One requires of a non-degenerate point on the sonic line that the hodograph plane in its vicinity should consist of a single sheet, and that along the characteristics through this point no discontinuities should be propagated. We inquire after the form of the expansion of the hodograph solution in the vicinity of such a point.

Let the point considered be the origin of the η, ϑ system of coordinates. In Section VII, 9 we have inquired after the particular solutions which indicate no discontinuities along the characteristics passing through the origin. This has resulted in the natural particular solutions $\psi_{h/6}$ ($h = 0, 1, \ldots$). The expressions $\psi_{h/2}$ and $\psi_{(1/3)+(h/2)}$ are polynomials in η and ϑ (cf. p. 174). These functions, naturally, continue smoothly through the region between the characteristics EO and HO in Fig. 69. They are, however, also the only particular solutions for which this is true for the following reasons. The expressions $\psi_{h/6}$ are either symmetric or antisymmetric with respect to the η axis. The same is then true of the continuation of these terms in the region between the characteristics AO and OB. It must be required of this continuation that along the characteristic $\xi = 1$ it must agree in the functional value with the solution $\psi_{h/6}$. One notices, however, from Eqs. VII, 4 (7) and VII, 4 (9), that the solutions, which along the positive axis are either symmetric or antisymmetric for the values of μ here considered, namely $\frac{1}{4} + (h/2)$, appear always as a superposition of both the particular solutions possible along $\xi = 1$. One of these solutions, however, is always singular. In accordance with the discussion of Section VII, 13 each solution can, within the region C' in Fig. 69, be represented by a superposition of functions

$\psi_{h/6}\,(h = 0, 1, 2, \ldots)$, as long as the point zero is not singular and no discontinuities are propagated along the characteristics EO and HO. The additional requirement that the solution can be continued into the space between these characteristics, without introducing singularities along the characteristics, excludes the functions $\psi_{(1/6)+(h/2)}$ so that $\psi_{h/2}$ and $\psi_{(1/3)+(h/2)}$ remain as the only possibilities.

The function $\psi_{1/3}$ must always be included among these particular solutions, since all the others, considered separately, map the hodograph plane into more than one sheet of the physical plane. For these solutions, going around the point O in the hodograph plane, y in the physical plane vanishes more than once In the vicinity of O the solution containing the lowest power of ϱ predominates and controls, therefore, the structure of the physical plane.

2. The Reflection of a Discontinuity at the Sonic Line

It is well known that in supersonic flow a discontinuity in the higher derivatives of ψ is propagated along a characteristic. One asks next what happens when such a characteristic reaches the sonic line. We shall find that the discontinuity is reflected, retaining always the same character even if the reflection follows quite complicated laws, and that a discontinuity can never disappear at the sonic line. It is then, of course, also impossible for a discontinuity to originate at the sonic line (GUDERLEY [27]).

In the preceding section we have discussed points on the sonic line at which no discontinuities occurred. One should not expect that the occurrence of discontinuities will introduce important changes in the structure of the hodograph plane. This means that, even if discontinuities are permitted, one must construct solutions which in the vicinity of the point where the singular characteristic reaches the sonic line cover the η, ϑ plane once completely.

Along the line $\xi = 1$ each solution $G(\xi, \mu)$ is expressed by a superposition of

$$(1 - \xi^3)^{(1/12)-\mu}\, F\left(\frac{1}{12} - \mu, \frac{7}{12} - \mu, 1 - 2\mu, 1 - \xi^3\right) \tag{1a}$$

and

$$(1 - \xi^3)^{(1/12)+\mu}\, F\left(\frac{1}{12} + \mu, \frac{7}{12} + \mu, 1 + 2\mu, 1 - \xi^3\right). \tag{1b}$$

Except for a change in the sign in the coefficient of the hypergeometric series, this representation is valid both for $\xi < 1$ and for $\xi > 1$.

The corresponding particular solutions $\psi = \varrho^{-(1/12)+\mu}\, G(\xi, \mu)$ are then, in principle, the functions which occurred already in Section VII, 9, i.e.

$$\left(\frac{\eta}{\xi}\right)^{-(1/4)+3\mu} P(1 - \xi^3) \tag{2a}$$

and

$$\left(\frac{\eta}{\xi}\right)^{-(1/4)+3\mu} (1 - \xi^3)^{2\mu} P(1 - \xi^3). \tag{2b}$$

At each point of the line $\xi = 1$, with the exception of the origin, the first expression is regular, while the second exhibits a singular behaviour in view of the factor $(1 - \xi^3)^{2\mu}$. (Integer or half-integer values of μ are at first excluded.) The propagation of a discontinuity is thus expressed by Eq. (2b). When μ is negative, the second term tends to infinity and the characteristic, discussed, maps into infinity. This is, of course, of no interest. For positive values of μ the contribution of Eq. (2b) to x and y is zero, as may be seen from Eqs. VII, 3 (7) and VII, 3 (8). In order for the solution in the region *EDFGH* in Fig. 69 to join, without a gap in the physical plane, the solution in the region *EOH* it is only necessary to require that the solutions in the two regions agree with respect to the expression given by Eq. (2a). The coefficients of the expression given by Eq. (2b) are arbitrary and need not be the same for the representations corresponding to $\xi < 1$ and $\xi > 1$.

For the calculation of reflections of discontinuities at the sonic line it is useful to employ the concept of separation of each solution into a symmetric and an antisymmetric part. Solutions which are symmetric or antisymmetric in the regions $-\infty < \xi < 1$ or $1 < \xi < \infty$ were given by Eqs. VII, 4 (6) through VII, 4 (17). In order to find the expressions which cover the entire region, these solutions must be made to agree for $\xi = 1$. (Symmetric and antisymmetric solutions must, of course, be treated separately.) To this end it is only necessary, in view of our above discussion, that the coefficient of that part of the solution which is regular for $\xi = 1$ be the same in both regions.

The solution in the region $1 < \xi < \infty$ which is matched to $G^{(a)}$ for $-\infty < \xi < 1$ is then given by Eq. VII, 4 (9) multiplied by $2 \sin [\pi(\mu + \frac{1}{4})]$. Then the coefficient of the first term in this equation agrees with that of the first term in Eq. VII, 4 (17d).

Correspondingly, as a continuation of a function $G^{(s)}$, defined for $-\infty < \xi < 1$, we have in the region $1 < \xi < \infty$ the function defined by Eq. VII, 4 (7) multiplied by $\frac{1}{2} \sin[\pi(\mu + \frac{3}{4})]$.

Let α be the coefficient of the particular solution singular along $\xi = 1$, in the region $\xi < 1$ and β the corresponding coefficient for $\xi > 1$. For the antisymmetric particular solutions the ratio of these coefficients is

$$\frac{\beta}{\alpha} = -\cot\left[\pi\left(\mu + \frac{1}{4}\right)\right], \tag{3a}$$

while for the symmetric particular solutions one obtains

$$\frac{\beta}{\alpha} = -\cot\left[\pi\left(\mu - \frac{1}{4}\right)\right]. \tag{3b}$$

Any other case can be represented by a linear combination of the above expressions.

The characteristic, along which one approaches the sonic line with the flow, can be interpreted as carrying a discontinuity approaching the sonic line. The "reflection" of this discontinuity is then propagated along the other characteristic. One could attempt to determine an approaching discontinuity in such a manner that the reflected discontinuity would vanish. For this it would be necessary that the singular components of the antisymmetric and of the symmetric particular solutions should cancel one another along the reflected characteristic or, in other words, that both the ratios given by Eqs. (3a) and (3b) should be the same for both antisymmetric and symmetric particular solutions. It is easy to show that because of the nature of the cotangent function this cannot be the case for a real positive value of μ. A discontinuity can never disappear at the sonic line and can, therefore, also never originate at the sonic line.

In our discussions, up to this point, there occurred on both sides of a characteristic singular expressions which, in general, possessed different coefficients. These coefficients can be determined from the flow field. For example, one could expand ψ along a line $\eta = \text{const}$ in terms of $(1 - \xi^3)$. In accordance with the structure of the solutions this expansion would include a power series in $(1 - \xi^3)$ which is the same on both sides of the characteristic and corresponds to the solution given by Eq. (2a). It would, further, contain another power series multiplied by $(1 - \xi^3)^{2\mu}$ on one side of the characteristic and by $(\xi^3 - 1)^{2\mu}$ on the other side. The coefficients of the second part can be different on both sides of the characteristic. These coefficients can be found from an expansion of ψ along a given line in η, ϑ plane.

When μ is an integer or a half-integer then this procedure fails since then, on both sides of the characteristic, one obtains only a power series in $(1 - \xi^3)$. These power series can differ from one another in certain terms. From these deviations one can obtain the difference between the coefficients which for other values of μ were singular, but not the coefficients themselves. This is exactly the very interesting case in which a discontinuity in the curvature, or in a higher derivative of the streamline, is propagated along the characteristic. Also in another respect this case represents an exception. Since the third argument in the first hypergeometric series occurring, for example, in Eq. VII, 4 (7), is a negative integer, a solution cannot be represented in this case by hypergeometric series. The second hypergeometric series occurs in the solution multiplied by $\ln (1 - \xi^3)$. When the singularity approaching the sonic line is characterized only by a discontinuity in a higher derivative, but does not contain a logarithmic term, the solution can for $\xi = 1$ and $\xi > 1$ be represented only by

$$(1 - \xi^3)^{+(1/12)+\mu} F\left(\frac{1}{12} + \mu, \frac{7}{12} + \mu, 1 + 2\mu, (1 - \xi^3)\right)$$

where the coefficients for $\xi < 1$ and for $\xi > 1$ are different. Only the difference between these coefficients is given. The solution is fully determined by the fact that the solution in the physical plane must be joined along the reflected characteristic. Along the reflected characteristic there occur then logarithmic terms; thus a change in the character of the singularity occurs on reflection. Successive reflections result, however, in no further complications.

A necessary condition for the usefulness of such solutions is that their Jacobian must be negative everywhere in the flow field, and thus also along the characteristic $\xi = 1$. The criteria for the sign of the Jacobian are given by the relationships in Section VII, 8. In general one finds that for $\mu > \frac{1}{2}$ the Jacobian is positive along $\xi = 1$. Such solutions are, on their own, without any physical meaning. They become important, however, when superimposed on the solution for $\mu = 5/12$, i.e. $\psi = \eta$. This latter solution is regular at the point O and dominates the singular function.

If μ lies between $\frac{5}{12}$ and $\frac{1}{2}$, and if this solution is superimposed on $\psi = \eta$, then the sign of the Jacobian depends on the coefficients of the singular terms. Only such solutions are of interest, of course, in which no limiting lines occur along the characteristics approaching the sonic line. Otherwise the flow field would be, *a priori*, impossible. GUDERLEY [27] has shown that, even under this restriction, limiting lines can occur in the reflected waves. This means that in the physical plane a shock can occur due to the reflection of an originally harmless singularity at the sonic line.

One may ask next what is the effect of the singularities, discussed here, on the physical plane, for example, on the shape of the streamlines. In accordance with our previous discussions, a solution in which a singularity is propagated along the characteristic $\xi = 1$ is given in general terms by

$$\psi = \text{const}\, \eta + \eta^{-(1/4)+3\mu} \times$$

$$\times \{a_0 + a_1 \Delta\xi + a_2 \Delta\xi^2 + \cdots + \Delta\xi^{2\mu}(b_0 + b_1 \Delta\xi + b_2 \Delta\xi^2 + \cdots)\},$$

where

$$\Delta\xi = \xi - 1. \tag{4}$$

The first term in this expression originates from the solution which predominates at O and which has no singularities. The further terms are due to the particular solutions containing singularities. Even this component of the solution contains a term which has no singularity for $\xi = 1$, the important term is the second part of the curly bracket. A superposition onto these solutions of further "smooth" solutions would not alter anything. Along a streamline $\psi = \text{const.}$ Then, from the last equation η can be expressed as a function of $\Delta\xi$ in the form of a series

$$\eta = \eta_0 + c_1 \Delta\xi + c_2 \Delta\xi^2 + \cdots + c_\nu \Delta\xi^\nu + c'_\nu \Delta\xi^{2\mu} +$$

$$+ c_{\nu+1} \Delta\xi^{\nu+1} + c'_{\nu+1} \Delta\xi^{2\mu+1} + \cdots.$$

Here η_0 and $c_1, c_2 \ldots c'_\nu \ldots$ are suitable constants. The constants $c_1, c_2 \ldots$ result from the non-singular parts of the solution; the primed coefficients derive from the singular components of the solution. ν is the largest integer smaller than 2μ.

We express further ϑ as a function of η, with the aid of Eq. VII, 3 (2)

$$\vartheta = \frac{2}{3}\left(\frac{\eta}{\xi}\right)^{2/3}.$$

With suitable constants $\vartheta_0, d_1, d_2, \ldots$, one obtains then

$$\vartheta = \vartheta_0 + d_1 \Delta \xi + \cdots + d_\nu \Delta \xi^\nu + d'_\nu \Delta \xi^{2\mu} + + d_{\nu+1} \Delta \xi^{\nu+1} + d'_{\nu+1} \Delta \xi^{2\mu+1} + \cdots. \quad (5)$$

The x coordinate can be expressed as a function of $\Delta \xi$, with the aid of Eq. VII, 3 (9). Introducing new constants $x_0, e_1, e_2, \ldots e_\nu \ldots e'_\nu$, one obtains

$$x = x_0 + e_1 \Delta \xi + \cdots + e_\nu \Delta \xi^\nu + e'_\nu \Delta \xi^{2\mu} + + e_{\nu+1} \Delta \xi^{\nu+1} + e'_{\nu+1} \Delta \xi^{2\mu+1} + \cdots. \quad (6)$$

This can be solved for $\Delta \xi$ and, for $\nu \geqslant 1$, one finds

$$\Delta \xi = g_1 \Delta x + \cdots + g_\nu \Delta x^\nu + g'_\nu \Delta x^{2\mu} + \cdots, \quad (7a)$$

while for $\nu = 0$

$$\Delta \xi = \left(\frac{\Delta x}{e'_0}\right)^{\frac{1}{2\mu}} \left(1 - \frac{e_1}{2\mu} (e'_0)^{-\frac{1}{2\mu}} \Delta x^{\frac{1-2\mu}{2\mu}} + \cdots\right). \quad (7b)$$

The second case occurs when the singular term predominates in the vicinity of $\xi = 1$. Introducing the last equations in Eq. (5) one obtains, for $\nu \geqslant 1$,

$$\vartheta = \vartheta_0 + d_1 g_1 \Delta x + \cdots + (d'_\nu g_1^{2\mu} + d_1 g'_\nu) \Delta x^{2\mu} + \cdots, \quad (8a)$$

and for $\nu = 0$

$$\vartheta = \vartheta_0 + \frac{d'_0}{e'_0} - \frac{d'_0}{e'_0} e_1 \left(\frac{\Delta x}{e'_0}\right)^{1/2\mu} + \cdots, \quad (8b)$$

where ϑ denotes the inclination of the streamline. Let $\tilde{y}$ be the deviation of a given streamline from a line $y = \text{const}$

$$\frac{d\tilde{y}}{dx} y = \vartheta,$$

then for $\nu \geqslant 1$ we have

$$\tilde{y} = \tilde{y}_0 + \vartheta_0 x + \frac{1}{2} d_1 g_1 \Delta x_2 + \cdots + (d'_\nu g_1^{2\mu} + d_1 g'_\nu) \frac{\Delta x^{2\mu+1}}{2\mu + 1}, \quad (9a)$$

while for $\nu = 0$

$$\tilde{y} = \tilde{y}_0 + \theta_0 x + \frac{1}{2} \frac{d'_0}{e'_0} \Delta x^2 - \frac{d'_0}{e'_0} \frac{e_1}{(e'_0)^{1/2\mu}} \frac{2\mu}{2\mu + 1} \Delta x^{\frac{2\mu}{2\mu+1}} + \cdots. \quad (9b)$$

In general, μ is a non-integer. The terms containing $\Delta x^{2\mu+1}$ or $\Delta x^{2\mu/(2\mu+1)}$ indicate the effect of the singularity in the hodograph plane on the form of the streamlines. In the range of validity of the first equation, the power of Δx occurring in the description of the singularity decreases with decreasing μ. For $\mu < \frac{1}{2}$ the second equation applies and the power of the term describing the singularity increases with decreasing μ. For $\mu = \frac{1}{2}$ both expressions yield the same power, namely a jump in the curvature. As mentioned before, this represents an exception in which a logarithmic term occurs along the reflected wave. A discussion of the physical plane shows that the strongest singularity which can be propagated in the physical plane along the characteristic is a jump in the curvature. This means that without any further discussion one can expect that, because of the logarithmic singularity, a shock emanates from the sonic line.

If the discontinuity in the boundary streamline, and thus the exponent in the singular solution, are prescribed one obtains two values of μ for the representation of the hodograph solution. To explain this ambiguity we recall the construction of supersonic flows with the aid of the method of characteristics (Section I, 7). We have introduced there the quantities λ and μ. In the present approximation λ can be expressed, apart from the factor $180/\pi$, by

$$\lambda = \eta^{3/2} \frac{1}{3} (\xi^{-3/2} - 1).$$

For small values of $\Delta \xi$ there results

$$\lambda = -\frac{1}{2} \eta^{3/2} \Delta \xi .$$

Thus from Eq. (7a) one obtains

$$\lambda = -\frac{1}{2} \eta_0^{3/2} g_1 \Delta x$$

and correspondingly from Eq. (7b)

$$\lambda = -\frac{1}{2} \eta_0^{3/2} \left(\frac{\Delta x}{e_0'}\right)^{1/2\mu} .$$

The density of MACH lines per unit length of the streamline is then given by

$$\frac{d\lambda}{dx} = -\frac{1}{2} \eta_0^{3/2} g_1$$

or

$$\frac{d\lambda}{dx} = -\frac{1}{2} \eta_0^{3/2} (e_0')^{-\frac{1}{2\mu}} \frac{1}{2\mu} \Delta x^{\frac{1-2\mu}{2\mu}} .$$

In the immediate vicinity of the singular characteristic the first expression is finite and different from zero; the second expression is zero since in that case $\mu < \frac{1}{2}$.

One arrives thus at the following picture of the properties of the flow field: We have found that in a supersonic region embedded in a subsonic flow the waves approaching the sonic line are rarefaction waves while those returning from the sonic line are compression waves. The curvature of the walls must be such that the compression waves, arriving from the sonic line, are converted into rarefaction waves. We consider now a wall, whose tangent direction and curvature are continuous but which at one point has a discontinuity in the terms of higher order. Let this wall occur in various flow fields, so that in the vicinity of the singular point the density of the waves originating at the sonic line can assume different values. If this density of the approaching compression waves is not too large, then the density of the rarefaction waves leaving the wall is different from zero. One obtains then the solution for $\mu > \frac{1}{2}$. If the density of compression waves approaching from the sonic line is just large enough for the density of the emitted rarefaction waves at the singular point to become exactly zero, we have the case of $\mu < \frac{1}{2}$. If the density of the approaching waves increases further, then the wall reflects compression waves which coalesce even before reaching the sonic line and generate a shock, so that in the vicinity of the sonic line a solution of the form described here no longer exists. As mentioned before, it is possible even when $\mu < \frac{1}{2}$ that a reflection of a singularity at the sonic line results in a limiting line, and hence in a shock.

3. The Flow in the Throat of a De Laval Nozzle

We have already met an example of the flow in the throat of a De Laval nozzle. The expansion of the velocity distribution along the axis of the nozzle began there with a term linear in x. One can ask whether there exists a physical reason for this choice of the velocity distribution (Guderley [27])*. We restrict ourselves to nozzles symmetrical with respect to the x axis. The expression for the stream function is then antisymmetric with respect to $\vartheta = 0$ ($\xi = -\infty$) and the term of lowest order in ϱ is, in the hodograph plane, represented by

$$\psi = \varrho^{-(1/2) + \mu} G^{(a)}(\xi, \mu).$$

At the origin ψ must, of course, be finite, i.e. $\mu > \frac{11}{12}$. The behaviour of such solutions along the x axis is given by

$$\eta = \text{const} (\Delta x)^{\frac{1}{(1/2) + 3\mu}}$$

and Eq. VII, 4 (17) represents the solution along the characteristic $\xi = 1$. An application of the criterion of Eq. VII, 8 (5d) shows that for $\mu > \frac{1}{6}$ the solutions are impossible. The solution which we have met previously corresponds to $\mu = \frac{1}{6}$. Solutions for $\mu < \frac{1}{6}$ are also possible, in those, however, the Mach line which reaches the sonic line at the center of the nozzle carries a discontinuity in a higher derivative.

This can be interpreted as follows: If $\mu > \frac{1}{6}$, the pressure would decrease along the axis of the nozzle faster than linearly, this means that at the intersection of the sonic line with the axis of the nozzle the velocity distribution would have a vertical tangent. To obtain such a pressure drop it would be necessary to cause the flow to expand very rapidly. Even the largest curvature of the wall would not be sufficient for this; one would have to generate expansion waves within the flow itself. In the calculation this is expressed by the occurrence of a limiting line. It was shown in Section V, 3 that limiting lines can be interpreted in this manner. Such flow fields are, of course, physically impossible.

If, on the other hand, the pressure drop were slower than linear, i.e. if it took place with a horizontal tangent at the intersection of the sonic line and the axis of the nozzle, one would have to insure that the density of the expansion waves,

* This question was posed by Tollmien.

travelling towards the sonic line, should not tend to O as the limiting characteristic is approached. This requires a special shape of the nozzle wall. Thus the pressure distribution, which is linear in the vicinity of the limiting characteristic, is the only one which can occur in the flow without any special arrangements being made.

Onto the function $\psi_{1/6}$ which from the above appears natural, particular solutions $\psi_{(1/6)+(h/3)}$ may be superimposed. If no discontinuities are propagated along the limiting characteristic, this results, in accordance with Section VII, 13, in a complete representation of the hodograph solution in the vicinity of the origin. Singularities would be expressed by further particular solutions $\psi^{(a)}$.

If the calculation of the DE LAVAL nozzle in the physical plane is carried out on a basis of the complete potential equation, for example with the aid of a series expansion, one begins normally with a linear velocity distribution along the axis. This yields the solution for the flow field corresponding to the expression $\psi_{1/6}$. It will be seen, in such a calculation, that certain parameters can be chosen freely, namely the coefficients of a TAYLOR series for the velocity along the axis. The counterpart of these parameters, in the hodograph plane, are the coefficients of the particular solutions $\psi_{(1/6)+(h/3)}$. This explains the matching procedure to the further boundary conditions, prescribed upstream of the throat in the physical plane. One notices, further, that the series expansion of the solution, obtained by assuming a linear velocity distribution, represents in fact the part of the solution predominant in the vicinity of the throat.

In all these discussions the region downstream of the limiting characteristic was neglected on purpose since there the flow is obtained automatically with the aid of the method of characteristics. To this end the contour of the nozzle must, of course, be known. If this is an analytic continuation of the contour upstream of the limiting characteristic one can employ, of course, simply the continuation of the particular solutions $\psi_{(1/6)+(h/3)}$ past the characteristic $\xi = 1$ in the hodograph plane. Because of the properties of the particular solutions $\psi_{(1/6)+h}$ one obtains then automatically the triple coverage of the hodograph plane, which is to be expected.

Investigations of this kind can, of course, be carried out for other discontinuities occurring along the sonic line. For example, one might consider the points B and C in Fig. 48.

4. Discussion of Special Boundary Value Problems of TRICOMI's Equation

The theory of boundary value problems associated with TRICOMI's equation is not developed as far as one would desire from the point of view of applications. It is therefore very convenient that, with the aid of the particular solutions, special boundary value problems can be treated and the conditions of solubility, as well as the properties of the solutions, can be investigated (GUDERLEY [29]). Such considerations cannot, however, replace the required theorems. The regions in which the particular solutions, discussed so far, can be used with particular advantage are bounded by lines $\xi = \text{const}$ and $\varrho = \text{const}$. One considers, for example, frequently a triangular region bounded by $\varrho = \text{const} = \varrho_0$ and two lines $\xi = \text{const} = c_1$ and $\xi = \text{const} = c_2$. The boundary conditions can be of the first or of the second kind.

In the case of boundary conditions of the first kind, ψ is prescribed along the contour. Transforming the boundary conditions of the second kind [Eq. V, 11 (12)] into the ϱ, ξ system, one obtains

$$9\,\varrho^{7/6}\varphi_\varrho \frac{\xi}{(1-\xi^3)^{7/6}} + \varphi_\xi \frac{(1-\xi^3)^{5/6}}{\varrho^{5/6}} \frac{d\varrho}{d\xi}$$

$$= F_5\left[\varrho^{-1/2}(1-\xi^3)^{-1/2}\frac{d\varrho}{d\xi} + \varrho^{1/2}\frac{3\,\xi^2}{(1-\xi^3)^{3/2}}\right]. \tag{1}$$

Here F_5 is the RHS of Eq. V, 11 (12). If, with the aid of Eq. VII, 3 (5a), one performs integrations similar to those which occurred in connection with Eq. V, 11 (11), there results exactly the RHS of the last equation.

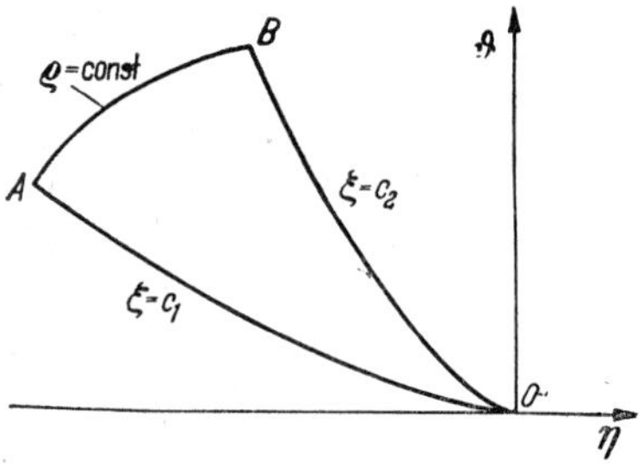

FIG. 107 Subsonic boundary value problem. (According to GUDERLEY [29]).

In accordance with Eq. (1), in the case of boundary conditions of the second kind, φ_ξ is prescribed along a line ξ const and φ_ϱ along a line $\varrho = \text{const}$. No difficulties arise, in principle, when the boundary values are different from zero along the boundaries $\xi = c_1$ and $\xi = c_2$. For the sake of simplicity we shall assume these boundary values, however, to be zero. If c_1 and c_2 are in the subsonic region ($c_1 < c_2 < 0$), as shown in Fig. 107, then one is faced with a purely elliptic boundary value problem. Depending on whether boundary conditions of the first or of the second kind are prescribed along $\xi = c_1$ and $\xi = c_2$, one puts there either $G = 0$ or $G' = 0$ and thus defines systems of functions G through eigenvalue problems. Since, in this case, the sign of the coefficients of G in Eq. VII, 3 (6b) is always negative, the eigenvalue problem yields only positive eigenvalues μ^2. Along the line ϱ, which forms a part of the boundary, one can prescribe either ψ or ψ_ϱ. Let, for $\varrho = \varrho_0$, either

$$\psi = f_1(\xi)$$

or

$$\psi_\varrho = f_2(\xi).$$

Using the notation of Section VII, 9 the solution can be written in the form

$$\psi = \sum_{h=1}^{\infty} a_h \varrho^{-(1/12)+\sqrt{\lambda_h}}\, G_h(\xi).$$

The boundary conditions along $\varrho = \varrho_0$ yield either

$$\sum_{k=1}^{\infty} a_h \varrho_0^{-(1/12)+\sqrt{\lambda_h}}\, G_h(\xi) = f_1(\xi)$$

or

$$\sum_{k=1}^{\infty} a_h \left(-\frac{1}{12} + \sqrt{\lambda_h}\right) \varrho_0^{-(13/12)+\sqrt{\lambda_h}} G_h(\xi) = f_2(\xi).$$

Hence, with the aid of the orthogonality relations of Eqs. VII, 9 (7a) and VII, 9 (8), which are valid also in this case, and when in the lower limit of the integral $-\infty$ is replaced by c_1, one obtains

$$a_h = \left[\int_{c_1}^{c_2} \frac{\xi}{(1-\xi^3)^{7/6}} f_1(\xi)\, G_h(\xi)\, d\xi\right] \left[C_h \varrho_0^{-(1/12)+\sqrt{\lambda_h}}\right]^{-1}$$

or

$$a_h = \left[\int_{c_1}^{c_2} \frac{\xi}{(1-\xi^3)^{7/6}} f_2(\xi)\, G_h(\xi)\, d\xi\right] \left[C_h \varrho_0^{-(13/12)+\sqrt{\lambda_h}} \left(-\frac{1}{12} + \sqrt{\lambda_h}\right)\right]^{-1}.$$

The functions G_h differ, of course, depending on the boundary conditions prescribed along $\xi = c_1$ and $\xi = c_2$. If along these two lines we prescribe the boundary condition $dG/d\xi = 0$, then one of the eigenvalues is $\sqrt{\lambda} = \frac{1}{12}$ and the corresponding eigenfunction is $G = 1$. The appropriate particular solutions are

$$\psi = 1$$

and

$$\psi = \varrho^{-1/6}.$$

If the value of ψ is prescribed along $\varrho = \varrho_0$ this offers no difficulties. If, on the other hand, ψ_ϱ is given then the particular solution $\psi = 1$, which is regular at the origin, provides no contribution to ψ_ϱ. In this case, therefore, the entire orthogonal system is no longer available for the purpose of satisfying the prescribed boundary conditions along $\varrho = \varrho_0$; the function $G = 1$ is missing. Boundary conditions of the second kind can only be satisfied when

$$\int_{c_1}^{c_2} f_2(\xi) \frac{\xi}{(1-\xi^3)^{7/6}} d\xi = 0.$$

This is another form of the condition given by Eq. V, 11 (11), which we have established previously in the discussion of the boundary value problem of the second kind.

It is not possible to prescribe both ψ and ψ_ϱ arbitrarily along the line $\varrho = \varrho_0$. Of course, one could assume a solution in the form

$$\psi = \sum_{h=1}^{\infty} \left(a_h \varrho^{-(1/12)+\sqrt{\lambda_h}} + b_h \varrho^{-(1/12)-\sqrt{\lambda_h}}\right) G_h(\xi)$$

and calculate the coefficients a_h and b_h formally. Since, however, the particular solutions $\varrho^{-(1/12)-\sqrt{\lambda_h}}$ tend to infinity when the origin is approached, and this the faster, the larger λ_h, this series can only converge when the coefficients decrease sufficiently fast. This cannot, in general, be expected to be the case (cf. p. 21).

Next let us consider a hyperbolic boundary value problem ($0 < c_1 < c_2 < 1$). This problem is properly formulated when it can be solved with the aid of the method of characteristics. This, however, is the case when both ψ and ψ_ϱ are prescribed along $\varrho = \varrho_0$, namely

$$\psi = f_1(\xi),$$
$$\psi_\varrho = f_2(\xi)$$

and, in addition, when along the lines $\xi = c_1$ and $\xi = c_2$ one prescribes either $\psi = 0$ or $\psi_\xi = 0$. Again a classical eigenvalue problem results for the functions G and determines a complete orthogonal system of these functions. In accordance with Section VII, 9, in this case $\lambda < \frac{1}{12}$. A solution in the form

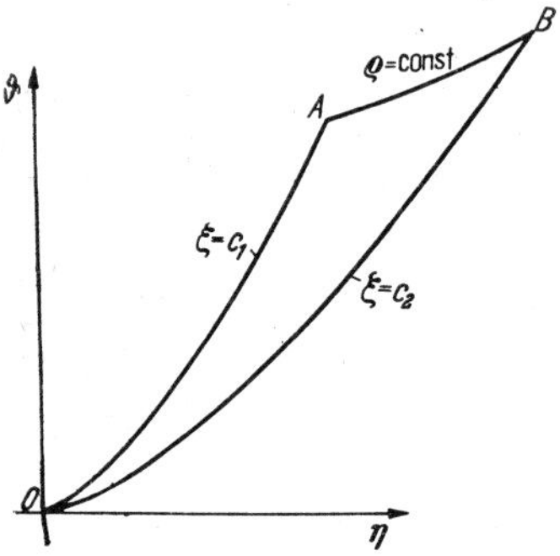

FIG. 108 Supersonic boundary value problem. (According to GUDERLEY [29]).

$$\psi = \varrho^{-1/12} \sum_{h=1}^{\infty} \{a_h \cos[\sqrt{-\lambda_h} \log \varrho] + $$
$$+ b_h \sin[\sqrt{-\lambda_h} \log \varrho]\} G_{-h}(\xi) \qquad (2)$$

utilises the entire system of particular solutions which can be constructed with the aid of the eigenfunctions. Since along a line $\xi =$ const these functions are, except for a factor $\varrho^{-1/12}$, trigonometric functions of ln ϱ, no convergence problems of the kind occurring in subsonic flow occur in this case. The coefficients a_h and b_h can be determined without difficulty using the orthogonality relations.

The factor $\varrho^{-1/12}$, which occurs here in connection with each particular solution, is noteworthy. Because of it, all particular solutions become infinite at the origin. One may ask if this is also true of the complete solution. In special cases in which the summations in Eq. (2) contain only finite numbers of terms, this can be seen immediately to be the case, since, because of the orthogonality relations, the individual functions cannot cancel one another.

For more general cases one can conclude with the following. Along each line $\varrho =$ const, a given solution ψ can be expressed by a superposition of the eigenfunctions G whose coefficients are obtained with the aid of the orthogonality relations. They are expressed as integrals containing the values of ψ along the particular line $\varrho =$ const and, in each case, one of the functions G. If ψ is bounded and $c_2 < 1$, then these integrals are bounded, and hence also the above coefficients of the functions G are bounded. On the other hand, the solution given by Eq. (2), which represents also an expansion of in terms of G along each line $\varrho =$ const, indicates that the coefficients of G in the vicinity of $\varrho = 0$ are not bounded. It follows from this that the original assumption of ψ being bounded in the vicinity of O is not correct.

In this discussion it was necessary to assume $c_2 < 1$. The case of $c_2 = 1$ affords an exception inasmuch as it would then be improper, in a construction using the method of characteristics, to prescribe a boundary condition along $\xi = c_2 = 1$.

The example shown in Fig. 109 leads to a deeper understanding of the transition to the limit $c_2 \to 1$. Let $\psi = 0$ be prescribed along the sonic line and, further, let ψ be given along a characteristic AC. Thus, as may be seen from the method of characteristics, the solution in the region ACD is determined. If the boundary values of ψ at the point C show no singularity, the solution at the point D is not singular, since the point C is no different from any other point of the characteristic AC. Let us now assume, for the sake of simplicity, that $\psi = 0$ at the point C. The solution can then also be obtained by the following calculation. We choose, in Fig. 110, the origin of the η, ϑ system on the sonic line, below D, and draw a line $\xi = \text{const}$ through the point C and a line $\varrho = \text{const}$ through the point A. Along the line OCB we prescribe $\psi = 0$. Now in the region ACB one can construct a function satisfying TRICOMI's equation, which along AC has the prescribed values of ψ and for which along CB $\psi = 0$. This function and its derivative with respect to ϱ have, along AB, values designated by $f_1(\xi)$ and

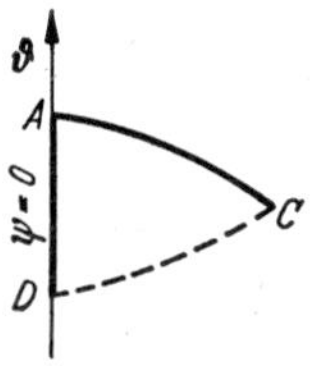

FIG. 110

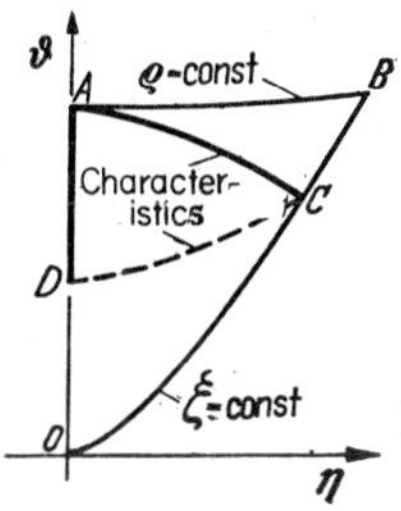

FIG. 109

$f_2(\xi)$, respectively. Let us now reverse the procedure and construct, with the aid of the method discussed in the preceding example, a solution which satisfies the condition $\psi = 0$ along AD and OB and which, along AB, has the values $\psi = f_1(\xi)$ and $\psi_\varrho = f_2(\xi)$. This solution is then equivalent to that which we have just obtained by the method of characteristics because of the uniqueness of the boundary value problems in the region ABC. Thus the solution assumes along AC the values of ψ prescribed originally. Further, it satisfies along $\xi = 0$ the original boundary condition $\psi = 0$ and thus represents, in the region ADC, the required solution which is determined by the data prescribed along AD and AC. This solution is certainly not identically equal to zero along DC since then, because of the condition $\psi = 0$ prescribed along AD, it would vanish identically in the entire region ADC.

This behaviour does not change when the origin is allowed to approach D; in particular the solution in the region ACD remains the same. In any case, in the vicinity of the point O, the value of ψ increases without limit and, further, in the triangle DCO the decrease in the values of ψ, resulting along DC, leads to zero along the line OC. If O coincides with D one obtains a jump in the value of ψ which can be interpreted as a lost solution similarly as in Section V, 10. This explains why the boundary values prescribed along $\xi = c_2$ have no influence on the solution in the limiting case of $c_2 \to 1$. The real character of the solution is shown by the transformations indicated in Section VII, 13.

This discussion forms a preparation for the mixed boundary value problem. Particularly interesting is the case in which the contour in the supersonic region is closed, contrary to TRICOMI's problem. Let the contour be given in the subsonic region by a line $\varrho = \text{const} = \varrho_0$ and by a line $\xi = c_1 = -\infty$ (Fig. 111). Let, further, the contour in the supersonic region be given by a line $\xi = c_2$ and by one of the characteristics passing through the point of intersection of the line $\varrho = \varrho_0$ and the sonic line. Let ψ be given along the line ABC and, further, let $\psi = 0$ be prescribed along the lines $\xi = c_1 = -\infty$ and $\xi = c_2$. The discussion is almost exactly the same as that for the boundary value problem of the second kind. The formulation of this problem deviates from that of TRICOMI's problem

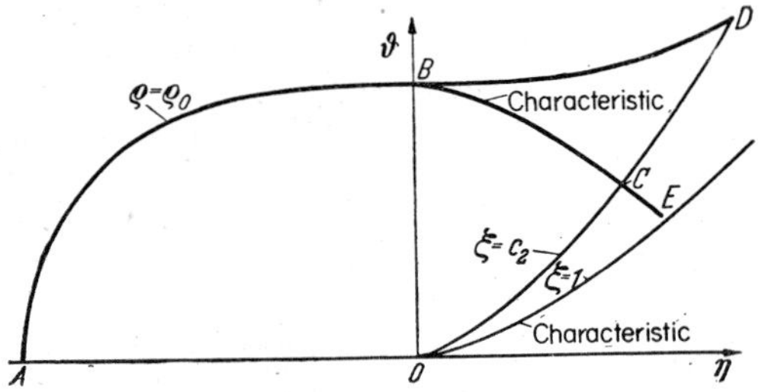

FIG. 111 Mixed boundary value problem. (According to GUDERLEY (29]).

inasmuch as the boundary does not contain the gap characteristic of TRICOMI's problem. One would suppose then that a solution exists only when certain conditions, imposed on TRICOMI's solutions, are omitted. We shall see that we must allow the solution to become singular, in a definite manner, at one of the points of intersection with the sonic line.

To obtain a boundary value problem in which the contour is described only by lines $\xi = \text{const}$ and $\varrho = \text{const}$ we extend the line $\varrho = \varrho_0$ into the supersonic region, up to an intersection with the line $\xi = c_2$. It is assumed that at the point C ψ is equal to O. We prescribe $\psi = 0$ along CD. It is then possible (as in the preceding example) to construct a function ψ, in the region BCD, from the values prescribed along the characteristic BC and along the line CD. The boundary condition along BC can be replaced by the values of ψ and ψ_ϱ, obtained from this construction along BD, and by the condition $\psi = 0$ along CD. We assume the solution to have the form

$$\psi = \sum_{h=1}^{\infty} a_h \left(\frac{\varrho}{\varrho_0}\right)^{-(1/12)+\sqrt{\lambda_h}} G_h(\xi) +$$

$$+ \sum_{h=1}^{\infty} \left(\frac{\varrho}{\varrho_0}\right)^{-1/12} \left(b_h \sin\left[\sqrt{-\lambda_h}\ln\frac{\varrho}{\varrho_0}\right] + c_h \cos\left[\sqrt{-\lambda_h}\ln\frac{\varrho}{\varrho_0}\right]\right) G_{-h}(\xi).$$

It contains all the particular solutions resulting from negative eigenvalues, as well as those solutions corresponding to positive eigenvalues, which tend to zero at the origin. If a solution of the above problem, which at the origin does not increase to infinity faster than $\varrho^{-1/12}$, exists at all, it must, in accordance with

Section VII, 10, be of this form. The particular solutions $(\varrho/\varrho_0)^{-(1/12)+\sqrt{\lambda_h}}G_h(\xi)$ and $(\varrho/\varrho_0)^{-1/12}\cos\left[\sqrt{(-\lambda_h)}\ln(\varrho/\varrho_0)\right]G_{-h}(\xi)$ assume along $\varrho=\varrho_0$ exactly the form $G_h(\xi)$ and $G_{-h}(\xi)$, so that a complete orthogonal system is available in order to satisfy the boundary condition for ψ along this line. With the aid of Eq. VII, 9 (7a) one can obtain explicit expressions for the coefficients a_h and c_h. The coefficients b_h must be chosen in such a way that the values of ψ_ϱ, prescribed along $\varrho=\varrho_0$ are, for $0<\xi<c_2$ correctly represented. No simple procedure leading to this result is known. One could, for example, satisfy the boundary conditions point by point or choose the coefficients b_h in such a manner that the mean error in the boundary values is held to a minimum. In any case the following is important; whatever the values obtained for the coefficients b_h, the fact that the coefficients c_h are, in general, different from O is sufficient to show that the solutions must become infinite at the origin. The argument leading to this conclusion follows the lines employed in the supersonic example.

This example shows what would be expected if a boundary value problem is formulated in an "improper" manner, i.e. with a closed contour in the supersonic region. The importance of this problem lies in the fact that the physical boundary value problem, occurring in a subsonic flow with an embedded supersonic region, is just of this mathematically improper form. This is a problem of considerable theoretical interest. Although, in the author's opinion, it may be considered resolved, its uniform comprehension is not, however, as yet general. The fundamental concepts together with their physical interpretations can be found in an article by GUDERLEY [34]. A new contribution of decisive importance is due to MORAWETZ [63]. A complete discussion of this problem must be left out because of space limitations. (cf. also FRANKL [16]).

The fact that the contour in the hodograph has an infinite curvature at the origin could be construed as a defect of the above example; one might even be inclined to consider this to be the reason for the solutions becoming infinite. The behaviour of particular solutions for contours which do not have this special feature has been discussed in an article by BUSEMANN and GUDERLEY [5] and in a further article by GUDERLEY [25], without, however, a proof of convergence which would be necessary to make such an analysis completely conclusive. Corresponding singularities are obtained in such cases.

If c_2 is allowed to tend to 1, one would expect a transition to TRICOMI's problem which is analogous to the example of purely supersonic flow. The details of this are, however, difficult to follow since the solution in the region CEO influences the subsonic solution and thus, indirectly, also the region BCO. For $c_2=1$ a singularity occurs at the origin. The discussion of Section VII, 13 shows how this can occur, in spite of the fact that at the origin the particular solutions for negative eigenvalues tend to infinity as $\varrho^{-1/12}$.

The uniqueness of the flow with $M=1$ requires the solution of the boundary value problem of the second kind, even for a contour of TRICOMI's type, to be subject to an additional condition (cf. p. 239). In an article by GUDERLEY [29] an attempt is made to discover the nature of this condition with the aid of examples of a similar type.

CHAPTER XI

AXISYMMETRIC FLOWS

SOME ofour investigations of two-dimensional flows can be extended to axisymmetric problems. This is of considerable practical interest, for example, with regard to missiles or supersonic aircraft which approximate much more closely bodies of revolution than two-dimensional bodies. The concern with axisymmetric flows is important also for another reason; one is inclined to extend results obtained for two-dimensional flows to bodies of other forms. This can, however, be misleading. In a linearised treatment of transonic flow we have found that the difficulties characteristic of such a flow are much less pronounced in the axisymmetric than the two-dimensional case. An even incomplete knowledge of axisymmetric flows would warn against incorrect analogies.

1. Flows with $M = 1$

The hodograph method, which in two-dimensional flow leads to a linearised equation, no longer offers this advantage in an axisymmetric case. To find a form of the solution which would describe the behaviour of an axisymmetric flow at infinity, one may be guided by the example of two-dimensional flow. There, in Eq. VIII, 2 (3), we have found that the line ξ = const maps into a generalised parabola. Along such a parabola y is proportional to $\varrho^{-5/6}$. In accordance with Eqs. V, 7 (7) and VIII, 2 (1), the transformed potential is along the line ξ = const proportional to $\varrho^{-1/3}$. The same is also true of the potential in the physical plane. It can therefore be represented by

$$\Phi = y^{2/5} f\left(\frac{x}{y^{4/5}}\right).$$

More generally one can assume the form (GUDERLEY and YOSHIHARA [44])

$$\Phi = y^m f(\zeta, n), \tag{1}$$

with

$$\zeta = (\gamma + 1)^{-1/3} \frac{x}{y^n}. \tag{1a}$$

Here m and n are constants and in the course of the calculation one finds

$$m = 3n - 2. \tag{1b}$$

The factor $(\gamma + 1)^{-1/3}$ was introduced in the expression for ζ to make the equation for f free of γ. The form of Eq. (1) is suitable also for axisymmetric flows, when the distance from the x axis is denoted by y. This distance was previously denoted by r.

Without reference to our understanding of two-dimensional flows, the form of Eq. (1) can be justified as follows. One may assume that the potential varies with some power of the distance when infinity is approached in the physical plane. It is important, however, in this connection, along which line in the physical plane one approaches infinity. It is easy to see that one is led to trivial solutions when infinity is approached along straight lines. The next attempt would be to approach infinity along the generalised parabolas. This leads to Eq. (1). The flows discussed in Chapter IV are, incidentally, of just this form.

Equation (1) can be introduced into the transonic approximation to the axisymmetrical potential equation, Eq. II, 8 (2). The same result is obtained if Eq. (1) is substituted in the exact potential equation and only the higher powers of y are retained in the latter. In order to obtain an ordinary differential equation for f Eq. (1b) must be valid. In the axisymmetric case one obtains

$$(f' - n^2\zeta^2)\, f'' + (5n - 4)\, n\zeta f' - (3n - 2)^2 f = 0. \tag{2}$$

With n given, the solutions of this equation can be obtained numerically. It is desirable, however, to obtain a picture of the manifold of solutions in advance, particularly since the differential equation of flow contains a non-linear term and the singularities of the solution are therefore not known *a priori*. Dimensional analysis shows that when the scale of measurement of ζ and the scale of measurement of f are respectively multiplied by C and C^3, the differential equation remains unchanged. This points to the fact that the flow field transforms into itself when a similarity transformation is performed simultaneously with a change of scale in the physical plane. If a function $f = g(\xi)$ is a solution of Eq. (2) then

$$f = C^3\, g(\zeta C) \tag{3}$$

is also a solution.

If a solution has this property of invariance with respect to such a group of transformations then its order can be reduced by one. This reduction is affected by the introduction of a new variable, such that the free constant C cancels*. Thus we introduce

$$s = \zeta^{-3} f, \tag{4a}$$

$$t = \zeta^{-2} f'. \tag{4b}$$

Hence

$$\frac{dt}{d\zeta} = -2\zeta^{-3} f' + \zeta^{-2} f'' = \zeta^{-1}(-2t + \zeta^{-1} f''), \tag{5a}$$

$$\frac{ds}{d\zeta} = -3\zeta^{-4} f + \zeta^{-3} f' = \zeta^{-1}(t - 3s). \tag{5b}$$

* C in Eq. (3) can be interpreted as a constant of integration occurring in the solution of Eq. (2). Since, with the introduction of the new variable, this constant of integration no longer appears, one expects that the differential equation, in terms of the new variable yields one less integration constant, i.e. that its order was reduced by 1.

and one obtains

$$f'' = \zeta \left[\frac{dt}{ds} (t - 3s) + 2t \right].$$

Then Eq. (2) yields

$$\frac{dt}{ds} = \frac{2t^2 + (3n - 4)\, nt - (3n - 2)^2 s}{(n^2 - t)\,(t - 3s)}, \tag{6}$$

and ζ can be calculated from Eq. (5b).

Equation (6) offers no advantages in a numerical treatment of the problem, on the contrary, the relationship between the variables t and s and the quantities

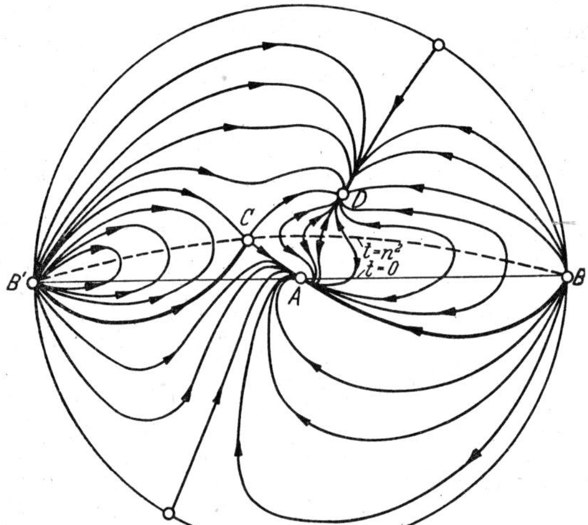

FIG. 112 The manifold of solutions in the s, t plane for $n = 4/7$. Arrows show direction of increasing values of $|\zeta|$. (According to GUDERLEY and YOSHIHARA [44]).

of physical interest is much less lucid than in Eq. (2). On the other hand, since Eq. (6) is of the first order, the behaviour of the solution curves can be easily deduced. The general behaviour of these solutions is shown in Fig. 112. It is obtained by finding a family of integral curves in the s, t plane using the directions prescribed by the differential equation. To include also the infinity of the s, t plane, the latter is projected onto a hemisphere with the center of the sphere as the center of projection. Thus the entire s, t plane transforms into the northern hemisphere while infinity transforms into the equator. Finally this hemisphere is deformed into a circle. Only the qualitative behaviour of the integral curves is important.

The sonic line in the s, t plane is given by $t = 0$ in view of Eqs. (4b) and (1). The line $t = n^2$ is also of importance. On it the coefficient of f'' in Eq. (2) vanishes. In accordance with Eq. (6) together with Eq. (5b), ζ has an extremum when an integral curve intercepts the line $t = n^2$. If one moves along an integral curve in a suitable direction, ζ decreases, until this line is reached, and then increases again. Thus the lines $\zeta =$ const initially sweep a part of the physical plane up to an extreme value of ζ and then cover the same region of the physical plane a second time. This is an example of occurrence of limiting lines in axisymmetric flows. According to the sign of the pressure change at the limiting line the latter represents either a coalescence of pressure waves, which are due to the boundary conditions of the problem, or it is formed by fanning out rarefaction waves. The first case requires the formation of a compression shock while the second cannot be realised physically.

Further the singular points of the direction field, in which ds/dt is indeterminate, are important. At those points both the numerator and the denominator on the RHS of Eq. (6) vanish simultaneously. As long as these points are not at infinity, one finds for their coordinates

Point A $$s = 0, \quad t = 0,$$

Point C $$s = n^3 \frac{(5n - 4)}{(3n - 2)^2}, \qquad t = n^2,$$

Point D $$s = \frac{2}{9}, \qquad t = \frac{2}{3}.$$

To determine the character of the solutions in the vicinity of these points the numerator and the denominator in Eq. (6) are linearised in the vicinity of the appropriate point. For example in the vicinity of C one obtains

$$\frac{dt}{ds} = \frac{(3n - 2)^2 [\Delta t (7n^2 - 4n) - \Delta s (3n - 2)^2]}{\Delta t (6n^4 - 4n^2)},$$

where

$$\Delta t = t - n^2,$$

$$\Delta s = s - n^3 \frac{(5n - 4)}{(3n - 2)^2}.$$

Since this equation was obtained by linearisation, it is homogeneous (i.e. it is again invariant with respect to a group of transformations) and can, therefore, be integrated. One obtains in this manner the integral curves in the immediate vicinity of a singular point. The details of this calculation will not be considered here. Only two integral curves pass through the point C while all the other curves show a hyperbolic-type behaviour. For the directions of the two special integral curves, one obtains either by the above method or by direct substitution

$$\frac{dt}{ds} = \frac{\Delta t}{\Delta s}.$$

For $t = n^2$ Eq. (4) yields

$$f' = n^2 \zeta^2.$$

Since, as a result of Eqs. (1) and (1a),

$$\Phi_x = (\gamma + 1)^{-1/3}\, y^{2n-2} f'(\zeta), \tag{7}$$

one obtains

$$\Phi_x = (\gamma + 1)^{-1/3}\, y^{2n-2}\, n^2 \zeta^2. \tag{8}$$

The slope of the line $\zeta =$ const is, in general,

$$\frac{dx}{dy} = n\zeta(\gamma + 1)^{-1/3}\, y^{n-1}.$$

Hence for $t = n^2$

$$\frac{dx}{dy} = (\gamma + 1)^{1/2}\sqrt{\Phi_x}\,.$$

In accordance with Eq. I, 6 (10), this is the slope of a characteristic; thus all the lines $\zeta =$ const corresponding to points on the line $t = n^2$ have the slope of a characteristic.

The second condition

$$s = n^3\,\frac{(5n - 4)}{(3n - 2)^2} \tag{9}$$

for the singular point B represents a compatibility condition for a characteristic, Eq. I, 6 (11), i.e.

$$-\frac{dx}{dy}\,\frac{d\Phi_x}{dy} + \frac{d\Phi_y}{dy} + \frac{\Phi_y}{y} = 0. \tag{10}$$

To show this we use Eqs. (7) and (8), as well as

$$\Phi_y = y^{3n-3}\,[(3n - 2)\, f - n\zeta f'].$$

For $\zeta =$ const one obtains

$$\frac{d\Phi_x}{dy} = (2n - 2)\, y^{2n-3} f'(\zeta)\,(\gamma + 1)^{-1/3},$$

$$\frac{d\Phi_y}{dy} = (3n - 3)\, y^{3n-3}\,[(3n - 2)\, f - n\zeta f')].$$

Introducing this in Eq. (10), and taking Eq. (4) into account, one obtains Eq. (9).

Thus the line $\zeta =$ const, corresponding to the point C, is a characteristic and, in particular, it is a limiting characteristic such as we have already encountered in two-dimensional flows. Since only the special integral curves reach the point C, it appears advisable to start the integration of the differential equations (6) or (2) at the limiting characteristic.

To determine the slopes of the integral curves at $t = 0$, $s = 0$ one puts

$$\frac{dt}{ds} = \frac{t}{s}.$$

From this

$$\frac{t}{s} = \frac{3n-2}{n},$$

which indicates the desirability of introducing a new variable u, in order to facilitate the determination of the solution in the vicinity of this point. This new variable is given by

$$u = t - \frac{3n-2}{n} s$$

or

$$t = u + \frac{3n-2}{n} s. \tag{11}$$

Hence

$$\frac{dt}{ds} = \frac{du}{ds} + \frac{3n-2}{n}.$$

Retaining only terms of first order in both the numerator and the denominator of Eq. (6)

$$\frac{du}{ds} = \frac{2u}{2s - un}$$

and hence

$$s = -\frac{n}{2} u \ln (C_1 u) \tag{12}$$

and

$$u = 0. \tag{12a}$$

Here C_1 denotes a constant of integration. From Eq. (5b) there results

$$\ln \zeta = \int \frac{ds}{t - 3s} = -\frac{n}{2} \int \frac{d[u \ln (C_1 u)]}{u - \frac{2}{n} s} = -\frac{n}{2} \int \frac{d[u \ln (C_1 u)]}{u + u \ln (C_1 u)},$$

and hence

$$\zeta = \text{const}\, u^{-n/2}. \tag{13}$$

Thus further

$$\begin{aligned} \Phi_y &= y^{3n-3} [(3n-2) f - n\zeta f'] \\ &= y^{3n-3} \zeta^3 [(3n-2) s - nt] = -y^{3n-3} \zeta^3 n u. \end{aligned} \tag{14}$$

Upon substitution from Eq. (13) there results

$$\Phi_y = \text{const}\, y^{3n-3} \zeta^{3-(2/n)}$$

and hence, finally, with the aid of Eq. (1a)

$$\Phi_y = \text{const}\, y^{-1} x^{3-(2/n)}.$$

This means that in this solution the x axis is covered with singularities. In a similar manner one obtains also Φ_x.

The solution given by Eq. (12a) is exceptional in that it represents the case, from the physical point of view particularly interesting, in which the x axis is free of singularities. From Eqs. (12a) and (14) one obtains namely

$$\Phi_y = 0.$$

A complete discussion of the integral curves must include also their behaviour at infinity. In this respect the reader is referred, however, to the original article. It is shown there that the straight line at infinity (the equator in the projection onto a sphere) also represents an integral curve along which some singular points occur. Points lying on the equator and on the same diameter should be identified with one another (the points B and B' are thus equivalent). They represent the y axis of the physical plane. Within the physical plane the y axis is of no special importance. The fact that the corresponding point in the s, t plane is singular is due to the choice of the variables s and t.

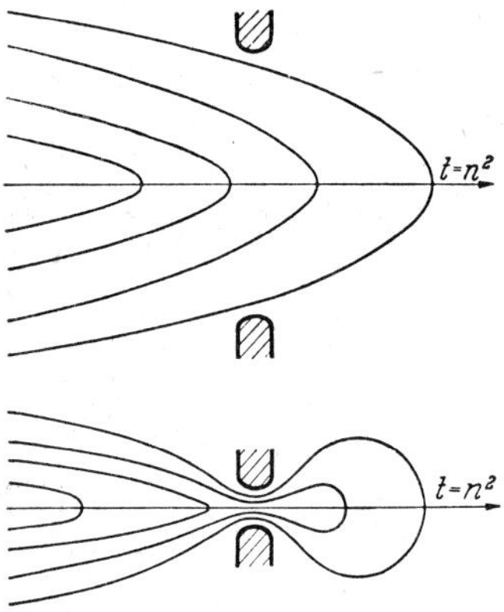

Fig 113 Illustrating the behaviour of the solution curves in the vicinity of the points B or B' in Fig. 112.

If t is expressed in terms of Φ_x, x and y, one finds that at the point B $t = 0$. The behaviour of an integral curve passing through the point B in the s, t plane and in the vicinity of that point can be deduced from Eq. (4) in conjunction with Eq. (1a). At B, as at any other point, Φ and Φ_x are continuous so that only a change in the sign of s occurs.

The behaviour of the manifold of solutions in the neighborhood of B is explained by the fact that in the physical plane some solutions reach a limiting line ($t = n^2$) before the region swept by curves $\zeta = \text{const}$ can extend to the y axis. These solutions never reach the point B. For other solutions the y axis belongs to their region of validity and then it occurs twice. Thus the point B appears twice on the corresponding integral curve. The upper half of Fig. 113 shows a family of curves for which s has a maximum along the straight line corresponding to $t = n^2$. Let this family of curves be contracted at a given point, whose counterpart in Fig. 112 is B or B', without altering the relative location of the curves. This yields the lower half of Fig. 113. The behaviour of the integral curves in the vicinity of B and B' corresponds exactly to the sketch, to the left of the restriction in Fig. 113 one obtains the field of the vicinity of B, while to the right of the restriction the field in the vicinity of B'. The structure of the manifold of solutions in the vicinity of B is therefore not as surprising as it appeared originally.

We can now describe the desired solution for a flow with $M = 1$ in general terms. The point A corresponds to the x axis. Upstream of the immersed body one expects a subsonic velocity and along the x axis no sources can occur. Therefore at the point A one must employ the solution curve which proceeds towards negative values of t and whose beginning is described by Eq. (12a). The subsequent behaviour of the solutions depends on the value of n. All the solutions, sooner or later, cross the sonic line and a class of them subsequently reaches the line $t = n^2$, i.e. a limiting line occurs. Such solutions are of no use. For another class of solutions, i.e. of values of n, the line $t = n^2$ is never reached; the solutions pass the point C in Fig. 112 and terminate at A, approaching from the supersonic side. Solutions of this kind cover the entire physical plane from the negative to the positive axis. The positive axis is covered with sources, i.e. one obtains the flow past a semi-infinite body. Similar flow fields for the two-dimensional case were discussed in Section VIII, 5. The transition between the two classes of solutions occurs at a definite value of n. At this value the integral curve passes exactly through C. This is the desired solution with a limiting characteristic.

To find this solution it is necessary to determine the integral curves which originate at both A and C for various values of n.

As indicated already, the calculation is carried out with the aid of Eq. (2). This equation is solved once starting from the x axis and again starting from the limiting characteristic. It would be a pure coincidence if the constant C, occurring in Eq. (3), was the same for both these calculations. To prove the agreement between the two solutions it is best to eliminate C by introducing the variables t and s and then determining n such that for a given value of s the two solutions yield the same value of t.

This calculation was performed by GUDERLEY and YOSHIHARA [44] and was recently checked very accurately by GERTRUDE BLANCH. As a result, the value of $n = 4/7$ was obtained with a great degree of accuracy. The results are shown in Table 2 and also in Fig. 119. Except for the scale, which of course depends on the size of the body, the flow at infinity is described by these results. The figure contains further information regarding the flow. This will be discussed in Section XI, 5. For the limiting characteristic one can always choose the value $\zeta = 1$. The first terms of an expansion of f at the point $\zeta = 1$ are then, for $n = 4/7$, given by

$$f = \frac{-128}{49} + \frac{16}{49}(\zeta - 1) + \frac{36}{49}(\zeta - 1)^2 + \cdots . \tag{15}$$

The calculation of the behaviour at infinity forms only the first step in the determination of a real flow field*. To obtain a result which corresponds, at least approximately, to a practical problem one has to calculate the flow field in the vicinity of an immersed body. Whether the shape of this body is prescribed or whether it is obtained first in the course of the calculation, is of little importance. For a body of revolution the problem is rather difficult because the differential equation of flow is not linear and cannot, as in the case of two-dimensional flow, be linearised by a hodograph transformation.

YOSHIHARA [86] has calculated the flow past a cone-cylinder combination using relaxation methods.

* This step is, however, of great importance. It is shown on p. 47 that the difficulties of the linearised theory, i.e. the fact that the pressures become infinite at the body, originate at infinity.

2. An Improved Analysis of the Solution at Infinity

The body appropriate to the solution of the preceding section is always represented by a singularity on the x axis. In the solution for the flow past a body of finite dimensions there occur, just as in the corresponding two-dimensional case, further terms which describe the changes due to the presence of such a body. These additional solutions will be discussed in the following paragraphs (GUDERLEY (28]).

To this end we consider the deviations of the actual solution from the expressions obtained in the preceding section to be small and neglect the higher powers of these deviations in the differential equation of the flow. Let the potential be given by

$$\Phi = \Phi_0(x, y) + \overline{\Phi}(x, y). \tag{1}$$

The term $\Phi_0(x, y)$ represents the function given by Eq. XI, 1 (1) and $\overline{\Phi}(x, y)$ represents the deviation caused by the presence of the body. Equation (1) is introduced into the differential equation of transonic flow. Neglecting terms of higher order, one obtains the following linear differential equation for $\overline{\Phi}$

$$-(\gamma + 1)(\Phi_{0x}\overline{\Phi}_{xx} + \Phi_{0xx}\overline{\Phi}_{x}) + \overline{\Phi}_{yy} + \frac{\overline{\Phi}_y}{y} = 0. \tag{2}$$

Particular solutions of this equation are obtained by putting

$$\overline{\Phi} = y^{\nu} g(\zeta, \nu), \tag{3}$$

which leads to the ordinary differential equation

$$(f' - n^2\zeta^2)\, g'' + [f'' + (2\nu n - n^2)\,\zeta]\, g' - \nu^2 g = 0. \tag{4}$$

As in the corresponding two-dimensional problem, the question of completeness of a system of such particular solutions has to be resolved. Fortunately this differential equation can also be reduced to a form of an eigenvalue problem, so that all the arguments offered in connection of the two-dimensional problem can be applied. Introducing namely

$$g(\zeta, \nu) = h(\zeta)^{\nu}\, G(\zeta, \nu), \tag{5}$$

where h is determined by the differential equation

$$\frac{h'}{h} = -\frac{n\zeta}{f' - n^2\zeta^2} \tag{6}$$

one obtains the following equation for G

$$(f' - n^2\zeta^2)\, G'' + (f'' - n^2\zeta)\, G' - \lambda \frac{f'}{f' - n^2\zeta^2}\, G = 0. \tag{7}$$

Here

$$\lambda = \nu^2 + n\nu. \tag{7a}$$

The self-adjoint form of this equation is

$$\frac{d}{d\zeta}\left(\frac{f' - n^2\zeta^2}{h^n} G'\right) - \lambda \frac{f'}{h^n (f' - n^2\zeta^2)} G = 0. \tag{8}$$

Using Eq. (5) we can write Eq. (3) in the form

$$\varphi = \varrho^\nu G(\zeta, \nu), \tag{9}$$

where

$$\varrho = y h(\zeta). \tag{9a}$$

The particular solutions may be considered referred to a ϱ, ζ system of coordinates (Fig. 114).

The singular points of Eq. (8) are $\zeta = \pm\infty$ (the x axis) and the value of ζ at which $f' - n^2\zeta^2 = 0$ (the limiting characteristic). It may be assumed that for

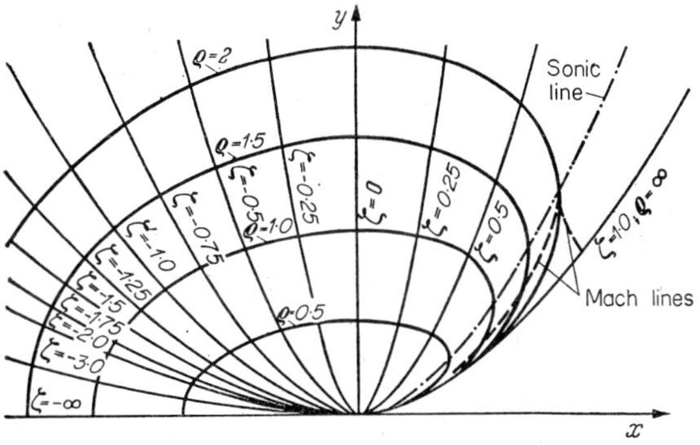

Fig. 114 The ϱ, ζ system of coordinates in the x, y plane for axisymmetric flows. (According to Guderley [28]).

the limiting characteristic $\zeta = 1$. The form of the solutions G at the point $\zeta = 1$ will be determined next. To this end one expands the coefficients of G', G'', and G in terms of $\zeta - 1$ in Eq. (7) and retains in each case the first term only. This yields

$$(\zeta - 1)(f''(1) - 2n^2) G'' + (f'(1) - n^2) G' - \lambda \frac{f'(1)}{(f''(1) - 2n^2)(\zeta - 1)} G = 0.$$

[$f'(1)$ or $f'(1)$ means of course f' or f'' at $\zeta = 1$]. Hence at $\zeta = 1$ one obtains for the first terms of an expansion of G

$$G = (\zeta - 1)^{\frac{1}{f''(1) - 2n^2}\left\{-\frac{n^2}{2} \pm n\sqrt{\frac{n^2}{4} + \lambda}\right\}} P(\zeta - 1). \tag{10}$$

The corresponding expansions for g [Eq. (4)] are of the form

$$g = P(\zeta - 1) \qquad \text{and} \qquad g_{\pm} = (\zeta - 1)^{\frac{2}{f''(1) - 2n^2}\sqrt{\frac{n^2}{4} + \lambda}} P(\zeta - 1). \tag{10a}$$

With the aid of Eqs. XI, 1 (15) and (7a) this can be reduced to the form

$$G = (\zeta - 1)^{-\frac{1}{5} \pm \frac{7}{10}\left(\nu + \frac{2}{7}\right)} P(\zeta - 1) \tag{11}$$

or

$$G = (\zeta - 1)^{\frac{7}{10}\nu} P(\zeta - 1) \tag{11a}$$

and

$$G = (\zeta - 1)^{-\frac{2}{5} - \frac{7}{10}\nu} P(\zeta - 1). \tag{11b}$$

For g one obtains

$$g = P(\zeta - 1) \tag{12a}$$

and

$$g = (\zeta - 1)^{-\frac{2}{5} - \frac{7}{5}\nu} P(\zeta - 1). \tag{12b}$$

Thus one of the solutions is regular in the vicinity of $\zeta = 1$, while the second one represents, for negative ν, the propagation of a singularity along the limiting characteristic. The solution for $\nu > (2/7)$ would tend to infinity and therefore contradicts the assumption of small disturbances. For negative ν the solution, given by Eq. (12b), can become regular when the exponent is an integer. This occurs when

$$\nu = -\frac{2}{7} - \frac{5}{7}h \qquad (h = 1, 2 \ldots). \tag{13}$$

In this case a logarithmic term occurs in the second solution and hence also a singularity for $\zeta - 1$, in at least one of the derivatives.

The lower limit of the interval to be considered is, of course, the x axis. There we must require that the y component of the additional velocity should vanish.

In defining the particular solutions with the aid of an eigenvalue problem one should take, as the upper limit of the integral, a line $\zeta = c_2 < 1$, located in the supersonic region. The transition to the limit $c_2 \to 1$ is performed later.

The system of particular solutions, obtained in this manner, again has positive and negative eigenvalues λ. The corresponding values of ν are

$$\nu = -\frac{n}{2} \pm \sqrt{\lambda + \frac{n^2}{4}}. \tag{14}$$

The eigenvalues for which $\lambda > -(n^2/4)$ yield particular solutions of the form

$$\overline{\Phi} = \varrho^{-\frac{n}{2} \pm \sqrt{\lambda + \frac{n^2}{4}}} G(\zeta, \nu), \tag{15a}$$

while the particular solutions corresponding to the eigenvalues $\lambda < -(n^2/4)$ are of the form

$$\overline{\Phi} = \varrho^{-n/2} \begin{matrix}\cos\\ \sin\end{matrix} \left[\sqrt{-\lambda - \frac{n^2}{4}} \log \varrho\right] G(\xi, \nu). \tag{15b}$$

The form of Eq. (8) and of the boundary conditions permit us to obtain orthogonality relations. An analysis, analogous to that of Section VII, 10, shows that each solution of the linearised differential equation (2), which satisfies the boundary conditions prescribed along $\zeta = -\infty$ and $\zeta = c_2$ can be represented as the superposition of these particular solutions The boundary condition prescribed along $\zeta = c_2$ becomes meaningless when this line becomes identical with the limiting characteristic.

In that case it is also necessary to distinguish between the particular solutions defined by the eigenvalue problem and between the "natural" particular solutions which are determined by the requirement that along the limiting characteristic all derivatives are bounded (cf. p. 185). The connection between the two kinds of particular solutions can probably be established by means of the method of Section VII, 13.

The first "natural" particular solutions result from simple considerations of a general nature. One can, for example, start with the remark that both

$$\Phi = y^{3n-2} f(\zeta)$$

and

$$\Phi = C^{3n-2}\, y^{3n-2} f(C^{1-n} \zeta) \tag{16}$$

are solutions of the potential equation for transonic flow. The second form results from the first when the coordinates x and y are multiplied by C. If C is approximately equal to 1 then the difference between the two solutions represents a disturbance of the original field described by Eq. (2). This solution is obtained by differentiating with respect to C and then putting $C = 1$.

$$\bar{\Phi} = y^{3n-2}\,[(3n-2) f + (1-n)\,\zeta f'].$$

Putting $n = 4/7$ and comparing with Eq. (3) one obtains

$$\nu = -\frac{2}{7}, \tag{16a}$$

$$g = \left(-\frac{2}{7} f + \frac{3}{7}\,\zeta f'\right). \tag{16b}$$

If, as the second solution, one takes the function

$$\Phi = y^{-2/7} f\left(\frac{(\gamma+1)^{-1/3}(x+C)}{y^{4/7}}\right),$$

then a similar discussion may be applied. This form implies the displacement of the singular point along the x axis. Differentiation with respect to C yields

$$\nu = -\frac{6}{7},$$

$$g = f'(\zeta).$$

The next two natural particular solutions occur, in accordance with the calculations of GUDERLEY [28], when $\nu = -(9/7)$ and $\nu = -(12/7)$ (Table 1). These values of ν were calculated by a numerical procedure and therefore may not be accurate*.

Table 1. The variation of g and g' with ζ

$\nu = -9/7$			$\nu = -12/7$		
ζ	g	g'	ζ	g	g'
1·0	1·0000	−5·0624	1·0	0	0
0·9	1·3973	−2·9404	0·9	−0·1497	0·00825
0·8	1·6038	−1·1887	0·8	−0·2165	0·02713
0·7	1·6519	1·2272	0·7	−0·2269	0·04930
0·6	1·5738	1·3352	0·6	−0·1957	0·07043
0·5	1·3990	2·1818	0·5	−0·1403	0·08722
0·4	1·1542	2·7347	0·4	−0·0727	0.09787
0·3	0·8634	3·0821	0·3	0·0036	0·10169
0·2	0·5476	3·2328	0·2	0·0597	0·09888
0·1	0·2252	3·2159	0·1	0·1120	0·09029
0	−0·0886	3·0606	0	0·1505	0·07714
−0·1	−0·3815	2·7963	−0·1	0·1739	0·06095
−0·2	−1·6439	2·4519	−0·2	0·1827	0·04312
−0·3	−1·8692	2·0549	−0·3	0·1787	0·02595
−0·4	−1·0536	1·6315	−0·4	0·1642	0·00790
−0·5	−1·1955	1·2054	−0·5	0·1422	−0·00742
−0·6	−1·2956	0·79724	−0·6	0·1158	−0·02032
−0·7	−1·3567	0·42380	−0·7	0·08775	−0·03030
−0·8	−1·3828	0·09733	−0·8	0·06052	−0·03791
−0·9	−1·3789	−0·17470	−0·9	0·03592	−0·04273
−1·0	−1·3507	−0·38945	−1·0	0·01510	−0·04528
−1·2	−1·2459	−0·65869	−1·2	−0·01380	−0·04554
−1·4	−1·1047	−0·75307	−1·4	−0·02782	−0·04140
−1·6	−0·9559	−0·75494	−1·6	−0·03147	−0·03549
−1·8	−0·8164	−0·65987	−1·8	−0·02957	−0·02939
−2·0	−0·6939	−0·56576	−2·0	−0·02505	−0·02393
−2·2	−0·5899	−0·47335	−2·2	−0·02034	−0·01939
−2·4	−0·5035	−0·39158	−2·4	−0·01618	−0·01574

The solution for $\nu = -(12/7)$ is not only a "natural" particular solution but, within the accuracy of the calculation, represents also the first particular solution defined by an eigenvalue problem**. The corresponding positive eigenvalue is $\nu = (8/7)$. The corresponding function G is shown in Fig. 115.

* Although the value $n = 4/7$ was also obtained by numerical calculation it was found, however, to be so accurate that there is hardly any doubt that it can be exactly expressed by the fraction. This leads to the supposition that the values of ν mentioned above are exact and that there is a general rule governing the distribution of values of ν belonging to natural particular solutions.

** This is quite remarkable since the two types of particular solutions can, for negative ν, coincide only for those values given by Eq. (13). In a plane two-dimensional problem this never occurs.

This discussion can be extended to the three-dimensional case by including in Eq. (2) a term of the form $\bar{\Phi}_{\omega\omega}/y^2$. This term appears then also in the linearised equation for the disturbances. Instead of Eq. (3) we consider the form

$$\bar{\Phi} = y^{\nu}\, g(\zeta, \nu, m) \cos m\, \omega. \tag{17}$$

m is usually an integer. For g there results the differential equation

$$(f' - n^2 \zeta^2)\, g'' + (f'' + 2n\,\nu - n^2 \zeta)\, g' - (\nu^2 - m^2)\, g = 0. \tag{18}$$

All further transformations are obtained in the same way, e.g. it is again possible to find an orthogonal system of functions.

With the aid of these systems of particular solutions all small deviations from the solution of the preceding section can, in principle, be represented. These deviations can be due to the shape of the body or to a finite angle of attack.

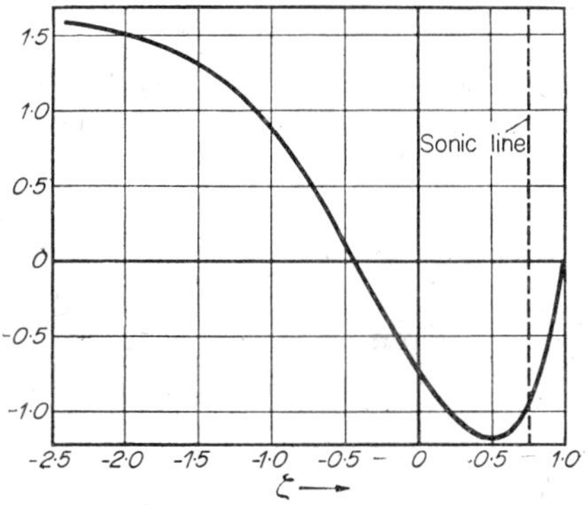

FIG. 115 The eigenfunction G for $\nu = -12/7$ or $\nu = 8/7$ (axisymmetrical case).

The importance of these solutions is, of course, limited by the fact that they assume a linearisation in the neighborhood of Φ_0. In the vicinity of a body immersed in the flow this assumption is certainly not permissible.

3. Applications

GUDERLEY and YOSHIHARA [44] have originally introduced these particular solutions in order to calculate a first example of the flow past a body of revolution with an approach MACH number of 1. They simply superimposed a function $\bar{\Phi}$, which results for $\nu = -(9/7)$, onto the solution Φ_0 and have determined the resulting shape of the body. This was done on the assumption that the linearisation undertaken in Eq. (2) is valid even in the neighborhood of the profile.

It would be more satisfactory to employ the representation, which we have just indicated, at a large distance from the immersed body and, within the region in which the linearisation is no longer permissible, to calculate the flow by an analytic continuation, using the complete differential equation II, 8 (2). Such calculations have, as yet, not been performed.

The particular solutions of the preceding section enable us to discuss axi-symmetric flow fields with an approach MACH number close to 1 (GUDERLEY [29]). Similar concepts to those we have met in connection with two-dimensional flow field apply also in this case. The non-linearity of the differential equation results, however, in some complications in the train of thought.

Let us start with a flow at $M = 1$. One must assume that a change in the boundary conditions at a large distance from the profile introduces only a small change in the flow field in the vicinity of the profile, even if at the point where the changes are introduced substantial disturbances occur. Such a change can then in the vicinity of a profile be represented by a linearisation. If one considers, for example, a body of revolution in a choked wind tunnel then a linearisation of the flow field at $M = 1$ is permissible in the vicinity of the profile but not, however, near the wall. If the width of the tunnel is increased then the region in which the linearisation is possible is also increased.

The region in which a linearisation is to be performed must, however, be subdivided still further. In the vicinity of the profile the original flow is quite complicated and cannot, of course, be represented simply by the function $\Phi_0 (x, y)$. At a larger distance from the profile, but still within a region in which a linearisation is permissible, Φ_0 offers a good representation of the original flow. There the system of particular solutions, derived in the preceding section, can be used to represent the disturbed flow field.

We construct now in the region, in which the linearisation is permitted, the particular solutions which leave the surface of the profile unchanged. Such particular solutions can certainly not be small at a large distance from the profile in comparison with the function $\Phi_0 (x, y)$, since then the superposition could be extended to infinity and the flow at $M = 1$ would not be unique. Therefore, among the particular solutions which leave the surface of the body unchanged, at least one of the particular solutions, Eq. XI, 2 (2) must be present with a positive exponent. Thus in the region in which a representation with the aid of such particular solutions is possible, the functions which leave the surface of the body unchanged have, in principle, the following form

$$\overline{\Phi} = y^{\nu_h} g(\zeta, \nu_h) + \tilde{\varphi}_h. \tag{1}$$

Here ν_h is the positive value of ν, appropriate to the eigenvalue λ_h. $\tilde{\varphi}_h$ is a solution of the linearised equation, which at infinity is at most of the same order of magnitude as Φ_0, i.e. $0\,(y^{-2/7})$. The change in the flow field at a large distance from the body, due to the boundary conditions, is represented by a superposition of expressions of the form of Eq. (1). The smaller the disturbance introduced at a large distance, i.e. the smaller the deviation of the flow from one at $M = 1$, the smaller the coefficients multiplying the functions, given by Eq. (1) in the superposition. At the same time, however, the distance, up to which the deviations from a flow at $M = 1$ can be represented by a superposition of expressions of the form of Eq. (1), increases. At a large distance from the body the first term predominates in Eq. (1) and the entire flow, including Φ_0, is represented by

$$\Phi = a_0 \Phi_0 + \sum a_h y^{\nu_h} g(\zeta, \nu_h). \tag{2}$$

The functions $\tilde{\varphi}_h$ occurring in Eq. (1) are determined by the shape of the body. Since these functions do not occur in the last equation, the influence of the special features of the body is eliminated. Only the coefficient of the function Φ_0 is still a function of the shape of the body.

The remaining coefficients in the last equation must be chosen in such a way that a continuation of this expression, with the aid of the complete potential equation of transonic flow, satisfies the boundary conditions prescribed at a large distance from the body. In this connection one can consider the conditions appropriate to a fixed tunnel wall or the boundary conditions corresponding to a supersonic MACH number. For a given type of the boundary condition and for a flow field characterized by the MACH number M_0, let Eq. (2) be the expression which satisfies this boundary condition. The coefficients a_h are functions of the boundary conditions. For example, Eq. (2) could represent a flow at a supersonic MACH number M_0.

In order to find now the corresponding expression for another characteristic MACH number M one must perform a distortion in accordance with the similarity rule for transonic flow. At the same time, however, one must perform a general distortion of the scales of measurement so that the coefficient a_0 of the first term, which depends on the size of the body, remains unchanged. In accordance with the results of Section II, 6 one obtains

$$\Phi = a_0 x_0 \tau \left(\frac{y}{x_0}\tau^{1/2}\right)^{3n-2} f\left(\frac{(\gamma+1)^{-1/3}\dfrac{x}{x_0}}{\left(\tau^{1/2}\dfrac{y}{x_0}\right)^n}\right) +$$

$$+ \sum_{h=1}^{\infty} a_h x_0 \tau \left(\frac{y}{x_0}\tau^{1/2}\right)^{\nu_h} g_h\left(\frac{(\gamma+1)^{-1/3}\dfrac{x}{x_0}}{\left(\tau^{1/2}\dfrac{y}{x_0}\right)^n}\right).$$

Here $n = (4/7)$. To make the first term invariant x_0 must be chosen equal to $\tau^{-2/3}$. The calculations outlined in the preceding section yield for the first eigenvalue $\nu = (8/7)$. For small values of τ one obtains then the following expression

$$\Phi = a_0 y^{-2/7} f(\zeta) + a_1 \tau^{5/3}\left[y^{8/7} g\left(\zeta, \frac{8}{7}\right)\right] + \cdots.$$

Since $M - 1$ is proportional to τ this expression can also be written, with a slightly changed constant a_1, in the form

$$\Phi = a_0 y^{-2/7} f(\zeta) + a_1 (M-1)^{5/3} y^{8/7} g\left(\zeta, \frac{8}{7}\right) + \cdots.$$

If these functions are to be continued towards the body, then the particular solutions $y^{\nu_h} g(\zeta, \nu_h)$ must be replaced by the complete functions of Eq. (1). The first term of the last equation represents then the flow at $M = 1$, while the successive terms represent corrections which have to be applied. The correction of lowest order is introduced in the last equation. The resulting change in the pressure distribution is proportional to $(M - 1)^{5/3}$. It follows thus that a curve of the drag coefficient, referred to $\varrho^* w^{*2}/2$ as stagnation pressure, plotted versus the MACH number of the approaching flow, has at $M = 1$ a horizontal tangent but its curvature is infinite.

This fact cannot be discerned in the experimental results; the slope, for example, of the curve of the drag coefficient, plotted versus the MACH number, is always shown positive. It is possible that the present analysis is valid only for such a small range of MACH numbers that our results are smothered by the inaccuracies in the measurements*.

In this connection another consideration should be included. The results of this section are valid not only for rotationally symmetrical bodies, but for all bodies of finite dimensions. This is true because of the fact that at a large distance from the immersed body the deviations from axisymmetry become unimportant. A yawed wing of finite length belongs to this type of obstacle. Except for end effects, however, the velocity component parallel to the chord is in this case of decisive importance. This means that for a large part of the wing the transition through $M = 1$ introduces no really fundamental change in the flow field. In such a case the behaviour described in the present section can be noticeable only within a very small range of MACH numbers in the vicinity of 1.

4. Special Two-Dimensional and Axisymmetric Flows with Compression Shocks

The assumed form of a solution of the transonic potential equation, used in Section XI, 2 can also be employed when compression shocks occur in the flow field and when these extend along the line $\zeta = \text{const}$ (GUDERLEY and BARISH [1]). In order to show this, let us consider the shock conditions. Let the flow field upstream of the shock be of the form given by Eq. XI, 1 (1). Then

$$\Phi_x = +y^{2n-2} f_1(\zeta) \quad \text{and} \quad \Phi_y = y^{3n-3} f_2(\zeta),$$

where f_1 and f_2 are appropriate functions of ζ. The shock is assumed to extend along the line $\zeta = \text{const} = \zeta_0$. Its slope is then given by

$$\frac{dy}{dx} = \frac{(\gamma + 1)^{-1/3}}{n \zeta_0 y^{n-1}}.$$

These quantities are introduced into the shock conditions given by Eq. II, 4 (6) putting, in accordance with the remarks of Section II, 8, $\tau = 1$ and writing x, y, z in place of ξ, η, ζ. We must further consider that because of the meaning of the quantity f, occurring in Eq. XI, 4 (6),

$$\frac{\left(\frac{\partial f}{\partial \eta}\right)^2 + \left(\frac{\partial f}{\partial \zeta}\right)^2}{\left(\frac{\partial f}{\partial x}\right)^2} = \left(\frac{dx}{dy}\right)^2.$$

* Recent measurements performed at NACA appear, however, to confirm this theory.

For the state downstream of the shock we obtain then

$$\Phi_{x\,\mathrm{II}} = y^{2n-2} f_3(\zeta).$$

Similarly, with the aid of Eq. II, 4 (7a), $\Phi_{y\,\mathrm{II}} = y^{3n-3} f_4(y)$. The velocity, therefore, behind the shock appears again in a form which fits Eq. XI, 1 (1).

The shock conditions in the s, t plane can be formulated particularly easily. We say that in the transonic region the entropy changes can be neglected and that the velocity potential, which can be introduced because of this, is continuous through the shock. The continuity of the potential expresses the fact that the tangential component of the velocity remains constant in passing through the shock. Since, of course, the values of ζ immediately upstream and immediately downstream of the shock are the same, the quantity s [Eq. XI, 1 (3)] (not to be confused with the entropy) does not change in the transition through the shock, i.e.

$$s_{\mathrm{I}} = s_{\mathrm{II}}.$$

As in Chapter II the subsripts I and II denote respectively the quantities upstream and downstream of the shock. Introducing further Eq. XI, 1 (1) into the shock conditions [Eq. II, 4 (6)] there results

$$t_{\mathrm{II}} = 2n^2 - t_{\mathrm{I}}.$$

This means that across a shock one jumps from a given point in the s, t plane to its mirror image, with respect to the line $t = n^2$. Since the shock results always in an increase in pressure, and therefore a decrease in the velocity, only jumps from a larger to a smaller value of t are permissible. This result is valid for both two-dimensional and axisymmetric flows.

The corresponding conditions can, for two-dimensional flows, be also formulated in the hodograph plane.

5. Applications

These relations were utilized by GUDERLEY and BARISH to complete the picture of the flow at $M = 1$. Up to now the flow field at infinity was calculated only up to the limiting characteristic. We are now interested in the flow field at infinity downstream of this line.

Immediately downstream of the immersed body one finds, at least in the two-dimensional case, a supersonic velocity. This can be recognized from the following. The state at the point A in Fig. 116 is determined by the fact that the velocity vector there is horizontal and that A is located on one of the characteristics, emanating from the sonic line. It is assumed that the change of state across a shock, which could cross the characteristic, does not differ very much from the changes of state which are possible along a characteristic. One should compare in this respect Fig. 44 which contains the shock polar and the characteristics. The velocity vector along the sonic line maps into the line CO of the hodograph, so that the starting point of the characteristic BA lies on this line. Such characteristics, however, certainly intersect the line $\vartheta = 0$.

All the waves approaching from the sonic line are compression waves. This is true also of those waves which downstream of the body cross the wake. These waves probably coalesce and form a shock. The behaviour of this shock, at a large distance from the immersed body, will be discussed here.

While in the vicinity of the profile the method of characteristics was found convenient, at large distances an analytical method is desirable. One would expect that the flow field is represented by the function given by Eq. XI, 1 (1) also downstream of the limiting characteristic. In the s, t diagram (Fig. 112) there exist two continuations of the solution curve past the point C, namely CD and CA. Both continuations are physically conceivable and both lead to the positive

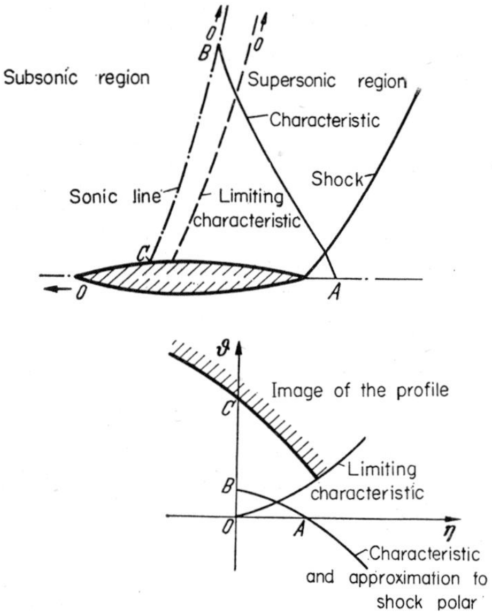

Fig. 116 Illustrating the discussion of the state at the point A.

x axis. A more exact calculation would show that the curve CA enters the point A in such a manner that a distribution of sources would arise along the positive x axis. This condition corresponds, therefore, to a semi-infinite body, whose convex curvature accepts the compression waves originating from the sonic line in such a manner that no shock is generated.

The solution CD is the analytic continuation of the solution upstream of the limiting characteristic. One would expect that this is the correct solution, since the limiting characteristic differs from the remaining characteristics only in regard to its behaviour at infinity and not within the flow field. It would be surprising, therefore, if the character of the solution were to change at the limiting characteristic. This solution, however, also does not satisfy the boundary condition along the positive x axis, which requires that the y component of the velocity be equal to zero. In this solution both the x and the y components become infinite at the point D, since there ζ becomes infinite. To recognize this fully a somewhat more detailed discussion would be necessary.

Since the solution CD lies above the line $t = n^2$, a shock can occur in this part of the flow and it can extend along the curve $\zeta =$ const. In the flow field downstream of the shock the y component of the velocity must be zero along the x axis. This condition requires that the solution curve at the point A should be determined by Eq. XI, 1 (12a). The flow field past the shock yields thus a prescribed curve in the s, t diagram. The state before the shock is given by the curve CD. By reflecting this curve at the line $t = n^2$ one obtains the locus of states which can be reached through a shock. The intersection of this curve with CA gives the locations of the shock. Figure 117 shows this construction for the axisymmetric case.

At the shock two flow fields are thus to be connected together; these result from quite separate calculations. In this matching process the constant C in

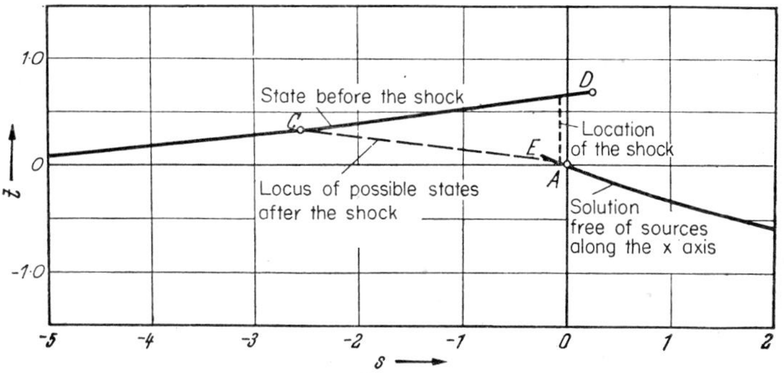

FIG. 117 The t, s diagram and the determination of a compression shock for an axisymmetric flow at $M = 1$. (According to BARISH and GUDERLEY [1]).

Eq. XI, 1 (3) must, for one of the fields, be chosen in such a way that at the shock the same value of ζ is obtained in both flows.

To obtain the shape of the streamlines, i.e. the deviation of a streamline from a line $y =$ const, it is necessary to integrate the slope of the streamline along the line $y =$ const $= y_0$. Thus one determines the integral

$$\tilde{y} = \int \vartheta(y_0, x)\, dx.$$

The calculation becomes simpler if one applies the continuity equation in a manner similar to that in Section II, 8. In a two-dimensional case we consider for an arbitrary region of the physical plane the expression

$$\iint (-(\gamma + 1)\, \Phi_x \Phi_{xx} + \Phi_{yy})\, dx\, dy = 0$$

and transform it by an integration

$$\oint \left[-(\gamma + 1) \left(\frac{\Phi_x^2}{2} \right) dy - \Phi_y\, dx \right] = 0.$$

The integration is to be performed in an anticlockwise sense around the region considered. Choosing, as the limits of the region, lines $y = 0$, $y = y_0$, $x = -\infty$ and $\zeta = \text{const} = \zeta_0$, the integral simplifies to

$$\tilde{y} = \int_{-\infty}^{x_0} \Phi_y \, dx = \left\{ \int_0^{y_0} \left[\frac{(\gamma + 1)}{2} \Phi_x^2 + \Phi_y \frac{dx}{dy} \right] dy \right\}_{\zeta = \zeta_0} .$$

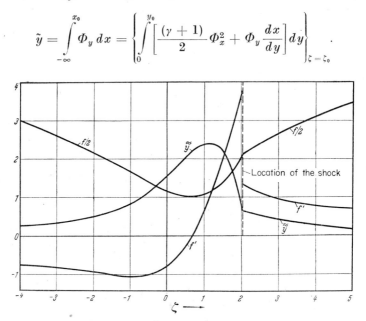

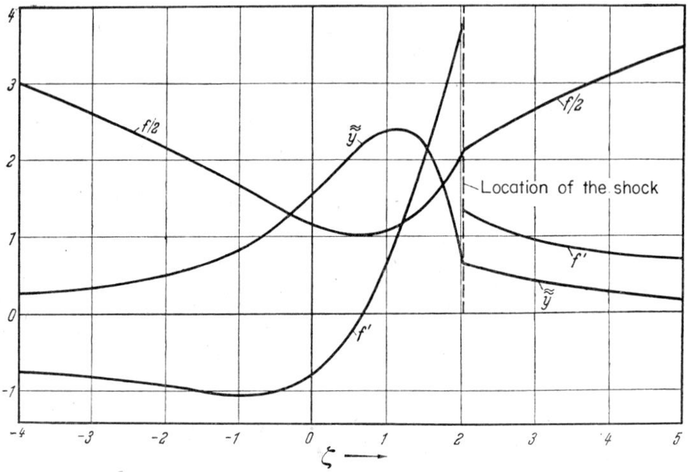

FIG. 118 The functions f, f and $\tilde{\tilde{y}}$ for the two-dimensional case. (According to BARISH and GUDERLEY [1]).

Thus for $n = 4/5$ one finds, with the aid of Eq. XI, 1 (1),

$$\tilde{y} = y_0^{1/5} (\gamma + 1)^{1/3} \tilde{\tilde{y}} ,$$

where

$$\tilde{\tilde{y}} = \frac{5}{2} f'^2 + \frac{8}{5} \zeta (f - 2 \zeta f') .$$

Similarly for the axisymmetric case

$$\tilde{y} = y_0^{-5/7} (\gamma + 1)^{1/3} \tilde{\tilde{y}} ,$$

where

$$\tilde{\tilde{y}} = \frac{7}{4} f'^2 - \frac{4}{7} \zeta (f + 2 \zeta f') .$$

These results are shown in Tables 2 and 3 and in Figs. 118 and 119. The fact that the coordinates downstream of the shock are not given by round numbers, is due to the determination of these values only after the shock conditions are satisfied.

It is noteworthy, but not surprising, that in the two-dimensional case the deformation of the streamlines does not tend to zero as y is allowed to increase beyond all limits. In the axisymmetric case the deformation of the streamlines does tend to zero but the surface, contained between the deformed and the undeformed physical plane, does not.

One other application of this discussion may be pointed out. If the flow approaches the body with a high subsonic velocity then a local supersonic regime

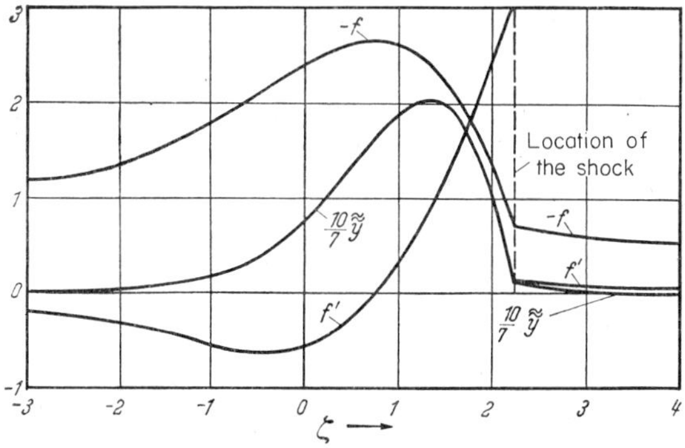

FIG. 119 The functions f, f and $\tilde{\tilde{y}}$ the for axisymmetrical case. (According to BARISH and GUDERLEY [1]).

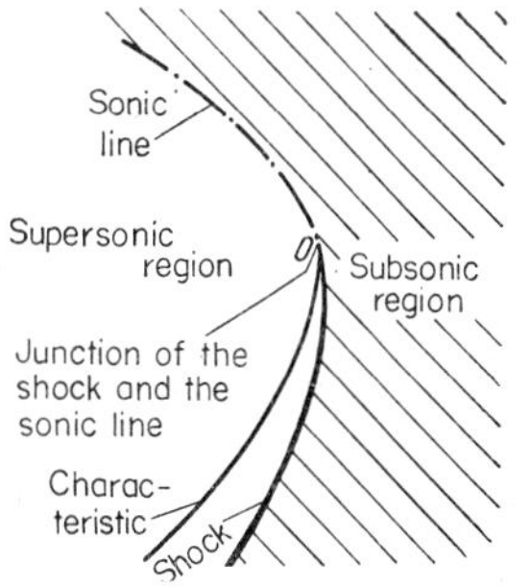

FIG. 120
Hypothetical form of the junction of a shock and a sonic line.
A solution of this type cannot be determined.

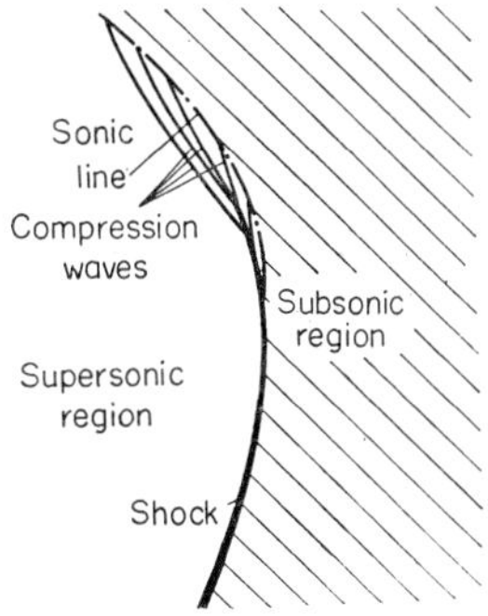

FIG. 121 Possible form of behaviour of a shock in the vicinity of a sonic line. The shock originates in the supersonic region due to coalescence of compression waves. The analysis of such an example has not, as yet, been undertaken.

is generated and this often ends in a shock. One is led to suppose that this shock starts at the sonic line and one could ask whether the neighborhood of the point, at which the shock meets the sonic line, could be described by solutions of the type described here (Fig. 120). The only assumption underlying these solutions is that the potential in the vicinity of such a point varies, along suitable general-

Table 2. The function $f(\zeta)$ for axisymmetric flow upstream and downstream of a compression shock

	ζ	f	f'
	−2·4	−1·261	−0·2493
	−2·2	−1·314	−0·2785
	−2·0	−1·373	−0·3126
	−1·8	−1·439	−0·3519
	−1·6	−1·514	−0·3965
	−1·4	−1·588	−0·4457
	−1·2	−1·693	−0·4975
	−1·0	−1·797	−0·5480
	−0·8	−1·911	−0·5917
	−0·6	−2·033	−0·6218
	−0·4	−2·159	−0·6311
	−0·2	−2·283	−0·6128
	0	−2·401	−0·5612
	0·2	−2·505	−0·4715
	0·4	−2·587	−0·3403
	0·6	−2·639	−0·1648
	0·8	−2·650	0·0570
	1·0	−2·613	0·3265
	1·2	−2·517	0·6451
	1·4	−2·352	1·016
	1·6	−2·109	1·435
	1·8	−1·777	1·906
	2·0	−1·346	2·428
	2·2	−0·849	3·001
	2·24	−0·712	3·119
shock			
	2·24	−0·712	0·1528
	2·274	−0·710	0·1516
	2·366	−0·691	0·1390
	2·554	−0·669	0·1253
	2·774	−0·641	0·1099
	3·113	−0·605	0·0916
	3·795	−0·547	0·0615

ized parabolas, in the first approximation with a power of the distance from the point considered. A more detailed analysis, using the hodograph method, was undertaken by Walter Ludwig and resulted in the fact that such a possibility does not arise*. Apparently the flow field is much more complicated. A possible form of this part of the flow is shown in Fig. 121. It would, of course, be desirable if an analytical example of this kind could be calculated.

* Since the result was negative the investigation has remained unpublished.

Table 3. The function $f(\zeta)$ for two-dimensional flow upstream and downstream of a compression shock

	ζ	f	f'
	−3·4	5·531	−0·7801
	−3·2	5·373	−0·8002
	−3·0	5·211	−0·8216
	−2·8	5·044	−0·8442
	−2·6	4·873	−0·8681
	−2·4	4·696	−0·8933
	−2·2	4·515	−0·9195
	−2·0	4·328	−0·9465
	−1·8	4·136	−0·9736
	−1·6	3·939	−0·9999
	−1·4	3·736	−1·0238
	−1·2	3·529	−1·0430
	−1·0	3·319	−1·0540
	−0·8	3·108	−1·0524
	−0·6	2·899	−1·0322
	−0·4	2·697	−0·9866
	−0·2	2·507	−0·9079
	0	2·336	−0·7886
	0·2	2·194	−0·6214
	0·4	2·091	−0·3999
	0·6	2·038	−0·1886
	0·8	2·048	0·2269
	1·0	2·133	0·6400
	1·2	2·308	1·122
	1·4	2·587	1·678
	1·6	2·958	2·308
	1·8	3·516	3·013
	2·0	4·196	3·795
	2·03	4·208	3·807
shock			
	2·03	4·208	1·361
	3·167	5·504	0·933
	4·749	6·802	0·732

6. Description of Flow Fields whose Approach Mach Number is Close to 1

The results of the preceding section provide us with a more exact representation of a flow field at an approach Mach number of unity. We want to consider now how this flow field develops when the Mach number of 1 is approached from below and how, with a further increase in the Mach number, the known supersonic flow fields are obtained.

Let a symmetrical body be approached at various Mach numbers. If the Mach number of the approaching flow is low then one obtains a purely subsonic flow (as long as the body has no convex corners). At a certain higher Mach number, which depends on the shape of the body, there results for the first time a small local supersonic region. This most frequently terminates in a shock. With a further increase in the approach MACH number, this supersonic region expands further and further and extends finally behind the submerged body. If this is the case, then the supersonic region always ends in a compression shock. The compression waves originating at the sonic line are then no longer received by the surface and instead approach the boundary of the supersonic region. This boundary cannot, however, be a sonic line since, in accordance with Section VI, 1, all waves terminating at the sonic line must be expansion waves. Thus this boundary must be formed by a shock. Although the convex surface of a body transforms the waves which it reflects into, generally, rarefaction waves; at the trailing edge,

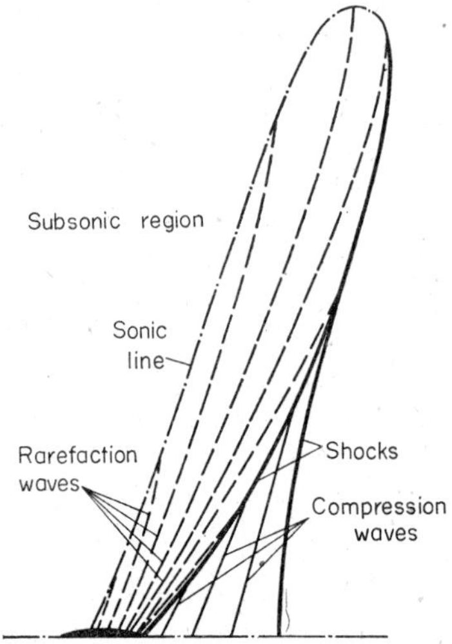

FIG. 122 Structure of the flow at a high subsonic velocity. (According to BARISH and GUDERLEY [1]).

however, there exists a concave corner from which a shock originates. If the angle of the trailing edge is zero then one has to have a concave curvature and, although the shock does not form directly at the trailing edge, it does develop in its vicinity. This compression shock need not lead to a subsonic flow. In its further course it joins the compression waves, which penetrate the wake, and finally also the compression shock which forms the boundary of the supersonic region.

When the MACH number of the oncoming flow approaches unity from below the shock which limits the subsonic region moves further and further downstream. The compression shock emanating from the trailing edge assumes, in conjunction with the compression waves travelling through the wake, at a larger distance from the body a form such as calculated in the preceding section. A deviation from this form occurs again at still larger distances, when our shock combines with that which forms a boundary of the supersonic region (Fig. 122).

Since, in accordance with the calculations of the preceding section, the velocities after the shock are very close to the critical velocity, particularly in the axisymmetric case, it is possible that the shock which closes the subsonic region behind the body is very weak; one gains thus the impression that a return to subsonic velocities is always caused by a shock which emanates from the trailing edge of the body.

Since the subsonic region, which develops downstream of the obstacle, is related to the subsonic region upstream of the body, the two influence one another mutually. Thus a real solution of the flow field, for a subsonic MACH number, must include the influence of the compression shock ending the supersonic region on the entire subsonic field. This is exceedingly difficult to achieve. An example was given recently by YOSHIHARA [87].

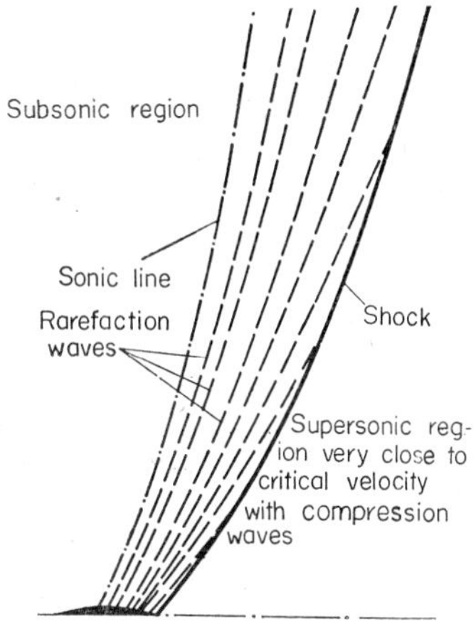

FIG. 123 General form of a flow at $M = 1$. (According to BARISH and GUDERLEY [1]).

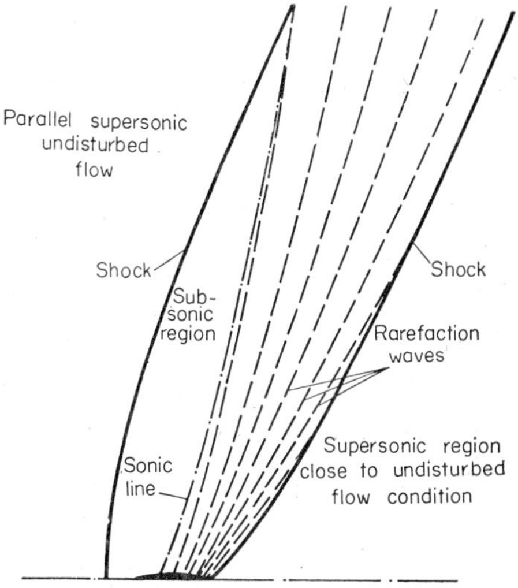

FIG. 124 Structure of a supersonic flow past a profile. (According to BARISH and GUDERLEY [1]).

Figure 123 shows the corresponding flow at $M = 1$.

When the MACH number of the oncoming flow slightly exceeds unity, one obtains a detached compression shock at a considerable distance upstream of the obstacle. The sonic line emanating from the obstacle terminates at the compression shock. The compression waves originating at the sonic line, and passing through the wake, unite with the waves which emanate from the trailing edge of the body and form a shock, such as we have encountered in the preceding section. A deviation from the flow discussed in the preceding section occurs in the vicinity of the intersection of this latter shock with the detached one which starts upstream of the body (Fig. 124). At higher MACH numbers the detached shock approaches closer and closer to the obstacle. Progressively fewer rarefaction waves reach the sonic line and correspondingly fewer compression waves emanate from the sonic line. From the point of view of the pressure distribution at the profile, the flow downstream of the trailing edge is for all supersonic flow fields of no interest.

If, at a higher supersonic MACH number one follows a characteristic (for example ABC in Fig. 125) which starts in the supersonic region before the shock

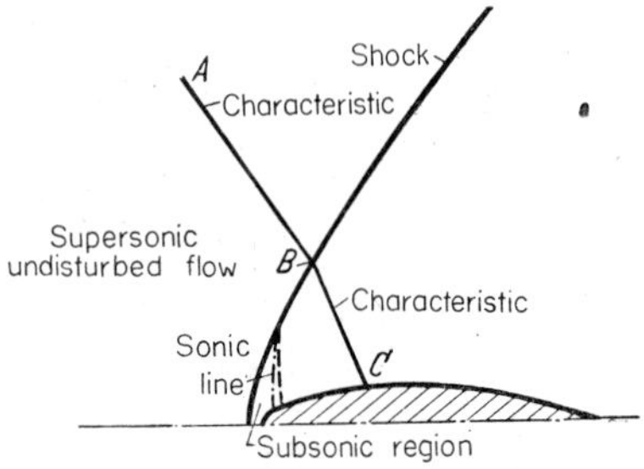

FIG. 125 Illustrating the determination of the pressure distribution on the downstream part of a profile in the presence of an attached shock.

and, after crossing the shock, reaches the profile, then in the hodograph plane one moves approximately along a characteristic. This is because the jump in the velocity vector which occurs across the shock is, in the hodograph plane, represented quite well by the jump occurring along a characteristic. It follows from this that in a two-dimensional flow the pressures at those points of the profile, which are reached by characteristics of this kind, are the same as in a purely supersonic flow. As the MACH number of the oncoming flow increases this type of pressure distribution covers a progressively larger portion of profile, starting from the trailing edge.

BIBLIOGRAPHY

1. Articles Cited in the Text

1. Barish D.T. and Guderley K. G. (1953) Asymptotic Forms of Shock Waves in Flows over Symmetrical Bodies at Mach One. *J. Aero. Sci.*, **20,** 491.
2. Busemann A. (1937) Hodographenmethode der Gasdynamik. *Z. angew. Math. Mech.*, **17,** 73.
3. Busemann A. (1931) Chapter on Gas dynamics in Wiens–Harms: *Handbuch der Experimentalphysik*, Vol. 4, Part 1, Leipzig.
4. Busemann A. (1953) Theory of the Propeller in Compressible Flow. *Proc. Third Midw. Conf. Fluid Mech., Univ. Minnessota.*
5. Busemann A. and Guderley K.G. (March 1947) The Problem of Drag at High Subsonic Speeds. British Ministry of Aircraft Production, Volkenrode Reports and Translations, No. 184.
6. Bergmann S. (1950) *The Kernel Function and Conformal Mapping.* American Mathematical Society.
7. Chang C.C. and O'Brien V. (1953) Some Exact Solutions of Two-Dimensional Flows of Compressible Fluids with Hodograph Method. NACA Tech. Note 2885.
8. Christianowich S.A. (1940) Flow Past Bodies at High Subsonic Velocities, Rep. No. 481. Joukowski Central Aero-Hydro Institute.
9. Cole J.D. (1954) Transonic Limits of Linearized Theory. Guggenheim Aeronautical Laboratory, California Institute of Technology, Office of Scientific Research, Technical Note 228.
10. Cole J.D. (1954) Acceleration of Slender Bodies of Revolution through Sonic Velocity. Guggenheim Aeronautical Laboratory, California Institute of Technology, Office of Scientific Research, Technical Note 5–55.
11. Crocco L. (1937) Singolarità della corrente gassosa iperacustica nell'intorno di una prora a diedro. *Aerotechnica, Roma*, **17,** 519.
12. Computation Laboratory, National Applied Mathematics Laboratories, National Bureau of Standards: (1948 and 1949) *Table of Bessel Functions of Fractional Order*, Vol. I and II, Columbia University Press, New York.
13. Eggink H. Über Verdichtungsstöße bei abgelöster Strömung. *Forschungsbericht.* 1850.
14. Falkowich S.V. (1947) On a class of Laval Nozzles, *Appl. Math. Mech., Leningr.*, **11,** 223. (Translation by the Graduate Division of Applied Mathematics, Brown University, Headquarters Air Material Command, Wright Patterson AFB, Rech. Report F–TS–1223–IA.)
15. Frankl F.I. (1946) Effect of the Acceleration of Elongated Bodies of Revolution upon the Resistance in Compressible Fluid, *Appl. Math. Mech., Leningr.*, **10,** No. 4.; also NACA Tech. Memorandum 1230.
16. Frankl F.I. (1947) On the Formation of Shock Waves in Subsonic Flows with Local Supersonic Velocities. *Appl. Math. Mech., Leningr.*, **11,** 199; also Brown University translation.
17. Frankl F.I. (1947) Asymptotic Resolution of Chaplygin's Functions. *C.R. Acad. Sci. U.R.S.S.*, **58,** (5) 000; also Brown University translation.
18. Frankl F.I. (1947) The Flow of a Supersonic Jet from a Vessel with Plane Walls. *C.R. Acad. Sci. U.R.S.S.*, **58,** No. 3.; also Brown University translation.
19. Frankl F.I. Investigation of the Theory of Wings of Infinite Span Moving at the Speed of Sound. *C.R. Acad. Sci. U.R.S.S.*, **57,** 991.

20. FRANKL F.I. On the Problem of Chaplygin for Mixed Subsonic-Supersonic Flows. *C.R. Acad. Sci. U.R.S.S.*, **9**, also NACA Tech. Memorandum 1155.
21. FRIEDRICHS K.O. On the Non-Occurrence of a Limiting Line in Transonic Flow. *Commun. Appl. Math.*, (1948) 287; *Appl. Mech. Rev.* (1950) Review 753.
22. GARDNER C.S., and LUDLOFF H.F. (1950) Influence of Accelerations on Aerodynamic Characteristics of Thin Airfoils in Supersonic and Transonic Flight. *J. Aero. Sci.*, **17**, **47**.
23. GÖRTLER H. (1939) Zum Übergang von Unterschall zu Überschallgeschwindigkeiten in Düsen. *Z. angew. Math. Mech.*, **19**, 325.
24. GRAHAM E.W. (1949) Solution of a Non-Linear Equation for Transonic Flow with Rotational Symmetry. Douglas Aircraft Co. SM-13677.
25. GUDERLEY K.G. (1947) On the Transition from a Transonic Potential Flow to a Flow with Shocks. Tech. Report F–TR–2160 ND, Headquarters Air Materiel Command. Wright Field, Dayton, Ohio, ATI No. 22–278.
26. GUDERLEY K.G. (1947) Considerations on the Structure of Mixed Subsonic-Supersonic Flow Patterns. Tech. Report F–TR–2168–ND Headquarters Air Materiel Command, Wright Field, Dayton, Ohio.
27. GUDERLEY K.G. Singularities at the Sonic Velocity. Tech. Report F–TR–1171–ND, Headquarters Air Materiel Command, Wright Patterson Air Force Base, Dayton, Ohio.
28. GUDERLEY K.G. (October 1950) Axial Symmetric Flow Patterns at a Free Stream Mach Number Close to One. US Air Force Tech. Report No. 6285.
29. GUDERLEY K.G. (May 1951) Two-Dimensional Flow Patterns with a Free Stream Mach Number Close to One. US Air Force Tech. Report No. 6346.
30. GUDERLEY K.G. (1952) A Formula for the Normalization Constant in Eigenvalue Problems. *Quart. Appl. Math.* **10**, 176.
31. GUDERLEY K.G. (1953) On Wind Tunnel Corrections in the Lower Transonic Range. Wright Air Development Center Tech. Report No. 53–506.
32. GUDERLEY K.G. (1953) On Transonic Simplifications of the Hodograph Equation. Wright Air Development Center Tech. Report No. 53–183.
33. GUDERLEY K.G. (1953) Two-Dimensional Bodies at Slightly Supersonic Mach Numbers. Wright Air Development Center Tech. Report No. 53–454.
34. GUDERLEY K.G. (1953) On the Presence of Shocks in Mixed Subsonic-Supersonic Regions. *Advanc. Appl. Mech.*, **3**, Acad. Press.
35. GUDERLEY K.G. (1953) The Wall Pressure Distribution in a Choked Tunnel. Wright Air Development Center. Tech. Report No. 53–509.
36. GUDERLEY K.G. (1954) The Flow over a Flat Plate with a Small Angle of Attack. *J. Aero. Sci.*, **21**, 261.
37. GUDERLEY K.G. (1955) The Flat Plate with an Angle of Attack in a Choked Wind *J. Aero. Sci.*, **22**, 844.
38. GUDERLEY K.G. (1956) On the Development of Solutions of Tricomi's Equation in the Vicinity of the Origin. *J. Rational Mech. Anal.*, **5**, 747.
39. GUDERLEY K.G. (1956) On Transonic Air Foil Theory. *J. Aero. Sci.*, **23**, 961.
40. GUDERLEY K.G. Asymptotische Darstellungen für die Partikularlösungen der Hodographengleichung. Ministry of Supply 3E/244T. Obtainable through PB 96095 Publ. Bd. Department of Commerce, Washington D.C.
41. GUDERLEY K.G. (1942) Rückkehrkanten in ebener kompressibler Potentialströmung. *Z. angew. Math. Mech.*, **22**, 121.
42. GUDERLEY K.G. (1947) Störungen in ebenen and achsensymmetrischen Schall- und Überschall-Parallelestrahlen. *Z. angew. Math. Mech.*, **25/27**, 190.
43. GUDERLEY K.G. and YOSHIHARA H. (1950) The Flow Over a Wedge Profile at Mach Number One. *J. Aero. Sci.*, **17**, 723.
44. GUDERLEY K.G. and YOSHIHARA H. (1951) An Axial-Symmetric Transonic Flow Pattern. *Quart. Appl. Math.*, **8**, No. 4.
45. GUDERLEY K.G. and YOSHIHARA H. (1953) Two-Dimensional Unsymmetric Flow Patterns at Mach Number One. *J. Aero. Sci.*, **20**, 757.
46. HAMEL G. (1949) *Integralgleichungen*, 2nd ed. Springer, Berlin.

47. Hantzsche W. and Wendt H. Mit Überschall angeblasene Kegelspitzen. *Jb. dtsch. Luftfahrtf.*, (1942); also NACA Tech. Memorandum No. 1157 (1947).
48. Heaslet M.A., Lomax H. and Spreiter J.R. (1950) Linearized Compressible Flow Theory for Sonic Flight Speeds, NACA Rep. 956.
49. Huckel V. (1948) Tables of Hypergeometric Functions for Use in Compressible Flow Theory. NACA Tech. Note 1716.
50. Imai I. Application of the WKB-Method to the Flow of a Compressible Fluid I, II. *J. Math. Phys.*, (1949) 173; (1950) 205.
51. Jones R.T. (1946) Properties of Low Aspect Ratio Pointed Wings at Speeds Below and Above the Speed of Sound. NACA Rep. 835.
52. Jacobs W. (1956) Geschwindigkeitsverteilungen in zwei-dimensionalen gekrümmten Laval-Düsen. *Jb. wiss. Ges. Luftf.*
53. Jahnke and Emde *Tafeln höherer Funktionen*, Teubner, Stuttgart.
54. von Kármán T. (1961) The Similarity Law of Transonic Flow. *J. Math. Phys.*, **26,** 182.
55. Keune F. Low Aspect Ratio Wings with Small Thickness at Zero Lift in Subsonic and Supersonic Flow. Royal Institute of Technology. Stockholm, Sweden KTH Aero TN 21.
56. Keune F. The Influence of Camber and Geometrical Twist on Low Aspect Ratio Wings of Finite Thickness in Subsonic Transonic and Supersonic Flow. Royal Institute of Technology, Stockholm, Sweden, KTH Aero TN 29.
57. Liger M. (1953) Nouvelles Équations âpprochées pour l'Étude des écoulements subsoniques et transsoniques. *Publ. Off. nat. Étud. aéro*, No. 64.
58. Lighthill M.J. (1947) The Hodograph Transformation in Transonic Flow Parts I-III. *Proc. Roy. Soc.*, [A], **191,** 323.
59. Langer R.E. (1931) On Asymptotic Solutions of Ordinary Differential Equations with an Application to Bessel Functions of Large Order. *Trans. Amer. Math. Soc.*, 23.
60. Marschner B.W. (1956) The Flow Over a Body in a Closed Wind Tunnel and in a Sonic Free Jet. *J. Aero. Sci.* **23,** 368.
61. Meyer Th. (1908) Dissertation, Göttingen.
62. Molenbroek P. (1890) Über einige Bewegungen eines Gases mit Annahme eines Geschwindigkeitspotentials. *Arch. Math. Phys., Lpz.*, **9,** 157.
63. Morawetz C.S. (February 1956) On the Non-Exitence of Continuous Transonic Flows Past Profiles I. *Comm. Pure Appl. Math.* **9.**
64. Morawetz C.S. (1954) A Uniqueness Theorem for the Frankl Problem. *Comm. Pure Appl. Math.*, **7,** 691.
65. Mangler K.W. Calculation of the Pressure Distribution over a Wing at Sonic Speed. RAE-Report No. 2439 (1951); Aero Research Council, London Rep. Mem. 2888 (1955).
66. Nikolski A. A. and Taganoff G. I. Flow of a Gas in a Local Supersonic Zone and Some Conditions for the Breakdown of Potential Flow. Inst. of Mechanics of the Academy of Sciences U.S.S.R. *Appl. Math. Mech. Leningr.*, **10** (1946); also Brown University translation.
67. Oswatitsch K. Zur Ableitung des Croccoschen Wirbelsatzes. *Luftfahrtforsch.*, **20,** 260.
68. Oswatitsch K. (1950) Die Geschwindigkeitsverteilung bei lokalen Überschallgebieten an flachen Profilen. *Z. angew. Math. Mech.*, **30,** 17.
69. Oswatitsch K. and Berndt S.B. (1950) Aerodynamic Similarity of Axisymmetric Transonic Flow around Slender Bodies. Stockholm: Royal Institute Techn. (KTH Aero TN 15).
70. Oswatitsch K. and Keune F. Ein Äquivalenzsatz für nichtangestellte Flügel kleiner Spannweite in schallnaher Strömung. KTH Aero Report 155 (1954) and *Z. Flugwissensch.* **III** (1954) 29.
71. Spreiter J.R. (1954) On Alternative Forms for the Basic Equations of Transonic Flow Theory. *J. Aero. Sci.*, **20,** 360.
72. Seifert H. (1942) Zur asymptotischen Integration von Differentialgleichungen. *Math. Z.*, **48,** 173.
73. Tollmien W. (1937) Zum Übergang von Unterschall- in Überschallströmungen. *Z. angew. Math. Mech.*, **17,** 117.

74. Tollmien W. (1941) Grenzlinien adiabatischer Potentialströmungen. *Z. angew. Math. Mech.*, **21,** 140.
75. Tomotika S. and Tamada K. Studies on Two-Dimensional Transonic Flows of Compressible Fluids Parts I, II, III. *Quart. Appl. Math.*, (1950) p. 127, p. 381; (1951) p. 129.
76. Chaplygin A. (1904) Über Gasstrahlen. *Wiss. Ann. Univ. Moscow, Phys. und Math. Klasse* **21,** 1 (translation by DVL).
77. Temple G. (1944) The Method of Characteristics in Supersonic Flow. ARC Reports and Memoranda 2091.
78. Tricomi F. (1923) Sulle equazioni lineari alle derivate parziali di 2° ordine di tipe misto. *R.C. Accad. Lincei,* **14,** 134.
79. Vincenti W.G. and Wagoner C.B. (1952) Transonic Flow Past a Wedge Profile with Detached Bow Wave. NACA Rep. 1095.
80. Vincenti W.G. and Wagoner C.B. (1954) Theoretical Study of Transonic Lift of a Double Wedge Profile with Detached Bow Wave. NACA Rep. 1180.
81. Vincenti W.G., Wagoner C.B. and Fisher N.H. Jr. Calculations of the Flow over an Inclined Plate at Free-Stream Mach Number 1. NACA TN 3723.
82. Weise A. (1943) Theorie des gegabelten Verdichtungsstoßes. *Tech. Ber.* **10,** No. 12.
83. Withcomb R.T. (1952) A Study of the Zero Lift Drag Rise Characteristics of Wing Body Combinations near the speed of Sound. NACA RM–L 52 HO 8.
84. Withcomb R.T. (1956) Zero Lift Characteristics of Wing-Body Combinations at Transonic Speeds. *Aeronaut. Engng. Rev.*
85. Yoshihara H. On the Flow Over a Wedge in the Upper Transonic Region. Second *Nat. Congr. Appl. Mech.* Ann. Arbor, Mich. 1954. Published by the American Society of Mechanical Engineers.
86. Yoshihara H. (1953) The Flow Over a Cone Cylinder Body at Mach Number One. Wright Air Development Center. Tech. Report No. 52–295; and *Proc. Third Midw. Conf. Fluid Mech., Univ. Minnesota.*
87. Yoshihara H. (1956) On the Flow Over a Finite Wedge in the Lower Transonic Region.
88. Wright Air Development Center Tech. Report 56–268; and *Proc. Internat. Conf. Appl. Math. Brussels.*

2. Textbooks

1. Sauer R. (1952) *Einführung in the theoretische Gasdynamik,* 2nd ed. Springer, Berlin.
2. Oswatitsch K. (1952) *Gasdynamik,* Springer, Wien.
3. Liepmann H.W. and Puckett A.E. (1947) *Introduction to Aerodynamics of Compressible Fluid,* Wiley, New York.
4. Shapiro A.H. (1953) *The Dynamics and Thermodynamics of Compressible Fluid Flow,* Vol. I and II. Ronald Press, New York.
5. Sears W.R. (Editor) (1954) *General Theory of High Speed Aerodynamics and Jet Propulsion,* Vol. VI. Princeton University Press.
6. von Kármán Th. and Biot M. *Mathematical Methods in Engineering,* McGraw-Hill, New York.
7. Courant R. and Hilbert D. (1931) *Methoden der Mathematischen Physik,* I and II, 2nd ed. Springer, Berlin.
8. Whittaker E.T. and Watson G.N. *A Course of Modern Analysis,* MacMillan, New York.
9. Copson E.T. *An Introduction to the Theory of a Complex Variable.* Oxford University Press, Oxford.

3. Additional References

1. Agmon S., Protter N. and Protter M.H. (Nov. 1953) A Maximum Principle for a Class of Hyperbolic Equations and Applications to Equations of Mixed Elliptic-Hyperbolic Type. *Commun. Pure Appl. Math.*

2. von Baranoff A. (1955) Sur la résistance d'un corps de révolution effilé en mouvement acceleré ou déceleré. *C.R. Acad. Sci., Paris,* **240.**
3. Barish D.T. (1952) Interim Report on a Study of Mach One Wind Tunnels. Wright Air Development Center Tech. Report No. 52–88.
4. Bergdolt V.E. (1953) Airflow about Cone-Cylinders with Curved Shock Waves. *J. Aero. Sci.,* **20,** 751.
5. Bers L. (1954) Results and Conjectures in the Mathematical Theory of Subsonic and Transonic Gas Flows. *Commun. Pure Appl. Math.,* **7.**
6. Bergman S. (1947) Two-Dimensional Subsonic Flows of a Compressible Fluid and their Singularities. *Trans. Amer. Math. Soc.,* **62,** 452.
7. Berndt S.B. (1950) Similarity Laws for Transonic Flow about Wings of Finite Aspect Ratio. Stockholm, Sweden: Royal Institute of Technology KTH Aero TN 14.
8. Bryson A.E.J. (1952) An Experimental Investigation of Transonic Flow Past Two-Dimensional Wedge and Circular Arc Sections Using a Mach Zehnder Interferometer. NACA Rep. 1094.
9. Busemann A. (1949) A Review of Analytical Methods for the Treatment of Flows with Detached Shocks. NACA TN 1858.
10. Busemann A. (1949) The Drag Problem at High Subsonic Speeds. *J. Aero. Sci.,* **16,** 337.
11. Busemann A. (1952) Application of Transonic Similarity. NACA TN 2687.
12. Busemann A. (1953) The Non-Existence of Transonic Potential Flow. *Fluid Mechanics, Proc.* Symp. Applied *Math.* Vol. IV. MacGraw-Hill, New York, p. 29.
13. Biot M.A. (1949) Transonic Drag of an Accelerated Body. *Quart. Appl. Math.* **7,** 101.
14. Cabannes H. (1951) Détermination Théoriques de l'Écoulement d'un Fluide derrière une Onde de Choc Détachée. *Note tech. Off. nat. Étud. aéro.,* No. 5.
15. Cabannes H. (Jan. March 1952) Contributions to the Theory of Compressible Fluids, Transonic Flow, Shock Waves. *Ann. sci. Éc. norm. Sup., Paris,* **9.**
16. Carrier G.F. and Ehlers F.E. (1948) On Some Singularities of the Tricomi Equation. *Quart. Appl. Math.,* **6,** 331.
17. Chang C.C. (1952) General Considerations of Problems in Compressible Flow Using the Hodograph Method. NACA TN 2582.
18. Chang C.C. and Chu B.T. (July 1951) Linearized Theory of Subsonic, Transonic and Supersonic Flow with Assigned Velocity Gradient. The John Hopkins University, Department of Aeronautics.
19. Cherry T.M. (March 1950) Uniform Asymptotic Formulae for Functions with Transition Point. *Trans. Amer. Math. Soc.,* **68,** 224.
20. Cherry T.M. Flow of a Compressible Fluid about a Cylinder Part I. *Proc. Roy. Soc. London,* [A], **192,** (1947) 45; Part II, *ibid.,* **196,** (1949) 1.
21. Clauser M.U. and Clauser F.H. (1937) New Methods of Solving the Equation for the Flow of Compressible Fluids. Doctorate Thesis, Cal. Institute of Technology.
22. Cole J.D. (1951) Drag of a Finite Wedge at High Subsonic Speeds. *J. Math. Phys.,* **30,** 79.
23. Cole J.D., Solomon G.E. and Willmarth W.W. (1953) Transonic Flow Past Simple Bodies. *J. Aero. Sci.,* **20,** 627.
24. Craggs J.W. (1948) The Breakdown of the Hodograph Transformation for Irrotational Compressible Fluid Flow in Two Dimensions. *Proc. Camb. Phil. Soc.* **44,** 360.
25. Demtschenko B. (1933) Sur la relation entre la dynamique des fluides compressibles et celle des fluides incompressible. *Publ. Math. Univ. Belgrade,* **2,** 85.
26. Diaz J.B. and Ludford G.S.S. A Transonic Approximation. University of Maryland, Institute for Fluid Dynamics and Applied Mathematics. TN BN-24.
27. Diaz J.B. and Ludford G.S.S. On Two Methods of Generating Solutions of Linear Partial Differential Equations by Means of Definite Integrals. University of Maryland, Institute for Fluid Dynamics and Applied Mathematics. TN BN-26.
28. Drougge G. The Flow Around Conical Tips in the Upper Transonic Region. The Aeronautical Research Institute of Sweden, Report No. 25, Stockholm–Ulvsunda.
29. Ehlers F.E. (1955) On Some Solutions of the Hodograph Equation which Yield Transonic Flow Through a Laval Nozzle. *J. Aero. Sci.,* **22.**

30. Falkowich S.V. (1946) On the Theory of the Laval Nozzle. *Appl. Math. Mech., Leningr.*, **10,** 503.
31. Frankl F.I. (1945) On the Theory of the Laval Nozzle. Rep. of Academy of Sciences USSR Math. Series **9.**
32. Frankl F.I. (1947) On a Family of Particular Solutions of the Equation of Darboux Tricomi and Their Applications to the Critical Current in a Given Plane Parallel Nozzle. *C.R. Acad. Sci., U.R.S.S.* **58,** 683.
33. Frankl F.I. (1947) Asymptotic Resolution of Chaplygin's Function. *C.R. Acad. Sci. U.R.S.S.*, **58,** 575.
34. Fischbach J.W. (Jan. 1953) Computation of the Transonic Flow Over a Wedge with Detached Shock Wave by the Method of Steepest Descent. Ballistic Research Laboratory, Aberdeen Proving Ground Maryland, BRLM 642.
35. Garrick I.E. and Kaplan C. (1944) On the Flow of a Compressible Fluid by the Hodograph Method. Fundamental Set of Particular Flow Solutions of the Chaplygin Differential Equation. NACA Rep. 790.
36. Germain P. and Bader R. (1953) Solutions élémentaires de certaines Équations aux dérivées partielles du type mixte. *Bull. Soc. math. France.*
37. Germain P. and Bader R. (1953) Sur le problème de Tricomi. *R.C. Circ. mat. Palermo* (II), **2,** 1.
38. Germain P. and Bader R. (1952) Sur quelques problèmes relatifs a l'équation de type mixte de Tricomi. *Publ. Off. nat. Étud. aéro.*, No. 54.
39. Germain P. (1954) Remarks on the Theory of Partial Differential Equations of Mixed Type and Applications to the Study of Transonic Flow. *Commun. Pure Appl. Math.*, **7,** (1).
40. Germain P. (1954) New Applications of Tricomi Solutions to Transonic Flow. *Proc. Second Nat. Congr. Appl. Mech.*
41. Germain P. (July 1956) An Expression for the Green's Functions for a Particular Tricomi Problem. *Quart. Appl. Math.*
42. Germain P. and Ligert M. Une nouvelle Approximation pour l'Étude des Écoulements Subsoniques et Transoniques. *C. R. Acad. Sci., Paris*, **234,** 1846.
43. Griffith W. (1952) Shock Tube Studies of Transonic Flow Over Wedge Profiles. *J. Aero. Sci.*, **19,** 265.
44. Guderley K.G. Theoretical Considerations Concerning the Flow Pattern in a Two-Dimensional Diffusor. Tech. Rep. F-TR-II 14 ND Headquarters Air Materiel Command, Wright Field, Dayton, Ohio.
45. Guderley K.G. (1. Nov. 1947) New Aspects of Transonic Flow Theory, *ATI Tech. Data Dig.* Wright Field.
46. Gullstrand T.R. (1951) The Flow Over Symmetrical Air Foils without Incidence in the Lower Transonic Range. Stockholm: Royal Institute of Technology, KTH Aero TN 20.
47. Gullstrand T.R. (1952) The Flow Over Symmetrical Air Foils without Incidence at Sonic Speed. Stockholm: Royal Institute of Technology, KTH Aero TN 24.
48. Gullstrand T.R. (1952) A Theoretical Discussion of Some Properties of Transonic Flow Over Simple Two-Dimensional Air Foils at Zero Lift with a Simple Method to Estimate the Flow Properties. Stockholm: Royal Institute of Technology. KTH Aero TN 25.
49. Gullstrand T.R. (1952) The Flow Over Two-Dimensional Airofoils at Incidence in the Transonic Speed Range. Stockholm: Royal Institute of Technology. KTH Aero TN 27.
50. Gullstrand T.R. (1952) Transonic Flow Past Two-Dimensional Air Foils. *Z. Flugwissensch.*, 38.
51. Harder K.C. (1952) Transonic Similarity Rules for Lifting Wings. NACA TN 2724.
52. Hilton J.H., Jr. (1952) Flow Characteristics of a Lifting Wedge of Finite Aspect Ratio with Attached and Detached Shock Waves at a Mach Number 1.40. NACA TN 2712.
53. Imai I. (Jan.–Febr. 1954) Extension of von Karman's Transonic Similarity Rule. *J. Phys. Soc. Japan* **9.**
54. Jacob C. (1937) Étude d'un Jet gazeux. *Bull. sci. Éc. polyt. Timisoara* **7** (1, 2).
55. Johnston G.W. (1953) An Investigation of the Flow about Cones at and beyond the Critical Angle. *J. Aero. Sci.*, **20,** 378.

56. KAPLAN C. (1948) On Similarity Rules for Transonic Flow. NACA Rep. 894.
57. KAPLAN C. (1953) On Transonic Flow Past a Wave-Shaped Wall. NACA Tech. Report 1149.
58. VON KÁRMÁN T. (1946) Some Investigations on Transonic and Supersonic Flow. Sixth *Int. Congr. Appl. Mech.*
59. VON KÁRMÁN T. (1947) Supersonic Aerodynamics-Principles and Applications. *J. Aero. Sci.*, **14**, 373.
60. KAWAMURA T. (1954) Contribution of the Change of Entropy to the Directions of Spines of Shock Polar. *J. Phys. Soc. Japan*, **9**, 396.
61. KAWAMURA T. A Trial Calculation on the Analysis of the Flow behind a Curved Shock with Special Reference to Chaplygin's Approximation. Inst. of Physics, Pure and Domestic Science Division, The Nara Women's University, Nara, Japan.
62. KEUNE F. and OSWATITSCH K. (1953) Nichtangestellte Körper kleiner Spannweite in Unter- und Überschallströmung. *Z. Flugwissensch.*, 137.
63. KEUNE F. and OSWATITSCH K. An Integral Equation Theory for the Transonic Flow around Slender Bodies of Revolution at Zero Incidence. Stockholm: Royal Institute of Technology (KTH Aero TN 37).
64. KEUNE F. On the Subsonic, Transonic and Supersonic Flow around Low Aspect Ratio Wings with Incidence and Thickness. Stockholm: Royal Institute of Technology (KTH Aero TN 28).
65. KEUNE F. Bericht über eine Theorie der Strömung um Rotationskörper ohne Anstellung bei Mach-Zahl 1. *Forsch.-Ber. Wirtschafts- und Verkehrsministerium Nordrhein-Westfalen* No. 218. Köln and Opladen: Westdeutscher Verlag.
66. KEUNE F. Zusammenfassende Darstellung und Erweiterung des Äquivalenzsatzes für schallnahe Strömungen. Deutsche Versuchsanstalt für Luftfahrt E.V., Bericht No. 8.
67. KRAFT H. and DIBBLE C.G. (1944) Some Two-Dimensional Adiabatic Compressible Flow Patterns. *J. Aero. Sci.*, **11**, 283.
68. KRYUCHIN A.F. (1954) Flow around a Wedge Shaped Profile with Detached Line of Strong Discontinuity. *C.R. Acad. Sci. U.R.S.S.*, **97**, 37; M.D.Friedman, Russian Translation. 2 Pine Street, West Concord, Mass.
69. KRYUCHIN A.F. (1954) Drag of a Rhomboid Profile at Transonic Speeds. *C.R. Acad. Sci. U.R.S.S.*, **97**, 205; M.D.Friedman, Russian Translations, 2 Pine Street, West Concord, Mass.
70. LAITONE E.V. (1952) A Study of Transonic Gasdynamics by the Hydraulic Analogy. *J. Aero. Sci.*, **19**, 249.
71. LANDAHL M.T. The Flow around Oscillating Low Aspect Ratio Wings at Transonic Speeds. Stockholm: Royal Institute of Technology (KTH Aero TN 40).
72. LEVEY H.C. (March 1954) Exact Solutions for Transonic Flow Past Cusped Air Foils. Aeron. Research Lab. Melbourne Rep. A 87.
73. LIEPMANN H.W. and BRYSON A.E., JR. (1950) Transonic Flow Past Wedge Sections. *J. Aero. Sci.*, **17**, 745.
74. LIEPMANN H.W. (1946) The Interaction between Boundary Layer and Shock Waves in Transonic Flow. *J. Aero. Sci.*, **13**.
75. LOEWNER C.A. (1950) A Transformation Theory of Partial Differential Equations of Gasdynamics. NACA TN 2065.
76. LOMAX H. and HEASLET M.A. (1949) Linearized Lifting Surface Theory for Swept Back Wings with Slender Plan Forms. NACA TN 1992.
77. MANGLER K.W. Calculation of the Load Distribution over a Wing with Arbitrary Camber and Twist at Sonic Speeds. RAE Report Aero. 2515.
78. MANWELL A.R. (1952) A Note on the Hodograph Transformation. *Quart. Appl. Math.* **10**, 177.
79. MANWELL A.R. (Jan. 1955) A New Singularity of Transonic Plane Flows. *Quart. Appl. Math.*
80. MITCHELL A.R. and RUTHERFORD D.E. (1951) Application of Relaxation Methods to Compressible Flow Past a Double Wedge, *Proc. Roy. Soc. Edinb.*, [A], **63**, Part II, 139.

81. MORAWETZ C.S. (1956) Note on a Maximum Principle and a Uniqueness Theorem for an Elliptic Hyperbolic Equation. *Proc. Roy. Soc. London* [A]‘ **236,** 141.
82. MORAWETZ C.S. and KOLODNER I.I. (1953) On the Non-Existence of Limiting Lines in Transonic Flow. *Commun. Pure Appl. Math.* **6,** 97.
83. OSWATITSCH K. (1950) Die Geschwindigkeitsverteilung an symmetrischen Profilen bei Auftreten lokaler Überschallgebiete. *Acta phys. austr.* **4,** No. 2/3.
84. OSWATITSCH K. The Effect of Compressibility on the Flow Around Slender Bodies of Revolution. Stockholm: Royal Institute of Technology. KTH Aero TN 12 (1950); and *Arch. Math.* II, 6 (1949/1950).
85. OSWATITSCH K. and WIEGHARDT K. Theoretische Untersuchungen über stationäre Potentialströmungen und Grenzschichten bei hohen Geschwindigkeiten. *Lilienthal-gesellschaft für Luftfahrtforschung, Bericht* S. 13/1d (1942), 7. (NACA TN 1189, 1948).
86. PACK D.C. and MACKIE A.G. (1952) Transonic Flow Past Finite Wedges. *Proc. Camb. Phil. Soc.* **48,** Part 1, 178.
87. PACK D.C. and MACKIE A.G. Transonic Flow Past Finite Wedges. *J. Rational Mech. Anal.* **4** (1), Indiana University.
88. PACK D.C. (1946) Investigation of the Flow Past a Finite Wedge of 20 Degrees and 40 Degrees Apex Angle at Subsonic and Supersonic Speeds Using a Mach-Zehnder Interferometer R and M, 2321 British ARC.
89. PROTTER M.H. (1951) A Boundary Value Problem for an Equation of Mixed Type. *Trans. Amer. Math. Soc.,* **71,** 416.
90. RIABOUCHINSKI D. (1932) *C. R. Acad. Sci. Paris,* 194, 1215.
91. RINGLEB F. (1940) Exakte Lösungen der Differentialgleichung einer adiabatischen Gasströmung. *Z. angew. Math. Mech.* **20,** 185.
92. RINGLEB F. (1940) Über die Differentialgleichungen einer Gasströmung und den Strömungsstoß. *Dtsch. Math.* **5,** 377.
93. SAKURAI T. (1956) The Flow Past a Flat Plate Accompanied with an Unsymmetric Dead Air at Mach Number One. *J. Phys. Soc. Japan* **11** (6).
94. SIRIEIX M., GOLAZ P. and REBUFFET P. (1952) Résultats expérimentaux obtenus aux voisinage de la vitesse du son sur une maquette d'aile à profile losangique. *C. R. Acad. Sci., Paris,* **235,** 459.
95. SOLOMON G.E. (1954) Transonic Flow Past Cone Cylinders. NACA TN 3212.
96. SPREITER J.R. (1953) On the Application of Transonic Similarity Rules to Wings of Finite Span. NACA Rep. 1153.
97. SPREITER J.R. (1956) On the Range of Applicability of the Transonic Area Rule. NACA TN 3673.
98. SPREITER J.R. and ALKSNE A. (1954) Theoretical Prediction of Pressure Distributions of Non-Lifting Airfoils at High Subsonic Speeds. NACA TN 3096.
99. STACK J. (1951) Experimental Methods for Transonic Research, Proc. Third Anglo-American Aeron. Conf. Brighton Sept. 4–7, p. 586.
100. TAMADA K. and SHIBOAKA Y. (1955) On Supersonic Flow Past a Finite Wedge at the Crocco Mach Number. *J. Aero. Sci.,* **22,** 261.
101. TAYLOR G.I. (1930) Recent Work on the Flow of Compressible Fluids. *J. Lond. Math. Soc.,* **5,** 224.
102. TSIEN H.S. and KUO Y.H. Two-Dimensional Irrotational Mixed Subsonic and Supersonic Flow of a Compressible Fluid and the Upper Critical Mach. Number. NACA TN No. 995.
103. TIMMAN R. (April 22, 1949) Asymptotic Formulae for Special Solutions of the Hodograph Equation in Compressible Flow. Nat. Luchtlab. Amsterdam Rep. No. F 46.
104. VINCENTI W.G., DUGAN D.W. and PHELPS E.R. An Experimental Study of the Lift and Pressure Distribution on a Double Wedge Profile at Mach Number near Shock Attachment. NACA TN 3225.
105. VINCENTI W.G. (1955) Measurements of the Effects of Finite Span on the Pressure Distribution over Double Wedge Wings at Mach Numbers near Shock Attachment, NACA TN 3522.

106. WARREN C. H. E. (April 1956) Recent Advances in the Knowledge of Transonic Air Flow. *J. R. Aero. Soc.*
107. WEINSTEIN A. (1951) On Tricomi's Equation and Generalized Axially Symmetric Potential Theory. Institute for Fluid Dynamics and Applied Mathematics. University of Maryland.
108. WILLMARTH W. W. (1953) The Lift of Thin Airfoils at High Subsonic Speeds. Ph. D. Thesis, Cal. Inst. of Tech.
109. WOOD G. P. (1952) Experiments on Transonic Flow around Wedges. NACA TN 2829.

INDEX